GEORGE C. BEAKLEY
ERNEST G. CHILTON

With Contributions by

MICHAEL J. NIELSEN

ARIZONA STATE UNIVERSITY

The Macmillan Company, New York   Collier-Macmillan Publishers, London

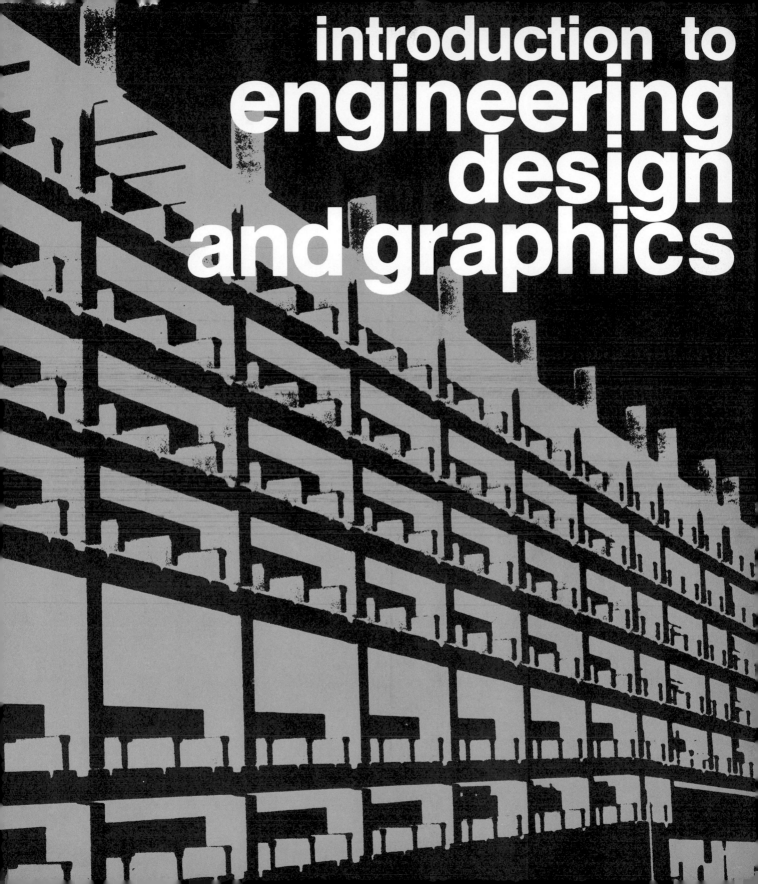

introduction to
engineering
design
and graphics

The Macmillan Company
866 Third Avenue, New York, New York 10022

Collier-Macmillan Canada, Ltd., Toronto, Ontario

Library of Congress catalog card number: 77-186438

Printing: 1 2 3 4 5 6 7 8   Year: 3 4 5 6 7 8 9

preface

to the student

Welcome to the exciting and challenging experiences of engineering and to an exploration of some methods and procedures that will help to solve the broad spectrum of problems facing our civilization. Doubtlessly you have had a number of ideas within the past few years that seemed worthy of further consideration. After you have studied this book you may be able to test their workability and effectiveness. It is this capacity for generating these ideas that will contribute to your interest in design, engineering, and technical studies. Therefore this will be a time of personal involvement with realistic and relevant problems. History is full of the accounts of young people who have dared to translate their ideas into actions. Some began at a very early age. Wolfgang Mozart, for example, wrote his first sonatas at age 7 and Ludwig van Beethoven completed his first composition at 13; Blaise Pascal had written a book on geometry at age 16 and invented the adding machine at 19; Michael Faraday at age 21 began work in electromagnetics that led to his invention of the electric motor; Thomas Edison patented his electrical vote recorder at age 21; Samuel Colt invented the first revolver at age 21; and Alexander the Great at age 20 reigned as king of Macedonia and at age 27 had conquered the civilized world. Concerning the accomplishments of the young, it was Benjamin Disraeli who once said, "Almost everything that is great has been done by youth." ° We believe that it is not too early in your life to consider the principles of design that are contained in this book, and whose mastery will vastly improve your chances for success as a "problem-solver" and engineer.

to the instructor

In one sense youth is a state of mind. Therefore, this book has not been molded in the traditional pattern of textbooks with regard to either content or form of presentation. For the past several decades authentic engineering design experiences in the curriculum have been delayed until the final semester of the students' baccalaureate program. It was generally assumed that underclassmen were too immature and lacking in educational background to attempt *real* designs. In contradiction to this rather widespread belief, we have found over

° Don Fabun, ed., *The Dynamics of Change*, Prentice-Hall, Englewood Cliffs, N.J. (1967).

a number of years that freshman and sophomore students *are* innovative and able to cope with problems of considerable sophistication. Also they become motivated to continue their studies toward their chosen career objective if they are allowed to engage in realistic and authentic design experiences as a regular part of the curriculum. For this reason, the content of this book has been written for the individual student—to motivate and to instruct. Some material can be learned best in a classroom environment, while other of the material is specifically prepared for self-paced individual learning.

The text format is also atypical. We hope the departures employed will make the text material more interesting, relevant, and informative for both you and the students. For years we have been much impressed with the consistently high quality publication *Kaiser News*—an internationally distributed company magazine whose Publications Editor is Don Fabun—and several features used regularly in this publication have been incorporated in the textbook.

The text is divided conveniently into three sections—informational and motivational, design, and graphics. Any of the chapters of the three parts may be used, or not, as you may desire. This flexibility allows and encourages the individuality of each school or each instructor and the freedom to organize a course with unique emphasis. Chapters not included in the regular course syllabus can be used for extra reading or reference. Although the text is not presented in a programmed learning format, the majority of the chapters and pertinent parts of the Appendix have been prepared to facilitate individual self-paced instruction. An exceptionally large number of photographs, quotations, annotated drawings, and examples have been prepared to accompany the text material for clarification and enrichment.

The designer's ability to communicate his ideas is enhanced greatly if he has mastered certain fundamental visual skills that are associated with technical sketching, engineering drawing, descriptive geometry, and data presentation. Traditionally instruction in these important subjects has been constrained to a study of the *theory* and practice in the *skill* involved, and too little emphasis has been placed upon the use of graphics as an indispensable tool. In this text, Part III has been prepared to be used either independently or in conjunction with Parts I and II. In either case graphics should be recognized as being one of the designer's most important and useful mediums of communication.

This is an introductory text—both for design and for graphics. Because of this, breadth of coverage of subject matter has been given preference over depth, particularly with regard to the aspects of design, which are extensive and many-faceted. We hope that each teacher will take advantage of this type of presentation and amplify and enrich the students' encounter with design by adding material from other books, case studies, and his personal experience.

We have purposely organized the material to allow the instructor maximum freedom in organizing his course as he chooses, recognizing that there will be a large spectrum of such desires. For example, some will want to give preference to design—others to graphics. In this respect most of the chapters are free-standing and their sequence may be altered at will. Most have been written to serve the dual purpose of either formal class use or personalized self-paced instruction.

to all

The preparation of this book has been a voluminous and complex assignment. The task was complicated by the dual nature of our purpose. We wanted to introduce the broad spectrum of design, from the miraculous and infinitely complex designs of nature—including delicate ecological balances—to the entirely human but no less important relationships involving the market enterprise system. We also wanted to provide the student with a fundamental understanding of the basic graphic tools that are used by engineers and designers for purposes of communication. To our knowledge these multiple objectives have never been addressed before under a single cover and some of the suggested material is completely new for an elementary text of this type.

We are most grateful to our many professional colleagues who have provided counsel and advice with regard to the selection of material for this text, and particularly with regard to reading portions of the manuscript.

A corps of consultants have assisted us in preparing the manuscript. In particular we would like to cite the work of Professors Gordon Bender, Ph.D., James Schamadan, M.D., and Charles Hoyt, Ph.D. They prepared, respectively, the basic material for Chapters 3, 9, and 10. Roy Dike prepared the majority of sketches used in Chapter 13 and Donald Autore served as a consultant for Part III of the text.

Special commendation should go to Esther Taylor, who typed and proofread the manuscript. The majority of the drawings for Parts I and II were drawn by David C. Gironda, while those of Part III have been prepared by David W. Hudgins. John W. Radder, P.O. Box 54, Stratford, Connecticut 06497, made available for this book problems 13-12, 13-13, 13-14, 14-13, 14-14, 16-11, 16-12, 16-13, and 16-14. We are also grateful to John Beck, Leo Malek, and Andrew Zutis at The Macmillan Company for their care and devotion to the development, production, and internal design of this book.

A series of workbooks particularly suited to complement the text material in Part III is available from the publisher. A workbook emphasizing analytical and problem solving is available from the authors.

G. C. B.
E. G. C.

acknowledgments

Chapter Opening, 1 General Electric Company
Figure 1-1 Uniroyal, Inc.
Figure 1-2 U.S. Army Strategic Communications Command
Figure 1-3 H. Armstrong Roberts Photo
Figure 1-4 Bethlehem Steel Corporation
Figure 1-5 Floyd A. Craig, Christian Life Commission, Southern Baptist Convention
Figure 1-6 Planned Parenthood-World Population
Figure 1-8 Planned Parenthood-World Population
Figure 1-9 Planned Parenthood-World Population
Figure 1-10 Monsanto Company
Figure 1-11 Ambassador College Photo
Figure 1-12 Ministers Life and Casualty Union
Figure 1-13 Republic Steel Corporation
Figure 1-14 Citizens for Clean Air
Figure 1-15 Planned Parenthood-World Population
Figure 1-16 Merrill, Lynch, Pierce, Fenner & Smith, Inc.
Figure 1-17 Torit Corporation
Figure 1-18 Nyle Leatham, *Arizona Republic*
Figure 1-18A United States Tobacco Company
Figure 1-19 Federal Water Pollution Control Administration
Figure 1-20 U.S. Department of Housing and Urban Development
Figure 1-21 Floyd A. Craig, Christian Life Commission, Southern Baptist Convention
Figure 1-22 Floyd A. Craig, Christian Life Commission, Southern Baptist Convention
Figure 1-23 Bethlehem Steel Corporation
Figure 1-24 Floyd A. Craig, Christian Life Commission, Southern Baptist Convention
Figure 1-25 Shell Oil Company
Figure 1-26 Phil Stitt, *Arizona Architect*
Figure 1-27 The MITRE Corporation
Figure 1-28 Hewlett-Packard
Figure 1-29 Hewlett-Packard
Figure 1-30 *Kaiser News*
Figure 1-31 L. P. Gaucher
Figure 1-32 General Electric Company
Figure 1-33 Photograph Courtesy Institute of Traffic Engineers
Figure 1-34 Shell Oil Company
Figure 1-35 Planned Parenthood-World Population
Figure 1-36 General Electric Company
Figure 1-37 Parsons, Brinckerhoff, Quade & Douglas and Bay Area Rapid Transit District and American Society of Civil Engineers
Figure 1-38 Institute of Traffic Engineers
Figure 1-39 North American Rockwell
Figure 1-40 American Express Co.
Figure 1-41 Polaroid Corporation, Cambridge, Massachusetts
Figure 1-42 Reprinted with permission from General Telephone & Electronics
Figure 1-43 Thomson-CSF, Versailles, France
Figure 1-44 Floyd A. Craig, Christian Life Commission, Southern Baptist Convention
Figure 1-45 Modified after drawing of Ron Thomas, *Kaiser News*
Figure 1-47 Humble Oil & Refining Company
Figure 1-48 General Electric Company

Chapter Opening, 2 General Motors Research Laboratories
Figure 2-1 North American Rockwell
Figure 2-2 EG&G International Geodyne Division
Figure 2-3 Western Electric
Figure 2-4 Great Books Division of Encyclopaedia Britannica, Inc.
Figure 2-5 North American Rockwell
Figure 2-7 Floyd A. Craig, Christian Life Commission, Southern Baptist Convention
Figure 2-10 Esso Research & Engineering Company
Figure 2-13 North American Rockwell
Figure 2-14 Coca Cola Company, Atlanta, Georgia
Figure 2-15 Allis-Chalmers
Figure 2-16 Photograph by Phillip Leonian

The consulting author for Chapter 3 was Gordon L. Bender, Ph.D.
Chapter Opening, 3 General Motors Research Laboratories
Figure 3-1 Stennett Heaton Photo, Courtesy Neil A. Maclean Co., Inc.
Figure 3-2 Moody Institute of Science
Figure 3-3 Moody Institute of Science
Figure 3-4 Photo by Gordon Smith from National Audubon Society
Figure 3-5 Photo by Treat Davidson from National Audubon Society
Figure 3-6 RCA Electronic Components
Figure 3-8 Photo by John H. Gerard from National Audubon Society
Figure 3-9 Interior-Sport Fisheries & Wildlife Photo by Charles E. Most
Figure 3-10 Photo by Harold V. Brown from National Audubon Society
Figure 3-11 Bell Helicopter Company
Figure 3-12 Bell Telephone Laboratories
Figure 3-13 Schweizer Aircraft Corp.
Figure 3-14 General Dynamics Convair Division
Figure 3-15 Carolina Biological Supply Company
Figure 3-16 Arizona Game and Fish Department
Figure 3-17 Photo by Karl W. Kenyon from National Audubon Society
Figure 3-18 USDA Photo
Figure 3-19 Photo by Karl H. Maslowski from National Audubon Society
Figure 3-20 North Carolina Department of Mental Health, Division of Research
Figure 3-21 Photo by N. E. Beck, Jr. from National Audubon Society
Figure 3-22 U.S. Department of Agriculture
Figure 3-23 Photo by Carl Koski from National Audubon Society
Figure 3-24 U.S. Department of Agriculture
Figure 3-25 U.S. Department of Agriculture
Figure 3-26 U.S. Department of Interior, Bureau of Reclamation
Figure 3-27 U.S. Department of Interior, Bureau of Reclamation
Figure 3-28 Photo by G. Ronald Austing from National Audubon Society
Figure 3-29 North Carolina Department of Mental Health, Division of Research
Figure 3-30 North Carolina Department of Mental Health, Division of Research
Figure 3-31 Dow Chemical Company
Figure 3-34 General Electric Company
Figure 3-35 Photo by Treat Davidson from National Audubon Society
Figure 3-37 *Machine Design*

Figures 3-40 and 3-41 Ralph Buchsbaum, *Animals Without Backbones*, University of Chicago Press, 1948
Figure 3-42 Photo by Robert C. Hermes from National Audubon Society
Figure 3-43 Moody Institute of Science
Figure 3-44 Moody Institute of Science
Figure 3-45 Carolina Biological Supply Company
Figure 3-46 Carolina Biological Supply Company
Figure 3-47 U.S. Department of Agriculture
Figure 3-48 Carolina Biological Supply Company
Figure 3-49 Carolina Biological Supply Company
Figure 3-50 Moody Institute of Science
Figure 3-51 Moody Institute of Science
Figure 3-52 Moody Institute of Science
Figure 3-53 Carolina Biological Supply Company
Figures 3-54, 3-55, 3-56 Ralph Buchsbaum, *Animals Without Backbones*, University of Chicago Press, 1948
Figure 3-57 Photo by Mitchell Campbell from National Audubon Society
Figure 3-58 Photo by Arthur W. Ambler from National Audubon Society
Figure 3-59 USDA Photo
Figure 3-60 Photo by G. E. Kirkpatrick from National Audubon Society
Figure 3-61 Carl Zeiss Inc., New York
Figure 3-62 Moody Institute of Science
Figure 3-63 American Iron and Steel Institute
Figure 3-64 Photo by Lynwood M. Chace from National Audubon Society

Chapter Opening, 4 General Motors Research Laboratories
Figure 4-1 USDA Photo
Figure 4-3 Koppers Company, Inc.
Figure 4-4 Reynolds Metals Company
Figure 4-5 North American Rockwell
Figure 4-6 Union Electric Company
Figure 4-7 Uniroyal, Inc.
Figure 4-8 Eastern Airlines Incorporated
Figure 4-9 Hercules Incorporated
Figure 4-10 Culver Pictures
Figure 4-11 Renault, Inc.
Figure 4-12 American Airlines
Figure 4-13 American Airlines
Figure 4-14 American Airlines
Figure 4-15 American Airlines
Figure 4-16 American Airlines
Figure 4-17 Lockheed Missiles and Space Company
Figure 4-18 U.S. Naval Ordnance Laboratory
Figure 4-19 Official U.S. Navy Photograph
Figure 4-20 Photo by Mike Jakub
Figure 4-21 The Boeing Company
Figure 4-22 Pipeline and Compressor Research Council of the Southern Gas Association
Figure 4-23 General Motors Styling Staff
Figure 4-24 AT & T
Figure 4-25 Zenith Radio Corporation
Figure 4-26 Honeywell Inc.
Figure 4-27 Clay Adams
Figure 4-28 Zenith Radio Corporation
Figure 4-29 American Welding Society
Figure 4-30 Reynolds Metals Company
Figure 4-31 Humble Oil & Refining Company
Figure 4-35 USDA Photo

Figure 4-36 USDA Photo
Figure 4-37 Illinois Gear Division, Wallace-Murray Corporation
Figure 4-39 Tinius Olsen Testing Machine Company
Figure 4-40 Bell Telephone Laboratories
Figure 4-42 Bell Telephone Laboratories
Figure 4-46 North American Rockwell
Figure 4-49 Martin Marietta Corporation
Figure 4-50 Weatherby, Inc.
Figure 4-51 RCA
Figure 4-52 Martin Marietta Corporation
Figure 4-55 General Dynamics Convair Division
Figure 4-56 Carl Zeiss, Inc., New York
Figure 4-57 California Computer Products, Inc.
Figure 4-58 Eastman Kodak Company
Figure 4-59 Photo by Charles Conley
Figure 4-60 Inland Steel Company
Figure 4-66 Du Pont Lucite® Paints
Figure 4-71 Raleigh Industries of America, Incorporated
Figure 4-72 SKF Industries, Inc.
Figure 4-73 Interarms Limited
Figure 4-74 Ford Motor Company
Figure 4-75 Knoll International, Inc.
Figure 4-76 Zippo Manufacturing Company
Figure 4-77 Luxo Lamp Corporation
Figure 4-78 General Radio Company
Figure 4-79 Chemex Corporation
Figure 4-80 American Motors Corporation
Figure 4-81 Photo courtesy Herman Miller, Inc.
Figure 4-82 American Airlines
Figure 4-83 IBM Corporation, Office Products Division
Figure 4-84 Cummins Engine Company, Model V8-300 Marine Engine, designed by Eliot Noyes
Figure 4-85 Porsche-Audi Division, Volkswagen of America, Inc.

Chapter Opening, 5 Carl Zeiss, Inc., New York
Figure 5-2 Modine Manufacturing Company
Figure 5-4 National Air Pollution Control Administration
Figure 5-5 Ford Motor Company Design Center
Figure 5-6 Ford Motor Company Design Center
Figure 5-7 Uniroyal, Inc.
Figure 5-8 United States Steel Corporation
Figure 5-9 Thai-American Audio Visual Service
Figure 5-10 Deere & Company
Figure 5-11 American Iron and Steel Institute
Figure 5-12 Campus Crusade for Christ International
Figure 5-13 Martin Marietta Corporation
Figure 5-14 Chrysler Corporation
Figure 5-15 The Boeing Company, Vertol Division
Figure 5-16 Hughes Aircraft Company
Figure 5-17 United Aircraft
Figure 5-18 Enjay Chemical Company

Chapter Opening, 6 Carl Zeiss, Inc., New York
Figure 6-1 Zenith Radio Corporation
Figure 6-2 *Water Power*
Figure 6-7 Digital Equipment Corporation
Figure 6-8 *Kaiser News*
Figure 6-9 General Motors Research Laboratories
Figure 6-11 General Motors Corporation and American Society of Civil Engineers
Figure 6-12 Allis-Chalmers
Figure 6-13 Toyota Motor Sales, U.S.A., Inc. and Road & Track/ Bond Publishing Co.

Figure 6-17   Triborough Bridge & Tunnel Authority
Figure 6-18   National Aeronautics and Space Administration
Figure 6-20   Al Capp
Figure 6-21   Chesebrough-Pond's Inc.
Figure 6-23   Photo by Charles Conley
Figure 6-24   National Aeronautics and Space Administration
Figure 6-25   Pacific Northwest Laboratory Operated by Battelle Memorial Institute of the USAEC
Figure 6-35   Adapted from drawing, *Kaiser News*
Figure 6-36   *Sperry Rand Engineering Review*
Figure 6-39   Photo by Ernest Braun, FMC Corporation
Figure 6-43   U.S. Steel Corporation
Figure 6-44   General Dynamics Convair Division
Figure 6-45   B. F. Goodrich Company
Figure 6-46   Sikorsky Aircraft
Figure 6-47   Digital Equipment Corporation
Figure 6-48   Reynolds Aluminum, Reynolds Metals Co.
Figure 6-49   General Electric Company
Figure 6-51   Ford Motor Company
Figure 6-52   General Motors Corporation
Figure 6-53   F. W. Dodge Division, McGraw-Hill Information Systems Company
Figure 6-54   Rocketdyne, North American Rockwell
Figure 6-55   Phil Stitt, *Arizona Architect*
Figure 6-56   Phil Stitt, *Arizona Architect*
Figure 6-57   Industrial Research Inc., Photo by Micrographics
Figure 6-58   *Industrial Research*
Figure 6-60   The Carborundum Company
Figure 6-61   Planned Parenthood-World Population
Figure 6-62   United States Department of Agriculture
Figure 6-63   Phil Stitt, *Arizona Architect*
Figure 6-64   Max O. Urbahn Associates, Inc. Architecture & Planning
Figure 6-65   Eric Lantz Photograph
Figure 6-66   Paramount Die Casting
Figure 6-67   Somerset Importers, Ltd.
Figure 6-68   Texas Instruments Incorporated
Figure 6-69   Pratt & Whitney Aircraft
Figure 6-71   RCA

Chapter Opening, 7   General Motors Research Laboratories
Figure 7-1   General Motors Proving Ground
Figure 7-2   Bell Telephone Laboratories
Figure 7-3   Federal Highways Administration
Figure 7-4   New York Life Insurance Company
Figure 7-5   Frank Roberge and *Arizona Republic*
Figure 7-6   The Boeing Company
Figure 7-7   United Aircraft Photo
Figure 7-8   McDonnell Douglas Corporation
Figure 7-9   Martin Marietta Corporation
Figure 7-10   United Aircraft
Figure 7-11   Esso Research & Engineering Company
Figure 7-12   Deere & Company
Figure 7-20   Texas Instruments Incorporated
Figure 7-21   M. W. Kellogg Company
Figure 7-22   Westinghouse Electric Corporation and Instrument Society of America
Figure 7-27   Structural Analysis Associates
Figure 7-29   Electronics Associates, Inc.
Figure 7-31   Pipeline and Compressor Research Council of the Southern Gas Association
Figure 7-32   Pipeline and Compressor Research Council of the Southern Gas Association
Figure 7-33   *Professional Engineer*

Chapter Opening, 8   General Electric Company
Figure 8-1   Ambassador College Photo
Figure 8-2   International Paper Company
Figure 8-3   Reynolds Metals Company
Figure 8-4   American Wire & Steel Institute
Figure 8-5   United States Steel Corporation
Figure 8-6   United States Steel Corporation
Figure 8-7   Photo by John L. Brown, Georgia Institute of Technology, Courtesy Engis Equipment Company
Figure 8-8   Electronics Division of Aerojet-General Corporation
Figure 8-9   Bethlehem Steel Corporation
Figure 8-10   Koppers Company, Inc.
Figure 8-11   Los Alamos Scientific Laboratory
Figure 8-14   American Foundrymen's Society
Figure 8-16   American Foundrymen's Society
Figure 8-17   American Foundrymen's Society
Figure 8-19   Aluminum Company of America
Figure 8-21   Photo by Charles Conley
Figure 8-24   Photo by Charles Conley
Figures 8-25, 26, 27, 28, 30, 32, 33, 34, 36, 38, 41   Adapted from Moore & Kibbey's *Manufacturing Materials and Processes*, Richard D. Irwin, Inc., by permission
Figure 8-29   Precisions Materials Group, Chemical & Metallurgical Division, GTE Sylvania Incorporated
Figure 8-31   The Warner & Swasey Company
Figure 8-35   Denison Division, Abex Corporation
Figure 8-37   Photo by Charles Conley
Figure 8-39   Aluminum Company of America
Figure 8-40   Aluminum Company of America
Figure 8-42   General Motors Research Laboratories
Figure 8-43   Norton Company
Figure 8-45   American Welding Society
Figure 8-47   Lockheed Missiles and Space Company
Figure 8-49   The Foxboro Company
Figure 8-53   Federal-Mogul Corp.
Figure 8-54   Ford Motor Company
Figure 8-55   © Rube Goldberg. Permission granted by King Features Syndicate
Figure 8-58   Photo by Charles Conley
Figure 8-59   Photo by Charles Conley
Figure 8-60   Federal-Mogul Corp.
Figure 8-62   Photo by Charles Conley
Figure 8-63   Atlas Chain & Precision Products Co., Inc.
Figure 8-64   Smithsonian Institution
Figure 8-65   Illinois Gear Division, Wallace-Murray Corporation
Figure 8-66   American Society of Mechanical Engineers

The consulting author for Chapter 9 was James L. Schamadan, M.D.
Chapter Opening, 9   General Motors Research Laboratories
Figure 9-1   Ford Motor Company
Figure 9-3   A. H. Robins Company
Figure 9-5   Phipps & Bird, Inc.
Figure 9-7   General Dynamics, Convair Division
Figure 9-8   Brown Brothers
Figure 9-9   Konica Autoreflex Photo, Konica Camera Corp.
Figure 9-10   A-T-O Inc.
Figure 9-11A   Carl Zeiss, Inc., New York
Figure 9-11B   *Sperry Rand Engineering Review*
Figure 9-11C   *Sperry Rand Engineering Review*
Figure 9-11D   *Industrial Research*
Figure 9-12   Institute of Environmental Sciences
Figure 9-14   Andrea Raab Corporation

Figure 9-15 Keystone Steel & Wire Division of Keystone Consolidated Industries, Inc.
Figure 9-16 Dr. H. Richard Blackwell and Institute for Research in Vision, Ohio State University
Figure 9-17 Xerox Corporation
Figure 9-18 Rod Moyer Photo, *Arizona Republic*
Figure 9-20 Denver Division, Martin Marietta Corporation
Figure 9-21 Torit Corporation
Figure 9-22 U.S. Department of Agriculture
Figure 9-23 Keuffel & Esser Company
Figure 9-24 *Sperry Rand Engineering Review*
Figure 9-25 National Aeronautics and Space Administration
Figure 9-27 Lockheed Missiles & Space Company
Figure 9-28 National Aeronautics and Space Administration
Figure 9-29 Cessna Aircraft Company
Figure 9-30 S. C. Johnson & Son, Inc.
Figure 9-31 Humble Oil and Refining Company
Figure 9-32 Hercules Incorporated
Figure 9-33 Photographed by Jim Adair for Eli Lilly and Company
Figure 9-34 Cornell Aeronautical Laboratory, Inc.
Figure 9-35 *American Medical News*
Figure 9-36 Electronics Division of Aerojet-General Corporation

The consulting author for Chapter 10 was Charles C. Hoyt, Ph.D.
Chapter Opening, 10 Sperry Rand Microanalysis Laboratory, Rockville, Md.
Figure 10-4 RCA Electronic Components
Figure 10-5 Texas Instruments Incorporated
Figure 10-6 Ford Motor Company Design Center
Figure 10-7 Midas, Inc.
Figure 10-8 Battelle Development Corporation
Figure 10-9 Texas Instruments Incorporated
Figure 10-11 Texas Instruments Incorporated
Figure 10-12 Vermont Research Corporation. Design by Hill, Holliday, Connors, Cosmopulos Advertising, Boston
Figure 10-13 U.S. Patent 3,163,925, R. K. Ulm
Figure 10-14 Hewlett-Packard Calculator Products Division

Chapter Opening, 11 General Motors Research Laboratories
Figure 11-1 Massachusetts Mutual Life Insurance Company
Figure 11-2 Sandia Laboratories
Figure 11-3 Texas Instruments Incorporated

Chapter Opening, 12 Texas Instruments Incorporated
Figure 12-1 Cessna Aircraft Company
Figure 12-5 Gramercy
Figure 12-7 Zenith Radio Corporation
Figure 12-11 Keuffel & Esser Company
Figure 12-13 Gramercy
Figure 12-16 General Dynamics, Convair Division
Figure 12-17 Gramercy
Figure 12-21 RapiDesign, Inc.
Figure 12-35 Hewlett-Packard, Medical Electronics Division
Figure 12-55 Gramercy

Chapter Opening, 13 General Motors Research Laboratories
Figure 13-1 Ford Motor Company
Figure 13-16 Travelodge International, Inc.
Figure 13-17 Robertshaw Controls Company, Milford Division
Figure 13-39 Koppers Company, Inc.
Figure 13-40 M. W. Kellogg Company
Figure 13-70 Texas Instruments Incorporated

Figure 13-72 RapiDesign, Inc.
Figure 13-80 GraphiCraft
Figure 13-81 United States Gypsum Company

Chapter Opening, 14 Electron Optics Laboratory, Engis Equipment Company

Chapter Opening, 15 General Motors Research Laboratories
Figure 15-1 Reynolds Metals Company
Figure 15-2 American Iron and Steel Institute
Figure 15-3A A. W. Faber, Castell
Figure 15-5A Mobil Oil Corporation
Figure 15-14A Reynolds Metals Company
Figure 15-23A General Motors Research Laboratories
Figure 15-32 Bell Telephone Laboratories
Figure 15-37 Inland Steel Company

Chapter Opening, 16 Carl Zeiss, Inc., New York
Figure 16-7 ANSI (Y 14.5-1966)
Figure 16-29 ANSI (Y 14.5-1966)
Figure 16-32 ANSI (Y 14.5-1966)
Figure 16-49 FMC Corporation
Figure 16-55 ANSI (Y 14.5-1966)
Figure 16-56 ANSI (Y 14.5-1966)
Figure 16-57 ANSI (Y 14.5-1966)
Figure 16-60 ANSI (Y 14.2-1957)
Figure 16-94 Los Alamos Scientific Laboratories
Figure 16-99 Texas Instruments Incorporated

Chapter Opening, 17 General Motors Research Laboratories
Figure 17-54 Bell Telephone Laboratories
Figure 17-55 Bell Telephone Laboratories
Figure 17-56 The Boeing Company
Figure 17-57 International Business Machines

A-I Photograph by William G. Hyzer. Reprinted from *Research/Development,* August 1971. © 1971 by Technical Publishing Company
A-II General Motors Corporation
A-II-Metric System U.S. Dept. of Commerce
A-III Reprinted from the January 19, 1970, issue of *Design News,* a Cahners publication.
A-III-Material Specification Systems Society of Automotive Engineers
A-V General Motors Corporation
A-VI Chicago *Tribune*
A-VII Salton
A-VIII Vermont Research Corporation. Design by Hill, Holliday, Connors, Cosmopulos Advertising, Boston
A-VIII-1 Gillette Safety Razor Company
A-VIII-2 Gillette Safety Razor Company
A-VIII-3 Gillette Safety Razor Company
A-VIII-4 Gillette Safety Razor Company
A-VIII-5 Gillette Safety Razor Company
A-VIII-6 Engineering Case Program, Stanford University
A-VIII-7 Engineering Case Program, Stanford University
A-VIII-8 Engineering Case Program, Stanford University
A-VIII-9 Engineering Case Program, Stanford University
A-VIII-10 Engineering Case Program, Stanford University
A-VIII-11 Engineering Case Program, Stanford University
A-VIII-12 Engineering Case Program, Stanford University
A-VIII-13 Engineering Case Program, Stanford University
A-VIII-14 Engineering Case Program, Stanford University

contents

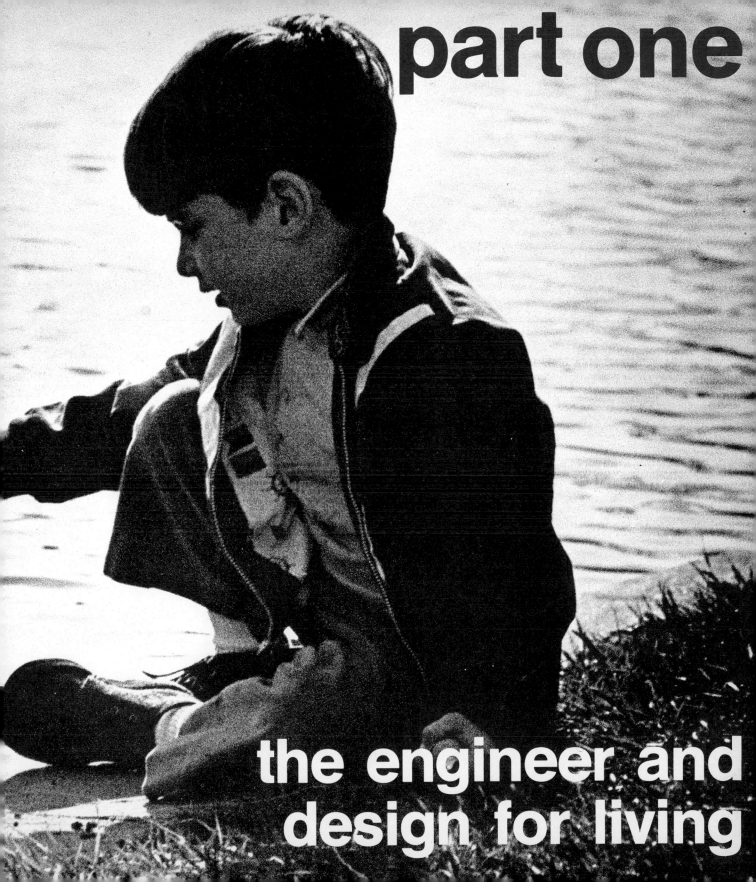

part one

the engineer and
design for living

These enormously magnified needlelike whiskers of sapphire resemble musicians tuning up for a concert. Finer than human hair, they have a tensile strength of more than 1 million pounds per square inch and can be used to reinforce metals in the same way that steel rods are used to strengthen concrete.

1-1
The System

t he earth has always been a constantly changing system. Until man arrived on the scene the changes that took place over the geological ages have been primarily the result of natural processes. However, through time, as man's numbers have grown, he has exerted his own influence upon the system. During the past century his population has begun to increase at such an alarming rate that his "artificial" changes have taken precedence over the slower natural changes of the system.

Perhaps more than the members of any other profession, engineers throughout history have made possible the incremental changes in our way of life—some desirable, some undesirable. However, too infrequently has the engineer also been involved in the political, religious, economic, demographic, and military decisions that have determined the ultimate use and effect of his creations—his designs.

The system—the earth—has undergone many artificial but significant changes in the last 100 years, many of which are detrimental to maintaining a desirable quality of life and too many of which are irreversible in their influence. Once man questioned, "Am I my brother's keeper?" Now the answer is no longer one of uncertainty; it is, "Yes, I am!" To survive on this earth we *must* be concerned about our neighbor's well-being. For example, when insecticides such as DDT can be plowed into farmlands in the midwest and a few months later their traces found in animals in such remote locations as the Antarctic, man can no longer ignore the ultimate consequences of his actions—his designs. The situation is becoming critical and people in all parts of the world *must* begin to show a special concern for the welfare of their fellow-men and of the plants and animals that share this planet with man.

In particular, the engineer of the future must be more cognizant of the effects that his designs could have upon the system, upon the lives of his fellow-men, and upon his own well-being. He is responsible also to warn those in government and business of the consequences and possible misuse of his designs.

Before we realistically can evaluate the effects of our designs, we must first have a good understanding of the natural order of the system in which we and our fellow-men live. Since the whole realm of natural, physical, and biological sciences is devoted to gaining such understanding, no attempt will be made in this text to address this part of the task. This first chapter is devoted to an exploration of the natural constraints of the system and particularly to the major challenges facing the engineer today—especially with regard to restoring the system to a state of change more nearly in harmony with its natural rate of change. However, lasting solutions to complex problems of this magnitude are possible *only* if the general populace demands and supports a national priority sufficient to supply the engineer with resources adequate to sustain his designs.

the system

The earth and its inhabitants form a complex system of constantly changing interrelationships. From the time of creation until a few thousand years ago, the laws of nature programmed the actions of all living things in relation to each other and to their environments. From the beginning, however, change was ever present. For example, as glaciers retreated, new forests grew to reclaim the land, ocean levels and coast lines changed, the winding courses of rivers altered, lakes appeared, and fish and animals migrated, as appropriate, to inhabit the new environments. Changes in climate and/or topography always brought about consequential changes in the distribution and ecological relationships of all living things—plants and animals alike. Almost invariably these changes brought about competitive relationships between the existing and migrating species. In this way certain competing forms were forced to adapt to new roles, while others became extinct. As a result of this continual change in the ecological balance of the earth over eons of time, there currently exist some 1,300,000 different kinds of plants and animals that make their homes in rather specific locations. Only a few, such as the cockroach, housefly, body louse, and house mouse, have been successful in invading a diversity of environments—this because they chose to follow man in his travels. Presumably, even these would be confined to specific regions if man did not exist on the earth.

Primitive man was concerned with every facet of his environment, and he had to be acutely aware of many of the existing ecological interrelationships. For example, he made it his business to know those places most commonly frequented by animals that he considered to be good to eat or whose skins or pelts were valued for clothing. He distinguished between the trees, plants, and herbs, and he knew which would provide him sustenance. Although by today's standards of education men of earlier civilizations might have been classified as "unlearned," they certainly were not ignorant. The Eskimo, for example, knew long ago that his sled dogs were susceptible to the diseases of the wild arctic foxes, and the Masai of East Africa have been aware for centuries that malaria is caused by mosquito bites.[1]

From century to century man has continued to add to his store of knowledge and understanding of nature. In so doing he has advanced progressively from a crude nomadic civilization in which he used what he could find useful to him in nature, to one sustained by domestication and agriculture in which he induced nature to produce more of the things that he wanted, and currently to one in which he is endeavoring to use the technologies of his own design to control the forces of nature.

For thousands of years after man first inhabited the earth, popula-

[1] Peter Farb, *Ecology*, New York: Time, Inc., 1963, p. 164.

Today is the first day of the remainder of your life.

"AND ON THE SEVENTH DAY"

In the end,
There was Earth, and it was with form and beauty.
And Man dwelt upon the lands of the Earth, the meadows and trees, and he said,
"Let us build our dwellings in this place of beauty."
And he built cities and covered the Earth with concrete and steel.
And the meadows were gone.
And Man said, "It is good."

On the second day, Man looked upon the waters of the Earth.
And Man said, "Let us put our wastes in the waters that the dirt will be washed away."
And Man did.
And the waters became polluted and foul in smell.
And Man said, "It is good."

On the third day, Man looked upon the forests of the Earth and saw they were beautiful.
And Man said, "Let us cut the timber for our homes and grind the wood for our use."
And Man did.
And the lands became barren and the trees were gone.
And Man said, "It is good."

On the fourth day, Man saw that animals were in abundance and ran in the fields and played in the sun.
And Man said, "Let us cage these animals for our amusement and kill them for our sport."
And Man did.
And there were no more animals on the face of the Earth.
And Man said, "It is good."

On the fifth day, Man breathed the air of the Earth.
And Man said, "Let us dispose of our wastes into the air for the winds shall blow them away."
And Man did.
And the air became heavy with dust and all living things choked and burned.
And Man said, "It is good."

On the sixth day, Man saw himself and seeing the many languages and tongues, he feared and hated.
And Man said, "Let us build great machines and destroy these lest they destroy us."
And Man built great machines and the Earth was fired with the rage of great wars.
And Man said, "It is good."

On the seventh day, Man rested from his labors and the Earth was still, for Man no longer dwelt upon the Earth.
And it was good.

New Mexico State Land Office

The air, the water and the ground are free gifts to man and no one has the power to portion them out in parcels. Man must drink and breathe and walk and therefore each man has a right to his share of each.

JAMES FENIMORE COOPER
The Prairie, 1827

ecology—the study of plants and animals in relation to their natural environment.

Harper's Encyclopedia of Science, 1967

And God blessed them, and God said unto them, be fruitful, and multiply, and *replenish* the earth, and *subdue* it: and have dominion over the fish of the sea, and over the fowl of the air, and over every living thing that moveth upon the earth.

GENESIS 1:28
THE HOLY BIBLE

1-2

tions were relatively small and, because man was mobile, the cumulative effect of his existence upon his environment was negligible. If, perchance, he did violence to a locality (for example, caused an entire forest to be burned), it was a relatively simple matter for him to move to another area and to allow time and nature to heal the wound. Because of the expanded world population, this alternative is no longer available to him. He affects not only his immediate environment but that of the whole earth.

Man's existence is a part of, not independent of, nature—and specifically it is most concerned with that part of nature that is closest to the surface of the earth known as the *biosphere*.[2] This is the wafer-thin skin of air, water, and soil comprising only a thousandth of the planet's diameter and measuring less than 8 miles thick.[3] It might be said to be analogous to the skin of an apple. However, this relatively narrow space encompasses the entire fabric of life as we know it—from virus to field mouse, man, and whale. Most life forms live within a domain extending from a half-mile below the surface of the ocean to 2 miles above the earth's surface, although a very few creatures can live in the deep ocean or above a 20,000-foot altitude. A number of processes of nature provide the biosphere with a delicate balance of characteristics that are necessary to sustain life. The life cycles of all living things, both fauna and flora, are interdependent and inextricably interwoven to form a delicately balanced *ecological system* that is as yet not completely understood by man. We do know, however, that not only is every organism affected by the environment of the "world" in which it lives, but it also has some effect on this environment.[4] The energy necessary to operate this system comes almost entirely from the sun and is utilized primarily through the processes of photosynthesis and heat. Any changes that man exerts on any part of the system will affect its tenuous balance and cause internal adjustment of either its individual organisms, its environment, or both. The extent and magnitude of the modifications that man has exerted on this ecological system have increased immeasurably within the past few years, particularly as a consequence of his rapid population growth. Certain of these modifications are of particular concern to the engineer.

Even during the period of the emergence of agriculture and domestication of animals, man began to alter the ecological balance of his environment. Eventually, some species of both plants and animals became extinct, while the growth of others was stimulated artificially. All too often man was not aware of the extent of the

[2]*Our Polluted Planet*, Pasadena, Calif.: Ambassador College Press, 1968, p. 54.
[3]R. C. Cook (ed.), "The Thin Slice of Life," *Population Bulletin*, Vol. 24, No. 5, p. 101.
[4]Marston Bates, "The Human EcoSystem," *Resources and Man*, San Francisco: W. H. Freeman, 1969, p. 25.

consequences of his actions and, more particularly, of the irreversibility of the alterations and imbalances that he had caused in nature's system. His concerns have more often been directed toward subduing the earth than replenishing it. Over the period of a few thousand years nature's law of "survival of the fittest" was gradually replaced by man's law of "survival of the most desirable." From man's short-term point of view, this change represented a significant advantage to him. Whereas once he was forced to gather fruit and nuts and to hunt animals to provide food and clothing for himself and his family—a life filled with uncertainty, at best—now he could simplify his food-gathering processes by increasing the yield of crops such as wheat, corn, rice, and potatoes. In addition, certain animals, such as cows, sheep, goats, and horses, were protected from their natural enemies and, in some instances, their predators were completely

There is another design that is far better. It is the design that nature has provided. . . . It is pointless to super-impose an abstract, man-made design on a region as though the canvas were blank. It isn't. Somebody has been there already. Thousands of years of rain and wind and tides have laid down a design. Here is our form and order. It is inherent in the land itself—in the pattern of the soil, the slopes, the woods—above all, in the patterns of streams and rivers.

WILLIAM H. WHYTE
The Last Landscape

1-3
There are too few beautiful areas to be found today that have been spared the ravages of man.

7

1-4

We shape our buildings; and forever afterwards our buildings shape us.

SIR WINSTON CHURCHILL
Speech in House of Commons, October, 1943

1-5
Man's continued misuse of the world's resources can only lead to a depletion of the essentials for life.

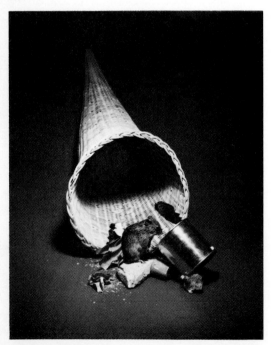

annihilated. Such eradication seemed to serve man's immediate interests, but it also eliminated nature's way of maintaining an ecological balance. Man, in turn, was also affected by these changes. At one time only the strongest of his species survived, and the availability or absence of natural food kept his population in balance with the surroundings. With domestication these factors have become less of a problem and "survival of the fittest" no longer governs his increase in numbers. In general, today both strong and weak live and procreate. Because of this condition the world's population growth has begun to mount steadily and *alarmingly* . . . because of the manifold problems that accompany large populations and for which solutions are still to be found.

In many respects the young engineer of today lives in a world that is vastly different from the one known to his grandfather or great grandfather. Without question he enjoys a standard of living unsurpassed in the history of mankind; and yet, in spite of the significant agricultural and technological advances made in this generation, over half the world's population still lives in perpetual hunger. Famine, fever, and war continue to run rampant throughout portions of the earth. The wastes from his own technology continue to mount steadily. Nevertheless, his population growth continues unabated, further compounding these problems.

the population explosion—a race to global famine

Until comparatively recent times the growth of the human race was governed by the laws of nature in a manner similar to that controlling the growth of all other living things. However, as man's culture

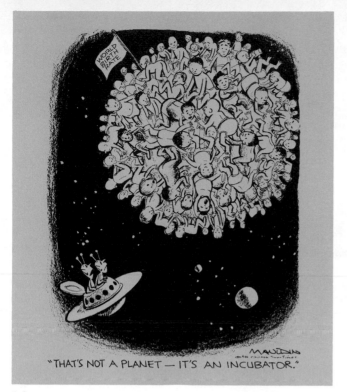

"THAT'S NOT A PLANET — IT'S AN INCUBATOR."

1-6

1-7

changed from nomadic to agrarian to technological, he began to alter nature's population controls significantly. Through control of disease and pestilence his average life span has been extended over three times. His ability to supply his family consistently with food and clothing has also been improved immeasurably. Combinations of these two factors have caused his population to increase in geometric progression: 2–4–8–16–32–64–128, etc.[5] Initially it took hundreds of thousands of years for a significant change to occur in the world population. However, as the numbers became larger, and particularly in more recent times as man's life span began to lengthen as a result of his gaining some control over starvation, disease, and violence, the results of geometric growth began to have a profound effect. Whereas it has taken an estimated 2 million years for the world population to reach slightly over 3 billion persons, it will take only 35 years to add the next 3 billion *if present growth rates remain unchanged*. The significance of this problem is illustrated by [1-7].

As in the case of man's altering his ecological environment, he has not always been wise enough to anticipate all the various effects of his changes. In the case of his own propagation, he has managed

[5] T. R. Malthus, 1798, *An Essay on the Principle of Population As It Affects the Future Improvements of Mankind*, facsimile reprint in 1926 for J. Johnson, Macmillan, London.

1-8
Traditionally, one person signifies loneliness; two persons—companionship; three persons—a crowd. In more recent times a new concept has been added: multitudes signify pollution and loneliness.

U.S. POPULATION GROWTH

1900 - 76 MILLION

1940 - 131.6 MILLION

1960 - 180 MILLION

2000 - 340 MILLION

1-9   SOURCE: U.S. BUREAU OF THE CENSUS

to introduce "death control," but birth rates have continued to climb, particularly in the underdeveloped countries. It is estimated that the average annual increase in world population in 1650 was only 0.3 per cent.[6] In 1900 this annual growth rate had increased to 0.9 per cent; in 1930, 1.0 per cent; in 1960, 2.0 per cent; and in 1970 over 2.1 per cent. Unless these rates decline significantly, which does not now seem likely, a worldwide crisis is fast approaching.

The earth's land area, only 10 per cent of which appears to be arable, is fixed and unexpandable, and a shortage of food and water is already an accepted fact of life in many countries. Although conditions in some slum areas of the United States are very bad, they bear little resemblance to many areas of the world where people grovel in filth and live little better than animals. Dr. Paul Ehrlich describes a recent visit to India:[7]

I have understood the population explosion intellectually for a long time. I came to understand it emotionally one stinking hot night in Delhi a couple of years ago. My wife and daughter and I were returning to our hotel in an ancient taxi. The seats were hopping with fleas. The only functional gear was third. As we crawled through the city, we entered a crowded slum area. The temperature was well over 100, and the air was a haze of dust and smoke. The streets seemed alive with people. People eating, people washing, people sleeping. People visiting, arguing, and screaming. People thrusting their hands through the taxi window, begging. People defecating and urinating. People clinging to buses. People herding animals. People, people, people, people. As we moved slowly through the mob, hand horn squawking, the dust, noise, heat, and cooking fires gave the scene a hellish aspect.

Over one third of the human beings now living on the earth are starving, and another one third are ill fed. The underdeveloped countries of the world are incapable of producing enough food to feed their populations. This deficiency is 16 million tons of food each year and will grow to a staggering 88 million tons of food per year by 1985. For these people to be fed an adequate diet, the current world food production would have to double by 1980, *which appears to be an impossible task*.[8] The quantity of food available is not the only problem; it must also be of the proper quality. For example, in Central Africa every other baby born dies before the age of five *even though food is generally plentiful*. They die from a disease known as *kwashiorkor*, which is caused by a lack of sufficient protein in the diet. The magnitude of the problem continues to grow as the world population increases. More population means more famine. It also means more crowding, more disease, less sanitation, more

[6]J. M. Jones, *Does Overpopulation Mean Poverty?* Washington, D.C.: Center for International Economic Growth, 1962, p. 13.
[7]P. R. Ehrlich, *The Population Bomb*, New York: Ballantine Books, 1968, p. 15.
[8]*Famine! Can We Survive?* Pasadena, Calif.: Ambassador College Press, 1969, p. 14.

waste and garbage, more pollution of air, water, and land, and ultimately . . . the untimely death of millions, or possibly, the end of human life on earth.

In the United States, just as in the underdeveloped countries of the world, the population has tended to migrate to cities and some of the cities have grown to monstrous size, often called megalopolises. These treks have been brought about by the widespread use of mechanized agriculture and the impoverishment of the soil. With these migrations special problems have arisen. No longer is a city dweller self-sufficient in his ability to provide sustenance, shelter, and security for his family. Rather his food, water, fuel, and power must all be brought to him by others, and his wastes of every kind must be taken away. Most frequently his work is located many

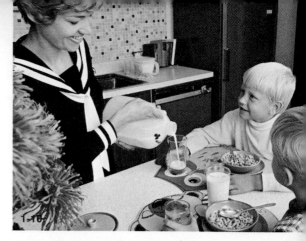

One half of the people in the world had food to eat this morning. . . .

. . . the other one half faced starvation.

Very few Americans, picking and choosing among the piles of white bread in a supermarket, have ever appreciated the social standing of white bread elsewhere in the world. To be able to afford white bread is a dream that awaits fulfillment for billions of the world's population. To afford it signifies that one enjoys all the comforts of life.

ISABEL CARY LUNDBERG
Harpers Magazine, December, 1948

We can only dimly perceive the kind of society we will have a decade or so hence. But we can see the directions of change. The issues coming to the fore in our time have in common a concern with the quality of life, and I believe we are entering an era in which the quality of life for every citizen will move far ahead of the gross national product as the measure of our well-being. Increasingly some of the classical views of property will disappear, giving way to the view that resources are not free for the taking but belong fundamentally to the people. Increasingly this will mean that technological innovations are not automatically judged to be improvements. Nor will the marketplace be a sufficient test of their value. Increasingly we will demand of technological innovations that both in use and in the process by which they are created they enhance the public good. Or, to put it more accurately, we will demand that they function with the least possible hazard to ourselves and the environment.

WILLIAM D. McELROY
Address, The Society of the Sigma Xi, 1970

miles from his home, and his reliance upon a transportation system becomes critical. He finds himself vulnerable to every kind of public emergency, and the psychological pressures of city life often lead to mental illness or escape into the use of alcohol and drugs. The incidence of crime increases, and his clustering invites a more rapid spread of disease and pestilence than ever. In general, his cities are enormous consumers of electrical and chemical energy and producers of staggering amounts of wastes and pollution. Today 70 per cent of the people in our country live on 1 per cent of the land, and the exodus from the countryside continues.

What are the implications for the engineer of these national and international sociological crises? The engineer is particularly affected

1-13
Wheat is one of the world's most important food crops because each grain contains a relatively large amount of useful protein. Even though engineering designs and advances in agricultural science have made possible a substantially increased production, the disparity between food supply and world population continues to increase.

because he is an essential participant among those whose creative efforts should be directed *to improving* man's physical and economic lot. First, he must learn all he can about the extent and causes of the technological problems that have resulted, and he must direct his energies and abilities to solving them. In general, he must recognize his responsibility to restore the equilibrium to the ecological system of nature in those cases in which it has become unbalanced. This requires that he be cognizant of the manifold effects of his designs *prior to their implementation*. The task is not an easy one, and the challenge is great, but the consequences are too severe to be disregarded.

Just as the engineer has learned that the physical laws of nature *do* govern the universe, so also must he be aware that nature's laws governing the procession and diversity of life on this planet are equally valid and unyielding. In the remainder of this chapter we shall consider the severity and complexity of several problems that confront today's society and, more particularly, the engineer's social responsibility for their solution.

For this is the word that the Lord has spoken.
The earth dries up and withers,
The whole world withers and grows sick;
   the earth's high places sicken,
and the earth itself is desecrated by the feet of those who
     live in it,
because they have broken the laws, disobeyed the statutes
and violated the eternal covenant.

ISAIAH 24:3b–5
THE HOLY BIBLE, The New English Translation

our polluted planet

In the last few years the average American citizen has become aware that our "spaceship earth" is undergoing many severe and detrimental ecological changes, which may take hundreds of years to repair. Unfortunately, he is not always able to distinguish effects that are of a temporary nature from those with long-term consequences. Frequently, his most damaging actions to the environment are either of an incremental or visually indistinguishable nature, and for this reason he participates willingly in them. In some measure man's reactions are dulled by the slowness of deterioration. This is somewhat analogous to the actions of a frog that will die rather than jump out, when placed in a bucket of water that is being *slowly* heated. In contrast, if the frog is pitched into a bucket of boiling water, he will immediately jump out and thereby avoid severe injury. The engineer in particular must learn to understand such cause and effect relationships so that his designs will not become detrimental to the orderly and natural development of life.

the air environment

The atmosphere, which makes up the largest fraction of the biosphere, is a dynamic system that absorbs continuously a wide range of solids, liquids, and gases from both natural and man-made sources. These substances often travel through the air, disperse, and react with one another and with other substances, both chemically and

The sky is the daily bread of the eyes.
RALPH WALDO EMERSON
Journal May 25, 1843

THE ENGINEER AND DESIGN FOR LIVING

A recent scientific analysis of New York City's atmosphere concluded that a New Yorker on the street took into his lungs the equivalent in toxic materials of 38 cigarettes a day.

ROBERT RIENOW and LEONA TRAIN RIENOW
Moment in the Sun, 1967

1-14
What you think about air pollution—
depends on your vantage point.

1-15

physically. Eventually, most of these constituents find their way into a depository, such as the ocean, or to a receptor, such as a man. A few, such as helium, escape from the biosphere. Others, such as carbon dioxide, may enter the atmosphere faster than they can be absorbed and thus gradually accumulate in the air.[9]

Clean, dry air contains 78.09 per cent nitrogen by volume and 20.94 per cent oxygen. The remaining 0.97 per cent is composed of a gaseous mixture of carbon dioxide, helium, argon, krypton, and xenon, as well as very small amounts of some other organic and inorganic gases whose amounts vary with time and place in the atmosphere. Through both natural and man-made processes that exist upon the earth, varying amounts of contaminants continuously enter the atmosphere. That portion of these substances which interacts with the environment to cause toxicity, disease, aesthetic distress, physiological effects, or environmental decay has been labeled by man as a pollutant. In general, the actions of people are the primary cause of pollution and, as population increases, the attendant pollution problems also increase proportionally. This is not a newly recognized relationship, however. The first significant change in man's effect on nature came with his deliberate making of a fire. No other creature on earth starts fires. Prehistoric man built a fire in his cave home for cooking, heating, and to provide light for his family. Although the smoke was sometimes annoying, no real problem existed with regard to pollution of the air environment. However, when his friends or neighbors visited him and also built fires in the same cave, even prehistoric man recognized that he then had an *air-pollution problem*. People in some nineteenth-century cities with their hundreds of thousands of smoldering soft-coal grates coughed amid a thicker and deadlier smog than any modern city can concoct.[10] Today the natural terrain that surrounds large cities is recognized as having a significant bearing on the air-pollution problem. However, this is not an altogether new concept either. Historians tell us that the present Los Angeles area, which in recent years has become a national symbol of comparison for excessive smog levels,[11] was known as the "Valley of Smokes" when the Spaniards first arrived.[12] In recent years air pollution has become a problem of world concern.

[9]*Cleaning Our Environment: The Chemical Basis for Action*, Washington, D.C.: American Chemical Society, 1969, p. 23.

[10]Tom Alexander, "Some Burning Questions About Combustion," *Fortune*, February, 1970, p. 130.

[11]The term *smog* was coined originally to describe a combination of smoke and fog, such as was common in London when coal was widely used for generating power and heating homes. More recently it has come to mean the accumulation of photochemical reaction products that result largely from the action of the radiant energy of the sun on the emissions of internal combustion engines (automobile exhaust).

[12]H. C. Wohlers, *Air Pollution—The Problem, the Source, and the Effects*, Philadelphia: Drexel Institute of Technology, 1969, p. 1.

Imagine a series of clear plastic domes, one within another. You can only see them from the outside; from the inside they are invisible. You become aware of an environment—one of those domes that surround you—only when you get outside of it. At that point you can see it. But you can't see the one which is now about you.

HOWARD GOSSAGE
Ramparts, April, 1966

Hell is a city much like London—A populous and smoky city.

PERCY BYSSHE SHELLEY
Peter Bell the Third, 1819

1-16
One solution to the air pollution problem. Surely there must be a more desirable alternative!

Table 1-1. Sources of Air Pollutants in the United States**
[millions of tons/year (1969)]

Source	Totals	% of Totals	Carbon Monoxide	Sulfur Oxides	Hydro-carbons	Nitrogen Oxides	Particulate Matter	Other
Motor vehicles	86	60	66	1	12	6	1	*
Industry	25	17	2	9	4	2	6	2
Power plants	20	14	1	12	*	3	3	
Space heating	8	6	2	3	1	1	1	*
Refuse disposal	4	3	1	*	1	*	1	*
TOTALS	143	100	72	26	18	12	12	4

*Less than 1%.
** *Your Right to. Clean Air,* Washington, D.C.: The Conservation Foundation, 1970, p. 15.

The great question of the seventies is, shall we surrender to our surroundings, or shall we make our peace with nature and begin to make reparations for the damage we have done to our air, to our land, and to our water? . . . Clean air, clean water, open spaces—these should once again be the birthright of every American. If we act now, they can be.

PRESIDENT RICHARD M. NIXON
State of the Union Message, January 22, 1970

In the United States the most common air pollutants are carbon monoxide, sulfur oxides, hydrocarbons, nitrogen oxides, and particles (Table 1-1). Their primary sources are motor vehicles, industry, electrical power plants, space heating, and refuse disposal, with approximately 60 per cent of the bulk being contributed by motor vehicles and 17 per cent by industry. It seems probable that by the year 2000 America's streets will contain twice as many automobiles as the current 100 million. This is a foreboding prospect *unless improved engineering designs are able to alleviate the situation.*[13] Restoring the quality of the atmosphere ranks as one of the most difficult and challenging tasks of our generation. As with the determined effort of the 1960's to explore the moon, an engineering venture of this complexity requires a coordinated national effort of great magnitude. With every man, woman, and child in the United States producing an average of 1,400 pounds/year of air pollutants, the problem is one of serious proportions. The National Air Quality Standards Act of 1970, which specified that motor vehicle exhaust emissions should be reduced by 90 per cent by January 1, 1975, could provide the impetus for a sincere and necessary national commitment.

It has been found that the significantly increasing volume of particulate matter entering the atmosphere scatters the incoming sunlight. This reduces the amount of heat that reaches the earth and tends to reduce its temperature. The decreasing mean global temperature of recent years has been attributed to the rising concentrations of airborne particles in the atmosphere.[14] A counteracting phenomenon, commonly referred to as the *greenhouse effect,* is caused by the increasing amounts of carbon dioxide found in the atmosphere. Although carbon dioxide occurs naturally as a constituent of the atmosphere and is not normally classified as an air pollutant, man

[13] *Our Polluted Planet,* Pasadena, Calif.: Ambassador College Press, 1968, p. 25.
[14] R. E. Newell, "The Global Circulation of Atmospheric Pollutants," *Scientific American,* January, 1971, p. 40.

1-17

Environment pollution . . . now affects the whole earth. Smog produced in urban and industrial areas is hovering over the countryside and beginning to spread over the oceans . . . cities will not benefit much longer from the cleansing effects of the winds for the simple reason that the wind itself is contaminated.

New York Times, January 6, 1969

Water, water everywhere, Nor any drop to drink.
SAMUEL TAYLOR COLERIDGE
The Rime of the Ancient Mariner, 1798

does generate an abnormally large amount of it in those combustion processes that utilize coal, oil, and natural gas. The presence of water vapor in the atmosphere, and to a lesser extent carbon dioxide and ozone, acts in a manner similar to the glass in a greenhouse. Light from the sun arrives as short-wavelength radiation (visible and ultra-violet) and is allowed to pass through it to heat the earth, but the relatively long-wavelength infrared radiation (heat radiation) that is emitted by the earth is absorbed—thereby providing an unnatural and additional heating effect to the earth. It has been estimated that if the carbon dioxide content in the atmosphere continues to increase at the present rate, the mean global temperature could rise by almost $4°C$ in the next 40 to 50 years. This might become a matter of great importance, because small temperature increases could cause a partial melting of the ice caps of the earth (causing flooding of coastal land, towns, and cities) with consequential and devastating effects to man.[15]

Air pollution can cause death, impair health, reduce visibility, bring about vast economic losses, and contribute to the general deterioration of both our cities and countryside. It is therefore a matter of grave importance that engineers of all disciplines consciously incorporate in their designs sufficient constraints and safeguards to ensure that they do not contribute to the pollution of the atmosphere. In addition, they must apply their ingenuity and problem-solving abilities to eliminating air pollution where it exists and restoring the natural environment.

the quest for water quality

Water is the most abundant compound to be found upon the face of the earth and, next to air, it is the most essential resource for man's survival. The per capita use of water in the United States is 1,000 gallons/day, and this demand continues to grow. Early man was most concerned with the quality (purity) of his drinking water, and even he was aware that certain waters were contaminated and could cause illness or death. In addition, modern man has found that he must be concerned also with the quantity of the water available for his use. An abundant supply of relatively pure water is no longer available in most areas. Today, water pollution, *the presence of toxic or noxious substances or heat in natural water sources,* is considered to be one of the most pressing social and economic issues of our time. Just how bad water pollution can become was dramatically illustrated when the oily, chocolate-brown Cuyahoga River in Cleveland, Ohio, caught fire and blazed for several days, nearly destroying

[15] Lord Ritchie-Calder, quoted in *Engineering Opportunities—College Edition,* February, 1970, p. 32.

two railroad bridges that spanned the river. This once beautiful river was so filled with municipal and industrial wastes that even the leeches and sludge worms, normally found only in polluted rivers, could not survive; it was, in effect, nothing more than a flammable sewer.[16] Unfortunately, many other water bodies in the United States are no less polluted, and now approximately one half the people in the nation "drink their own treated sewage." Many city water-treatment plants merely remove the particulate matter and disinfect the available water with chlorine to kill bacteria, since they were not originally designed to remove pesticides, herbicides, and other organic and inorganic chemicals that may be present.[17] This problem has become acute in a number of areas in recent months

1-19
Oil and grease discharges are responsible for polluting many of the rivers and lakes of America.

[16]Gene Bylinsky, "The Limited War on Water Pollution," *The Environment*, New York: Harper & Row, 1970, p. 20.
[17]*Ibid.*, p. 25.

1-20
Pollution does not necessarily need to accompany poverty, but it most frequently does.

as hundreds of new contaminants have been discovered in streams and lakes: bacteria and viruses, detergents, municipal sewage, acid from mine drainage, pesticides and weed killers, radioactive substances, phosphorus from fertilizers, trace amounts of metals and drugs, and other organic and inorganic chemicals. As the population continues to increase, the burden assumed by the engineer to design more comprehensive water-treatment plants also mounts. Indeed, the well-being of entire communities may depend upon his design abilities, because it is now a recognized condition of population increase that "everyone cannot live upstream."

The processes of nature have long made use of the miraculous ability of rivers and lakes to "purify themselves." After pollutants find their way into a water body they are subject to dilution, or settling, the action of the sun, and to being consumed by beneficial bacteria. The difficulty arises when man disturbs the equilibrium of the ecosystem by dumping large amounts of his wastes into a particular water body, thereby intensifying the demand for purification. In time the body of water cannot meet the demand, organic debris accumulates, anaerobic areas develop, fish die, and putrification is the result. This process also occurs in nature, but it may take many thousands of years to complete the natural processes of deterioration. Man can alter nature's time scale appreciably.

Lake Erie, the smallest of the Great Lakes, provides a classic example of what can happen when man ignores his responsibility to protect a natural resource.[18] *Eutrophication*, a term used to denote the process of nutrient enrichment by which lakes fill and die, has overtaken the lake prematurely, and because of this it is estimated to have aged over 15,000 natural years since 1925. These consequences, however, should come as no surprise. The lake is fed by a number of heavily polluted rivers, including the Cuyahoga and Buffalo Rivers. In addition, over 9.6 billion gallons of industrial waste and 1.5 billion gallons of sewage are dumped into the lake *each day* from adjoining states.[19] Among the most damaging pollutants in this lake appear to be detergents and fertilizer polyphosphates that serve to stimulate the growth of algae—tiny, green plants—which then multiply until they become large green mats that literally clog and stifle the lake. When the algae die, their decay depletes the water of its life-giving oxygen, choking forms of desirable aquatic life, including fish.[20]

The presence of radioactive wastes and excess heat are relatively new types of pollution to water bodies, but they are of no less importance for the engineer to take into account in his designs. All radioactive materials are biologically injurious. Therefore, radioac-

Modern man . . . has asbestos in his lungs, DDT in his fat, and strontium 90 in his bones.
Today's Health, April, 1970

If the people of Cleveland only realized that they are drinking their own and their neighbor's purified urine and fecal matter, they might be prompted to take a closer look at what is floating in one of the world's largest open sewers—Lake Erie and the rivers emptying into it.
Medical World News, September 26, 1969

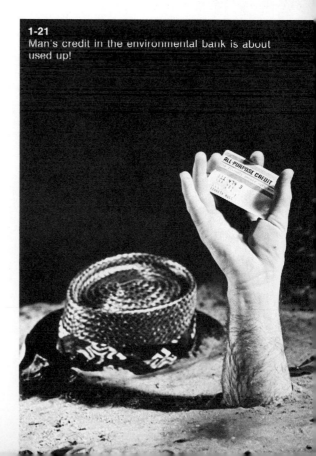

1-21
Man's credit in the environmental bank is about used up!

[18] V. W. Wigotsky, "Engineering and the Urban Crisis," *Design News*, December 7, 1970, p. 31.
[19] "Eat, Drink, and Be Sick," *Medical World News*, September 26, 1969, p. 32.
[20] Senator Gaylord Nelson, *Congressional Record*, February 26, 1970, p. S2444.

tive substances that are normally emitted by nuclear power plants are suspected of finding their way into the ecological food chain, where they could cause serious problems. For this reason all radioactive wastes should be isolated from the biological environment during the "life" of the isotopes (as much as 600 years in some cases).

The heat problem arises because nuclear electrical power generating plants require great quantities of water for cooling. Although the heated discharge water from a nuclear power plant is approximately the same temperature as that from a fossil-fuel power plant, the quantity has been increased by approximately 40 per cent. The warmer water absorbs less oxygen from the atmosphere, and this accelerates the normal rate of decomposition of organic matter. This unnatural heat also unbalances the life cycles of fish who, being cold blooded, cannot regulate their body temperatures correspondingly. With the prospect of the number of nuclear power plants doubling by 1980, this problem will loom larger than ever.

Engineering designs of the future must take into account all these factors to ensure for all the nation's inhabitants a water supply that is both sufficient in quantity and unpolluted in quality. This is not only the engineer's challenge, but his responsibility as well.

solid-waste disposal

We are living in a most unusual time—a time when possibly the most valuable tangible asset that a person could own would be a "bottomless hole." Never before in history have so many people had so much garbage, refuse, trash, and other wastes to dispose of, and at the same time never before has there been such a shortage of "dumping space." The proliferation of refuse, however, is only partly attributable to the population explosion. A substantial portion of the blame must be assumed by an affluent society that is careless with its increasing purchasing power and that has demonstrated a decided distaste for secondhand articles.[21] Table 1-2 lists the primary solid-waste constituents of the United States.

The most popular method of solid-waste disposal has long been "removal from the immediate premises." For centuries man has been aware of the health hazards that accompany the accumulations of garbage. Historians have recorded that a sign at the city limits of ancient Rome warned all persons to transport their refuse outside the city or risk being fined. Also, it has been recognized that in the Middle Ages the custom of dumping garbage in the streets was largely responsible for the proliferation of disease-carrying rats, flies, and insects that made their homes in piles of refuse.[22]

[21] Alex Hershaft, "Solid Waste Treatment," *Science and Technology*, June, 1969, p. 35.
[22] *Ibid.*, p. 34.

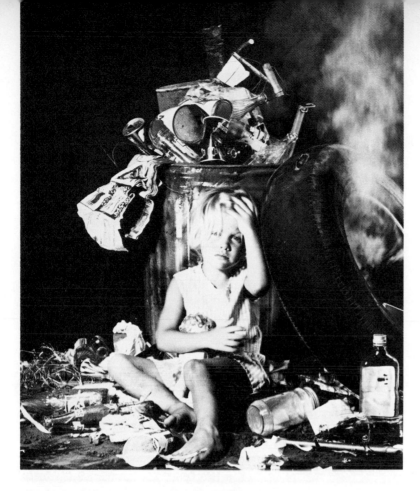

1-22
The character of a nation is revealed by
examining its garbage.

Table 1-2. Solid Waste of the United States*
1970

Category		Composition		Percentage Distribution	Estimated Production (10^6 tons/year)
Refuse	Garbage	Animal and vegetable kitchen wastes		15	
	Rubbish	Dry household, commercial, and industrial waste	Paper	28	230
			Yard waste	14	
			Glass and metal	10	
			Other	10	
	Municipal waste	Construction waste and street sweepings		23	
Industrial wastes		Industrial processing scrap and by-products			120
Scrap metal		Automobiles, machinery, major appliances			20
Sewage residue		Grit, sludge, and other residue from sewage-treatment plants			30
Mining displacement		Overburden and gangue			1200
Agriculture waste		Manure, animal carcasses, crop and logging debris			2400

*Drawn from compilation by Alex Hershaft, *Solid Waste Management*, Grumman Aerospace Corporation, Bethpage, N.Y., 1970.

1-24
Incineration may not be the answer.

1-25
Pollution is a personal matter.

1-23
America the ugly—or—America the beautiful? The choice is yours!

On the average, each person in the United States has established the following record with regard to the generation of solid waste, refuse, and garbage:

1920	2.75	pounds/person per day
1970	5.5	pounds/person per day
1980	8.0	pounds/person per day (estimated)

From New York to Los Angeles, cities throughout the nation are rapidly depleting their disposal space, and there is considerable concern that too little attention has been given to what is fast becoming one of man's most distressing problems—solid-waste disposal. Why is trash becoming such a problem? The answer seems to lie partially in man's changing value system. Just a generation or two ago, thrift and economy were considered to be important tenets of American life and few items with any inherent value were discarded. Today, we live in the era of "the throwaway." More and more containers of all types are being made of nondecomposable plastic or glass, or nonrustable aluminum, and everything from furniture to clothing is being made from disposable paper products, which are sold by advertising that challenges purchasers to "discard when disenchanted." In 1970 the American public threw away approximately 50 billion cans, 30 billion bottles, 35 million tons of paper, 5 million tons of plastic, and 100 million automobile tires. The problem of disposing of 7 million junked automobiles each year is also becoming a problem that can no longer be ignored—particularly when this volume is expected to climb to over 10 million per year by 1980.[23] The truth is that most "consumers" in America have instead become "users and discarders," but this fact has not been taken into account.

Unfortunately, most current waste-disposal practices make no

[23] *U.S. News & World Report,* September 8, 1969.

attempt to recover any of the potential values that are in solid wastes. The methods of disposing of refuse in most common use today are dumping and burning in the open, sanitary land fills, burial in abandoned mines or dumping at sea, and grinding in disposal systems followed by flushing into sewers. Some edible waste, such as garbage, is fed to hogs.

Since almost all the products of the engineer's design ingenuity will eventually be discarded, due to wear or obsolescence, it is imperative that consideration for disposal be given to each design *at the time that it is first produced*. In addition, the well-being of society as we know it appears to depend in some measure upon the creative design abilities of the engineer to devise new processes of recycling

I think that I shall never see
A billboard lovely as a tree
Indeed, unless the billboards fall
I'll never see a tree at all.

OGDEN NASH
Song of the Open Road, 1945

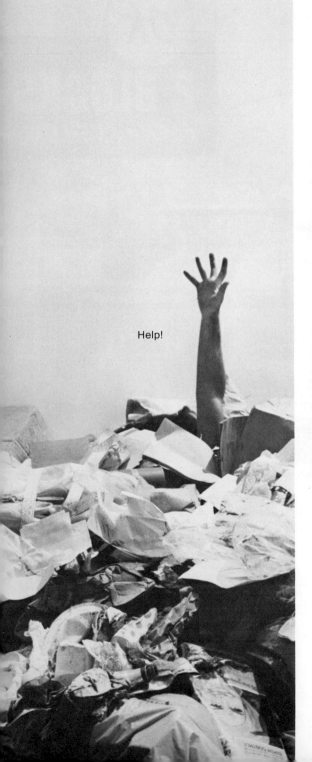

Help!

wastes,[24] by either changing the physical form of wastes or the manner of their disposal, or both. Such designs must be accomplished within the constraints of economic considerations and without augmenting man's other pollution problems: air, water, and sound. Basically, the solution of waste disposal is a matter of attitude, ingenuity, and economics—all areas in which the engineer can make significant contributions.

the rising crescendo of unwanted sound

A silent world is not only undesirable but impossible to achieve. Man's very nature is psychologically sensitive to the many sounds that come to his ears. For example, he is pleased to hear the gurgle and murmur of a brook or the soothing whispering wind as it filters through overhead pine trees, but his blood is likely to chill if he recognizes the whirring buzz of a rattlesnake or hears the sudden screech of an automobile tire as it slides on pavement. He may thrill to the sharp bugle of a far-off hunting horn, but his thoughts often tend to lapse into dreams of inaccessible places as a distant train whistle penetrates the night.[25] Yes, sounds have an important bearing on man's sense of well-being. Although the average city dweller's ears continue to alert him to impending dangers, their sensitivity is far less acute than that of people who live in less densely populated areas. It is said that, even today, aborigines living in the stillness of isolated African villages can easily hear each other talking in low conversational tones at distances as great as 100 yards, and that their hearing acuity diminishes little with age.[26] Even as man's technology has brought hundreds of thousands of desirable and satisfying innovations, it has also provided the means for the retrogression of his sense of hearing—for deafness caused by a deterioration of the microscopic hair cells that transmit sound from the ear to the brain. It has been found that prolonged exposure to intense sound levels will produce permanent hearing loss, and it matters not that such levels may be considered to be pleasing. [Some people purport to enjoy "rock" music concerts at sound levels exceeding 110 decibels[27] (Table 1-3).] Today noise-induced hearing loss looms as one of America's major health hazards.

Noise is generally considered to be any annoying or unwanted sound.[28] Noise (like sound) has two discernible effects on man. One

[24]*Environmental Science and Technology*, May, 1970, p. 384.

[25]*Noise: Sound Without Value*, Washington, D.C.: Committee on Environmental Quality of the Federal Council for Science and Technology, 1968, p. 1.

[26]*The Environment*, The Editors of *Fortune*, New York: Harper & Row, 1970, p. 136.

[27]A *decibel* (abbreviated dB) is a measure of sound intensity or pressure change on the ear.

[28]Michael Rodda, *Noise and Society*, London: Oliver & Boyd, 1967, p. 2.

Table 1-3.   Table of Sound Decibels

	Decibels	
	140	Threshold of pain
Hydraulic press at 3 ft	130	
Overhead jet aircraft at 400 ft	120	Pneumatic clipper at 5 ft
Unmuffled motorcycle	110	Construction noise
Rock and roll band	100	Inside subway car
10-hp outboard motor at 30 ft	90	Inside sedan in city traffic
Small truck accelerating	80	Office with tabulating machines
Automobile	70	Dishwasher
Conversational speech	60	Accounting office
	50	Light traffic at 100 ft
Average residence	40	
	30	Broadcasting studio music
Whisper	20	
	10	
	0	

1-28
Man is affected psychologically by the sounds that he hears.

causes a deterioration of his sensitivity of hearing, and the other affects his psychological state of mind. The adverse effects of noise have long been recognized as a form of environmental pollution. Julius Caesar was so annoyed by noise that he banned chariot driving at night, and, prior to 1865, studies in England reported substantial hearing losses among blacksmiths, boilermakers, and railroad men.[29]

Not many sounds in life, and I include all urban and all rural sounds, exceed in interest a knock at the door.
CHARLES LAMB
Valentine's Day, 1823

[29] Aram Glorig, *Noise As a Public Health Hazard,* W. D. Ward and J. E. Fricke (eds.), Washington, D.C.: The American Speech and Hearing Association, 1969, p. 105.

I love the sound of the horn, at night, in the depth of the woods.

ALFRED DE VIGNY
Le Cor, 1826

Noise is the most impertinent of all forms of interruption. It is not only an interruption, but also a disruption of thought.

ARTHUR SCHOPENHAUER
Studies in Pessimism, On Noise, 1851

1-29
If the ear were to shatter or bleed profusely when subjected to abuse from intense or prolonged noise, we might be more careful of its treatment.

$E = mc^2$

ALBERT EINSTEIN
Annalen der Physik, 1905
Statement of the mass–energy equivalence relationship.

It has only been in recent years, however, that noise has been recognized as a health hazard.[30]

It is estimated that the average background noise level throughout the United States has been doubling each 10 years. At this rate of increase, living conditions will be intolerable within a few years. Such a crescendo of sound results from the steady increase of population and the concomitant growth of the use of power on every hand—from the disposal in the kitchen and the motorcycle in the street to power tools in the factory. Buses, jet airliners, television sets, stereos, dishwashers, tractors, mixers, waste disposers, air conditioners, automobiles, jackhammers, power lawn mowers, vacuum cleaners, and typewriters are but a few examples of noise producers that are deemed desirable to today's high standard of living, but which may very well also prevent man from fully enjoying the fruits of his labors, unless the sound levels at which they operate are altered significantly.

Except in the case of minimizing aircraft noise, the United States lags far behind many countries in noise prevention and control. Virtually all man-made noise can be suppressed, and the same engineer who formulates the idea for a new type of kitchen aid or designs an improved family vehicle must also be capable of solving the acoustical problems that are associated with his designs. In this regard, he is responsible to generations yet unborn for the consequences of his actions.

man's insatiable thirst for energy

In man's earliest habitation of the earth he competed for energy with other members of the earth's ecological environment. Initially his energy requirements were primarily satisfied by food—probably in the range of 2,000 kilocalories (100 thermal watts) per person per day. However, as he has been able to make and control the use of fire, domesticate the plant and animal kingdoms, and initiate technologies of his own choosing, his per capita consumption of energy has increased appreciably. Today in the United States, man's thirst for energy (or *power*, which is the time rate use of energy) exceeds 10,000 thermal watts per capita per day,[31] which is about 100 times the average of underdeveloped nations.[32] This demand has followed an exponential pattern of growth similar to the growth of the world population *except that the annual rate of increase for nonnutrient*

[30] A. D. Hosey and C. H. Powell (eds.), *Industrial Noise*, Washington, D.C.: US Department of Health, Education, and Welfare, 1967.
[31] M. K. Hubbert, *Resources and Man*, San Francisco: W. H. Freeman, 1969, p. 237.
[32] S. F. Singer, "Human Energy Production As a Process in the Biosphere," *Scientific American*, September, 1970, p. 183.

energy utilization is growing at a rate (approximately 4 per cent per year) *considerably in excess of the world's growth in population* (approximately 2 per cent per year). This is brought about by man's appetite for more gadgets, faster cars and airplanes, heavier machinery, etc.

The principal sources of the world's energy prior to about A.D. 1200 were solar energy, wood, wind, and water. At about this time in England it was discovered that certain "black rocks" found along the seashore would burn. From this there followed in succession the mining of coal[33] and the exploration of oil and natural-gas reservoirs. More recently, nuclear energy has emerged as one of the most promising sources of power yet discovered. The safe management and disposal of radioactive wastes, however, continue to present problems for the engineer.

The graph [1-31] provides a record of the history of energy consumption in the United States since 1800, and represents a prediction of how the continually rising demand might expand in the future.[34] Of course, the future is unknown, and such a prediction of our energy sources for the year 2000 and beyond is mere conjecture. It depends to a large extent upon the background and experience of the predictor. External factors may also intervene. It may well be, for example, that although fossil fuels seem to be sufficient in quantity, they might be undesirable for expanded use because of their combustive pollutant effects. The solving of such problems represents a number of challenges for the engineer.

In the United States, the use of power is distributed approximately as follows:[35,36,37]

Household	20%
Commercial	10%
Industrial	40%
Transportation	20%
Other	10%

Considering the fact that currently the five most common air pollutants (carbon monoxide, sulfur oxides, hydrocarbons, nitrogen oxides, and solid particles) are primarily by-products of the combus-

[33]There are evidences that coal was used in China, Syria, Greece, and Wales as early as 1000 to 2000 B.C.

[34]L. P. Gaucher, "Energy Sources in the United States," *Journal of Solar Energy Society*, Vol. 9 (1965), p. 119.

[35]Garrett DeBall, "Energy," *The Environmental Handbook*, New York: Ballantine Books, 1970, p. 67.

[36]Chauncey Starr and Craig Smith, "Energy and the World of A.D. 2000," *Engineering for the Benefit of Mankind*, Washington, D.C.: National Academy of Engineering, 1970, p. 4.

[37]A. M. Weinberg and R. P. Hammond, "Limits to the Use of Energy," *American Scientist*, August, 1970, p. 413.

Man stands at the end of a long cycle of energy exchanges in which there is a calculable and irreversible loss of energy at each exchange. A grown adult irradiates heat equivalent to that of a 75 watt bulb. His total energy output, in 12 hours of hard physical work, is equivalent to only 1-kilowatt hour. He requires daily 2,200 calories of food intake, $4\frac{1}{2}$ pounds of water and 30 pounds of air, and he discards 5 pounds of waste. Considered as an energy converter, man is the least efficient link in his particular "food chain," and for this reason the most vulnerable to catastrophic ecologic change. Such a change can be caused by overloading the energy circuit. There are two new humans added to the globe's population *every second*.

1-30

F. D. Roosevelt
President of the United States
White House
Washington, D.C.

Sir:

Some recent work by E. Fermi and L. Szilard, which has been communited to me in manuscript, leads me to expect that the element of uranium may be turned into a new and important source of energy in the immediate future . . . that it may be possible to set up a nuclear chain reaction in a large mass of uranium by which vast amounts of power and large quantities of new radium-like elements would be generated. . .

ALBERT EINSTEIN
Old Grove Road, Nassau Point
Peconic, Long Island
August 2, 1939

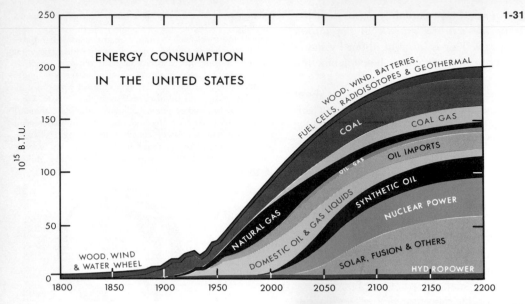

1-31

ENERGY CONSUMPTION
IN THE UNITED STATES

WOOD, WIND, BATTERIES,
FUEL CELLS, RADIOISOTOPES & GEOTHERMAL
COAL
COAL GAS
OIL GAS
OIL IMPORTS
NATURAL GAS
SYNTHETIC OIL
DOMESTIC OIL & GAS LIQUIDS
NUCLEAR POWER
WOOD, WIND
& WATER WHEEL
SOLAR, FUSION & OTHERS
HYDROPOWER

1-32
With proper planning, industrial installations, such as the nuclear power plant shown here, can perform their functions without polluting the environment.

It is better to more effectively insulate our homes than to compete for oil. It is better to design around a need for a scarce metal than to go to war over it.

MYRON TRIBUS
Roy V. Wright Lecture, ASME, 1971

It is our task in our time and in our generation to hand down undiminished to those who come after us, as was handed down to us by those who went before, the natural wealth and beauty which is ours.

JOHN FITZGERALD KENNEDY
March 3, 1961

tion of fossil fuels, it behooves the engineer to design and utilize energy sources that are as free from pollution as possible. It would appear that in the long run the earth can tolerate a significant increase in man's continuous release of energy (perhaps as much as 1,000 times the current United States daily consumption—or more) without deleterious effect.[38] Such increases would, of course, be necessary to accommodate a constantly increasing population. However, extrapolations and statements of this type concerning the future are meaningless unless the short-range problems—the problems of

[38] *Ibid.*, p. 418.

1-33

HIGHWAY TRAVEL IN THE UNITED STATES

RURAL

URBAN

100 BILLION MILES

0   2   4   6   8   10   12   14

1935   1940   1945   1950   1955   1960   1965   1970   1975   1980

today—are solved. Our society has invested the engineer with a responsibility for leadership in this regard and he must not fail.

go-go-go

At the present time American motorists are traveling over 1 million million miles per year on the nation's highways—an equivalent distance of over 2 million round trips to the moon. More than one half of this travel is in urban areas [1-33], where for the most part the physical layouts—the planning, the street design, and basic service systems—were created over 100 years ago.[39] As the population of the nation continues to shift to the urban areas, many of the *frustrating* problems of today will become *unbearable* in the future. Since 1896, when Henry Ford built his first car, the mores of the nation have changed gradually from an attitude of "pioneer independence" to a state of "apprehensive dependence"—to the point where one's possession of a means of private transportation is now considered to be a *necessity*.

Over three fourths of the families in the United States own at least one automobile, and over one fourth can boast of owning two or more. However, because of inadequate planning, this affluence has

When the motorcar was new, it exercised the typical mechanical pressure of explosion and separation of functions. It broke up family life, or so it seemed, in the 1920's. It separated work and domicile as never before. It exploded each city into a dozen suburbs, and then extended many of the forms of urban life among the highways until the open road seemed to become non-stop cities.

The motorcar ended the countryside and substituted a new landscape in which the car was sort of a steeplechaser. At the same time, the motorcar destroyed the city as a casual environment in which families could be reared. Streets, and even sidewalks, became too intense a scene for the casual interplay of growing up . . .

This is the story of the motorcar, and it has not much longer to run . . . Witness the portend of the crosswalk, where a small child has the power to stop a cement truck . . .

MARSHALL McLUHAN
Understanding Media, 1966

[39] *Tomorrow's Transportation*, Washington, D.C.: U.S. Department of Housing and Urban Development, 1968, p. 8.

Throughout the world, men and women and their families are leaving the countryside for the cities as we have known them in the past, but the farm base is definitely ceasing to have the significance it has had. Even where a farm base continues, life on the farm is vastly different; marginal coffee growers in Colombia now listen on their Japanese transistors to the quotations on the coffee exchange in New York.

TECHNOLOGICAL ADVANCES AND HUMAN VALUES
Ekistics, October, 1969

In the next 40 years, we must completely renew our cities. The alternative is disaster. Gaping needs must be met in health, in education, in job opportunities, in housing. And not a single one of these needs can be fully met until we rebuild our mass transportation systems.

LYNDON BAINES JOHNSON
1968

1-34
Automobile travel and parking problems of yesterday!

brought its share of problems for all concerned. Beginning about 3500 B.C. and until recent times roads and highways were used primarily as trade routes for the transport of commerce between villages, towns, and cities. The Old Silk Trade Route that connected ancient Rome and Europe with the Orient, a distance of over 6,000 miles, was used extensively for the transport of silk, jade, and other valuable commodities. The first really expert road builders, however, were the Romans, who built networks of roads throughout their empire to enable their soldiers to move more quickly from place to place. In this country early settlers first used the rivers, lakes, and oceans for transportation, and the first communities were located at points easily accessible by water. Then came the railroads. A few crude roads were constructed, but until 1900 the railroad was generally considered to be the most satisfactory means of travel, particularly when long distances were involved. With the advent of the automobile, individual desires could be accommodated more readily, and many road systems were improvised to connect the railroad stations with frontier settlements. At first these roads existed mainly so that farmers could market their produce, but subsequent extensions were the direct result of public demands for an improved highway system. People in the cities wanted to visit the countryside and people in the outlying areas were eager to "get a look at the big city." Within a few years we became a *mobile* people, but the road and highway system in use today was designed primarily to accommodate the transfer of goods rather than large volumes of people. Because of this, many of these "traffic arteries" are not in the best locations, nor of the most appropriate designs to satisfy *today's*

1-36
Parking problems today.

Motor trucks average some six miles an hour in New York traffic today, as against eleven for horse-drawn trucks in 1910—and the cost to the economy of traffic jams, according to a *New York Times* business survey, is five billion dollars yearly!

The Poverty of Abundance

demands. Thus, attempts to *drive* to work, *drive* downtown to shop, or take a leisurely *drive* through the countryside on a Sunday afternoon are apt to be "experiences in frustration." Vehicle parking is also becoming a critical problem.

Most cities have made only half-hearted attempts to care for the transportation needs of their most populous areas. Although those owning automobiles do experience annoying inconveniences, those without automobiles suffer the most—especially the poor, the handicapped, the elderly, and the young. Too often the public transit services that do exist are characterized by excessive walking distances to and from stations, poor connections and transfers, infrequent service, unreliability, slow speed and delays, crowding, noise, lack of comfort, and a lack of information for the rider's use. Moreover, passengers are often exposed to dangers to their personal safety while awaiting service.[40] Not to be minimized are the more than 4 million injuries and the 52,000 fatalities that result annually from motor vehicle accidents. (For perspective, since 1963 highway fatalities have exceeded more than ten times the total loss of American lives in the Vietnam War.)[41]

Traditionally, people have moved into a locality, built homes, businesses, and schools and then demanded that adequate transportation facilities be brought to them. We may now live in an era

[40] *Ibid.*, p. 6.
[41] K. P. Cantor, "Warning: The Automobile Is Dangerous to Earth, Air, Fire, Water, Mind, and Body," *The Environmental Handbook*, New York: Ballantine Books, 1970, p. 197.

when this independence is no longer feasible; rather, people eventually may be required to settle around previously designed transportation systems. (This is much the same as it was 100 years ago. However, during this time the transportation systems have changed greatly.) Engineers can provide good solutions for all these problems *if they are allowed to do so by the public*. However, there will be a cost for each improvement—whether it be a better vehicle design, computerized control of traffic flow, redesigned urban bus systems, rapid-transit systems, highway-guideway systems for vehicles, or some other entirely new concept. In some instances, city, state, or federal taxes must be levied; in others, the costs must be borne by each person who owns private transportation. The quality of urban life depends upon a unified commitment to this end.

the challenge of crime

Crime, one form of social pollution, is increasing rapidly in the United States in particular and throughout the world in general. The rate of increase in this country can be attributed variously to the population explosion, the increasing trend to urbanization, the changing composition of the population (particularly with respect to such factors as age, sex, and race), the increasing affluence of the populace, the diminishing influence of the home, and the deterioration of previously accepted value systems, mores, and standards of morality.[42] A recent survey of the National Opinion Research Center of the University of Chicago indicates that the actual amount of crime in the United States is known to be several times that reported. A comparison of recent increases in the seven forms of crime considered to be the most serious in this country is shown in [1-39]. A brief examination of these data indicates that the rate of increase of crime is now several times greater than the rate of increase of the population. In fact, crime is becoming such a serious social issue as to challenge the very fabric of our American way of life.

Not all people react in the same way to the threat of crime. Some are inclined to relocate their residences or places of business; some become fearful, withdrawn, and antisocial; some are resentful and revengeful; and a large percentage become suspicious of particular ethnic groups whom they believe to be responsible. A number, of course, seize the opportunity to "join in," and they adopt crime as an "easy way" to get ahead in life. The majority, however, merely display moods of frustration and bewilderment. In all cases, the

1-37
Rapid-transit systems have proved their usefulness in many major metropolitan areas.

1-38
Highway-guideway systems would relieve the driver of the tedious and tiring task of maneuvering his vehicle from one destination to another.

[42] *The Challenge of Crime in a Free Society,* A Report of the President's Commission on Law Enforcement and Administration of Justice, Washington, D.C., 1967, pp. 17–90.

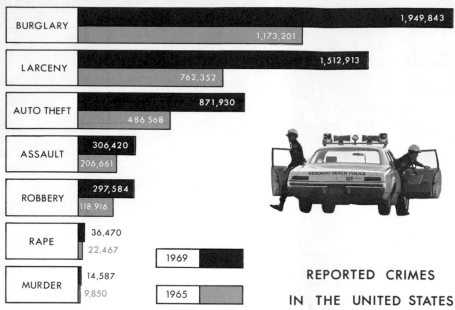

	1969	1965
BURGLARY	1,949,843	1,173,201
LARCENY	1,512,913	762,352
AUTO THEFT	871,930	486,568
ASSAULT	306,420	206,661
ROBBERY	297,584	118,916
RAPE	36,470	22,467
MURDER	14,587	9,850

1-39
Reported number of crimes in the United States.

REPORTED CRIMES

IN THE UNITED STATES

consequential results are detrimental to everyone concerned, because a free society cannot long endure such strains on public and private confidences, nor tolerate the continual presence of fear within the populace.

Traditionally, the detection, conviction, punishment, and even the prevention of crime have been functions of local, state, or federal agencies. Only in rare instances has private enterprise been called upon to assist in any significant way, and there has been no concentrated effort to bring to bear on these situations the almost revolutionary advances that have been made in recent years in engineering,

1-40
Many of us are unconcerned about the mounting epidemic of crime—until it gets personal.

1-42
Using the digicom system, the location of accidents can be quickly identified, and as many as five license-plate checks per minute can be made through the state computer file—an example of the use of engineering in the suppression of crime.

science, and technology. Rather, a few of the more spectacular developments have been modified or adapted for police operations or surveillance.

What is needed, and needed now, is a delineation of the vast array of problems that relate to the prevention, detection, and punishment of crime, with particular attention being directed toward achieving *general* rather than *specific* solutions. In this way technological efforts can be concentrated in those areas where they are most likely to be productive. For example, petty thefts may occur more frequently in one area of the city, murders more frequently in some other area, burglaries in another, and so on. What may be needed is a systems analysis of the city to delineate the contributing factors—rather than, for example, equipping all homes with burglary alarms. The engineer can make a significant contribution in this endeavor.

other opportunities and challenges

So far we have discussed primarily the environment as an area of challenge for the engineer today. Of necessity, many very important

1-43
Millions of people are alive today because of the availability of technical support systems that have been made possible by biomedical engineering design.

Modern electronic communications and information processing are marvelous extensions of man's senses and mind. But these same technologies are producing closer, more complex interactions between different peoples, and between people and machines, without the integrating force of common social purpose.

JACK MORTON
Innovation, 1969

. . . As never before, the work of the engineer is basic to the kind of society to which our best efforts are committed. Whether it be city planning, improved health care in modern facilities, safer and more efficient transportation, new techniques of communication or better ways to control pollution and dispose of wastes, the role of the engineer—his initiative, creative ability and hard work—is at the root of social progress in our time. . . .

PRESIDENT RICHARD NIXON
February, 1971

The world is very different now. For man holds in his mortal hands the power to abolish all forms of human poverty . . .

JOHN F. KENNEDY
January, 1961

challenges have not been discussed, such as the mounting congestion caused by the products of communication media and the threatening inundation of existing information-processing systems, ocean exploration with all of its varied technical problems and yet almost unlimited potential as a source of material, the expertise that the engineer can contribute to the entire field of health care and biological and medical advance, and the attendant social problems that are closely related to urbanization and population growth—such as mass migration, metropolitan planning, improved housing, and unemployment caused by outmoded work assignment.

It is axiomatic that technological advance always causes sociocultural change. In this sense the engineers and technologists who create new and useful designs are also "social revolutionaries."[43] After all, it was they who brought about the obsolescence of slave labor, the emergence of transportation machines that allowed redistribution of the population, the radio and television sets that provide "instant communication," and every convenience of liberation for the housewife—from mixers, waste disposers, dishwashers, ironers, and dryers to frozen foods. Frequently, society is not prepared to accept such abrupt changes—even though it is generally agreed that they are for the overall betterment of mankind. Because of this, the engineer has a dual responsibility to society. He not only

[43] Melvin Kranzberg, "Engineering, A Force for Social Change," *Our Technological Environment: Challenge and Opportunity*, Washington, D.C.: American Society for Engineering Education, 1971.

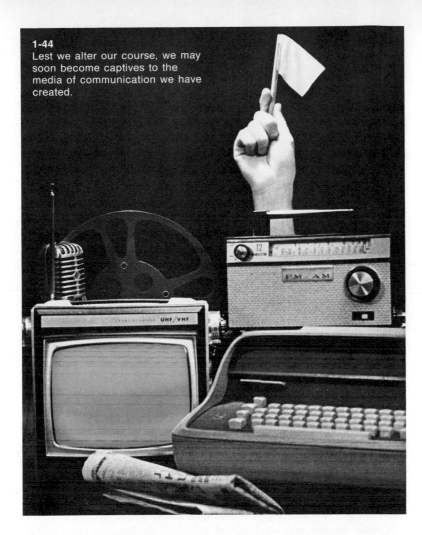

1-44
Lest we alter our course, we may soon become captives to the media of communication we have created.

1-45
In human communities, networks are the interfaces along which the interaction takes place between organic systems—Nature, Man, Society, and, of course, other Networks. Rural villages have fairly simple systems of networks, but urban communities interweave many systems of networks at various levels—water supply, sewage and waste disposal, electrical and natural-gas systems, movement of people and goods, telephone, radio, television and mass printed media. What is important about the vitality of an urban community is not its size or complexity but the degree to which the networks function efficiently. Shown are analogous network systems in Nature, Man, and an urban community.

must continue to bring about improvements for the benefit of society, but he must exert every possible means to acquaint society with its responsibility for continual change. Without such an active voice in community and governmental affairs, irrational forces and misinformation can prevail.

an environment of change

Man has always lived in an environment of change. As he has been able to add to his store of technical knowledge, he has also been able to change his economic structure and his sociological patterns. For centuries the changes that took place during a lifetime were hardly discernible. Beginning about 1600, the changes became more noticeable; and today technological change is literally exploding at

1-46
Growth of engineering and scientific knowledge.

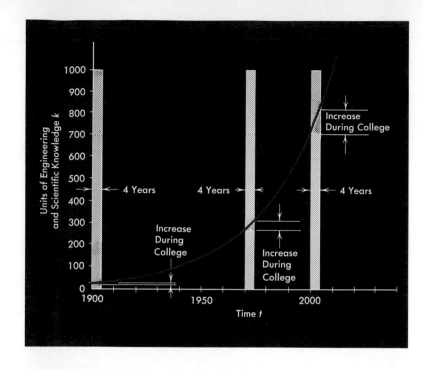

There is no excuse for western man not to know that the scientific revolution is the one practical solution to the three menaces which stand in our way—H-bomb war, overpopulations, and the gap between the rich and the poor nations.

LORD C. P. SNOW

The man who graduates today and stops learning tomorrow is uneducated the day after.

NEWTON D. BAKER

Physics is becoming so unbelievably complex that it is taking longer and longer to train a physicist. It is taking so long, in fact, to train a physicist to the place where he understands the nature of physical problems that he is already too old to solve them.
Eugene Wigner, as quoted by Colin Pittendrigh, 1971

an exponential rate. It is interesting to contemplate one's future if a growth curve relationship such as $k = a(i)^t$ is followed [1-46] (both a and i are constants).

In [1-46], engineering and scientific knowledge is assumed to be doubling every 15 to 20 years. Experience with other growth curves of this nature indicates that at some point a threshold will be reached and the rate will begin to level off and then decline. However, in considering the expansion of technology, no one can say with certainty when this slowing down is most likely to occur.

Similar factors are working to provoke changes in educational goals and patterns. In 1900, for example, the engineering student studied for 4 years to earn his baccalaureate degree, and he saw relatively little change take place in his technological environment during this period. Today, however, due to the accelerated growth pattern of engineering and scientific knowledge, many significant changes will have taken place between his freshman and senior years in college. In fact, complete new industries will be bidding for the services of the young graduate that were not even in existence at the time he began his freshman year of college. This is particularly true of the engineering student who continues his studies for a masters or a doctorate. It is also interesting to contemplate that at the present rate of growth, engineering and scientific knowledge will have doubled within 20 years after graduation. This places a special importance on continuing lifetime studies for all levels of engineering graduates.

These growth patterns, which are promoting change in all phases of society, are also causing educators and leaders in industry to reappraise existing educational practices with a view to increasing their scope and effectiveness. From time to time these changes, although not revolutionary, often provoke a sense of progress that shocks those who received their formal education a scant generation before.

the education of the engineer

Engineering students who will be best prepared for a career of change should have better than average abilities:

1. to think with imagination and insight;
2. to understand scientific principles and to apply analytical methods to the study of natural phenomena;
3. to conceive, organize, and carry to completion appropriate experimental investigations;
4. to synthesize and to design.[44]

In general, engineering programs in colleges and universities have concentrated upon providing a broad-based education that is not closely aligned to a specific state of the art. This has been necessary because for one to acquire even a small part of all the factual knowledge now available, a continuous memorization process would be required. It is, therefore, more appropriate to learn the basic laws of nature and certain essential facts that contribute to an understanding of problem solving. Emphasis must be placed upon developing mature minds and in educating engineers who can *think*. A means of condensing and concentrating the material to be learned is also of paramount importance. A powerful way of doing this is to employ mathematical techniques that can describe technical situations. For this reason mathematics is a most effective tool of the engineer and its mastery early in one's college career will allow for more rapid progress in such subjects as engineering mechanics, physics, and electrical circuit analysis. In a similar way, if a student learns the principles of physics, this knowledge will bind together such diverse engineering developments as magnetic materials, gas discharges, semiconductors, and dielectric and optical properties of materials. Similarly, there is no substitute for a mastery of the fundamental principles of other sciences, such as chemistry and biology.

Naturally, the education of an engineer must not end upon graduation from college. The pace of discovery is too great to consider

[44]Joseph Kestin, Brown University *Engineer*, No. 7 (May, 1965), p. 11.

The average person puts only 25% of his energy and ability into his work. The world takes off its hat to those who put in more than 50% of their capacity, and stands on its head for those few and far between souls who devote 100%.

ANDREW CARNEGIE

Education is what you have left over after you have forgotten everything you have learned.

1-47
Time is running out.

Thousands of engineers can design bridges, calculate strains and stresses, and draw up specifications for machines, but the great engineer is the man who can tell whether the bridge or the machine should be built at all, where it should be built, and when.

EUGENE G. GRACE

any other course of action than to study and keep abreast of the expanding realm of science and technology. Therefore, in addition to learning fundamental principles of science and engineering in college, the student must develop an intellectual and technical curiosity that will encourage him to continue study after graduation.

For the foreseeable future, opportunity for the engineer will continue to expand. Barring a national catastrophe or world war, available knowledge, productivity, and the living standard will probably continue to increase. It is hoped that man's appreciation for moral and esthetic values will continue to deepen and keep pace with this technological explosion.

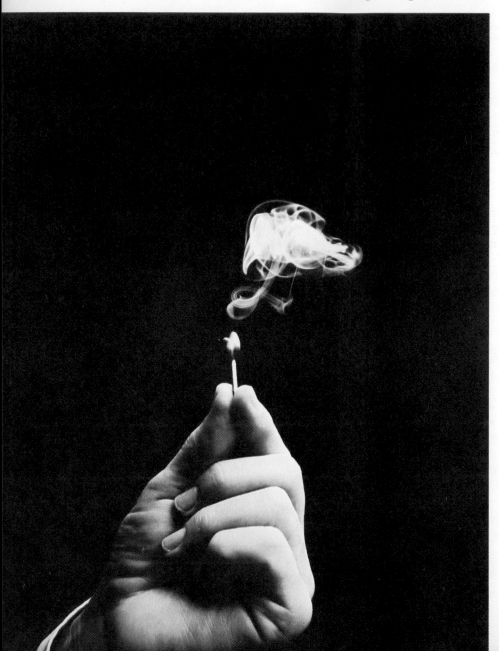

1-48
The challenge of engineering lies in providing light for man in the search for truth and happiness—without also bringing about some undesirable side effects.

problems

1-1. Describe one instance in which the ecological balance of nature has been altered unintentionally by man.

1-2. Plot the rate of population growth for your state since 1900. What is your prediction of its population for the year 2000?

1-3. What can the engineer do that would make possible the improvement of the general "standards of living" in your home town?

1-4. Investigate world conditions and estimate the number of people who need some supplement to their diet. How can the engineer help to bring such improvements about?

1-5. From a technological and economic point of view, what are the fundamental causes of noise in buildings?

1-6. Borrow a sound-level meter and investigate the average sound level in decibels of (a) a busy freeway, (b) a television "soap opera," (c) a college classroom lecture, (d) a library reading room, (e) a home vacuum cleaner, (f) a riverbank at night, (g) a "rock" combo, (h) a jackhammer, (i) a chain saw, and (j) a kitchen mixer.

1-7. Which of the air pollutants appears to be most damaging to man's longevity? Why?

1-8. Explain the greenhouse effect.

1-9. Investigate how the *smog intensity level* has changed over the past 10 years for the nearest city of over 100,000 population. With current trends, what level would you expect for 1985?

1-10. Describe some effects that might result from a continually increasing percentage of carbon dioxide in the atmosphere.

1-11. Investigate the methods used in purifying the water supply from which you receive your drinking water. Describe improvements that you believe might be made to improve the quality of the water.

1-12. What are the apparent sources of pollution for the water supply serving your home?

1-13. Seek out three current newspaper accounts in which man has caused pollution of the environment. What is your suggestion for remedy of each of these situations?

1-14. Investigate the problems that might be caused by increasing the average water temperature of the nearest river 20°F.

1-15. What means is currently being used to dispose of solid waste in the city where you live? Would you recommend some alternative procedure or process?

1-16. Estimate the amount of electrical energy consumed by the members of your class in 1 year.

1-17. Considering the expanding demand for energy throughout the world, list ten challenges that require better engineering solutions.

1-18. What are the five most pressing problems that exist in your state with regard to transportation? Suggest at least one engineering solution for each.

1-19. List five new engineering designs that are needed to help suppress crime.

1-20. In the United States, what are the most pressing communications problems that need solving?

1-21. List five general problems that need engineering solutions.

1-22.[45] The Marginal Chemical Corp. is a small company by Wall Street's standards, but it is one of the biggest employers and taxpayers in the little town in which it has its one and only plant. The company has an erratic earnings record, but production has been trending up at an average of 6 per cent a year—and along with it, so has the pollution from the plant's effluents into the large stream that flows by the plant. This stream feeds a large lake that has become unfit for bathing or fishing.

The number of complaints from town residents about this situation has been rising, and you, as a resident of the community and the plant's senior engineer, also have become increasingly concerned. Although the lake is a gathering place for the youth of the town, the City Fathers have applied only token pressure on the plant to clean up. Your immediate superior, Mr. Jones, the plant manager, has other worries, because the plant has been caught in a cost/price squeeze and is barely breaking even.

After a careful study, you propose to Jones that, to have an effective pollution-abatement system, the company must make a capital investment of $1 million. This system will cost another $100,000 per year in operating expenses (e.g., for treatment chemicals, utilities, labor, laboratory support). Jones's reaction is

"It's out of the question. As you know, we don't have an extra million around gathering dust—we'd have to borrow it at 10 per cent interest per year and, with the direct operating expenses, that means it would actually cost us $200,000 a year to go through with your idea. The way things have been going, we'll be lucky if this plant *clears* $200,000 this year, and we certainly can't raise prices. Even if we had the million handy, I'd prefer to use it to expand production of our new pigment; that way, it would give us a better jump on our competitors and on overseas competition. You can create a lot of new production—and new jobs—for a million dollars. This town needs new jobs more than it needs crystal-clear lakes, unless you want people to fish for a living. Besides, even if we weren't putting anything in the lake, it still wouldn't be crystal clear—there would still be all sorts of garbage in it."

During further discussion, the only concessions you can get from Jones is that you can spend $10,000 so that one highly visible (but otherwise insignificant) pollutant won't be discharged into the stream, and that if you can come up with an overall pollution-control scheme that will pay for itself via product recovery, he will give it serious consideration. You feel that the latter concession does not offer much hope, because not enough products with a ready market appear to be recoverable.

If you were this engineer, what do you think you *should* do? Consider the alternatives below.

A. Report the firm to your state and other governmental authorities as being a polluter, and complain about the laxness of city officials (even though the possible outcome might be your dismissal, or the company deciding to close up shop).

B. Go above Jones's head (i.e., to the president of the company). If he fails to overrule Jones, quit your job, and then take step A.

[45] Problems 1-22 through 1-25 are reprinted by special permission from *Chemical Engineering*, November 2, 1970, pp. 88–93, copyright ©, McGraw-Hill, New York.

C. Go along with Jones on an interim basis, and try to improve the plant's competitive position via a rigorous cost-reduction program so that a little more money can be spent on pollution control in a year or two. In the meantime, do more studies of product-recovery systems, and keep him aware of your continued concern with pollution control.

D. Relax, and let Jones tell you when to take the next antipollution step. After all, he has managerial responsibility for the plant. You have not only explained the problem to him, but have suggested a solution, so you have done your part.

E. Other action (explain).

1-23. (a) You are the division manager of Sellwell Co., a firm that has developed an inexpensive household specialty that you hope will find a huge market among housewives. You want to package this product in 1-gallon and $\frac{1}{2}$-gallon sizes. A number of container materials would appear to be practical—glass, aluminum, treated paper, steel, and various types of plastics. A young engineer whom you hired recently and assigned to the manufacturing department has done a container-disposal study which shows that the disposal cost for 1-gallon containers can vary by a factor of 3—depending upon the weight of the container, whether it can be recycled, whether it is easy to incinerate, whether it has good landfill characteristics, etc.

Your company's marketing expert believes that the container material with the highest consumer appeal is the one to use, although it happens to present the biggest disposal problem and cost to communities. He estimates that the sales potential would be at least 10 per cent less if the easiest-to-dispose-of, salvageable container were used, because this container would be somewhat less distinctive and attractive.

Assuming that the actual costs of the containers were about the same, to what extent would you let the disposal problem influence your choice? Would you

(1) Choose the container strictly on its marketing appeal, on the premise that disposal is the community's problem, not yours (and also that some communities may not be ready to use the recycling approach yet, regardless of which container material you select)?

(2) Choose the easiest-to-dispose-of container, and either accept the sales penalty or try to overcome it by stressing the "good citizenship" angle (even though the marketing department is skeptical about whether this will work)?

(3) Take the middle road, by accepting a 5 per cent sales penalty to produce a container that is midway on the disposability scale?

(4) Other action (explain).

(b) Do you think the young engineer who made the container-disposal study (but who is not a marketing expert) has any moral obligation to make recommendations as to which container to use? Explain your position.

1-24. Stan Smith, a young engineer with 2 years of experience, has been hired to assist a senior engineer in the evaluation of air- and water-pollution problems at a large plant—one that is considering a major expansion that would involve a new product. Local civic groups and labor unions favor this expansion, but conservation groups are opposed to it.

Smith's specific assignment is to evaluate control techniques for the effluents in accordance with state and federal standards. He concludes that the expanded plant will be able to meet these standards. However, he is not completely happy, because the aerial discharge will include an unusual by-product whose effects are not well known, and whose control is not considered by state and federal officials in the setting of standards.

In doing further research, he comes across a study that tends to connect respiratory diseases with this type of emission in one of the few instances when such an emission took place over an extended time period. An area downwind of the responsible plant experienced a 15 per cent increase in respiratory diseases. The study also tends to confirm that the pollutant is difficult to control by any known means.

When Smith reports these new findings to his engineering supervisor, he is told that by now the expansion project is well along, the equipment has been purchased, and it would be very expensive and embarrassing for the company suddenly to halt or change its plans.

Furthermore, the supervisor points out that the respiratory-disease study involved a different geography of the country and, hence, different climatic conditions, and also that apparently only transitory diseases were increased, rather than really serious ones. This increase might have been caused by some unique combination of contaminants, rather than only the one in question, and might not have occurred at all if the other contaminants had been controlled as closely as they will be in the new facility.

If Smith still believes that there is a reasonable possibility (but not necessarily a certainty) that the aerial discharge would lead to an increase in some types of ailments in the downwind area, should he

A. Go above his superior, to an officer of the company (at the risk of his previously good relationship with his superior)?

B. Take it upon himself to talk to the appropriate control officials and to pass their opinions along to his superior (which entails the same risk)?

C. Talk to the conservation groups and (in confidence) give them the type of ammunition they are looking for to halt the expansion?

D. Accept his superior's reasoning (keeping a copy of pertinent correspondence so as to fix responsibility if trouble develops)?

E. Take other action (explain)?

1-25. Jerry Williams is a chemical engineer working for a large diversified company on the East Coast. For the past 2 years he has been a member—the only technically trained member—of a citizens' pollution-control group working in his city.

As a chemical engineer, Williams has been able to advise the group about what can reasonably be done about abating various kinds of pollution, and he has even helped some smaller companies to design and buy control equipment. (His own plant has air and water pollution under good control.) As a result of Williams's activity, he has built himself considerable prestige on the pollution-control committee.

Recently, some other committee members started a drive to pressure the city administration into banning the sale of phosphate-containing detergents. They have been impressed by reports in their newspapers and magazines on the harmfulness of phosphates.

Williams believes that banning phosphates would be misdirected effort. He tries to explain that although phosphates have been attacked in regard to the eutrophication of the Great Lakes, his city's sewage flows from the sewage-treatment plant directly into the ocean. And he feels that nobody has shown any detrimental effect of phosphate on the ocean. Also, he is aware that there are conflicting theories on the effect of phosphates, even on the Great Lakes (e.g., some theories put the blame on nitrogen or carbon rather than phosphates, and suggest that some phosphate substitutes may do more harm than good).

In addition, he points out that the major quantity of phosphate in the city's sewage comes from human wastes rather than detergent.

Somehow, all this reasoning makes little impression on the backers of the "ban phosphates" measure. During an increasingly emotional meeting, some of the committeemen even accuse Williams of using stalling tactics to protect his employer who, they point out, has a subsidiary that makes detergent chemicals.

Williams is in a dilemma. He sincerely believes that his viewpoint makes sense, and that it has nothing to do with his employer's involvement with detergents (which is relatively small, anyway, and does not involve Williams's plant). Which step should he now take?

A. Go along with the "ban phosphates" clique on the grounds that the ban won't do any harm, even if it doesn't do much good. Besides, by giving the group at least passive support, Williams can preserve his influence for future items that really matter more.

B. Fight the phosphate foes to the end on the grounds that their attitude is unscientific and unfair, and that lending it his support would be unethical. (Possible outcomes: his ouster from the committee, or its breakup as an effective body.)

C. Resign from the committee, giving his side of the story to the local press.

D. Other action (explain).

bibliography

ALEXANDER, TOM, "Some Burning Questions About Combustion," *Fortune*, February, 1970.

BATES, MARSTON, "The Human EcoSystem," *Resources and Man*, San Francisco: W. H. Freeman, 1969.

BYLINSKY, GENE, "The Limited War on Pollution," *The Environment*, New York: Harper & Row, 1970.

CANTOR, K. P., "Warning: The Automobile Is Dangerous to Earth, Air, Fire, Water, Mind, and Body," *The Environmental Handbook*, New York: Ballantine Books, 1970.

Cleaning Our Environment: The Chemical Basis for Action, Washington, D.C.: American Chemical Society, 1969.

DeBALL, GARRETT, "Energy," *The Environmental Handbook*, New York: Ballantine Books, 1970.

"Eat, Drink, and Be Sick," *Medical World News*, September 26, 1969.

EHRLICH, P. R., *The Population Bomb*, New York: Ballantine Books, 1968.

Environmental Science and Technology, May, 1970.

FARB, PETER, *Ecology*, New York: Time, Inc. 1963.

FERKISS, V. C., *Technological Man: The Myth and the Reality*, New York: George Braziller, 1969.

GAUCHER, L. P., "Energy Sources in the United States," *Journal of Solar Energy*, Vol. 9 (1965), p. 119.

GLORIG, ARAM, *Noise as a Public Health Hazard*, W. D. WARD and J. E. FRICKE (eds.), Washington, D.C.: The American Speech and Hearing Association, 1969.

HERSHAFT, ALEX, "Solid Waste Treatment," *Science and Technology*, June, 1969.

HUBBERT, M. K., *Resources and Man*, San Francisco: W. H. Freeman, 1969.

Industrial Noise, A. D. HOSEY and C. H. POWELL (eds.), Washington, D.C.: U.S. Department of Health, Education and Welfare, 1967.

JONES, J. M., *Does Overpopulation Mean Poverty?* Washington, D.C.: Center for International Economic Growth, 1962.

KRANZBERG, MELVIN, "Engineering, A Force for Social Change," *Our Technological Environment: Challenge and Opportunity*, Washington, D.C.: American Society for Engineering Education, 1971.

MALTHUS, T. R., 1798, *An Essay on the Principles of Population As It Affects the Future Improvements of Mankind*, facsimile reprint in 1926 for J. Johnson, London: Macmillan.

MALTHUS, THOMAS, JULIAN HUXLEY, and FREDERICK OSBORN, *Three Essays on Population*. New York: The New American Library, 1960.

McLUHAN, MARSHALL, *Understanding Media*, New York: McGraw-Hill, 1964.

NELSON, SENATOR GAYLORD, *Congressional Record*, February 26, 1970.

NEWELL, R. E., "The Global Circulation of Atmospheric Pollutants," *Scientific American*, January, 1971.

Noise: Sound Without Value, Washington, D.C.: Committee on Environmental Quality of the Federal Council for Science and Technology, 1968.

PRICE, D. J. D., *Little Science, Big Science*, New York: Columbia University Press, 1963.

RODDA, MICHAEL, *Noise and Society*, London: Oliver & Boyd, 1967.

SINGER, S. F., "Human Energy Production as a Process in the Biosphere," *Scientific American*, September, 1970.

STARR, CHAUNCEY, and CRAIG SMITH, "Energy and the World of A.D. 2000," *Engineering for the Benefit of Mankind*, Washington, D.C.: National Academy of Engineering, 1970.

The Challenge of Crime in a Free Society, Washington, D.C.: A Report of the President's Commission on Law Enforcement and Administration of Justice, 1967.

The Environment, The Editors of *Fortune*, New York: Harper & Row, 1970.

"The Thin Slice of Life," R. C. COOK (ed.), *Population Bulletin*, Vol. 24, No. 5.

Tomorrow's Transportation, Washington, D.C.: U.S. Department of Housing and Urban Development, 1968.

WEINBERG, A. M., and R. P. HAMMOND, "Limits to the Use of Energy," *American Scientist*, August, 1970.

WIGOTSKY, V. W., "Engineering and the Urban Crisis," *Design News*, December 7, 1970.

WOHLERS, H. C., *Air Pollution—The Problem, the Source, and the Effects*. Philadelphia: Drexel Institute of Technology, 1969.

Your Right to Clean Air, Washington, D.C.: The Conservation Foundation, 1970.

Closed-cell foam insulation. Gossamer-thin polyurethane membranes in refrigerator insulation refract light into multiple hues the same way a child's soap bubbles do. These "bubbles" are polyhedral cells with hexagonal faces bounded by rigid white ribs. Each cell contains a fluorocarbon gas or another inert gas. These gases are better insulators than air. Linked together by the thousands, closed cells form an almost impervious barrier to heat. This means that thin layers of this foam insulate as effectively as greater thicknesses of other materials. As a result, interior volume of an insulated area can be increased substantially without changing exterior dimensions.

2-1

The act of creation and the act of appreciation of beauty are not in essence, distinguishable.

H. E. HUNTLEY
The Divine Proportion, 1970

Imagination is more important than knowledge.

ALBERT EINSTEIN
On Science, 1931

All good things which exist are the fruits of originality.

JOHN STUART MILL
Liberty, 1859

s man counts time, the first act of recorded history was one of creation. When God created man, he endowed him with some of this ability to bring new things into being. Today the ability to think creatively is one of the most important assets that all men possess. The accelerated pace of today's technology emphasizes the need for conscious and directed imagination and creative behavior in the engineer's daily routine. However, this need is not new.

For centuries primitive man fulfilled his natural needs by using the bounty nature placed about him. Since his choice was limited by terrain, climate, and accessibility, he was forced to choose from his environment those things which he could readily adapt to his needs. His only guide—trial and error—was a stern teacher. He ate whatever stimulated his sense of smell and taste, and he clothed himself and his family in whatever crude materials he could fashion to achieve warmth, comfort, and modesty. His mistakes often bore serious consequences, and he eventually learned that his survival depended upon his ability to think and to act in accordance with a plan. He learned the importance of imaginative reasoning in the improvement of his lot.

Archaeologists have discovered evidence of early civilizations that made hunting weapons and agricultural tools, mastered the use of fire, and improvised fishing equipment from materials at hand—all at an advanced level of complexity. These remains are silent reminders of man's ingenuity. Only his cunning and imagination protected him from his natural enemies. The situation is much the same even today, centuries later. Many believe that in this respect man may not have improved his lot substantially over the centuries. The well-being of our civilization still depends upon how successfully we can mobilize our creative manpower. As a profession, engineering must rise to meet this challenge.

In scientific work the term *creativity* is often used interchangeably with *innovation*. However, the two are not synonymous although they do have some similarities. Both creativity and innovation refer to certain processes within an individual or group. Innovation is the discovery of a new, novel, or unusual idea or product by the application of logic, experience, or artistry. This would include the recombination of things or ideas already known. Creativity is the origination of a concept in response to a human need—a solution that is both satisfying and innovative. We call those individuals creative who originate, make, or cause something useful to come into existence for the first time or those who originate new principles. Innovation, on the other hand, may or may not respond to a human need, and it may or may not be valuable. In effect, creativity is innovation to meet a need.

Creativity is a human endeavor. It presupposes an understanding of human experience and human values, and it is without doubt one of the highest forms of mental activity. In addition to requiring innovation, creative behavior requires a peculiar insight that is set into action by a vivid but purposeful imagination—seemingly the result of a divine inspiration that some often call a "spark of genius." Indeed, the moment of inspiration is somewhat analogous to an electrical capacitor that has "soaked up" an electrical charge and then discharges it in a single instant. To sustain creative thought over a period of time requires a large reservoir of innovations from which to feed. Creative thought may be expressed in such diverse things as a suspension bridge, a musical composition, a poem, a painting, or a new type of machine or process. Problem solving, as such, does not necessarily require creative thought, because many kinds of problems can be solved by careful, discriminating logic.

A given engineer may or may not be a creative thinker, although all engineers should have mastered the basic techniques of problem solving (see Chapter 6). For problem solving, the engineer must be intelligent, well informed, and discerning, so that he can apply the principles of deductive reasoning to the various innovational alternatives when he encounters them.

Every new or original thought may not be a creative thought. A psychotic's hallucinations might well be unique, even though they do not have intrinsic value. Such thoughts are neither innovational nor creative. Although all creative thinkers must be innovators, it does not follow necessarily that all innovators have to be creative thinkers. Innovation occurs daily, on every hand and in every walk of life. True creative behavior is much rarer and usually requires the fulfillment of some deliberate contemplation.

All persons of normal intelligence possess some ability to think creatively and to engage in imaginative and innovative effort. Unfortunately, the vast majority of people are only partially aware of the range of their creative potential. This potential seldom is attained, even if recognized. This is true partially because one's social environment, home life, and education experiences either stimulate or depress the urge to be creative. Even at a very early age, children are often urged to conform to group standards. Any deviations may bring immediate rebuke from the adult in charge. As an example, in the first grade little Johnny may be assigned to color inside the boundaries of his outlined and predrawn horse. He must color his horse brown—because the teacher likes brown horses. Black horses, white horses, green horses or other choices that might occur to Johnny are ruled out. The outline has been predrawn because, in this way, all the children's work will appear to be reasonably good to the parents on PTA night. No child's work will have the obvious appearance of poor quality or extreme excellence—a very important item to please the majority of parents. Also, the teacher will not be embarrassed by horses with horns or wings. And so it goes as Johnny grows up to assume his place in adult life. As a teenager he is considered "different" or an "odd ball" unless he always joins

More today than yesterday, and more tomorrow than today, the survival of people and their institutions depends upon innovation.

JACK MORTON
Innovation, 1969

The age is running mad after innovation. All the business of the world is to be done in a new way. Men are to be hanged in a new way.

SAMUEL JOHNSON

The creative process is any thinking process which solves a problem in an original and useful way.

H. HERBERT FOX
A Critique on Creativity in Science

Greater than the tread of mighty armies is the idea whose time has come.

VICTOR HUGO
Histoire d'un Crime, 1852

Creativity is man's most challenging frontier!

Common sense is not so common.

VOLTAIRE
Dictionnaire Philosophique 1764

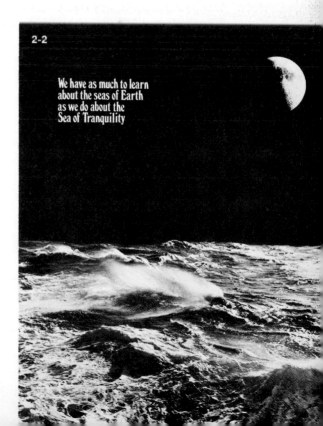

2-2

We have as much to learn about the seas of Earth as we do about the Sea of Tranquility

A child is highly creative until he starts to school.
STANLEY CZURLES
Director of Art Education, New York State College for Teachers

To think is to differ.
CLARENCE DARROW

The test of tolerance comes when we are in a majority; the test of courage comes when we are in a minority.
RALPH W. SOCKMAN, D.C.
Forbes Scrapbook of Thoughts in the Business of Life

An inventor is simply a fellow who doesn't take his education too seriously.
CHARLES F. KETTERING

Everybody is ignorant, only in different subjects.
WILL ROGERS

Iron rusts from disuse; water loses its purity from stagnation and in cold weather becomes frozen; even so does inaction sap the vigors of the mind.
LEONARDO DA VINCI
Forbes Scrapbook of Thoughts in the Business of Life

in with the majority. As a citizen, he is criticized as "antiAmerican" unless he affiliates with the political party that is in power at the moment. His neighbors "wonder" about him if he refuses to join a neighborhood drive to "achieve the Community Chest goal." His coworkers believe he is a "threat to our way of life" if he prefers independent action to letting some union speak in his behalf. And on and on we might continue. . . . It is no wonder that many well-informed persons today are creatively sterile, whereas others in former years (like Franklin and Edison) accomplished seemingly impossible results in spite of a poor formal education.

Years ago most American youths were accustomed to using innovative and imaginative design to solve their daily problems. Home life was largely one of rural experience. If tools or materials were not available, they quickly improvised some other scheme to accomplish the desired task. Most people literally "lived by their wits." Often it was not convenient, or even possible, to "go to town" to buy a clamp or some other standard device. Innovation was, in many cases, "the only way out." A visit to a typical midwestern farm or western ranch today, or to Peace Corps workers overseas, will show that these innovative and creative processes are still at work. However, today most American youths are city or suburb dwellers who do not have many opportunities to solve real physical problems with novel ideas.

A person is not born with either a creative or noncreative mind, although some are fortunate enough to have exceptionally alert minds that literally feed on new experiences. Intellect is essential, but it is not a golden key to success in creative thinking. Intellectual capacity certainly sets the upper limits of one's innovative and creative ability; but, nevertheless, motivation and environmental opportunities determine whether or not a person reaches this limit. Surprisingly, students with high IQ's are not necessarily inclined to be creative. Recent studies reveal that over 70 per cent of the most creative students do not rank in the upper 20 per cent of their class on traditional IQ measures.[1]

Everyone has some innovative or creative ability. For the average person, because of inactivity or conformity, this ability has probably been retarded since childhood. If we bind our hand or foot (as was practiced in some parts of the Orient) and do not use it, it soon becomes paralyzed and ineffective. But unlike the hand or foot, which cannot recover full usefulness after long inactivity, the dormant instinct to think creatively may be revived through exercise and stimulated into activity after years of near suspended animation. Thus everyone can benefit from studying the creative and innovative processes and the psychological factors related to them.

Imaginative thinking can be stimulated, and the basic principles

[1] E. P. Torrance, "Explorations in Creative Thinking in the Early School Years," in C. W. Taylor and Frank Barron (eds.), *Scientific Creativity*, New York: Wiley, 1963, p. 182.

Where does the firefly get its light?

2-4

of innovative thinking can be mastered. Parnes and Meadow[2] have shown that deliberate education in innovative thinking can significantly increase innovative and creative potential. In reporting this research, Osborn[3] notes that, for an experimental sample of 330 students, the subjects who enrolled in courses in creative problem solving produced 94 per cent more good ideas than subjects who did not get such training. Even if these results are somewhat optimistic, we certainly cannot deny that even a 50 per cent improvement in our own individual creative abilities would be worth achieving. Many organizations—including DuPont, General Electric, Aluminum Company of America, Westinghouse, Aerojet General Corporation, General Motors, and the Armed Forces—believe the fundamental principles of creative thinking and problem solving can be taught, and give their personnel such training. Therefore, all young engineering students should profit from studying the principles used to spark innovation and creative effort.

[2] S. J. Parnes and Arnold Meadow, "Development of Individual Creative Talent," in Taylor and Barron (eds.), *op. cit.*
[3] A. F. Osborn, *Applied Imagination*, New York: Scribner's, 1963, p. xii.

development of creative effort

Associated with innovative and creative thought are imagination, curiosity, and intuitive insight. As suggested above, the desire to use these faculties begins at an early age. Thwarting or suppressing this individuality of thought may change a child's personality. It is unfortunate that many of our mental resources are wasted in this way. Creative talent should be sought out, developed, and utilized wherever possible. But doing so is far from easy; although psychologists have described some general attributes and traits of the creative personality, it may be difficult to measure an individual's potential to perform creatively.

Although everyone has some capacity to be innovative and creative, *creative ability* is usually a scarce commodity. It need not be, however, because we can enumerate and measure the influence of the mental attitudes and thought processes that are most conducive to producing innovative and creative effort. Using some of these fundamental processes will certainly return valuable dividends. But first, one must have a proper mental attitude.

an attitude for innovative and creative thought

Unfortunately, there is no *one* set of ideal conditions that will always give the most effective imaginative and creative thought. The best conditions vary with personality and circumstances. However, it is important to approach all problems with an open mind—one as free from restrictions and preconceived limiting conditions as possible. Sentiments such as fear, greed, and hatred must be put aside. Try to approach problem situations with a clear mind stimulated *but not restrained* by past experiences. In general, your thought processes are influenced by *how* and *what* you have already learned, but tradition may hinder rather than help, especially if you have made incorrect or irrelevant assumptions. This is particularly true when certain attitudes, convictions, or feelings have stimulated your emotions excessively. In such instances, reasoning tends to be influenced so it will harmonize with these convictions. The engineer must learn to be receptive to new ideas, even though they may depart from conventional practices. He must always seek authenticity and truth, rather than trying to verify preconceived ideas or existing procedures.

The engineer must be *motivated* to use imaginative and innovative thought. Basically, most creative persons—whether they are artists, musicians, poets, scientists, or engineers—are motivated to work at a particular task partly because of the exhilaration, thrill, special

Creativity is the art of taking a fresh look at old knowledge.

All men are born with a very definite potential for creative activity.
JOHN E. ARNOLD

Reason can answer questions, but imagination has to ask them.

Why and *how* are words so important that they cannot be used too often.
NAPOLEON BONAPARTE

2-5
Man's potential habitation of the moon has been a
stimulus to his imagination.

Want is the mistress of invention.
SUSANNE CENTLIVRE
The Busybody, 1667–1723

satisfaction, pride, and pleasure they get from completing a creative task. It is perhaps natural that man should emulate his Creator in this respect. For, in each case, after creating the heavens and the earth, after adorning the earth with plant and animal life, and again after creating man and woman, God gave expression of His pleasure.

"And God saw everything that He had made, and behold, it was very good."[4]

But besides the sense of satisfaction that comes from the creative process itself, other factors also stimulate and motivate the engineer toward creative design efforts. These may be classified into two groups.

[4] *The Bible,* Revised Standard Version, Genesis 1:31.

1. *Basic motives:* food and self-preservation, faith, love, aspiration for fame or freedom.
2. *Secondary motives:* competition, pride, loyalty, fear.

Motivation is the power source that drives all engineers forward in their role as problem solvers, innovators, and creators. Some factors and circumstances will reinforce and stimulate natural motivation. Others will weaken and depress motivation. Engineers should be acquainted with both positive and negative motivating factors.

conditions that stimulate creative thinking

Some of the conditions that stimulate creative thinking are related to individual *personality* and *philosophy*. Other conditions are related to the individual's *state of mind*. In addition, the engineer must have particular personal qualities and attitudes to achieve maximum motivational stimulation.

The engineer must understand both nature and his environment. He must learn to carefully evaluate the results and consequences of his work. Many times it will be easy for him to draw an incorrect, though seemingly obvious, conclusion. The story is told of a young biologist who was investigating the sensitivity of a frog's sensory system. He devised an experimental apparatus with blinking lights and screeching sirens and positioned his frog for testing. He reasoned that the frog would become frightened by the noise and lights and attempt to escape. Beginning with the right rear leg, he carefully severed each leg in turn, and noted how far the frog could jump. When the frog did not move after its fourth leg was severed, he noted the following in his laboratory report:

All frogs are very sensitive to light and sound. However, at the moment the left foreleg is removed, they become deaf and blind.

We laugh at the young man's foolish statement, but daily we react in a similar manner as time after time we draw incorrect conclusions.

The engineer will devote a lifetime to changing and modifying his environment. His daily work will affect social and economic life. His actions and designs will be reflected in the lives of all people everywhere as their habits and customs change. He must recognize and assume a special responsibility in this regard because *all* his innovative designs will probably not be used for the *betterment* of his fellowmen and for uplifting their culture. He must recognize that the products of his imagination may, in fact, be used in ways that are detrimental to society. Generally, his designs are, within them-

Lord, grant that I may always desire more than I can accomplish.

MICHELANGELO

The thing of which I have most fear is fear.

MICHEL EYQUEM DE MONTAIGNE
Essays, 1533–1592

Important ideas are those that lie within the allowable scope of nature's laws.

You can observe a lot just by watching.

YOGI BERRA
Quoted in Eric Hodgin's Episode

Scientists study the world as it is, engineers create the world that never has been.

THEODORE VON KARMAN

selves, morally neutral. However, it is the use that people make of his designs that becomes recognized as forces for "good" or "evil." In addition, he must realize that his failures and his successes, all the fruits of his labor, are always on public display. President Herbert Hoover, himself an engineer, stated these conditions well:

Engineering training deals with the exact sciences. That sort of exactness makes for truth and conscience. It might be good for the world if more men had that sort of mental start in life, even if they did not pursue the profession. But he who would enter these precincts as a life work must have a test taken of his imaginative faculties, for engineering without imagination sinks to a trade.

It is a great profession. There is the fascination of watching a figment of the imagination emerge through the aid of science to a plan on paper. Then it moves to realization in stone or metal or energy. Then it brings jobs and homes to men. Then it elevates the standards of living and adds to the comforts of life. That is the engineer's high privilege.

The great liability of the engineer compared to men of other professions is that his works are out in the open where all can see them. His acts, step by step, are in hard substance. He cannot bury his mistakes in the grave like the doctors. He cannot argue them into thin air or blame the judge like the lawyers. He cannot, like the architect, cover his failures with trees and vines. He cannot, like the politicians, screen his short-comings by blaming his opponents and hope that the people will forget. The Engineer simply cannot deny that he did it. If his works do not work, he is damned. That is the phantasmagoria that haunts his nights and dogs his days. He comes from the job at the end of the day resolved to calculate it again. He wakes in the morning. All day he shivers at the thought of the bugs which will inevitably appear to jolt its smooth consummation.

On the other hand, unlike the doctor, his is not a life among the weak. Unlike the soldier, destruction is not his purpose. Unlike the lawyer, quarrels are not his daily bread. To the engineer falls the job of clothing the bare bones of science with life, comfort and hope. . . .

The engineer performs many public functions from which he gets only philosophical satisfactions. Most people do not know it, but he is an economic and social force. Every time he discovers a new application of science, thereby creating a new industry, providing new jobs, adding to the standards of living, he also disturbs everything that is. New laws and regulations have to be made and new sorts of wickedness curbed. . . . But the engineer himself looks back at the unending stream of goodness which flows from his successes with satisfactions that few professions may know.[5]

Chance favors only the prepared mind.

LOUIS PASTEUR

No one, regardless of his profession, is likely to be motivated to creative effort unless he has a strong and undiminishing love for his work. With this love, each day's task becomes more than a means of earning a living. Each successfully accomplished design provides a special satisfaction that comes only to those who have a strong

[5] Herbert Hoover, *Memoirs of Herbert Hoover,* Vol. 1, Years of Adventure, New York: Macmillan, 1951, p. 132.

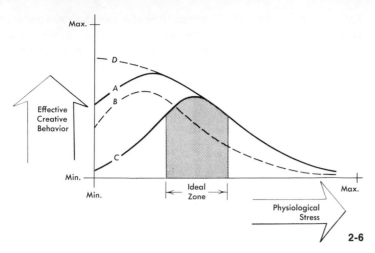

Effective Creative Behavior

Max.

Min.

Min.

Max.

Ideal Zone

Physiological Stress

2-6

ambition to succeed. The habit of work will become a part of the individual's personality until even his subconscious mind becomes saturated with the problem. These general conditions and circumstances provide very important climates for creative and imaginative thought.

To be most effective, a person should have a healthy body and a clear, intelligent mind, although a high IQ or a strong physique by no means guarantees innovative or creative ideas. Psychological freedom, in which the mind is unrestricted by past or present evaluations and judgments, is also very important. This requires breaking down early in life the erroneous idea that "if one attempts and fails, he will most certainly be a miserable person and be held in contempt by his peers." In fact, when the "fear of being wrong" has been removed, innovative and creative thought usually increases significantly for individuals as well as for groups of engineers working together.

Significant and imaginative thought processes are usually rare when the conscious mind becomes fatigued or when there is intense emotion (joy, sorrow, or fear). The relationship between *effective creative behavior* and *physiological stress* might be as illustrated in [2-6]. Each personality would have its own individual pattern or mathematical expression relating these variables.

The primary curve A indicates that, when the mind is without tension and the emotions are at rest, there is considerable possibility that imaginative and creative ideas can emerge. As supporting evidence for this conclusion, many creative people testify that their most novel ideas have appeared when they were engaged in such mild mental activities as bathing, listening to a musical concert, walking on the golf course, or riding the subway. Although this is not the usual case, such a situation might be represented by curve D. The secondary curves, B and C, indicate typical alternative paths that two different individuals might show. These curves also indicate

Our doubts are traitors and make us lose the good we oft might win by fearing to attempt.
WILLIAM SHAKESPEARE
Measure for Measure

We fear things in proportion to our ignorance of them.
TITUS LIVIUS
Histories, 50 B.C.–17 A.D.

It would seem quite apparent that there is no *one* creative process, and there may well be as many creative processes as there are creative people.

H. Herbert Fox
A Critique on Creativity in the Sciences

Observation, not old age, brings wisdom.

Behold the turtle, he makes progress only when his neck is out.

Dr. James B. Conant
President, Harvard University

I am a great believer in Luck. The harder I work the more of it I seem to have.

Coleman Cox

2-7
Frequently, man binds himself with constraints of his own making.

that some individuals do their most effective work when under some stress. Thus there is an ideal condition or emotional zone for each individual; for him it is most conducive to creative thought.

Other mental attributes that contribute positively toward creative thought are

1. An inquiring and questioning mind.
2. Abilities to concentrate and communicate.
3. Ability to accept conflict and tension without becoming frustrated.
4. Willingness to consider a new idea *even though it may seem to be in conflict* with previous experience.

In addition, there are personal qualities frequently associated with creative individuals. Developing them will enhance the likelihood that the individual will express himself creatively. They are as follows:

1. Intellectual curiosity.
2. Acute powers of observation.
3. Sensitivity to recognize that a problem exists.
4. Directed imagination.
5. Initiative.
6. Originality.
7. Memory.
8. Ability to analyze and synthesize.
9. Intellectual integrity.
10. Ability to think in analogies and images.
11. Intuition.
12. Being articulate in verbal response and alert in mental processes.
13. Patience, determination, and persistence.
14. Understanding of the creative process.

conditions that depress creative thinking

Just as certain conditions stimulate creative thinking, other conditions depress creative thinking and creative behavior. Thus, though the engineer may have high creative potential and intellectual ability to analyze, synthesize, and evaluate, he still may not be creative and innovative. These "road blocks to creative behavior" may be classified into three categories:

1. Barriers resulting from experience and perception.
2. Emotional barriers.
3. Social and cultural barriers.

Each of these will be considered briefly here.

Barriers to Creative Behavior Resulting from Experience and Perception

A recent experiment vividly illustrates the limitations that can be imposed by habit. This experiment involved a problem-solving situation in which two groups were asked to extract a Ping-Pong ball from the bottom of a long, small-diameter pipe standing vertically. When the members of the first group entered the experimental room, they saw assorted objects, including a screwdriver, pliers, string, thumbtacks, and a bucket of dirty water. None of the tools seemed useful, but, after some time, about half the group realized that the Ping-Pong ball could be recovered by pouring water into the pipe until the ball floated to the top.

A second group attacked the same problem. The small articles were displayed again. In this case, however, the container of water was missing. In its place was a dinner table set with china and silverware. On the table were a large pitcher of milk and a bucket of ice cubes. No one was able to solve the problem because the subjects could not relate the liquid (milk) or "solid water" (ice) used for dining to the totally different mechanical problem.

This experiment illustrates the danger of blind reliance on *restricted experience* in problem solving. In some instances, one may assume artificial restrictions that limit and bind his thought processes. As an example, consider the puzzle of the trees and the cows [2-8].

Problem: Six cows (shown as circles) are standing in a grove of trees (shown as X's). Draw three straight *connected* lines to join all the trees without touching any of the cows.

It's amazing what ordinary people can do if they set out without preconceived notions.

CHARLES F. KETTERING
Forbes Scrapbook of Thoughts in the Business of Life

2-8

Nothing in the problem statement implies that the lines represent fences or that the three lines must be restricted to the boundaries of the imaginary rectangular plot containing the cows and trees. However, most people automatically restrict themselves within this field and, under these artificial conditions, the problem becomes impossible to solve. This puzzle also illustrates the point that, in many instances, workable solutions to a problem are suggested by someone with minimal technical background related *directly* to the problem, but with a broad fundamental understanding of the principles governing the situation.

Strange as it may seem, it is nevertheless true that the more original and novel an idea is, the more vulnerable it is to criticism. Often the people most apt to prejudge a situation and allow past experiences to strangle a new idea are the ones whose analytical abilities have carried them to prior success. Certainly such skills *are essential* for minimum accomplishment in engineering. However, it sometimes seems easier to rely upon a previously successful mathe-

2-9

matical model than to consider the problem anew. It may well be that the original conditions have changed. We are all familiar with this tendency to "overconfidence" that sometimes overcomes those who excel in their field. It is particularly evident in athletics, where a less able person may be the eventual victor because he never recognizes that he is supposed to suffer defeat. The moral: Never prejudge; consider each situation on its own merits.

We are told that a man dying of thirst has little difficulty in seeing a mirage of a lake off in the distance. The image he *is* seeing seems to be affected in large measure by what his mind tells him that he *needs* to see. He is expectant and thirsty; therefore, it is easy for him to see the lake of water. In a sense, then, believing is seeing. The mind's recall of events and experiences also tends to influence one's observation, discernment, and judgment. For example, look at the two arrangements of straight lines.

In the first [2-11], do the vertical lines appear equal in length? Probably not. Are the two lines in the second [2-12] parallel to each other? "No," you say. Most people will think that these two simple questions are strange indeed. The answers appear obvious in both cases. However, if we tell you that the first is actually a picture of telephone poles standing in an abandoned field, and that the second

Some things have to be believed to be seen.
RALPH HODGSON
The Skylark and Other Poems

2-10

is a picture of a railroad track receding into the distance, you might quickly change your answers to "yes" or "maybe." In addition, the brief verbal descriptions that were added have given each picture a quality of depth that you did not recognize originally, demonstrating that we must sharpen our powers of observation, be alert to alternative explanations, and avoid the pitfalls of prejudgment and presumption that so often stifle our thought processes.

Another example might show how prior experience can artificially limit our thinking. Once two medical doctors were riding down the street together when they observed a head-on collision ahead. Upon arriving at the scene, they ran to the wrecked automobiles to render aid. After looking into one vehicle, the first physician moaned, "My wife and child!" Hearing this exclamation, the second physician pulled out a gun and killed the first physician. What is your analysis of the motive for this murder?

Writers of novels are skillful in maneuvering fiction plots so that the reader makes an invalid assumption. Perhaps you did this in the above example. Did you assume that both physicians were men? If both physicians were men, the story seems confused and no plausible explanation appears possible. However, the familiar triangular plot of secret love and consequential murder quickly unfolds when you realize that the second physician is a young woman.

Other barriers resulting from experience and perception are

1. Limited scope of basic knowledge.
2. Failure to recognize all the conditions relating to the problem—failure to get all the facts.
3. Preconception and reliance upon the history of other events.
4. Failure to investigate both the obvious and the trivial.
5. Artificial restriction of the problem.
6. Failure to recognize the *real* problem.
7. Inclusion of extraneous environmental factors.
8. Failure to distinguish between cause and effect.
9. Inability to manipulate the abstract.

Emotional Barriers

The graph of effective creative behavior versus physiological stress [2-6] illustrates that everyone's creative behavior diminishes to insignificance under high emotional stress. When under emotional strain, one is likely to narrow his field of observation, to make "snap judgments" that are not well thought out, and thus to disregard alternative and more valuable solutions. Overmotivated people are also likely to choose unrealistic and overambitious objectives. Emotional constraints are perhaps more damaging than other types because they can have such lasting influence upon one's personality. The emotional constraint most difficult to cope with is fear—fear

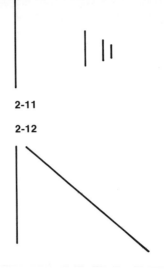

2-11

2-12

Habit is a cable; we weave a thread of it each day, and at last we cannot break it.

HORACE MANN
Forbes Scrapbook of Thoughts in the Business of Life

There are no foolish questions and no man becomes a fool until he has stopped asking questions.

CHARLES P. STEINMETZ

2-14

of failure, of criticism, of ridicule, of embarrassment, or of loss of employment. The fear of social disapproval can stifle initiative and reduce the flow of imaginative ideas. Controlled psychological experiments have shown that groups produce up to 70 per cent more innovative and novel ideas when group members do not *judge and evaluate each other's ideas* until later, thus largely removing the fears of ridicule and criticism. Brainstorming, a technique developed in the advertising business to produce more imaginative ideas, is one type of group effort that receives its stimulus by deferring judgment. Ways to implement this technique will be discussed later (see chapter 6).

An inferiority complex, resistance to change from the status quo, and a lack of reward stimulus can also be barriers to creative and innovative thought.

Social and Cultural Barriers

The history of civilization is essentially the record of man's creative behavior or lack thereof. Ancient cultures rose to great heights in Egypt (2700–1800 B.C.), Greece (600–300 B.C.), and Rome (400 B.C.–400 A.D.), but these civilizations eventually fell because of laxity of purpose, moral decay, and the people's overall lack of initiative. These conditions frequently arise when complacency, comfort, and luxury become primary objectives. When one must live or die by his wits, so to speak, his mind is stimulated to function more clearly than it would in a sheltered society. Younger generations who *inherit* the advantages of prosperity generally neither know nor appreciate the discipline of work. All these conditions reduce the motivation for creative thought.

Today, America faces a challenge much like those other cultures have faced in ages past. The physical frontiers that inspired our pioneer forefathers are fast disappearing from view. Fortunately, however, there are new frontiers, such as proper use and reuse of natural resources, ecological balance, outer space, ocean exploration, improved human relations and communications, disease eradication, new food and power sources, and waste and pollution elimination, which challenge our best and our maximum effort. These twentieth-century goals are, in many ways, more challenging than the frontier-day obstacles of a few hundred years ago. Even more significant, perhaps, is the fact that these new frontiers cannot be conquered successfully by applying known procedures or processes routinely. Individual initiative and motivation must continue to be the keys that unlock new ideas and stimulate creative thought. However, as with other cultures, intellectual decay must inevitably result if we desire security too strongly, choose undirected leisure instead of work, or deviate from our fundamental ideals.

Man is a social being and, as such, he needs the companionship of other men. His emotions, habits, and thoughts are strongly affected

There is no experiment to which a man will not resort to avoid the real labor of thinking.
SIR JOSHUA REYNOLDS

Daring ideas are like chessmen moved forward; they may be beaten, but they may start a winning game.
GOETHE

The probability is that tomorrow will not be an extrapolation of today.
ERNEST C. ARBUCKLE

Nothing can withstand the power of the mind. Barriers, enormous masses of matter, the remotest recesses are conquered; all things succumb; the very heaven itself is laid open.

MARCUS MANILUS, ca. 40 B.C.

by the cultural influences that surround him. At an early age, he learns that his associates disapprove of some of his actions and reward others with accolades and commendation. Such rewards may motivate him to make supreme efforts to gain recognition, but condemnation may make him afraid of deviating from his comrades' "group opinion" and thus stifle his creative and imaginative thought.

Overconformity to a group seems especially unfortunate, since a group or a committee as a discrete entity cannot, as such, produce creative thoughts. Creative thoughts come *only* from the minds of individuals. However, a committee or group can very definitely possess a unique personality that has strengths, weaknesses, and abilities—just as is the case for an individual. This fact does not discredit the accomplishments of teams, when the team members stimulate each other to produce novel and imaginative ideas. Not uncommonly, one team member's inspired idea will set off a chain reaction of ideas from other team members, whose subconscious memories have been awakened and stimulated into action. Team action is particularly effective in producing a large *volume* of ideas or getting a moderate course of action based on a *consensus*. Remember that hundreds of thousands of statues have been erected around the world . . . all to honor individuals. But so far, not one has been raised to honor a committee. It has been said, perhaps too harshly, that a committee never accomplishes anything unless it has three members, one of whom is always absent and one of whom is always ill. Winston Churchill is said to have once remarked that a committee was the organized result of a group of the incompetent who have been appointed by the uninformed to accomplish the unnecessary. Although his statement brings a smile to the lips of anyone who has served on very many committees, we must recognize that Churchill's own life showed that there is no substitute for bold, imaginative, individual thought.

Cultural restraints may be intangible, but they are very real. For example, someone assigned to reduce hunger in India might logically begin by looking at the availability of edible and nourishing foodstuffs in India. He would soon discover that India has a higher ratio of cows to people than any other country. Many of these cows could be slaughtered to provide enough meat, or clear meat broth, to sustain millions of people. Yet Indian culture, reinforced by the country's predominant religion, considers the cow a sacred animal that must not be harmed—certainly not killed and made into steaks and bouillon cubes.

In modern society most people are reluctant to accept change. Generally, they are either indifferent or negative to proposed ideas. This is why few creative people like Leonardo da Vinci, Copernicus, Galileo, and Mozart lived to see mankind accept the products of their imaginations. Modern civilizations have frequently been no more charitable to those who dared challenge contemporary mores.

If you want to kill an idea assign it to a committee for study.

. . . every idea is the product of a single brain.
BISHOP RICHARD CUMBERLAND

Society is never prepared to receive any invention. Every new thing is resisted, and it takes years for the inventor to get people to listen to him and years more before it can be introduced.

THOMAS ALVA EDISON

For example, John Kay was assaulted by weavers who feared his flying shuttle would destroy their means of livelihood; farmers scoffed at Charles Newbold's iron plow and insisted it would contaminate the soil; and the medical profession censured Dr. Horace Wells for using "gas" when extracting teeth.[6]

In more recent times, when the motel was first proposed as a new concept in innkeeping, the idea was greeted with scorn by leading hotel executives. However, the test of time has shown the immense value of the idea. Because of this built-in resistance to change, many new developments must necessarily originate outside the specialized area of endeavor.

Cultural blocks to creative behavior are not always as obvious as in these situations. For example, few of us would doubt the validity of a statement if we read it in a school textbook or in the daily newspaper. Under other circumstances, however, the same people might greet the same statement with considerable doubt, for example, if it appears to be the casual observation of a friend or associate with equal or lower social or intellectual standing. Yesterday everyone admired the young person who showed initiative in thinking for himself. Unfortunately, today we may not. Too often teachers, parents, and friends value the young person's ability to adapt himself to associates' dictates and his willingness to think and act in accordance with crowd sentiments above everything else. These social constraints tend to stifle and suppress our desire and ability to think independently and imaginatively and to behave creatively.

All these constraints therefore are detrimental to creative thought processes.

the stimulation of ideas

The engineer, as a professional man, must have keen analytical skill and the ability to synthesize. Without it he would be as handicapped as a boat without a rudder. His education must, necessarily, concentrate on this important part of the engineer's development. Both the engineer and his client must have confidence that his design calculations are both pertinent and accurate. However, an engineer who cannot produce a continuous flow of imaginative ideas is analogous to a boat without an engine. On the one hand, he may wander aimlessly, stumbling over his errors. But on the other hand, he may never get started at all. Therefore, engineering education must consider procedures for stimulating ideas.

It is highly desirable for the engineer to maintain the proper mental attitude toward the problem under study. High emotional stress, preconceived ideas based upon habit, or overemphasis on some assumed evaluation of an idea's ultimate value—all these are particu-

We do not have to teach people to be creative; we just have to quit interfering with their being creative.
ROSS L. MOONEY

Invention, strictly speaking, is little more than a new combination of those images which have been previously gathered and deposited in the memory. Nothing can be made of nothing; he who has laid up no materials can produce no combinations.
SIR J. REYNOLDS

BEWARE! Don't become victimized by habit.

The tyrant custom.
SHAKESPEARE
Othello

[6]A. F. Osborn, *Applied Imagination*, New York: Scribner's, 1963, p. 54.

Those who dream by day are cognizant of many things which escape those who dream only at night.

EDGAR ALLAN POE
Eleanora, 1841

2-16

Photograph by Phillip Leonian

larly damaging in the initial stages of idea development. Freedom of thought is essential. If it is restricted, intentionally or not, it makes little difference; the results are the same . . . reduced imaginative effort. Ancient history reveals that, before 3000 B.C., societies allowed the individual considerable freedom; artisans worked to enhance their own well-being rather than to expand the dominion of some ruler, king, or god-king. Inventions like the ax, the wheel, the plow, sailboats, writing, irrigation, the arch, pottery, spinning, and metallurgy are all examples of new ideas that appeared in this *free* environment. By about 1000 B.C. artisans found themselves working primarily to enhance the power of the ruler or king. Under these conditions, they produced considerably fewer new ideas.

Customs may also block imaginative thought. For example, archaeologists now believe that the pyramid-shaped structures built to protect Egyptian tombs originally were oblong buildings with sun-dried brick walls. Since rain deteriorated these walls, the Egyptians learned to slope the walls inward at the top, thus improving drainage and increasing durability. This custom persisted some 2,000 years later, long after stone had replaced the primitive clay bricks. Even though the outside walls no longer needed to be sloped for protection against erosion, *custom* dictated that they should slope inward at the top.

"The horror of that moment," the king went on, "I shall never, never forget!" "You will, though," the queen said, "if you don't make a memorandum of it."

LEWIS CARROLL

A man would do well to carry a pencil in his pocket, and write down the thoughts of the moment. Those that come unsought for are commonly the most valuable, and should be secured, because they seldom return.

BACON

If my theory of relativity is proven successful, Germany will claim me as a German and France will declare that I am a citizen of the world. Should my theory prove untrue, France will say that I am a German and Germany will declare that I am a Jew.

ALBERT EINSTEIN

The mind is not a vessel to be filled but a fire to be kindled.

PLUTARCH

Other examples have emphasized that the people who have imaginative ideas are the ones who "see with their minds" as well as their eyes. Many times we think of an idea that seems particularly exciting and innovative. When such a thought occurs, the substance of the idea should be recorded immediately so that it will not be lost. The engineer always should have a small notebook or card that can be carried easily in a shirt or coat pocket and a pencil or pen. He must be continually sensitive to impressions and to their significance. It is said that Galileo was walking about a cathedral one day when he noticed a large lamp swinging from side to side. From this observation he conceived his idea of the pendulum. There are similar possibilities for imaginative thought today, perhaps even more than in the ancient past.

Chapter 6 describes in some detail the several methods that are used in industry to deliberately stimulate ideas. These are

1. The use of check lists and attribute lists.
2. Reviewing of properties and alternatives.
3. Systematically searching design parameters.
4. Brainstorming.
5. Synectics.

general principles

The engineer who masters the fundamental principles of mathematics and science is able to understand the laws of nature. If this were the total requirement, the task of the engineer would be simplified. However, he never operates in a free environment where he is limited only by the laws of nature. The engineer always must endeavor to bridge between the "desires of man" and the "realities of nature." He must work both with nature and with people. Because of these practical considerations, he is limited by artificial or man-made restrictions, such as time, money, or personal preference. These restrictions necessitate compromises on the part of the engineer. Such is the nature of the real world, and the engineer must live and make his livelihood in it.

The engineer may be able to produce a novel solution that is seemingly desirable and economically justified, but it does not follow that his fellowman will always accept or implement it. People of all civilizations have resisted change; today's world is no exception. Although he will not suffer being thrown into jail, being whipped, shot, hung, or burned at the stake, as he might have years ago, the engineer with a radical idea may find that he is ignored, demoted, transferred to another part of the company, or even fired. Such is life in the real world.

It is important for the young engineer to recognize the importance of being able to sell his idea. Some suggestions to keep in mind are

1. People resist change. The status quo is comfortable and familiar. Any alterations or modifications to existing patterns must be "sold" to those who have the authority to approve decisions of change.
2. Never belittle a current practice or procedure in order to enhance the position of your own idea. Remember that your superior may have been responsible for implementing the technique that is now in use. Give him an opportunity to help you refine any improvement. If the idea is successful, there will be honor for all.
3. Present your design in a professional manner. Do not use sloppy sketches and poorly prepared commentary. Rather, take pride in your work. *Remember that its worth may be judged solely upon its clarity and appearance.*
4. Be prepared for all types of criticism. Try to think up as many reasons as you can why your idea *should not* be adopted. Prepare an answer for each objection.
5. Do not boast. It is better to minimize the overall effect of your idea and let others sell its virtue as a major contribution.
6. Do not become discouraged if you fail to sell your idea immediately. Time frequently acts as ointment to injured pride.

Since God created man in His own image, it is only *natural* for man to express himself in creative ways. The history of civilization is a history of man's creative efforts through the centuries. Man alone possesses the capacity for creative thought, and everyone has some capability for creative thinking. Remember that the real world is not always predictable, and that the art of compromise is in many cases the difference between success and failure. Remember also that creative behavior is a function of the individual personality rather than of organization, luck, or happenstance. For this reason, it is important to understand the characteristics of the creative person and to develop the attributes basic to imaginative and creative thought.

exercises in creative thinking

2-1. How can engineering help solve some of the major world problems?

2-2. Discuss some of the inventions that have contributed to the success of man's first lunar exploration.

2-3. Write a paragraph entitled "Fiction Today, Engineering Tomorrow."

2-4. Propose a method and describe the general features of a value system whereby we could replace the use of money.

2-5. List five problems that might now confront the city officials of your home town. Propose at least three solutions for each of these problems.

When dealing with people, remember you are not dealing with creatures of logic, but with creatures of emotion, creatures bristling with prejudice and motivated by pride and vanity.

DALE CARNEGIE

It takes courage to be creative. Just as soon as you have a new idea, you are a minority of one.

E. PAUL TORRANCE

Disciplined thinking focuses inspiration rather than constricts it.

It is better to wear out than to rust out.

BISHOP RICHARD CUMBERLAND
1697

There are two kinds of failures: The man who will do nothing he is told, and the man who will do nothing else.

PERLE THOMPSON

Satchel Paige championed six methods of staying young:
(1) Avoid fried meats which angry up the blood.
(2) If your stomach disputes, lie down and pacify it with cool thoughts.
(3) Keep the juices flowing by jangling around gently as you move.
(4) Go very light on the vices, such as carrying on in society. The social ramble ain't restful.
(5) Avoid running at all times.
(6) Don't look back. Something might be gaining on you.

2-6. Cut out five humorous cartoons from magazines. Recaption each cartoon such that the story told is completely changed. Attach a typed copy of your own caption underneath the original caption for each cartoon.

2-7. Propose a title and theme for five new television programs.

2-8. The following series of five words is related such that each word has a meaningful association with the word adjacent to it. Supply the missing words.

Example:

girl	blond	hair	oil	rich

(a) astronaut	_____	_____	_____	engineer
(b) pollution	_____	_____	_____	automobile
(c) college	_____	_____	_____	textbook
(d) football	_____	_____	_____	radio
(e) food	_____	_____	_____	trumpet

2-9. Suggest several highly desirable alterations that would encourage personal travel by rail.

2-10. What are five ways in which you might accumulate a crowd of 100 people at the corner of Main Street and Central at 6 A.M. on Saturday?

2-11. "As inevitable as night after day"—using the word "inevitable," contrive six similar figures of speech. "As inevitable as. . . ."

2-12. Name five waste products, and suggest ways in which these products may be reclaimed for useful purposes.

2-13. Recall the last time that you lost your temper. Describe those things accomplished and those things lost by this display of emotion. Develop a strategy to regain that which was lost.

2-14. You have just been named president of the college or university that you now attend. List your first ten official actions.

2-15. Describe the best original idea that you have ever had. Why has it (not) been adopted?

2-16. Discuss an idea that has been accepted within the past ten years but which originally was ridiculed.

2-17. Describe some design that you believe defies improvement.

2-18. Describe how one of the following might be used to start a fire: (a) scout knife, (b) baseball, (c) pocket watch, (d) turnip, (e) light bulb.

2-19. At night you can hear a mouse gnawing wood inside your bedroom wall. Noise does not seem to encourage him to leave. Describe how you will get rid of him.

2-20. Write a jingle using each of these words: cow, scholar, lass, nimble.

2-21. You are interviewing young engineering graduates to work on a project under your direction. What three questions would you ask each one in order to evaluate his creative ability?

2-22. Describe the most annoying habit of your girlfriend (boyfriend). Suggest three ways in which you might tactfully get this person to alter that habit for the better.

2-23. Suggest five designs that are direct results of ideas that have been stimulated by each of the five senses.

2-24. "A man's mother is his misfortune; his wife is his own fault" (*The London Spectator*). Write three similar epigrams on boy–girl relations.

2-25. Put a blob of ink on a piece of paper and quickly press another piece of paper against it. Allow it to dry, and then write a paragraph describing what you see in the resulting smear.

bibliography

ALLEN, M. S., *Morphological Synthesis*, Englewood Cliffs, N.J.: Prentice-Hall, 1962.

ANDERSON, H. H. (ed.), *Creativity and Its Cultivation*, New York: Harper & Row, 1959.

ARMSTRONG, F. A., *Idea Tracking*, New York: Criterion, 1960.

BEVERIDGE, W. I. B., *The Art of Scientific Investigation*, New York: Vintage Books, 1957.

CLARK, CHARLES, *Brainstorming*, Garden City, N.Y.: Doubleday, 1958.

CRAWFORD, R. P., *The Techniques of Creative Thinking*. New York: Hawthorn, 1954.

CRUTCHFIELD, R. S., "Conformity and Creative Thinking," *Contemporary Approaches to Creative Thinking*, New York: Atherton, 1963.

EASTON, W. H., "Creative Thinking and How to Develop It," *Creative Engineering*, New York: The American Society of Mechanical Engineers, 1954.

FLESCH, RUDOLPH, *The Art of Clear Thinking*, New York: Harper & Row, 1951.

GHISELIN, BREWSTER (ed.), *The Creative Process*, Berkeley: University of California Press, 1952.

GORDON, W. J. J., *Synectics*, New York: Harper & Row, 1961.

GUILFORD, J. P., "Creativity," *American Psychologist*, Vol. 5 (1950), pp. 444–454.

HAEFELE, J. W., *Creativity and Innovation*, London: Reinhold, 1962.

HUTCHINSON, E. D., *How to Think Creatively* (rev. ed.), New York: Abington-Cokeburg, 1949.

JEWKES, JOHN, DAVID SAWERS, and RICHARD STILLERMAN, *The Sources of Invention*, New York: Macmillan, 1961.

JONES, J. C., and D. G. THORNLEY (eds.), *Conferences on Design Methods*, New York: Macmillan, 1963.

LEFFORD, ARTHUR, "The Influence of Emotional Subject Matter on Logical Reasoning," *Journal of Psychology*, Vol. 34 (1946), p. 151.

OSBORN, A. F., *Applied Imagination*, New York: Scribner's, 1963.

PARNES, S. J., and H. F. HARDING (eds.), *A Sourcebook for Creative Thinking*, New York: Scribner's, 1962.

PLATT, WASHINGTON, and R. A. BAKER, "The Relation of the Scientific Hunch to Research," *Journal of Chemical Education*, Vol. 8, No. 10 (1931), p. 1969.

ROSSMAN, JOSEPH, *The Psychology of the Inventor*, Washington, D.C.: Inventors Pub. Co., 1931.

STEIN, M. I., and S. J. HEINZE, *Creativity and the Individual*, New York: Free Press, 1960.

TAYLOR, C. W., and FRANK BARRON (eds.), *Scientific Creativity*, New York: Wiley, 1963.

TAYLOR, J. W., *How To Create New Ideas*, Englewood Cliffs, N.J.: Prentice-Hall, 1961.

Think, A Special Issue: Man's Creative Mind, November–December, 1962.

TUSAK, C. D., *Inventors and Inventions*, New York: McGraw-Hill, 1957.

VON FANGE, E. K., *Professional Creativity*, Englewood Cliffs, N.J.: Prentice-Hall, 1959.

WHITING, C. S., *Creative Thinking*, London: Reinhold, 1958.

These copper-plated nickel flowers burgeoned during developmental work in electroforming. Strikingly beautiful but unwanted, the flowers generally sprout in high current density areas, robbing surrounding areas of deposits. Although these dendrites are small (the largest "bloom" is $\frac{3}{4}$ inch in diameter) and flower-like, such outgrowths can appear in many different shapes and sizes. The possibility of these products appearing can be minimized by close control of such parameters as temperature, current, voltage, and electrolyte composition.

What evidence would suggest that the inferior cockroach might out-last man, the most advanced creature that the world has known? Isn't man the most intelligent of all creations, and doesn't he adapt himself readily to changing geographic and climatic conditions, and to unusual and unique environments that are entirely foreign to his natural habitat? Aren't his recent journeys to the moon an excellent example of this ability? Yes, these are all true statements, and there are even stronger statements that could be made in behalf of man. For example, only man has been given intellectual faculties and a spiritual nature in addition to physical qualities. He alone possesses the ability to reason and he has lived a long, long time. In this regard, many scientists believe that man may have inhabited the earth for almost 2 million years.

And when the span of man has run its course
  Sitting upon the ruins of his civilization will be a
    cockroach,
Calmly preening himself
  In the rays of the setting sun.

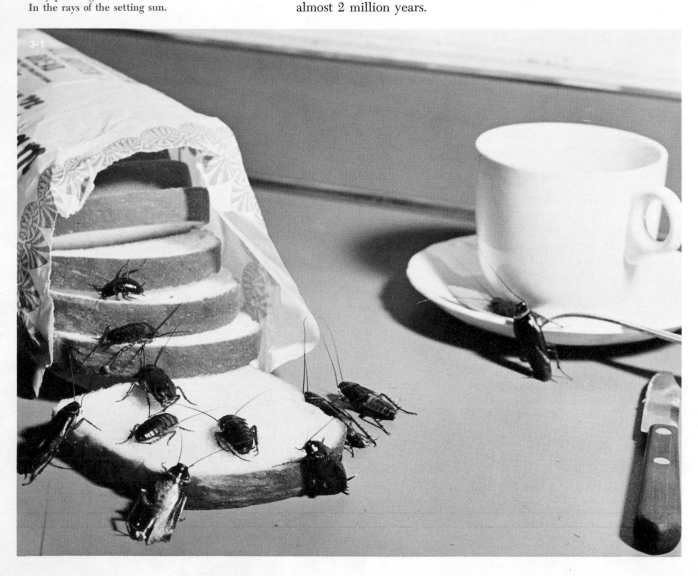

However, the cockroach has a much better "track record" for staying power. He has been around some 280 million years, or about 140 times as long as man. During man's *brief* tenure on earth the cockroach has competed successfully with him for food, lodging, and other necessities of life. Today, unlike numerous other animals and insects, his extinction does not appear to be imminent. Rather he seems to be gaining strength with each passing generation. Upon examination we find that the roach has been designed as a finely tuned instrument capable of adjusting to a tremendous range of conditions. He has a full complement of structures, organs, and behavior patterns that have been tested and honed to a fine edge by the evolutionary forces of nature. Although his physical size is small, his internal mechanisms are considerably more complex than the most sophisticated products of man's modern technology. Admittedly, he lacks intelligence and reasoning power, but he has never been observed to engage wilfully in activities that would guarantee his eventual annihilation. Yes, it *is* possible that man might learn many things from observing the actions of the lowly cockroach.

It is now believed that the earth is at least 3 billion years old. It is filled with many types of living things—animals and insects and plant life of countless varieties. Like the cockroach, each occupies a special place and each acts in a predictable behavior pattern in accordance with a long experience in meeting the requirements of nature under varying environmental conditions. To survive, each animal, insect, and plant has been forced to contrive actions, solutions, and *designs* that provide protective housing, that enhance the probability of sensing and capturing food, and that locate either prey or predator. Many of these designs are ingenious, and a large number are astonishingly beautiful. Many are simple designs. Others are quite complex, yet very efficient.

It is unfortunate that most often man has acted only as a casual observer of these ingenious *designs of nature*. More rarely, he has been a user of the products of nature's design (such as diatomic earth, spider-web threads, and bamboo). Least frequently, he has been an imitator of nature and been able to make use of the unique solutions that nature has made available to us (such as flying machines, honeycomb structures, and poison arrows). In fact, in the majority of cases man often has discovered the existence of some unique design in nature only after he himself had invented a similar device and learned to recognize its qualities. Examples are sonar and electric-field detection, and we will talk more about these later on.

This chapter has been written to encourage the engineering student to be especially observant of the behavior of animals, insects, and plants, to make an effort to discover how these "living designs of nature" have solved their problems, and to make use of this information in designing for human preservation and satisfaction.

The designs of nature can be divided into the general categories

In the works of Nature *purpose*, not accident, is the main thing.

ARISTOTLE
Nicomachean Ethics

If no way be better than another—that, you may be sure, is Nature's way.

LEIBNIZ
Théodicée, 1857

The chessboard is the world, the pieces are the phenomena of the universe, the rules of the game are what we call the laws of Nature. The player on the other side is hidden from us, we know that his play is always fair, just, and patient. But also we know, to our cost, that he never overlooks a mistake, or makes the smallest allowance for ignorance.

THOMAS HENRY HUXLEY
A Liberal Education, 1825–1895

Ever since I have been enquiring into the works of Nature I have always loved and admired the simplicity of her ways.

DR. GEORGE MARTINE
Medical Essays and Observations, 1747

3-2
The bolas spider takes her name from the bolas of the gaucho of the Argentine. She traps her prey by first forming a shining viscid glue ball and then twirling it overhead in a circular path to strike an unsuspecting moth or bug. The silky strand that tethers the sticky ball to the spider is elastic and will hold the struggling insect in spite of its gyrations. It is not known just what mechanism serves to attract the moth within throwing distance of the bolas.

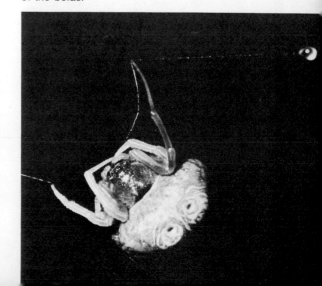

In nature's infinite book of secrecy
A little I can read.

SHAKESPEARE
Antony and Cleopatra

Nature abhors mathematics. What I really mean is that simple mathematics, as we have hitherto developed them, can never express the whole complex truth of natural phenomena. In other words, we must use such instruments as we have, such formulae as are convenient, such mathematical conventions as suit our human minds, such hypotheses as Newton's, Darwin's, or another's. But Nature, *elle ne s'y mêle pas*, as the Frenchman said. She knows. We try to know. We cannot know her formula however hard we try. But we shall play the game out with her to the end, and go on trying all the time; only so shall we get nearer and nearer every day; for only in that stern chase is any life worth living: *"to follow after valor and understanding."*

THEODORE ANDREA COOK
The Curves of Life, 1914

3-3
The bat is the only flying mammal. For food it hunts insects at night, and it finds them by an intricate sonar system. It issues periodic beeps of constant amplitude (as high as 113 decibels) but varying frequency—30,000–60,000 hertz—well beyond the range of human ears. The bat can tell from the echo reflected by its prey exactly how far away the prey is and where it is headed. This means that its ears must be extremely sensitive for receiving but unaffected by the loud sending signal. Careful study of the bat's ultrasonic sonar system has enabled engineers to design a device that allows blind people to "see."

of natural systems that are being used by man, natural systems that have been improved or repaired by man, and natural systems that are potentially useful to man.

natural systems that are being used by man

The Sonar of Bats

Long before man had heard of *sonar*, bats were using it to navigate and locate their prey. Insectivorous bats are able to locate and to capture insects smaller than mosquitoes while flying in complete darkness at full speed. They do so by giving off a series of ultrasonic cries and locating objects by the distance and direction of the sources of echoes.

The sounds emitted by bats are actually very loud with intensities as high as 113 decibels. We are unable to hear them because they

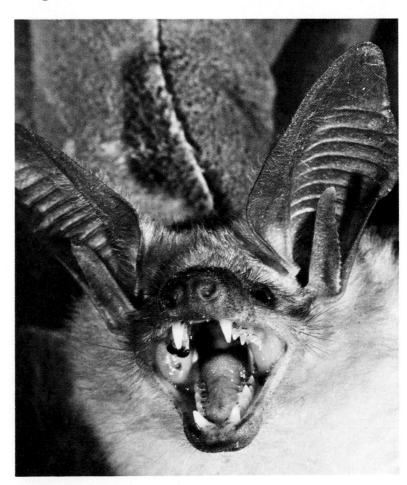

are out of the range of our sound sensitivities. The frequency modulation of the pulses ranges from 20,000 to 100,000 cycles per second. Man cannot hear sounds above 20,000 cycles per second. The wavelength of the pulses varies from 6 to 12 millimeters, which is about the same size as the insects that make up the normal prey of the bats.

While hunting, the bat sends 10 to 20 pulses per second until a returning echo tells him that an object is in his flight path. He then increases the pulse rate to as high as 200 per second. This improves his discrimination and enables him to find the prey more accurately.

A great deal of interest has been generated in the bat's "sonar" system because of two of its characteristics that are as yet unexplained. Some bats are able to locate fish beneath the surface of the water, and it is not understood how this is done. Also, attempts to "jam" the bat's sonar system with loud sound intensities have not been successful. In some way the bat is able to detect its own signals through a cacophony of sound. Military men have been looking for jam-proof systems and consequently are very interested in learning how the bat is able to accomplish this feat. Another use has been made of the principle in the designing of a sonar system to aid blind people to "see."

It is interesting to note that some night-flying moths which are the normal prey of bats have hearing apparatus that can detect the ultrasonic cries of the bats. When they hear a bat approaching, they may drop to the ground, soar upward, dive steeply, or otherwise take evasive action. The moth can detect the bat at a greater distance than the bat can detect it. However, the bat is capable of greater speed in flight. It is interesting that in this predator–prey relationship there is a precise balance between the ability of the bat to locate and react to a moth and the ability of the moth to detect and react to the bat.

The Eye of the Frog

The eyes of frogs are much less acute than those of man, and they are not movable in their sockets. However, they do have one capability that is very important to the frog's ability to obtain food. That is, they are able to detect movement and to differentiate between things flying toward him and those flying away from him. An engineering version of the retina of the frog is currently being tested to determine its application as a device to assist air-traffic controllers to prevent air collisions. The model contains more than 33,000 electrical components to accomplish this action.

Depth Control of Fish

Submarines adjust their vertical position in water by the use of air tanks that can be used to change the overall density of the submarine and thus cause it to rise, sink, or remain stable at one

Important ideas are those that lie within the allowable scope of nature's law.

Ere the bat hath flown
His cloister'd flight.

SHAKESPEARE
Macbeth

3-4

Frogs are practically blind, and their eyes are stationary in their sockets. However, they have other remarkable abilities. They receive, process, and relay information *important to the frog* and filter out everything else. For example, a juicy bug flying toward him is important; one flying away is not. The frog's eye signals his brain if

(a) An object is flying toward him,
(b) The object is "bug size,"
(c) The object is flying at "bug speed,"
(d) The object is within range.

Everything else is ignored. The frog's eye also makes other life and death decisions for him without bothering his feeble brain. A sudden shadow, for example, will trigger a danger signal causing the reflexive jumping mechanism to function.

It was a saying of Bion that though boys throw stones at frogs in sport, the frogs do not die in sport, but in earnest.

PLUTARCH
Which Are The Most Crafty, Water or Land Animals?,
46–120 A.D.

The pleasant'st angling is to see the fish
Cut with her golden oars the silver stream,
And greedily devour the treacherous bait.
SHAKESPEARE
Much Ado About Nothing

depth in the water. This same mechanism has been used for millions of years by those fish who have a swim bladder. These particular fish secrete gas into a flexible-walled container. Their bodies also are flexible so that the gas in the swim bladder expands or contracts as they change their depth in the water. Other species have swim bladders that are nearly inflexible, and they adjust for changes in pressure by means of a sphincter muscle that allows gas to escape when pressure is reduced. With some fish the swim bladder connects to the ear or is located very close to it. This results in an increased sensitivity to sound as the vibrations in the water are amplified around the bubble of gas in the swim bladder. A swim bladder connected to the ear in this manner may amplify the vibrations of sound by a factor of as much as 100. The cuttlefish lives at considerable depths, down to 150 meters, in the ocean. It is able to remain at this level with little effort because of a modification that serves the same purpose as a swim bladder. This modification is the cuttlebone, which consists of about 100 partitioned thin-walled chambers that are partially filled with gas and fluid. As fluid is withdrawn from the cuttlebone by osmotic forces, gases diffuse into the chambers until they are in equilibrium with the gases dissolved in the body fluid of the animal. In this way the animal is able to maintain its position in the water.

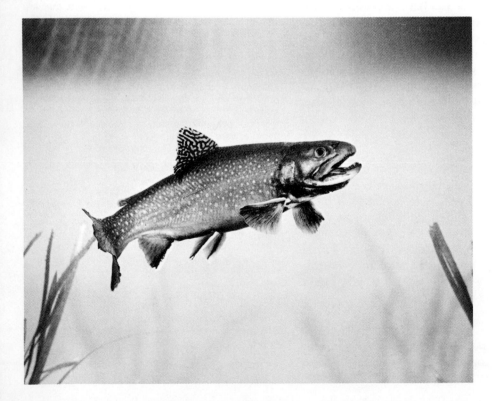

3-5
The locomotion and maneuverability of the fish are not well understood today, although these qualities have received much study over the past several thousands of years.

Flight Control of Flies

Gyroscopes have long been used to stabilize the position of structures and vehicles, such as ships and planes. They are based upon the principle of a rapidly spinning wheel or disc that is mounted so that it is free to rotate about one or both of two axes perpendicular to each other and to the axis of spin—thereby offering opposition to any torque that would change the direction of the axis of spin.

Flies have only one pair of functional wings. However, a pair of small knobbed structures known as *halteres* act as a second set of modified wings. These halteres vibrate up and down when the insect is in flight. As long as the insect is in level flight there are no abnormal strains at the point where the halteres are attached to the body. If the flying insect is inclined or tipped, however, the plane in which the halteres are vibrating is changed and stresses are set up in the attachment points to the body. The fly is then able to adjust his position to normal. In effect, the halteres act as "alternating gyroscopes."

The Light Meter of the Eye

Many modern cameras are advertised as having "through-the-lens focusing," automatic exposure control, and the capability of handling a wide range of film-emulsion speeds. Focusing for cameras is generally adjusted by the operator, whereas automatic exposure control is usually accomplished by means of a mechanism powered by a cadmium sulfide battery that operates independently once the film-emulsion speed has been set. Such cameras are very effective and efficient in taking pictures. However, these so-called "advanced features" were predated by millions of years by the eyes of mammals, which perform all the above, and more automatically. In fact, all the major mechanical features of cameras are modeled directly after the mammalian eye. The camera lens is modeled after the lens of

3-6

The multifaceted compound eye of the common housefly (enlarged over 100 times above) produces a mosaic made up of multiple images. In much the same way, engineers have designed new multielement phased-array radar sets that are freed from the foibles of mechanical failure and possess a near-instantaneous ability to "look" from one direction to another.

It was prettily devised of Aesop, "the fly sat upon the axle-tree of the chariot-wheel and said, 'What a dust do I raise.'"

FRANCIS BACON
Of Vainglory, 1561–1626

If a fly had an eye like ours, the pupil would be so small that diffraction would render a clear image impossible. The only alternative is to unite a number of small and optically isolated simple eyes into a compound eye, and in the insect Nature adopts this alternative possibility.

C. J. VAN DER HORST
"The Optics of the Insect Eye," Acta Zoolog., 1933,
p. 108

3-7
The human eye.

3-8

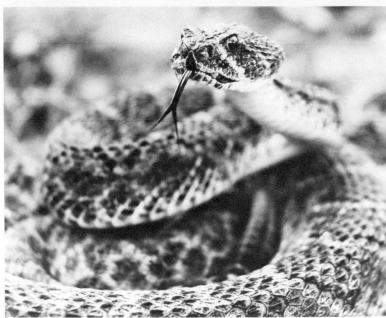

3-9

Man has much to learn from the snake. Over the years efforts have been made to imitate the design of the snake's fangs in the manufacture of hypodermic needles and to copy the heat-seeking infrared sensor mechanism of his nostril pits in missile-defense systems. What may offer even more valuable use, however, would be an understanding of his odor-air quality tester—the combined action of this flicking, darting tongue and a small organ of smell located in the roof of the mouth.

A snake lurks in the grass.

PUBLIUS VERGILUS MARO
Eclogues, 70-19 B.C.

the eye, the diaphragm is modeled after the iris diaphragm of the eye, and the retina of the eye is the forerunner of the tremendous range of film speed emulsions, both in black and white and color.

The Snake's Hypodermic Fang

In this day of antibiotics in medicine it is difficult for anyone to escape the sting of the hypodermic needle. Even when being subjected to the needle, few people take the opportunity to meditate on the fact that the hypodermic needle is an engineering copy of the fangs of rattlesnakes, which have served the snake very efficiently for millions of years. Rattlesnake fangs have exceedingly sharp points to break the skin and allow the entry of the fangs to the underlying tissues; the wedge-shaped design of the fangs spreads the tissues and allows the entry of the poison into the wound from an opening in the side of the fangs rather than from the tip. In this way, the possibility of the fangs becoming plugged by the tissue of the victim is minimized. The hypodermic needle has been designed with the same adaptive modification.

Some Old Ideas on Flying

Helicopters are widely used in civilian and military applications. Their ability to fly is based upon the principle of the airfoil, which in ordinary airplanes form the wings. In this case, the helicopter rotor blades are the airfoils that rotate and provide the necessary lift, even though the helicopter itself remains stationary. The successful application of this principle has been classified as an important engineer-

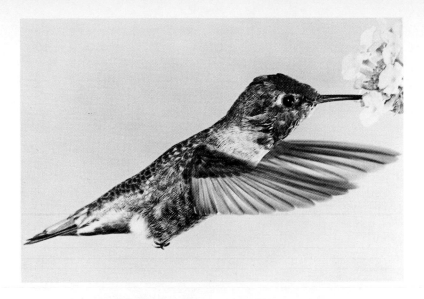

3-10
The hummingbird's wings beat very rapidly, up to 90 times per second. This action enables him to move backward or forward or remain stationary with equal facility.

3-11
The helicopter—man's hummingbird.

ing breakthrough in the development of heavier-than-air aircraft. However, this principle has been utilized for hundreds of centuries by hummingbirds and sphinx moths. The sight of hummingbirds hovering over a flower to obtain the nectar is a familiar one. They accomplish this feat by beating their wings forward and back, turning them upside down on the backstroke. In this manner, the lift of the wing is kept acting upward at all times. The net result is the same as that accomplished by the helicopter rotor blade.

Gliders and sailplanes have been modeled directly after soaring birds, such as buzzards, hawks, gulls, and albatrosses. Both birds and gliders utilize columns of warmer air known as *thermals*, which rise over heated areas of ground. Careful engineering studies of the aerodynamics of the flight of gliders and buzzards have shown very close correlations between airspeed, minimum gliding angles, and

3-12
Soaring birds have long been a fascination to man. This unusual drawing was achieved by electronically scanning an original photograph for values of grays, assigning each value a number, and storing the numbers in a computer. Later the numbers were used to reconstruct the photograph with symbols having the same quality of gray value.

3-13
Soaring is unpowered flight that utilizes the upward currents of air or shifts in wind velocity with small changes in altitude to maintain or make an overall gain in altitude. Currently, flights lasting in excess of 10 hours and distances of over 700 miles have been recorded.

minimum sinking speeds for both gliders and buzzards. By opening and closing the gaps between their primary feathers, which act as slotted airfoils, buzzards are able to adjust the lift coefficient to compensate for various gliding speeds. With gliders, similar adjustments are accomplished by means of wing flaps.

Propeller-powered fixed-wing aircraft also have close resemblances to basic designs of nature. Although it might appear at first glance that birds fly simply by beating their wings up and down, careful studies have shown that specialized primary feathers at the wing tips constantly change their angles and shapes as the wings move up and down. The flexible nature of the feathers, together with a movable connection to the framework of the wing, allows the feathers to adjust to varying speed and lift requirements. In this way the primary feathers produce much the same effect as the rotating propeller of a propeller-powered aircraft.

All heavier-than-air craft have the problem of reducing weight to a functional minimum. Man has imitated birds in meeting the requirements of light weight, great strength, and elasticity. In comparison with other animals, the skeleton of a bird is disproportionately light in weight. This design is accomplished by thin hollow bones, which are internally braced to increase their strength. One of the largest birds, the frigate bird, which may have a wingspan as great as 7 feet, has a bony skeleton that weighs 4 ounces or less. Modern aircraft utilize thin light aluminum skins reinforced by trussed girders to achieve lightness and strength.

Jet Propulsion in Nature

Even jet propulsion, which is so widely utilized to propel aircraft and boats, has its antecedent in designs of nature. One animal that

He is a fool who lets slip a bird in the hand for a bird in the bush.

PLUTARCH
Of Garrulity, 46–120 A.D.

3-14

Squids are remarkable creatures, and next to fish they are the most numerous of the advanced life forms of the ocean. Interesting features that we would do well to study are their jet-propulsion system, tentacles, beaks, dual optical systems (for seeing both in the darkened depths and on the surface), glowing light organs, adaptive camouflage, and black ink-like protective substance that serves to decoy and confuse attackers.

3-15
The dragonfly larva, or nymph, can walk or climb, and it swims efficiently by a jet-propulsion-like action. It captures its prey by means of a prehensile lower lip, which is folded under the head when not in use, but which can be extended suddenly to seize a prey by means of a pair of terminal hooks.

Courtesy Carolina Biological Supply Company

occurs in tremendous numbers in the oceans of the world is the *squid*. Squids are very important in the food chains in the oceans. In order to move, they employ the engineering principles employed by jet propulsion. Water is drawn into a cavity within the squid that is surrounded by elastic muscular walls. When the muscles contract, the size of the cavity is decreased and the water is forced out through a funnel-shaped structure, thereby pushing the squid forward in accordance with Newton's third law of motion. By changing the direction in which the funnel is pointed, the squid is able to change its direction of movement.

Immature forms of dragonflies also employ jet propulsion for locomotion. These nymphs live in the water for 2 or 3 years before changing into the more familiar form of dragonflies. While in the water, the nymphs breathe by means of gills located in a cavity at the posterior end of the intestine. When the size of the cavity is increased, water enters. When the muscular walls of the cavity contract, water is forced out the posterior end of the animal and the nymph is forced forward. As a result of this intermittent action, the nymph moves in a sequence of short spurts.

Heating and Cooling

Heat exchangers are widely utilized in the chemical industry and in mechanical devices. The automobile radiator, the heat pump, and the refrigerated air conditioner are modern-day examples of engineering designs wherein a circulating fluid transfers heat to an expanded surface area, where it is removed by radiation or convection. Similar designs are common among animals, where they play an important role in the animal's adaptations to its environment. Jackrabbits are widely distributed throughout the western states where they can be seen frequently, even during the heat of the day. Studies of their behavior have shown, however, that following prolonged exposure to the heat of the sun, jackrabbits will rest in the shade of a bush or tree for some period of time. During this time, their large ears are held erect and heat is lost by radiation into the atmosphere. The ears have a very large blood supply and a very large surface area. This combination produces an efficient heat-exchange mechanism. At the other end of the temperature scale, arctic seals frequently can be seen basking at the edge of an ice flow, sticking one flipper up into the sunshine. The flipper has a large surface area and is supplied abundantly with blood vessels. Heat is absorbed into the blood stream and carried throughout the body of the animal, thereby providing a localized source of heat for the animal. A closely related question is how the seal, which swims in icy waters, is able to maintain its body temperature within relatively narrow limits. Examination of the circulatory system in the flipper of the seal reveals the existence of a heat-exchange mechanism between the blood going to the flippers and that which returns from them. The arterial blood going to the flippers gives some of its heat to the venous blood returning from the flippers. In this way the venous blood is warmed, the arterial blood is cooled, and the exchange helps to keep the heat in the body of the animal.

Compost piles are familiar devices to almost any amateur gardener. They are devices for promoting the decomposition of organic material. Gardeners utilize them to convert lawn clippings into organic fertilizer, while sanitary landfills have utilized compost piles as a means of converting municipal garbage into usable organic fertilizer. In fact, quite a science has grown up around the construction and utilization of compost piles. It might appear that these designs have

The jackrabbit's large ears serve effectively as heat exchangers and help to cool the rabbit.

3-17
This Alaskan fur seal's flippers are supplied abundantly with blood vessels to serve as a heat-exchange mechanism and help to "heat up" the body.

been an origination of man's technology. Not so! In fact, a number of types of birds constructed and utilized compost piles long before man's appearance on the earth. Jungle fowl, brush turkeys, and mallee fowl are all known to construct such piles. The male mallee fowl constructs an incubator mound of earth and moist leaf litter as much as 3 feet high. The leaf litter begins to rot and, as it does so, heat is generated. After eggs are laid in the mound by the female, the male tends the mound to see that the temperature of the mound is maintained between 90 and 92°F. He does this by balancing the heat from the two major heat sources—fermentation and the sun. During the summer when the sun's radiation is intense, he protects the eggs by adding more soil to the mound to reduce the heating effect of the sun. During the winter he reduces the size of the mound to take advantage of the heating effects of the sun during the day, then rebuilds the mound at night to insulate the eggs against the colder temperatures of the night. He tests the temperature of the mound by thrusting his bill into the mound and withdrawing it filled with sand. The bill apparently serves as a thermometer. By these means the mallee fowl can maintain the temperature of the mound within a 2-degree range for the entire time that the eggs are incubating.

Visual Concealment

Camouflage, the art of concealment, has been developed to a science by the armed forces of almost every country. It is based upon several principles: (1) an object is made difficult to detect by coloring it so that it blends with its background, (2) an object is made less conspicuous by breaking up large color patterns into a number of smaller, irregular patterns, and (3) an object should be made to look like something else. Interestingly, similar techniques have been the basis for the survival of living organisms ever since life began.

The bark of birch trees is light in color. If both light- and dark-colored moths were to rest on the bark, the light-colored moths would be less conspicuous and therefore be less likely to be eaten by other animals than would the dark ones. There should therefore be more white moths in such geographical areas. This was the case in the vicinity of Manchester, England in 1850. However, by 1895 the dark-colored moths were found to be the most numerous. Investigation revealed that the increased industrialization at this time in history had brought about air pollution by coal soot and had so darkened the bark of the birch trees that the protective camouflage effect had been switched to the darker-colored moths. The resulting effect was an increase in their numbers and a decrease of light-colored moths. This change to darker color patterns as a result of industrial activity has been termed *industrial melanism.*[1]

[1] *Melanism*—the condition in which an unusually high concentration of dark pigment occurs in the skin, plumage, or pelage of an animal.

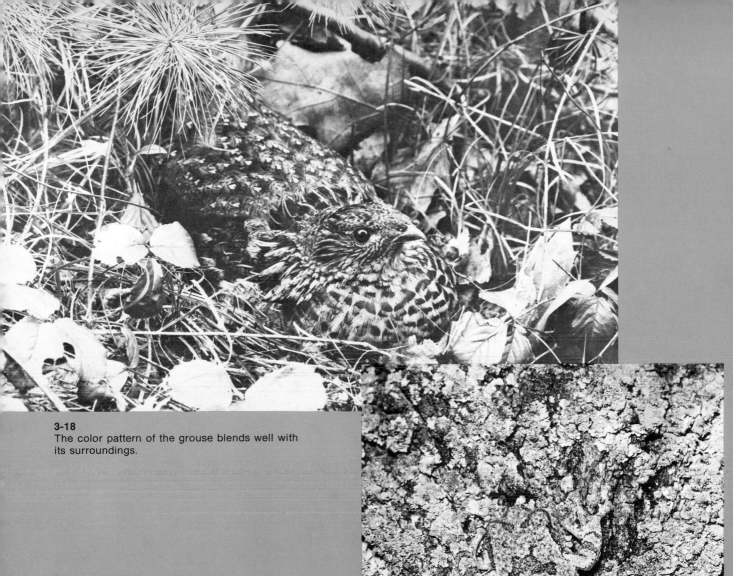

3-18
The color pattern of the grouse blends well with
its surroundings.

3-19
Few if any man-made camouflage designs can
match the effectiveness of the tree toad's coloring
and texture.

"Will you walk into my parlour?"
   said a spider to a fly;
"'Tis the prettiest little parlour
That ever you did spy."

MARY HOWITT
The Spider and the Fly, 1799-1888

3-20

Man is wonderfully ingenious and clever, but thus far he is incapable of matching the spider's efficient and effective spinning process. In this picture a female spider is seen from the rear as she spins a web. Note four large and two small spinnerets, a thread going from the anterior spinnerets to the surface anchoring the spider, a bundle of threads coming out of the posterior, and small spinnerets going through the hook of the eighth leg and connecting the spider to some place above. In this way the spider spends its whole life probing threads, pulling threads, and using threads as a means of moving around.

Many spiders spin webs which they use to capture prey. However, while sitting in the web, the spider himself is very conspicuous and subject to being eaten by other predators. Some spiders build into the web several structures that resemble themselves. These are designed to confuse prospective predators and increase the spider's chances for survival.

Many insects are very difficult to detect because of their resemblance in color or shape to some part of the plant upon which they

3-21
Walking sticks resemble their surroundings so closely that detection is difficult.

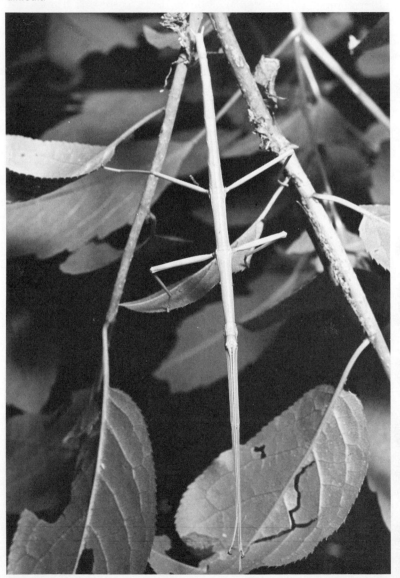

are usually found. Those that are green in color are found on leaves, bark-colored ones are found on tree trunks, and brightly colored forms may be found on flowers. In some cases, the color of the insect will change as the insect develops. In such cases the insect changes his resting places to match his changes in body color.

Walking sticks are examples of insects that achieve protection by closely resembling the plant part upon which they are usually found. In many cases, it would take a trained observer to spot a walking stick on its host plant.

Chameleons are famous for their ability to change body color to match the background upon which they are resting. However, many other animals exhibit similar abilities. Insects, spiders, lizards, and fish are among those which can change colors.

Limited Access Control

Many plants must utilize insects to carry pollen from one plant to another to allow fertilization to occur and to produce fruits and seeds. The relationships between plants and insects are often very close and are based upon both morphological and physiological considerations. Some flowers are so constructed that only insects of a certain size and weight are able to open them and reach the nectar pollen within the flower. Some flowers have colors and produce scents that are attractive to particular groups of insects. In others, the flowers open and close on a daily schedule coordinated with the activity times of the preferred insect pollinators. One outstanding example of design in nature related to pollination is that concerning yucca plants and the yucca moth. Only the yucca moth is able to bring about the pollination of these plants.

Seed Distribution

Many mechanisms for seed dispersal have been developed. Perhaps the most familiar are those in which parachute-like structures are formed to allow the seeds to be airborne for long periods of time. One such device consists of plumes of silky hairs. Milkweeds, dandelions, willows, and cottonwoods are examples of plants that have plumed seeds or fruits.

Other seeds and fruits have "wings" that enable them to be carried some distance by the wind. Plants that have winged seeds or fruits include the maple, ash, linden trees, and Tree of Heaven, as well as many herbacious plants. The basic design of these winged seeds has been copied by engineers to build containers for the purpose of dropping supplies safely from aircraft to the ground.

Mechanical means are also utilized for seed dispersal. In some cases valvelike structures in the fruit contract upon drying and force the seeds out. In some violets, seeds are thrown up to 15 feet; in the witch hazel plant, seeds are thrown more than 30 feet by such a mechanism.

How doth the little busy bee
  Improve each shining hour,
And gather honey all the day
  From each opening flower?

Isaac Watts
Divine Songs for Children, 1674–1748

3-22
The honey bee is a citizen of all continents and is found in all States of the United States. Without his pollination efforts it is estimated that over 100,000 species of plants would become extinct. Pollen also plays an important role in the life of the honeybee. The pollen, scraped from the bee's body and packed onto the hind legs for transporting back to the hive, provides the protein necessary for the rearing of the young.
The bee's almost miraculous navigation system is aided appreciably by the quality of his eyes that make them receptive to the polarization of the light in the sky. This quality enables him to navigate unerringly without recourse to the sun. The Pfundt sky compass, designed around this principle, has proved to be very useful for navigation in polar regions when neither sun nor stars are visible.
Bees are paradoxical in that individually they are cold-blooded insects but collectively they behave as a warm-blooded animal. To refrigerate the hive they bring in water for evaporation. For heating they cluster tightly to generate and conserve heat. Neither process is completely understood.

3-23
Plumed seeds, such as those of the milkweed, facilitate the transportation process. This unique type of parachute may offer man some interesting possibilities.

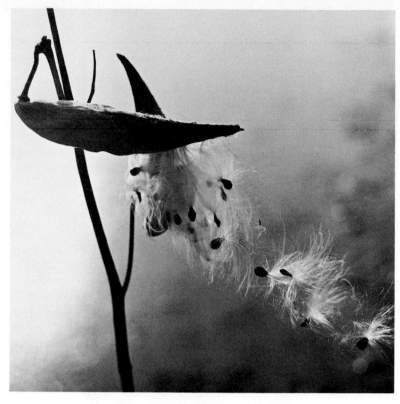

3-24
Certain seeds, such as the maple shown here, are aerodynamically designed for flight. When ripe, the seeds separate, and each wing rotates as it gently lowers the seed to the ground. Single wings of this design have been used as low-cost parachutes to drop food or equipment to isolated areas.

In other plants springlike sling mechanisms are used to throw the seeds. Some geranium plants are able to throw seeds in this way as much as 20 feet. Modern applications of this design principle include the catapult and the slingshot.

Mechanisms and Structures

Information gained from the study of animal movement has provided man with some of his most useful mechanical devices. Two of these are the hinge and ball-and-socket joint. The hinge is represented by the wrist, elbow, and finger joints of man; the hip and shoulders are examples of ball-and-socket joints. Mechanical examples of hinges include door hinges and piano hinges. Mechanical copies of ball-and-socket joints include trailer hitches and ball joints on the steering systems of automobiles.

Perhaps the animal that has been most closely associated with civil-engineering exploits is the beaver. His prowess at building dams is almost legendary and certainly well deserved. Using logs, branches, stones, and mud, the beaver has built dams, complete with spillways, that are marvels of efficiency. Studies of beaver dams have revealed that they are bow shaped with the bow facing upstream to provide the greatest strength against the pressure of the water. Large man-made dams also utilize this principle. Long before man constructed

3-25
With the tools at his disposal the beaver is a very capable design engineer.

his first crude dam, beavers were building coffer dams to divert water into canals to float logs to the desired dam construction site.

Nests of birds vary from mere depressions on the ground to elaborate multichambered structures of great complexity. The character of the nest is determined by heredity, the raw materials available, the site selected, and instinct. A particular species will build a characteristic nest. Investigators have reared four generations of birds, keeping them away from all building materials. Yet the descendants of these birds (when exposed to appropriate building materials) built perfect examples of the characteristic nest. The Rufous Ovenbird builds a nest of sturdy mortar from sand and cow dung that does not crack when dry.

3-26
The Hungry Horse Dam in Montana is a multiple-purpose dam that contributes significantly to flood control on the Columbia River and its tributaries. The powerplant has a maximum capacity of 285,000 kilowatts. The 564-foot-high dam is a variable-thickness concrete-arch structure.

Some birds dig burrows in the ground up to 2 meters in depth in which the eggs are laid. Others chisel out holes in trees; still others build nests of any available material. A robin's nest is typically cup shaped and composed of grasses, leaves, small roots, paper, or rags. It is plastered with mud and lined with grasses. Hanging nests, such as those of orioles, are perhaps among the most elaborate of nests. Some South American birds build hanging nests that are as much as 2 meters in length, and may have two or more chambers in them. The American Goldfinch builds its nest of moss and grasses and lines it with thistledown. These nests are so tightly woven that they will hold water.

PLAN

UPSTREAM ELEVATION
DEVELOPED

MAXIMUM SECTION THRU PENSTOCK
AND POWER PLANT

SECTION THRU SPILLWAY

CAPACITY AND DISCHARGE CURVES

3-27
The Hungry Horse Dam.

95

3-28
An understanding of materials—their strengths, weaknesses, and characteristics—is essential for all design engineers.

3-29
This web was built one day by an average adult female *Araneus diadematus* spider. Note the regularly spaced radii and the smooth spiral turns.

3-30
This web was built on the next day by the same female spider as in [3-29]. However, in this case, 12 hours before web building, the spider was given 0.5 gram/kilogram of *d*-amphetamine solution. The effect of the drug on the spider's design ability and accuracy is evident.

The most familiar form of spider webs has a radial pattern, although different kinds of spiders form characteristic webs. It has been demonstrated that if spiders are subjected to various kinds of drugs, they spin erratic and noncharacteristic webs. Spider webs are formed from "silk" spun by specialized glands on the body of the spider. Strands of this material are remarkably strong and uniform in size. For the spider the web serves as home, protection, and a means of capturing food. For man the web is variously an annoyance, a source of beauty, and a useful design component—for example, as a source of materials for the cross hairs of telescopic sights.

The spider's touch, how exquisitely fine!
Feels at each thread, and lives along the line.
ALEXANDER POPE
An Essay on Man, 1688–1744

natural systems repaired or improved by man

In addition to utilizing nature's designs to construct systems and devices useful to himself, man has been able to assist nature by repairing structures of organisms that have been damaged by disease, misuse, old age, or heredity. Here we refer primarily to man, although the techniques used on man can be used—and have usually been tried first—on animals. Vital organs frequently have their normal functions impaired and death would result if it were not for the technology of man, which is sometimes able to repair or replace the damaged organ or part with an artificial substitute.

Just as the human organism is more complex than that of the lower organisms, just as English life in the twentieth century is more complex than that of a primitive tribe, just as organisms are more complex than inorganic objects, so the highest thought and the greatest art are more complex than primitive knowledge or early ornamentation. The more highly developed phenomena are the result of more complex forces, and are therefore the more difficult to explain.

THEODORE ANDREA COOK
The Curves of Life, 1914

Artificial Kidney

It is estimated that about 60,000 persons in this country die from kidney failure every year. Transplant techniques have been devel-

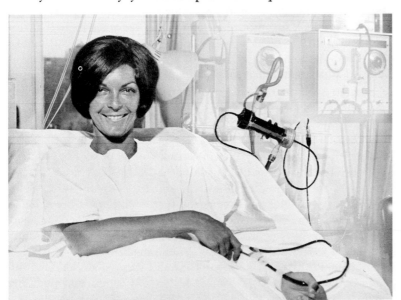

3-31
Disposable artificial kidneys contain more than 10,000 hollow fibers encased in a cell only slightly larger than a two-cell flashlight. Kidney failure kills an estimated 60,000 Americans every year. Kidney transplants are only about 60 per cent successful on the average. The only alternative is hemodialysis by means of an artificial kidney. A machine of this type cleanses a patient's blood in about 8 hours.

3-32
Artificial kidney.

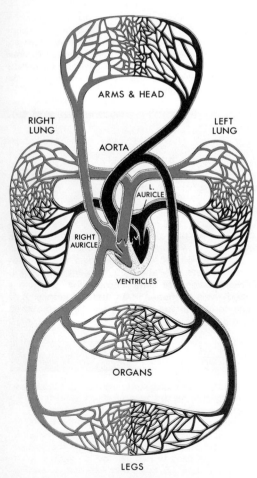

3-33
Man's blood circulatory system.

oped, but they have problems with biological rejection. As a result, a number of artificial kidneys have been developed. At present a person whose kidneys are not functioning normally must go to the hospital once or twice a week and have the artificial kidney machine attached to him; in about 8 hours his blood will be cleansed to normal. Although this procedure works, the costs are high. A major need now is to design an artificial kidney machine that will be less costly and small enough to be easily portable. One of the problems in developing a practical artificial kidney is to develop a proper membrane, such as a plasma membrane, through which the waste metabolites can pass.

Heart-assist Devices

Heart disease caused by improper functioning of some portion of the heart is still one of the major causes of death. Natural hearts have been transplanted from one person to another, but it seems unlikely that enough heart donors can be found to meet the demand in the near future. Mechanical devices to repair or replace the heart would seem to be the best solution for the immediate future. Many such designs are in the process of development.

Although the actual structure of the heart varies considerably from one group of animals to another, it is basically a muscular pumping organ for maintaining the flow of blood through the body. In performing this function it is incredibly effective. A man's heart pumps about 5 quarts of blood per minute or 75 gallons of blood per hour. During the average life span of 70 years, a man's heart will pump almost 18 million barrels of blood.

The heart of a human consists of four chambers, two auricles and two ventricles. The right side of the heart pumps the blood to the lungs; the left side pumps it to all other parts of the body. When a heart is removed from the body, it will continue to beat for some time, indicating that the initiation of the heart beat is in the heart itself. It is now known that the *pacemaker* consists of a small knot of specialized muscle tissue in the wall of the right auricle. An impulse generated by the pacemaker excites the muscle fibers of the heart within six hundredths of a second, causing the ventricles to contract simultaneously. Occasionally, the impulses from the pace- maker are unable to reach the ventricles and the heart's activity becomes asynchronous, with the beat of the ventricles falling off sharply. In these cases, an artificial pacemaker may be inserted into the body with its electrodes connected directly to the muscle tissue of the ventricles. Most artificial pacemakers are powered by mercury-cell batteries that must be replaced about every 2 to 3 years. Experiments are presently being conducted on nuclear- powered pacemakers, which should last the lifetime of the individual.

The ventricles are supplied with inlet and outlet valves that regu- late the direction of blood flow through the heart. Occasionally, one or more of these valves is faulty and allows the blood to leak through. This forces the heart to work harder to pump the same volume of blood through the body. A leaky heart valve can be heard as a heart murmur. In some cases it may be necessary to replace the defective valve with an artificial valve made of Dacron and Silastic rubber. To date, more than 20,000 persons have been fitted with artificial heart valves.

In some cases a heart may be damaged so severely that death of the individual will result if it is not repaired or replaced. Everyone is aware of the transplant operations in which a defective heart is replaced with a healthy one. However, many people are not equally aware of the engineering efforts that are being made to develop an artificial heart which will either assist the damaged heart to perform its functions or replace it completely.

Most heart-assisting devices are pumps. These artificial pumps are made of Dacron or silicone rubber, are attached to the heart or the aorta, and are activated by air pressure from outside the body. They relieve the heart of some of its work and allow damaged heart tissue to repair itself. It may then be disconnected and the heart allowed to resume its normal function.

Devices to completely replace damaged hearts are also being designed. Prototypes have been successfully tested in animals and perhaps represent the best hope of permanent assistance to a person

As dear to me as are the ruddy drops
That visit my sad heart.

SHAKESPEARE
Julius Caesar

The way to a man's heart is through his stomach.
SARA PAYSON PARTON
Willis Parton, 1811–1872

3-34

Thousands of persons suffering from a weakened or damaged heart are being helped by a new miniature pulse generator called a cardiac pacemaker. The tiny battery-powered device is implanted in heart patients without major surgery. When connected to the heart, it paces the heart muscle electrically to restore and maintain a normal heartbeat. Over 25,000 Americans ranging in age from 6 months to 94 years have been implanted with a pacemaker.

When I was one-and-twenty
  I heard a wise man say,
"Give crowns and pounds and guineas
  But not your heart away;
Give pearls away and rubies
  But keep your fancy free."
But I was one-and-twenty,
  No use to talk to me.

When I was one-and-twenty
  I heard him say again,
"The heart out of the bosom
  Was never given in vain;
'Tis paid with sighs a plenty
  And sold for endless rue."
And I am two-and-twenty,
  And oh, 'tis true, 'tis true.

ALFRED EDWARD HOUSMAN
A Shropshire Lad, 1859–1936

with a damaged heart. Models currently being developed are either air driven or hydraulically operated. The heart chambers are made of either rubber or plastic and are supplied with appropriate artificial valves to control blood flow.

Artificial Muscles

One of the key questions in biology is, "How do muscles move?" Although many people have studied this, there is still no definitive answer. A great deal has been learned about the structure of a striated muscle, however. The striated muscle gets its name from the fact that it has crossbands or striations on it. Striated muscles are the voluntary muscles of the body, making up the musculature of the arms, legs, abdomen, etc. A muscle fiber is made up of a number of smaller fibers called *myofibrils*, which are about 1 micron in diameter. Each myofibril in turn is made up of smaller filaments, each 50 to 100 angstroms[2] in diameter. There are two sizes of these smaller filaments held together by protein bridges. It is believed that when a muscle contracts, the two filaments slide past one another. However, the details of the process are not fully understood.

Engineers have been interested in developing "imitation muscles" or actuators that could do the work of muscles. One such attempt uses fibers of nylon fastened to a rubber tube. When the tube is inflated with air, it expands and thereby shortens the nylon fibers, much in the manner of a muscle shortening. Other experiments have been concerned with mechanical systems that will aid muscles in carrying out their action under conditions where the muscles alone might not be able to do the job. An example of this would be when a man is under very high gravity forces in aerial maneuvers or when normal movement is impeded by bulky protective clothing.

natural systems potentially useful to man

Those things are better which are perfected by nature than those which are finished by art.
MARCUS TULLIUS CICERO
De natura deorum, 106–43 B.C.

Living organisms have evolved some truly remarkable structures for specialized purposes. Among these are light-producing organs, electric organs, sonar systems, and other intricate guidance systems. Some of these natural systems are still not understood.

Cold Light

Nearly everyone has seen fireflies and has marveled at their ability to produce light. However, most people are not aware that a great number of organisms have this ability, including bacteria, fungi, sponges, corals, insects, snails, crustaceans, clams, millipedes, and centipedes. The emission of light by organisms is called bioluminescence and is the result of an enzyme-catalyzed chemical reaction.

[2] 1 angstrom = 10^{-7} millimeter $\approx$ 1 four-billionth of an inch.

The bioluminescent mechanism in different species is very similar, and it apparently evolved as a by-product of tissue metabolism. There has been a great deal of interest in the "cold light" produced by bioluminescence. Studies of its quantum efficiency have shown that firefly light production is almost 100 per cent efficient. Bioluminescence may be used as protection, as a lure, or as a mating signal. In some organisms its function is quite obscure. Colors produced by bioluminescence range over nearly the whole visible spectrum, with blue, blue-green, or white predominating. Green is the most frequent, but red and orange are relatively rare. There are three basic ways in which bioluminescence may be produced: (1) by symbiotic bacteria houses in special organs, (2) by light-emitting cells, and (3) by production of luminous secretions.

Some squids and deep-sea fish have symbiotic bacteria that are kept in specialized sacs where they grow. The emission of light is controlled by specialized structures, such as pigmented curtains, lenses, or reflectors that concentrate or diminish the light.

Luminous secretions are common among marine invertebrates. Secretions may completely cover the body or may appear as a luminescent cloud or discrete points of light. This luminescence is usually intermittent, with the control in the nervous system of the animal. In most advanced forms, light-emitting cells produce light within the cell. The most familiar example is the firefly.

Electricity in Nature

Electric charges are generated in all creatures with a nervous system. However, an external discharge of electricity has been noted only in certain groups of "electric" fish. This electricity is used for orientation, communication, and protection.

Electric organs are composed of electroplates, which are modified muscle cells. These plates are thin flattened structures whose two specialized surfaces are different from each other. There are large numbers of these cells, and those having similar surfaces are oriented in the same direction, horizontally or vertically. Each plate is housed in a compartment and embedded in a gelatinous material.

The electric eel has about 40 per cent of its body devoted to electroplates, arranged vertically in about 120 columns parallel to the spinal cord with each column containing 6,000 to 10,000 electroplates. The electroplates are arranged in series and are able to generate more than 500 volts. The high voltage is necessary to overcome the substantial electrical resistance of the freshwater in which the eel lives. On the other hand, the torpedo ray has electroplates stacked horizontally in about 2,000 columns with approximately 1,000 plates in each column. These columns are arranged in parallel, which enables the ray to develop a large amperage. This is most appropriate because the ray inhabits salt water, which offers a lower electrical resistance. The electric organs of both are used for stunning

3-35
Fireflies, glow worms, or fire beetles produce their characteristic bioluminescent glow by means of a complex and delicate chemistry that is not yet fully understood. *Luciferin* (a biochemical substance) oxidizes in the presence of an enzyme called *luciferase* and this serves as the fuel for the firefly's lantern. Both substances are produced in the abdomen of the firefly, where they are fed oxygen from the atmosphere by means of microscopic breathing ducts. While the usual incandescent lamp wastes 98 per cent of the energy supplied as heat, the efficiency of the cold-light production plant of the firefly is amazingly high, almost 100 per cent.

3-36
The electric catfish (Nile River).

3-37
The electric eel has built up a radar-like system to detect its prey. Special elastic organs discharge pulses of electricity that create an oscillating dipole field capable of detecting anything entering the field and distorting the pattern. Conductors tend to concentrate the lines of electrical current flow, whereas insulators repel them. Big, healthy electric eels can produce a 0.003-second jolt that has been measured at 887 volts and 1 ampere. If we really understood how the eel's electrical system worked, we could design vastly improved electrical-power-generating systems.

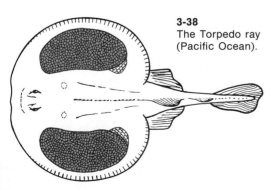

3-38
The Torpedo ray (Pacific Ocean).

prey or repelling predators, and the electrical charge developed is large enough to be a considerable deterrent.

Some fish produce almost continuous streams of electric pulses, the frequencies ranging from 50 to 1,600 pulses per second. These pulses are used to orient the fish and to enable it to detect objects near it.

An African fish *Gymnarchus niloticus* is able to detect objects as small as glass rods 2 millimeters in diameter by means of an electrical mechanism. The mechanism consists of an electric generating organ in the tail of the fish that is negative relative to the fish's head. In the head region the skin is perforated with pores that lead into tubes filled with a jelly-like substance. The lines of the electric current

3-39
The *Glymnarchus niloticus'* detection system.

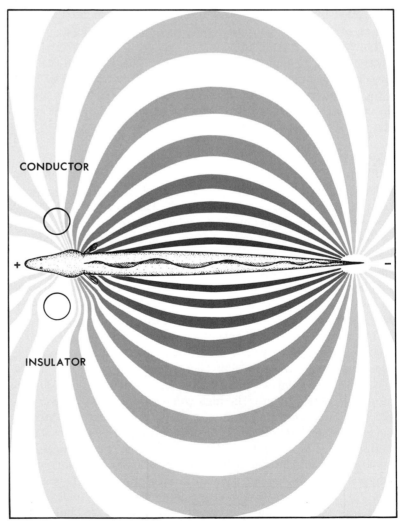

emitted from the tail are focused on these pores at the head end of the fish. Any objects in the electric field will distort the lines of current flow and tell the fish that an object is present in the field. The time it takes the fish to average out the information from 7 or 8 discharges of the electric organ has been found to be 25 milliseconds. How these sensory cells are able to accomplish this is still not known.

Unusual Mechanisms

Propulsion is very much a part of our modern world. A number of examples of the use of rockets and jet engines quickly come to mind. However, all man-made propulsion devices now in use have some problems, such as pollution, excessive consumption of fuel, etc. For the movement of an animal or the propulsion of a weapon of prey or defense, a number of methods are known in nature that have none of these drawbacks and that, if completely understood, might have some application to use by man. Studies are now being carried out to investigate these methods.

Studies of how fish swim have indicated great similarities between the tail fin of fish and variable propeller blades used on ships and submarines. Fish, of course, have to use a system of levers to produce a propelling effect. This system of levers consists of the vertebral column together with the tail fin. In fish the tail fin moves back and forth laterally; in whales and dolphins the tail fin moves up and down. Regardless of which way it moves, the speed of the tail fin varies during one cycle of movement. Its speed is greatest at the time the tail fin is in line with the axis of the vertebral column and decreases on either side of the axis.

The maximum speed at which fish can swim varies from $6\frac{1}{2}$ miles per hour for the trout to as much as 27 miles per hour for the barracuda, which is the fastest fish known. Mammals, such as the whales and dolphins, have been recorded swimming 20 and 22 miles per hour, respectively. Studies pertaining to large-sized mammals have indicated that their observed speed performance cannot be explained satisfactorily by ordinary hydrodynamic principles. *These animals are not capable of generating the power that has been calculated to be necessary to achieve the measured speeds.*

It has been suggested that whales and dolphins move much more efficiently than engineering calculations would suggest because they are able to reduce the turbulence of water flow over their bodies. One possibility of accomplishing this is that the continual bending of the body, combined with the nonrigid nature of the skin and underlying muscles, reduces the resistance due to turbulence. Further study of this condition might produce results that could be adapted to the design of undersea craft.

An interesting variation of purposeful movement is found in the action of the wings of some insects, which beat so rapidly that they

TENTACLE

3-40
The hydra's tentacles are composed of batteries of thread capsules. In this drawing two of the large stinging capsules are discharged. The circles containing a central dot represent the top view of the capsules.

3-41
Four types of thread capsules of the hydra. **A** and **B** are adhesive capsules, used to fasten the tentacles to solid objects when the hydra is looping. They also assist in capturing and holding the prey. **C** is a volvent type and aids in holding the prey by winding about it. **D** is a stinging capsule. It pierces the body of the prey and injects a poison.

RELAXED	DISCHARGED
A	
B	
C	
D	

become invisible to the human eye. Insect wings are thin sheets of cuticle strengthened by hollow ribs. The wings do not contain muscles but are moved by the action of two sets of muscles attached to the walls of the thorax. By changing the dimensions of the thorax, the wings are moved up and down at the hinge joint where they are attached. In this way, the wings are able to move much more rapidly than if they were activated in the normal manner by muscle action.

Hydra, an animal belonging to the family Phylum Coelenterata, which live in the sea, has batteries of poisonous threads that may be shot out to capture prey. These thread capsules are adhesive and help to hold the prey. They are spiral shaped to better entangle the prey, and barbed to facilitate piercing the body of the prey. In all cases, they are found in the outer layer of cells of the body with a fine extension or trigger projecting from the surface. When the trigger is stimulated, the pressure within the capsule is increased suddenly and the coiled threat is expelled. The threads immobilize the prey, which can then be swallowed by the hydra. The exact propulsive mechanism by which the threads are expelled is not fully understood, but the propelling force is believed to come from a sudden increase in pressure.

Jellyfish belong to the same group of animals, and anyone who has brushed against or stepped on a jellyfish while swimming in the ocean is aware of the stinging potential of the protective capsules they possess. The Portugese man-of-war has a central disc-shaped body as large as 12 feet in diameter with numbers of tentacles over 100 feet in length. These tentacles contain stinging capsules, and swimmers becoming entangled in these tentacles have been rendered unconscious by the poison and have died.

Predatory fungi or molds have mechanisms to catch animals. Some molds have sticky filaments in which the prey becomes entangled; others form networks of loops that secrete a very sticky fluid in which its prey is held fast. Other predatory fungi form small rings of filaments that are just the diameter of its prey. When the prey sticks its head into one of these rings, it triggers an almost instantaneous reaction with the ring inflating and catching the prey. The mechanism of the reaction is not well understood, but it has been suggested that it results from the intake of water caused by a change in *osmotic* pressure, or from changes in the structure of the *colloids* that make up the *protoplasm* of the cells.

Perhaps the best-known plants with a specialized means of obtaining food are the carnivorous plants, which include the cobra plant, pitcher plant, Venus's-flytrap, and the sundew.

The sundew plant has small red leaves less than half an inch across covered with tentacles that secrete a sticky substance for catching insects. Drops of this substance shine like dewdrops in the sunlight and are attractive to insects. When an insect touches one of the sticky

3-42

The Portugese man-of-war of the genus *Physalia* is supported on the water by a large gas-filled float, which can be exhausted or filled at will. It is most often accompanied by a fish that lives among the tentacles of the hydroid and shares the food caught. As long as the fish is healthy and has no wounds, it is not harmed by the *Physalia*. However, once wounded it too falls prey to its host. The nature and origin of its normal immunity to the stinging action is not understood.

3-43

The cobra plant is a type of pitcher plant that has a tall, slender, tapered trumpet with a beautifully curved hood over the top. Honey-like nectar is secreted as a lure for the insect prey that it will digest. Once it falls down into the hood, the insect encounters a pit of water and a forest of hairs that are arrayed to prevent his escape. The plant can then absorb the nutritive products from the insect.

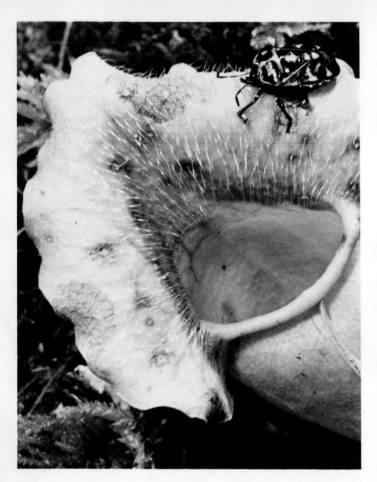

3-44

Many people consider meat-eating plants to be among the rarest of oddities, but there are over 450 species of plants that depend in part upon the food which they trap. The pitcher plant is such a carnivorous plant. Insects are lured over the edge or lip of the plant to reach nectar located just out of reach. Invariably, they fall into the abyss of the trap and into a watery soup designed to stupify, kill, and digest the insect. The inside walls of the trap have a very smooth surface, making it virtually impossible for the drenched insect to gain a footing.

Courtesy Carolina Biological Supply Company

3-45

Courtesy Carolina Biological Supply Company

The fly-paper type of insect-catching plant is typified by the sundew. These two pictures show how the tentacles of the plant react to the slightest movement of an insect, such as an ant. Since plants do not have muscles, the cause of this movement is indeed strange and has been the basis of constant investigation over the past 75 years.

3-47

3-48

Courtesy Carolina Biological Supply Company

3-49

Courtesy Carolina Biological Supply Company

3-50

The Venus' flytrap, found only in the southeastern part of the United States, was first discovered by Governor Arthur Dobbs of North Carolina, which he announced in a letter dated January 24, 1760. Each leaf of the plant is a small bear-trap-like mechanism consisting of two dished lobes that are effectively hinged along one side and armed with sharp spike teeth along the other edges. Within the inner surfaces are three tiny trigger hairs that, when touched ever so gently, cause the two lobes to snap shut and seal the doom of the insect prey within. After about 10 days the plant has assimilated the body tissues of the insect, and the jaws open ready for another catch. Although much effort has been expended in trying to solve the mechanism of the trap closure, there is as yet no definite answer. There is strong evidence, however, that the action is caused by electrical disturbances across the leaf of the trap.

tentacles, a reaction is triggered that results in the neighboring tentacles bending over the prey. The tentacles push the insect down onto the leaves of the plant where it is digested by the action of enzymes. The mechanism for the movement of the tentacles has attracted much interest because there are no muscles in plants to cause such movement. It has been determined that the movement is caused by growth phenomena. After the insect is digested, the tentacle unbends and is able to attract and catch another insect.

The Venus' flytrap is a small plant with leaves that are modified into two hinged lobes with sharp spines of teeth along the outer edge. Insects are attracted to the plant by secretions from glands located just inside the lips of the lobes. Each lobe has three small trigger hairs on its inner surface. Normally, the lobes are open until an insect enters and touches one of the trigger hairs. Then the lobes snap shut and the spines interlock to prevent the escape of the insect. The mechanism of snapping the lobes together is not well understood. Other glands on the inner surface of the lobes secrete the digestive enzymes that digest the insect. After the insect is digested, in perhaps 10 days, the lobes open again and are ready to capture another insect.

The archer fish lives mainly on insects, which it shoots out of the

The archer fish is quite gregarious, living on insects that hover over the surface of the water or alight on vegetation near the fishes' habitat. Considering that the fish must account for (a) the effect of gravity on the water jet, (b) the speed of the moving insect, and (c) the bending of light rays as they pass from air into water, it is remarkable that he is able to keep from starving to death.

3-51

3-52

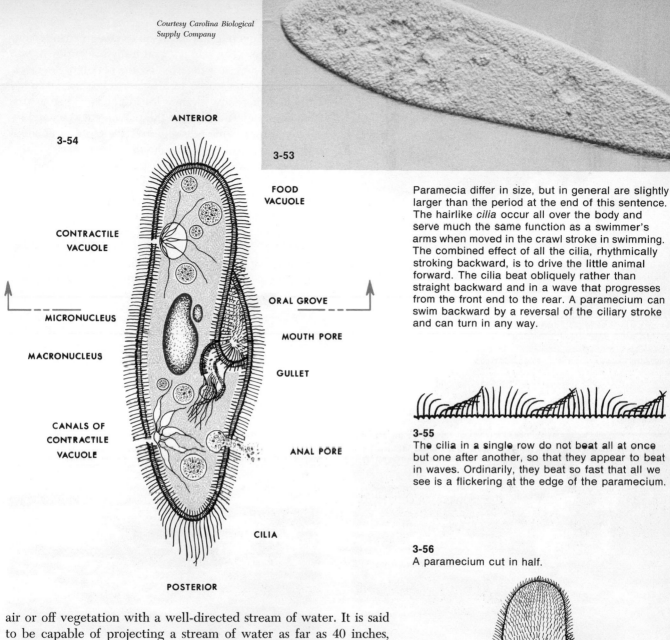

Courtesy Carolina Biological Supply Company

3-53

3-54

ANTERIOR

FOOD VACUOLE

CONTRACTILE VACUOLE

ORAL GROVE

MICRONUCLEUS

MOUTH PORE

MACRONUCLEUS

GULLET

CANALS OF CONTRACTILE VACUOLE

ANAL PORE

CILIA

POSTERIOR

Paramecia differ in size, but in general are slightly larger than the period at the end of this sentence. The hairlike *cilia* occur all over the body and serve much the same function as a swimmer's arms when moved in the crawl stroke in swimming. The combined effect of all the cilia, rhythmically stroking backward, is to drive the little animal forward. The cilia beat obliquely rather than straight backward and in a wave that progresses from the front end to the rear. A paramecium can swim backward by a reversal of the ciliary stroke and can turn in any way.

3-55
The cilia in a single row do not beat all at once but one after another, so that they appear to beat in waves. Ordinarily, they beat so fast that all we see is a flickering at the edge of the paramecium.

3-56
A paramecium cut in half.

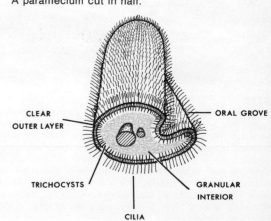

CLEAR OUTER LAYER

ORAL GROVE

TRICHOCYSTS

GRANULAR INTERIOR

CILIA

air or off vegetation with a well-directed stream of water. It is said to be capable of projecting a stream of water as far as 40 inches, although 12 to 20 inches is probably the normal range. The mechanism consists of a groove in the roof of the mouth. When the tongue is applied to this groove, it creates a tube through which water is forced by the action of the gill covers.

One general characteristic of living things is their ability to make purposeful movements. These movements may be the result of muscle contraction, action of cilia or flagella, jet propulsion, or a change in surface tension of a water film. In certain spiders, the legs are moved by hydrostatic pressure rather than by simple muscle action.

3-57

The trek of the salmon to reach their spawning grounds is a remarkable occurrence. In many cases these fish literally fight their way upstream, jumping seemingly impossible heights. To preserve the species (where dams have been constructed in a river, impeding such a journey) engineers have designed "fish ladders" and fishways to provide an alternative path upstream. Depending upon the size of the stream and the height of the dam, these bypasses vary from a simple succession of small pools, each about a foot higher than the preceding one, to multimillion dollar installations with a complex collection system built across the face of the dam. These structures also serve to allow the newly hatched young fry to move downstream. However, at best their designs leave much to be desired and designs of the future must be improved significantly.

The diversity of structures and methods of movement is tremendous.

Cilia are very small hairlike structures, which are widely distributed throughout the animal kingdom. They apparently perform two major functions: *contraction* and *conduction*. It is interesting that the rods and cones, which are the sensory structures of the vertebrate eye, have been evolved from cilia. Also, certain balancing organs in some animals have been derived from cilia. Some organisms, such as the one-celled paramecium, are covered with cilia whose movements are carefully coordinated to bring about locomotion.

Navigation

As man has continued to explore the physical world around him, he has been faced with the problems of navigating or finding his way. This has been particularly critical as he has ventured into the oceans and into flight in the air. Other animals have solved the problems of aquatic and aerial navigation very successfully in ways not completely understood by man. Intensive studies are being conducted on various navigational systems in nature.

The fact that salmon navigate hundreds of miles across the ocean to spawn is known to most people. Salmon spawn in freshwater streams, and the young migrate downstream to the ocean, where they may live for several years feeding and growing. When fully mature, they swim back to the stream where they were born to spawn and die. Experiments with marked fish have shown that they always return to the same stream, and, in fact, the same part of the stream.

A series of experiments both in the laboratory and in the field have indicated that the salmon utilize odors to guide them. Appar-

3-58
Green turtles have been known to swim over 300 miles in 10 days. Persistence rather than speed, however, is the attribute that enables them to migrate annually from breeding beach to feeding ground.

ently, different streams have characteristic odors to which the salmon are conditioned and to which they respond during the migration. The substances that contribute to the odor appear to be volatile organic materials. Obviously, the salmon must have tremendous ability to discriminate very small concentrations of these substances in order to use them as a guidance mechanism. The question of how they cross hundreds of miles of ocean and reach the mouth of a particular stream has yet to be answered satisfactorily.

Green turtles are found in warm oceans throughout the world. They breed in colonies that reproduce in specific isolated localities in various parts of the world. One such colony normally feeds along the Brazilian coast but migrates to Ascension Island to reproduce and lay its eggs. Ascension Island is 1,400 miles from the coast of Brazil and is only 5 miles wide, so the turtles must be able to navigate rather precisely if they are to reach the island.

The female turtle lays her eggs in sand, often some distance from the water. When the young turtles hatch, they head unerringly for the water, even though the water may not be visible from the nesting site. Once the young reach the sea, they swim out into it and essentially disappear. Almost nothing is known about their first year of life in the ocean. After a year in the ocean, they reappear. It has been suggested that the turtles use visual or olfactory cues to orient themselves and that they are able to use the sun for long-distance navigation. Experiments are now being carried on using satellite-relayed telemetry with radio-equipped turtles to establish their route of travel.

The most widely known examples of aerial navigation are found in birds. Each fall and spring in the United States more than 100 species migrate back and forth between their breeding and wintering grounds. Some of the migrations are truly heroic in extent. The arctic tern is the long-distance champion, as annually it conducts a migration between the Arctic and Antarctic regions, a distance of as much as 22,000 miles.

Inasmuch as most birds migrate unerringly to specific locations, they must use some internal design for navigation. Visual use of landmarks has been suggested as one possibility, and for birds such as homing pigeons this appears to be a possible answer. However, for those species which migrate great distances such a method does not appear to be satisfactory.

Experiments have shown that birds are able to utilize the sun as a compass while migrating during the daylight hours. However, many species migrate at night and navigate by the stars. This capability is inherited, as shown by experiments with birds raised in the laboratory and never exposed to the night sky. *These birds are able to orient to star patterns in a planetarium!*

Many phenomena associated with bird migration can be explained by visual landmarks, sun orientation, or star orientation. However,

3-59
Migratory behavior occurs among many different species of birds, animals, reptiles, and fish, and studies have been in progress for centuries relating to this amazing behavior and to the remarkable precision of timing and orientation that is achieved. None of the theories advanced thus far has been able to adequately explain even the origin of this behavior, much less the intricacies of the various navigation mechanisms employed.

the fact that birds can often migrate unerringly under conditions of zero visibility indicates that something more is involved. One suggestion is that they orient to the magnetic field of the earth. Experiments have shown that a number of other animals, including insects, protozoans, snails, and mammals, are capable of orienting to magnetic fields. However, definitive engineering experiments on birds' orientation to geomagnetic fields have not yet been completed.

The fact that a number of animals are known to respond to magnetic fields is interesting, because there are no known specific body receptors for such stimuli.

Special Senses

The organs of the body concerned with the special senses of seeing, hearing, feeling, and communicating are among the most highly specialized structures in living things. Some of these specialized structures are of great interest to the engineer.

Most animal forms are sensitive to light. In some forms the sensitivity is a function of the entire body; in others there are specialized structures or regions of the body that perceive light stimuli. Some of these are no more than pigmented spots; others are detailed complicated structures that are highly specialized for their specific function. The mammalian eye is an example of a highly specialized structure.

Most eyes of higher animals are based on the general plan exemplified by the mammalian eye. However, some have interesting modifi-

3-60
Zot!

cations that are adapted for the special purposes needed for the organism. One example is the eyes of chameleons, which are stalked and can be rotated in opposite directions. Such an adaptation aids the animal in capturing its prey. When the prey is in range, the chameleon shoots out its tongue (which is longer than its body) and picks up the prey on the enlarged sticky end of the tongue.

Time Sense

One of man's preoccupations in today's busy, complicated world is the accurate determination of time. Star time, time clocks, tuning-fork timers, and electronic timers are all monuments to man's attempts to calibrate time. A time sense is part of all living things. Birds, bees, squirrels, insects, and man have many of their activities tightly regulated by "biological clocks." Such diverse activities as waking, feeding, storing and consuming oxygen, clotting blood, and singing have been associated with these biological clocks. The clocks seem to be independent of light and can be reset experimentally. Anyone who has traveled long distances east or west by jet aircraft is familiar with the fact that it takes a few days to adjust to the new time zone.

The exact mechanism of these biological clocks and where it is centered in the organisms has not yet been determined.

shapes, aesthetics, and function

Many designs in nature might be justified on the basis of their beauty alone. However, investigation invariably reveals that also there is a highly functional reason for their structure. Some of these designs already have been adapted by man for his purposes. Others are still being studied but are not completely understood. As man learns more about their functions in nature, he may be able to adapt them to his purposes.

Diatoms are beautiful microscopic one-celled plants that exist in incredibly large numbers in both fresh and salt water. Each diatom secretes a shell of silicon around itself. Although the basic plan of these shells is the same, many of the 10,000 different species have very characteristic shapes, sizes, and structure. When alive, diatoms serve as a major food source for aquatic organisms. When they die, the shells fall to the bottom of the ocean, where they accumulate by hundreds of billions of tons. Many such deposits of diatomaceous earth from the floors of ancient seas are mined and used as insecticides, polishes, filters, insulation and as filler in paints, plastics, rubber, and roofing materials. Thus, diatoms are useful in both life and death.

Certainly comparable to diatoms in beauty, variety, and complexity are snowflakes. Although it is believed that no two snowflakes

What is a weed? A plant whose virtues have not yet been discovered.

RALPH WALDO EMERSON
1803-1882

Nature is the art of God.

DURANTE ALIGHIERI
De Monarchia, 1265-1321

The bee's architecture is "the most wonderful of known instincts—beyond this stage of perfection in architecture natural selection could not lead; for the comb of the hive-bee, as far as we can see, is *absolutely perfect* in economising labour and wax."
Darwin, quoted in *Growth and Form* by D'Arcy W. Thompson

3-61
Diatoms are not sea gems or jewely designs, but rather the exquisite little "glass" houses of single-celled aquatic plants so small that 15 million constitute a thimbleful. They live everywhere there is water; in every stream, lake, pond, and ocean. As living organisms they provide about 90 per cent of all the food in the ocean. In death their skeletons are used in a multitude of engineering applications.

are identical, all are constructed on a basic hexagonal plan. This shape apparently is dictated by the molecular forces within the water molecule. Man has often wondered why these forces seem to always result in producing hexagonally shaped snowflakes. However, the production of this geometric configuration is not limited to the action of inanimate forces. Rather, it is interesting to note that a number of living organisms produce structures that are hexagonal in shape; for example, for years it has been observed that when honeybees build honeycomb, they build hexagonal cells with trihedral bases. Mathematicians have long postulated that this shape is the most efficient for the purposes honeycomb fulfills. Not everyone agrees with this hypothesis. However, the honeybee seems unconcerned about the matter, and he continues to build hexagonal cells.

Also it has been found that honeybees demand rather precise spatial relationships. The discovery of the "bee space" by Root made possible man-made beehives and modern beekeeping. Stated simply, bees prefer passageways $\frac{3}{16}$ inch in diameter. If smaller openings occur, they are plugged up by the bees with beeswax or plant products; larger openings are reduced in size by similar means to the preferred "bee space." For this reason all commercial beehives are designed to satisfy the bees' specifications.

3-62
As the snowflakes make their spinning descent from the upper reaches of the atmosphere, they pick up molecules of water vapor that form delicate lacy unduplicated patterns.

3-63
Honeybees build hexagonal cells with trihedral bases. Engineers, particularly those in the aircraft industry, have made good use of this configuration in designing wing and fuselage components that require a high strength-to-weight ratio.

The variety of shapes, sizes, and colors of calcareous shells produced by animals has made confirmed shell collectors of many people. These shells serve initially as the home for a special kind of animal, but subsequently they may be highly modified for specialized purposes. Some of the boring mollusks have long pointed shells that aid in moving through solid materials; organisms such as the *sand dollar* are flattened so that they can adapt to life on the sand flats. "Shipworms" are not worms at all but greatly elongated clams whose shells have a roughened surface and are used in boring into the wood. The beauty and symmetry of the shells of the chambered nautilus are legendary.

the cell

Of all the systems known to man perhaps the most intricate and complicated is that of the living cell, the fundamental unit of all living organisms. With the development of the electron microscope it has become possible to study in detail the basic structure of the cell. Biochemists, molecular biologists, and other scientists are able to study the molecular and atomic structure as well as the major components.

Living things are able to exist only as long as there is a transformation of energy from one form to another. The type of transfer essential to life in plants is the transforming of light energy to chemical energy in the process of photosynthesis. This process is carried out in cell structures called *chloroplasts,* which contain the green coloring material, *chlorophyll.* This important process has received a great deal of attention and, even though it cannot yet be entirely explained, much is known about it and about the structure of the chloroplasts in which it occurs.

The chlorophyll molecules are stacked within the structures of the chloroplasts. These "stacks" are called *grana* and are separated from one another by membranes, much in the manner of plates of a wet-cell battery. Within these grana occur the mysterious reactions that result in light energy being converted to chemical energy.

Once light energy has been transformed to chemical energy, it has to be changed again to a form that is usable to the cell. This is accomplished by the *mitochondria,* which carry on the process of cell respiration in which *adenosine triphosphate* is formed as the usable source of energy for the cell. Mitochondria vary in number in a cell from 50 to 5,000, depending on the kind of cell and its function. Mitochondria are 3 to 4 microns long. Each mitochondrion consists of a double membrane with each membrane made up of a double layer of fat molecules covered with a protein layer, as in the plasma membrane discussed next and the chloroplasts. The inner membrane is greatly folded so as to increase the surface area.

membranes

It is interesting that many of the structures of the cell have a membranous structure. When we come to understand the properties of membranes completely, we shall have made a large stride toward understanding the cell.

One particular membrane still not well understood is the plasma membrane, which surrounds each cell and regulates that which enters and leaves the cell. Just how this regulation is accomplished is not known, but it has been suggested that there are pores through which substances may pass or not, depending upon the size of the substance. It has also been suggested that a substance can pass through if it can be dissolved in fat. Some cell membranes engulf particles or fluids. Although the structure of the membrane is not completely understood, it is believed that it consists of a double layer of fat molecules covered by two protein layers.

organization of communities

No organism lives completely by itself. It is part of a larger community consisting of plants and animals and the nonliving components. Such an organized entity is known as an ecosystem. As these ecosystems have been studied, it has become apparent that they are as tightly organized as individual organisms. It is now known that these ecosystems maintain their structure by the expenditure of energy, just as living organisms do. Energy flows into, through, and

Go to the ant, thou sluggard; consider her ways, and be wise.

PROVERBS 6:6
The Holy Bible

3-64
Man can learn much from nature about the intricacies of designing large group housing—communication, transportation, sanitation, food gathering, behavioral patterns and tendencies, and preservation of the species.

out of these ecosystems in a highly structured fashion. At present, little is known about the exact routes of flow of energy, but studies are underway to delineate them with a view to constructing a mathematical model that will depict the activities of the ecosystem. When such a model has been constructed and tested, it will be possible by use of computer technology to predict the effects on the ecosystem of changing any given portion of the system. The ecosystem can then be analyzed for efficiency and output much in the same manner as is now done for manufacturing plants and processes.

evolution of design

The structures and processes mentioned in this chapter are the present stage of design development that has been taking place over millions of years in living organisms. Indeed, all living things have been affected by evolutionary processes. Countless variations of these designs have been tried and tested against the selective demands of the environment, but only those designs which conferred some advantage to the organism under existing environmental conditions were able to survive and be passed on to later generations. Each new generation of organisms contains variations of the basic design, which are then tested against the demands of the environment. Each new generation represents a "new model year" for living things.

This constant shifting, winnowing, and honing has resulted in organisms remarkably well adapted to the various environmental conditions that they characteristically face. It should not be assumed, however, that the organisms that exist now are the end products of the evolutionary process and that they will remain as they now are. In addition to the design variations already mentioned, in each generation of organisms the environmental conditions are also continually changing, as witness the current problems of pollution of air, water, soil, and in fact the entire biosphere.

As the environmental conditions change, different design variations will be selected. A design that was successful under one set of environmental conditions may not be capable of surviving under the changed conditions, whereas a previously unimportant design variation may make the difference between dying and living. In this way the design is constantly updated to existing conditions. If there is anything certain about living organisms, it is the fact that they are constantly undergoing change.

Nature never deceives us; it is always we who deceive ourselves.

JEAN JACQUES ROUSSEAU
1772–1778

Nature has no watertight compartments. Every phenomenon affects and is affected by every other phenomenon. Any phenomenon which we choose to examine is *to us* conditioned by what we see and know. We exclude deliberately all other conditions. But Nature does not exclude them. A Nautilus growing in the Pacific is affected by every one of the million stars we see—or do not see—in the universe. But we examine it only by the light of what we know.

THEODORE ANDREA COOK
The Curves of Life, 1914

problems and questions

3-1. Pick a leaf from a broad-leaved tree and examine it carefully.
(a) What engineering principles are incorporated into this leaf to enable it to carry out its functions?

(b) Drop the leaf from a height of 6 feet and study its behavioral characteristics as it falls to the ground.

(c) What happens to the leaf if you put it in a pan of water?

(d) Compare the above results with those of a dry leaf of the same kind. Are the results the same? Explain.

3-2. Take a needle from a pine tree and examine it closely. These needles are said to be efficient in minimizing water losses to the plant. Enumerate the engineering principles involved for the needle to accomplish this.

3-3. Place a live frog on the desk before you. Observe his body and leg actions when he hops. Describe any physical or engineering principles involved in these movements.

3-4. Place a live frog in an aquarium or pan of water and carefully observe his actions and movements in swimming. Describe any physical or engineering principles involved in these movements.

3-5. Using your observations of a swimming or hopping frog, calculate the amount of work done per unit of time by each activity. Are the results the same for both activities? Explain.

3-6. Observe the activity of a dragonfly nymph in an aquarium. Notice particularly the various methods that he utilizes in locomotion. Try to determine his rate of movement for each method of locomotion.

3-7. Utilizing your observations of Question 3-6, calculate the forces involved and the amount of work done in each of the observed activities. Compare the results.

3-8. Obtain a 12-inch length of bamboo and a similar length of two or more other kinds of wood of the same diameter as the bamboo. Compare them in regard to weight, flotation, water displacement, and breaking strength. How are these characteristics related to the structure of each of the pieces of wood?

3-9. Given a live cockroach, a piece of string, some glue, and a strobe light, how would you go about determining the frequency of wing beat of the cockroach when it is flying?

3-10. Using sound as a measurement, how could you determine the frequency of the wing beat of a housefly?

3-11. Examine the wrist bones and joints of a human skeleton. Considering the functions that the wrist performs, how could its design be improved? Explain.

3-12. Examine a leg bone or wing bone of a chicken. Cut or break it open and examine its internal structure. What are the reasons for its strength-to-weight ratio?

3-13. Watch a dog or horse trot. What is the sequence of movement of the legs? How long does it take for one cycle of leg movements?

3-14. The statement has been made that a dog or horse trotting across a bridge has a greater chance of causing the bridge to collapse than does a much heavier object rolling across the bridge. Is there any basis for this claim? Explain.

3-15. What advantages or disadvantages does a four-footed animal have as compared to man in regard to

(a) Jumping

(b) Running

(c) Swimming

How important are the mechanical characteristics of the skeleton?

3-16. Obtain a package of seeds (squash, watermelon, sunflower) from the grocery store and examine them carefully. What functions are performed by seeds? How is their structure adapted to carry out these functions?

3-17. Examine the outside of an orange. What is the purpose of the apparent pores or depressions? Carefully peel the orange. Do the pores go all the way through the peel? What functions does the orange peel perform? How are these functions related to its structure?

3-18. Carefully separate the individual sections of an orange from one another. Notice their shape, structure, and the manner in which they are held together. Can you think of any design advantages to such a shape?

3-19. Examine the general shape of a grape, an orange, a tomato, and an apple. As far as plants are concerned, what functions are carried out by each? Of what value are their general shapes in carrying out these functions? Are there any special structural modifications that also help with these functions?

3-20. In "Indian wrestling" the two contestants place their elbows on the table and attempt to force their opponent's wrist down onto the table. Draw a force diagram of such a contest and indicate whether mechanically the advantage would be to the person with a long or a short elbow-to-wrist distance.

3-21. Some animals are built around a spherical body plan (like a sponge); others are built on an elongated body plan (like a fish). In general, animals which a spherical body plan are slow moving and sedentary and those with an elongated body plan are faster moving. What features of the two shapes might contribute to their movement capability?

3-22. Examine the structure of a feather. What functions do feathers perform for birds? How is the feather structure related to these functions?

3-23. Study the shape of any large tree. Does there seem to be any particular arrangement to the location of the branches? Is this arrangement true also for other kinds of trees? Describe your general observations. What is the advantage to the plant of such an arrangement—or lack of one?

3-24. One of the important functions of green leaves is to carry on food manufacture through the process of photosynthesis. Light is required for this process. Study the general shape and structure of a large tree. Can you detect any evidence of a positioning of branches and leaves that might be related to the function of food manufacture? *Explain.*

3-25. Examine a chicken egg. From a chicken's standpoint what is the function of an egg? Break the egg open. How is the external and internal structure of the egg related to its function?

3-26. Carefully wax half of a smooth surface. Sprinkle water on both halves and observe the shape of the water droplets. What shape do most of the droplets seem to have on the waxed portion of the surface? Are the droplets the same shape on the unwaxed portion? Explain the differences, if any, in the shapes.

3-27. Examine a human hair. What are some of the functions of hair to animals? How are these functions related to the general structure of a hair?

3-28. What is the function of hair in one's armpits? How else might this same function be accomplished?

3-29. Can people with big ears hear better than those with small ears?

What is the major function of the external ear? How does its design accomplish this function?

3-30. Name some mechanical devices for receiving sound in which the principles used by the external ears of animals have been adapted and employed.

3-31. Observe live fish in an aquarium. Describe the procedure whereby they swim through the water.

3-32. How would you proceed to determine the forces that are involved when a fish propels itself through the water?

3-33. Examine an unpainted piece of wood. What causes *grain* in wood? Of what value is grain to a tree?

3-34. Pull up a plant, being careful to get as much of the root system as possible. Carefully examine the roots, stem, and leaves and attempt to relate the design structure of each to its function for the plant.

3-35. Examine carefully the structure of a flower. Consider its main function to the plant to be that of reproduction. To accomplish this, it is most likely that insects must be attracted to the flower. Relate the structure of the various parts of the flower to these functions.

bibliography

ALLEN, A. A., *The Book of Bird Life*, New York: Van Nostrand Reinhold, 1930.

BENZINGER, T. H., "The Human Thermostat," *Scientific American*, January, 1961.

BUCHSBAUM, RALPH, *Animals Without Backbones*, Chicago: University of Chicago Press, 1948.

BUTCHER, DEVEREUX, "The Treacherous Pitcher Plant," *Natural History*, Vol. 45, No. 3 (March, 1940), p. 146.

DUNNING, D. C., and K. D. ROEDER, "Moth Sounds and the Insect-catching Behavior of Bats," *Science*, Vol. 147, No. 3654 (January, 1965), pp. 173–174.

EVEREST, F. A., *Hidden Treasure*, Chicago: Moody Press, 1951.

EVEREST, F. A., *The Prior Claim*, Chicago: Moody Press, 1953.

FEJES, TÓTH, "What the Bees Know and What They Do Not Know," *Bulletin of the American Mathematical Society*, Vol. 70 (July 1964), pp. 468–481.

GERTSCH, W. J., "Spiders That Lasso Their Prey," *Natural History*, Vol. 56, No. 4 (April 1947), pp. 152–158.

GRIFFIN, D. D., "Sensory Physiology and the Orientation of Animals," *American Scientist*, Vol. 41, No. 2 (April 1953), pp. 209–244.

HASLER, A. D., and J. A. LARSEN, "The Homing Salmon," *Scientific American* (August 1955).

"Hemodialysis for All Who Need It," *Medical World News* (April 30, 1971), pp. 29–36.

HOAR, W. S., *General and Comparative Psysiology*, Englewood Cliffs, N.J.: Prentice-Hall, 1966.

HODGE, W. H., "Carnivorous Plants," *Natural History*, Vol. 58, No. 6 (June, 1949), pp. 276–281.

HUXLEY, H. E., "The Contraction of Muscle," *Scientific American* (November, 1958).

LEHNINGER, A. L., "How Cells Transform Energy," *Scientific American* (September, 1961).

MANN, ALBERT, *Diatoms, The Jewels of the Plant World*, Smithsonian Misc. Collections, Vol. 48, No. 1574 (1905), pp. 50–58.

MASON, G. F., *Animal Tools*, New York: Morrow, 1951.

MURPHY, R. C., "The Most Amazing Tongue in Nature," *Natural History*, Vol. 45, No. 6 (May, 1940).

PASSMORE, LEE, "California Trapdoor Spider Performs Engineering Marvels," *National Geographic*, Vol. 64, No. 2 (August, 1933), pp. 195–211

PRINGLE, J. W. S., "The Gyroscopic Mechanism of the Halteres of Diptera," *Philosophical Transactions of the Royal Society of London*, Vol. 233B (1948), pp. 347–384.

RILEY, G. A., "Food from the Sea," *Scientific American*, Vol. 181, No. 4 (October, 1949), pp. 17–19.

ROEDER, K. D., "Moths and Ultra Sound," *Scientific American*, Vol. 212, No. 4 (April, 1965), pp. 94–102.

SAUER, E. G. F., "Celestial Navigation by Birds," *Scientific American* (August, 1958).

SCHAEFER, V. J., "A Method for Making Snowflake Replicas," *Science*, Vol. 93 (March, 1941), pp. 239–240.

SCHLOSSER, J. A., "An Account of a Fish from Batavia," *Transactions of the Philosophical Society*, Vol. 55 (1764), pp. 89–91.

SIEMENS, D. F., Jr., "The Mathematics of the Honeycomb," *Mathematics Teacher*, Vol. 58 (April, 1965), pp. 334–337.

SMITH, H. W., "The Kidney," *Scientific American*, Vol. 188, No. 1 (January, 1953), pp. 40–48.

STUHLMAN, OTTO, JR., and E. B. DARDEN, "The Action Potentials Obtained from Venus'-flytrap," *Science*, Vol. 3, No. 2888 (May 5, 1950), pp. 491–492.

WATERMAN, T. H., "Flight Instruments in Insects," *American Scientist*, Vol. 38, No. 2 (1950).

WIGGERS, C. J., "The Heart," *Scientific American* (May, 1957).

This striking mosaic pattern of iron oxide reflects the square symmetry of the atoms in the iron surface on which the oxide grew. This photomicrograph was taken while the oxide film was being dissolved. Changing film thickness produced different interference colors. From the color changes, scientists can determine the oxide film thickness from ten millionths of an inch to only one millionth. Such studies lead to a better understanding of what causes corrosion.

each of us has enjoyed an aesthetic experience. Often it is a barely detectable awareness of a pleasant sensation, an awareness of something attractive. Occasionally, it is a profound experience of such magnitude that we can scarcely contain it within ourselves. In either event, the aesthetic experience is a very personal one common to all of us. Because of this human quality, it has been the concern of artists for millenia, of philosophers for centuries, and of psychologists for decades. Throughout the ages this feeling has been expressed in different ways. Prehistoric men painted their aspirations on the walls of caves [4-2]; Socrates discussed beauty with Hippias Major; and psychologists suggested theories that ultimately influenced much

4-1
Bear grass on the slopes of Mt. Hood.

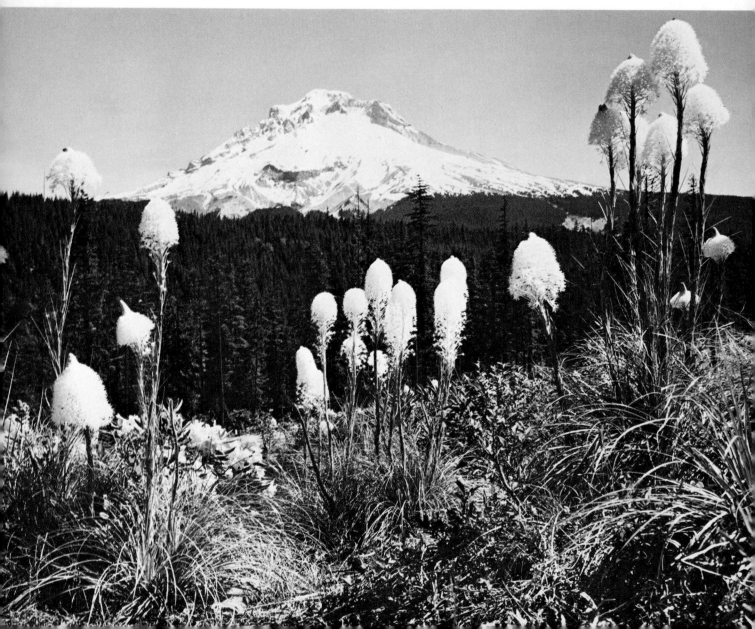

of modern art. Aesthetics has always been important to man, and concern for it is as valid today as it was at the dawn of mankind.

Aesthetics is expressed in the beauty of form that exists in the arts of poetry, literature, ballet [4-3], and music, the visual arts of painting and drawing, and the three-dimensional arts of sculpture [4-4], architecture, and engineering [4-5]. Engineers, more than any other group of people, are responsible for the variety of physical forms in the world today. The engineer designs many of the products that are bought and used by all of us; consequently, he must be conscious of standards of aesthetics as well as of functional demands that arise from our mode of life. In addition to his responsibility for functionally acceptable designs, the engineer must assume his responsibility to society for aesthetically pleasing designs. In particular, he should be aware of those elements of form that have been accepted as aesthetically satisfying through the centuries.

An aesthetically conscious engineer achieves something special in his designs that will reach across time and make them as aesthetically

4-2

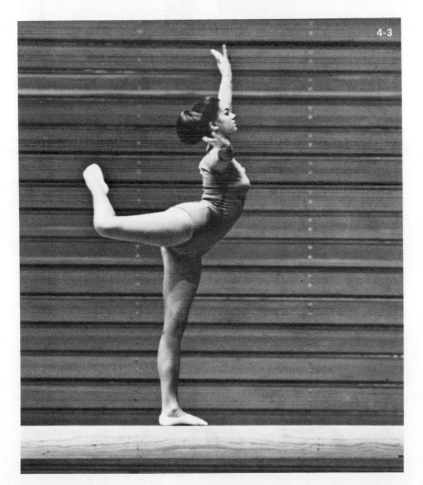

4-3

When the flush of a newborn sun fell first on Eden's
   green and gold,
Our father Adam sat under the Tree and scratched with
   a stick in the mould;
And the first rude sketch that the world had seen was
   joy to his mighty heart,
Till the Devil whispered behind the leaves, "It's pretty,
   but is it Art?"

RUDYARD KIPLING
The Conundrum of the Workshops, 1893

The Aesthetic Moment
"The aesthetic moment" is "that flitting instant, so brief as to be almost timeless, when the spectator is at one with the work of art. He ceases to be his ordinary self, and the picture or building, statue, landscape or aesthetic actuality is no longer outside himself. The two become one entity."

BERNARD BERENSON
The Pocket Dictionary of Art Terms (edited by Mervyn Levy)

Certain musical intervals have been found to be particularly harmonious (pleasing) to the ear: the octave, the major third, and the major sixth.

An aesthetic feeling is the emotion generated by the interaction between an object of beauty and an observer.

H. E. HUNTLEY
The Divine Proportion, 1970

125

4-4
"Falling Water," an aluminum sculpture created by Jack Zajac. The piece describes a column of water as it twists and changes in its fall.

4-5
The simplicity of aerodynamic designs enhances their aesthetic qualities.

acceptable in the future as when they were first created. This achievement is extremely difficult to define, but it is highly satisfying to experience. It goes beyond the mere doing of a job to the *creation* of something beautiful. Such creation results in a mixture of satisfaction and the desire to create again.

the definition of aesthetics

What is aesthetics? It has been defined as being sensitive to art; showing good taste; being artistic; being concerned with the study or appreciation of beauty. Many philosophers refer to aesthetics as beauty and the values that we attach to beauty.

Aesthetics surely is related to the concept of beauty. It would be useful to people of all walks of life, and particularly to the engineer and artist, if one could discover a scientific or mathematical formula that describes beauty and its application to design. This would be possible if beauty were an identifiable entity, external to the observer. Its fundamental ingredients could be isolated, analyzed, and assigned values. The resulting values could be applied to new designs, and all observers would generally agree that the new design was indeed beautiful. If such a simplification is possible, it has yet to be accomplished. However, there are some clues that tell us what is aesthetically acceptable. Men continually disagree among themselves concerning the question, what is beautiful? If they happen to agree that a particular object is beautiful, their reactions will likely be of different intensities. Thus, for the engineer, problems in aesthetics and beauty are quite unlike problems in mathematics that have a single, irrefutable answer.

Beauty has two recognizable attributes—the emotional and the intellectual. The first of these is related to the personality of the observer, to the period in which he lives, and to his environment. This quality ties beauty to man's emotions and to his senses. Its influence is judged mainly through intuitive processes. It is a subjective quality that is strongly influenced by one's social and cultural background. For this reason, it has resisted scientific analysis. The primary reason that a meaningful formula for beauty has not been accepted is that this subjective component of beauty is unique to each of us. Therefore, it cannot be easily measured and generalized. It is this undefinable, intuitive aspect of our personality that provides us with the means to gain an emotional appreciation of an object or of a particular design.

The second quality of beauty, intellect, is less subjective, since it involves one's mental ability to understand clearly and completely the function of a design. Specifically, it measures the suitability of an object for its intended use, taking into account particular speci-

beauty (bū'ti), n.
1. the quality attributed to whatever pleases or satisfies in certain ways, as by line, color, form, texture, proportion, rhythmic motion, etc. or by behavior, attitude, etc.
2. a very good-looking woman.
Webster's New World Dictionary

Could it be that:
$$B = E \times I$$
where
$$B = \text{Beauty}$$
$$E = \text{Emotion}$$
$$I = \text{Intellect}$$

Beauty is unity in variety.
J. BRONOWSKI
Science and Human Values, 1964

In the moment of appreciation. . . we re-enact the creative act, and we ourselves make the discovery again.
J. BRONOWSKI
Science and Human Values, 1964

127

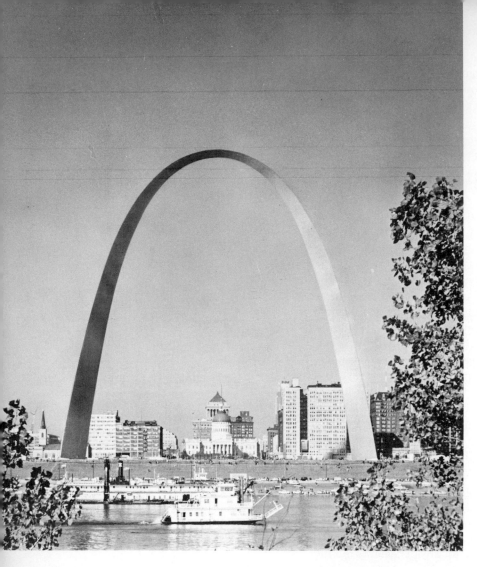

4-6
The St. Louis Gateway Arch.

4-7
Good design is an iterative process.

fications and conditions that have been imposed by materials and other identifiable constraints. This aspect of beauty provides one with the ability to rationally appreciate an object.

Since prehistoric times, man has created devices and products to assist him in his work and to make more amenable the environment in which he lives. Many of these devices have been designed to perform specific tasks, and, as the functions were more clearly understood, the form of the original concept gradually evolved. As an example, even a child can study a pneumatic tire and understand how it operates. Over many years this relatively simple form has gone through numerous changes to arrive at its present form [4-7]. It can be considered a form that is emotionally pleasing to view. It is also aesthetically pleasing in the intellectual sense because its construction and purpose can be easily understood. Much true beauty finds its origin and structure in "good engineering" and in the nature of materials and their fitness to a specified use.

The aesthetic qualities of heavier-than-air machines are accepted by the public because of the essential nature of the function performed. The evolution of this design [4-8 through 4-17] reflects man's awareness that form follows function and that the implementation of this principle leads to an intellectual appreciation of beauty. The emotional element of the design may be related to man's historical dream to fly.

The qualities of beauty cannot be measured independently because they are intrinsic components of the concept of *form*. Throughout the years, however, it has become evident that certain factors, particularly those concerning the intellectual qualities of beauty, can be identified and their effects consciously applied to the design of new objects. The location of mass can be determined, pleasing relationships of color have been established, and the proportions of forms have been documented. If these aesthetic qualities and many others are considered and incorporated into the final plan during the preliminary stages of the design, a far better product will result, because a unified and more aesthetically satisfying design can be achieved.

In the conception of a machine or a product of a machine, there is a point where one may leave off for parsimonious reasons, without having reached aesthetic perfection; at this point perhaps every mechanical factor is accounted for, and the sense of incompleteness is due to the failure to recognize the claims of the human agent. Aesthetics carries with it the implications of alternatives between a number of mechanical solutions of equal validity; and unless this awareness is present at every stage of the process, . . . it is not likely to come out with any success in the final stage of design.

LEWIS MUMFORD
Technics and Civilization

Beauty is truth, truth beauty, that is all
Ye know on earth, and all ye need to know.

JOHN KEATS
Ode on a Grecian Urn, 1820

A limited sense of aesthetic appreciation is given; the rest is acquired. For example, the mathematically uneducated can easily appreciate the dual symmetry of an ellipse; that is given. But the unlimited store of beauty of the conic sections is reserved for the mathematically trained: it is acquired. This indicates that the path to real aesthetic pleasure is through toil, a principle that holds far beyond the realm of mathematics.

H. E. HUNTLEY
The Divine Proportion, 1970

The ultimate object of design is form.

CHRISTOPHER ALEXANDER
Notes on the Synthesis of Form, 1964

concepts of aesthetics for engineering

In engineering, certain aesthetic concepts are useful. Many of these are analogous to fundamental concepts of engineering science, such as the centroids of geometric forms.

Concepts of aesthetics in engineering are numerous, but they are not subject to precise analysis and are not easily measured. The principles of aesthetics that are particularly useful to the engineer will be discussed here. Often, these principles, with minor modifications, are directly interchangeable with related concepts in aesthetics in other professional disciplines. It will be our purpose here

I do not mean by beauty of form such beauty as that of animals or pictures, which many would suppose to be my meaning: but says the argument, understand me to mean straight lines and circles, and the plane or solid figures which are formed out of them by turning-lathes and rulers and measurers of angles: for these I affirm to be not only relatively beautiful, like other things, but they are eternally and absolutely beautiful.

SOCRATES
from Plato's Philebus Jowett's translation

4-8
Man's dream.

4-9
This concept of man's attempt to harness birdpower, in an attempt to fly, first appeared in *The Man in the Moon,* published in Paris in 1648. In 1659, the same mode of air travel was depicted in another book, *The Flying Wanderer.* Here, Brussel-Smith has interpreted the original drawing through the medium of wood engraving.

4-10
The Wright brothers' flying machine, 1909.

4-11
Bréquet 14 Aircraft (1916).

4-12
Ford Tri-Motor in flight (1928).

4-13
Curtiss Condor (1934).

4-14
DC-3 in flight (1936).

4-15
Boeing 720 Astrojet in flight (1960).

4-16
The Boeing 747 (1970).

4-17
Space shuttles could become commonplace in the future.

4-18
A 3.48-mach shock wave.

4-19
Flow lines give visual evidence that "form follows function."

to consolidate all these related concepts under terms that can be easily identified by the engineer.

Function

The concept of *function* is probably the most important and the most easily understood principle of aesthetics. A famous architect, Louis Sullivan, is credited with coining the phrase "form follows function" [4-18]. It means, in effect, that a product or design should possess a form descriptive of the actual function that the product is intended to perform. This concept is very important, because many products today are quite complex and their function is difficult for the user to appreciate intellectually. It is important for the buyer of a product to recognize by means of the aesthetic treatment what the product is intended to do and how it is to be used. The intellectual capability of the engineer must be focused simultaneously upon the purpose for which an object is being made, the aesthetic considerations, the capacities of the material, the tools, and the process—in short, all the related aspects that must be controlled to assure completion of the design.

Function is not limited to the purely mechanical operation of an object. Cost, environment, user acceptance and familiarity, maintainence, and service, as well as aesthetics, are but a few examples of other functional considerations that also are the responsibility of the engineer in the development of a design. A good designer is neglecting his responsibility if he approaches any of these considerations in isolation, because they all contribute to the concept of *function* that controls the development of the product form.

Form

Design is the process of inventing physical things that display new physical order, organization, or form in response to function. *Form* involves the overall visual appearance of an object. It consists of many elements, such as line, proportion, color, and texture. These elements are organized to give a design its unique form [4-20]. The arrangement of these elements is either disorganized and unattractive

Form follows function, underlying it, clarifying it, crystalizing it, making it real to the eye.
LEWIS MUMFORD
Technics and Civilization

So that there will be no misunderstanding, when we speak of form in connection with three-dimensional objects, we mean not only the shape or outline, but all the gradation, and variation, and connotations of texture and color as well as the peculiar quality of the material itself.
F. C. ASHFORD
Designing for Industry, 1955

4-20
Lines and proportion
give meaning to form.

4-21
Disorder.

4-22
Order.

4-23

Form
follows
function.

4-24

4-25

or orderly and attractive [4-21 and 4-22]. A good form is one that successfully imparts to the user an understanding of what the designer intended the object to do; a good form clearly identifies itself and its function.

The first step in design is to define the need. In designing an object, the first consideration is its intended use—its functions. A useful approach for relating the form of a product to its function is to begin with a simple sketch of the product's main components and then arrange these components relative to their intended functions. The proper form of many products can be found by understanding the functional arrangements of the product's components. The engineer uses these functional arrangements as the basic structure of the final product form [4-23 through 4-25]. He then integrates the applicable aesthetic and technical components into a cohesive whole.

Developing a product's form concurrently with the technical aspects of the design is an ideal approach to use in all product development. It is unfortunate that all designs are not approached in this manner. In fact, there are many stereotyped ideas about machines that exist today, and once stereotyped they are difficult to change. As an example, most American automobiles have a forward-mounted engine, a hood, four wheels, and a trunk in the rear. These elements make up a stereotype form. Consequently, if the typical buyer of American cars does not find these arrangements when he is shopping for an automobile, he is likely to look elsewhere.

This factor of stereotype has a strong influence on the design of many products that might be more functional and attractive in some other form. Engineers in electronics have developed very effective designs because they have not been plagued with established stereotypes, for example, in the design of computers. Their designs more often than not have turned out to be aesthetically attractive [4-26].

4-26
Computer designs have developed free from the restrictions of custom.

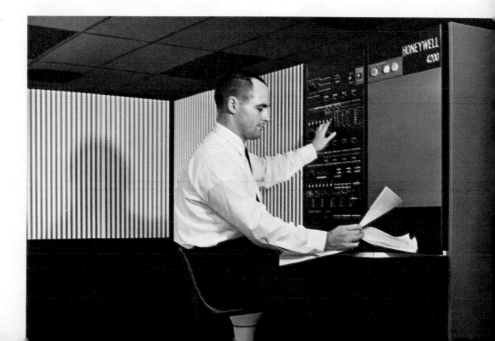

4-27
This centrifuge design embodies unity—the
concentrate of simplicity and completeness.

4-28
Unity in design is an essential quality.

Unity

Unity is another word for order or harmony. In aesthetics, unity is a harmonious combination of parts. The use of similar proportions and shapes and identical decorative motifs are examples of ways to provide unity in design. Using elements that are similar through all the products of a line is a typical means of expressing unity and of developing product identification for a manufacturer. Unity in a product means that it appears to be complete. Nothing is missing nor are there any superfluous elements [4-27]. Furthermore, there is a proportionate relationship between all the parts contributing to an orderly whole. A designer achieves unity by regarding an object as a total composition and not as an assembly of individually designed parts. Many engineers have designed efficient and functionally attractive subassemblies that, when joined to make the whole, failed to satisfy the concept of unity. A common example of the lack of unity is the components of stereo equipment found in many homes. Often the components of the system are extremely well designed, electronically, to provide the best in sound reproduction; but there may be loose, exposed connecting wires between components, and perhaps a walnut base on the turntable and a black metal cabinet around the stereo receiver. The system when viewed all together is not aesthetically pleasing; it does not provide a feeling of unity. This frequently happens because each designer has been responsible for one part of the design and no one has considered the whole system. To achieve an attractive, unified design—as in our example of the stereo system—an overall view of the design must be retained at all times [4-28].

I shall define beauty to be harmony of all parts in whatsoever subject it appears, fitted together with such proportions and connections that nothing could be added, diminished or altered but for the worst.

ALBERTI

. . . The first quality that we demand in our sensations will be order, without which our sensations will be troubled and perplexed, and the other quality will be variety without which they will not be fully stimulated.

ROGER FRY
Essay in Aesthetics

4-29
Too much of one thing can lead to monotony.

All heiresses are beautiful.

JOHN DRYDEN
King Arthur, 1631–1700

Proportion is not only found in numbers and measurement but also in sounds, weights, times, positions and in whatsoever power there may be.

LEONARDO DA VINCI

4-30
As with illicit love, *styling* is a pleasure of the moment and tarnishes with time.

Closely related visual elements exhibit a pattern or rhythm that is the epitome of unity; but in the hands of a poor designer, this rhythm can quickly deteriorate into monotony [4-29]. The need for variety is obvious, but, at the same time, the effective application of variety is an extremely difficult task. Too much variety results in the destruction of unity, because the relationship of the visual elements is lost. The designer must be able to recognize and create this delicate balance of unity with variety within the framework of an object's form.

Styling

Styling, decoration, ornamentation: these are different names for one of the most discussed and least understood aspects of aesthetics. Styling, the application of ornamentation, is in direct conflict with the concepts of function, form, and unity [4-30]. All too frequently styling is applied to an object *after* the function and form of a design have been fully developed. A good design does not need styling. On the other hand, if the function and form of a product have been developed improperly, it is impossible to achieve unity by applying decoration or ornamentation—in other words, by styling.

Styling is closely associated with marketing products. It is a common device used to promote the sale of goods, but it should not be confused with the aesthetic quality that results from proper function, form, and unity. Styling applied to products reflects the buying public's immediate interest and concept of "what is beautiful." The basic engineering design of the automobile has not changed for

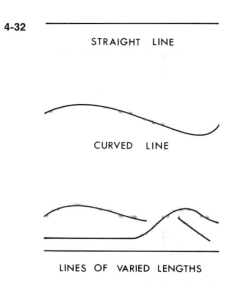

4-31
Styling is sensuous and appeals to the ego.

4-32

several years, but styling revision in the outward appearance have changed annually. These "new styles" are created each year to generate consumer interest.

Styling has much in common with commercial art. Many of the techniques are the same, as well as the motives and purpose. Styling is primarily concerned with the outward appearance [4-31]. It is the development of a form with little or no functional consideration. It is applied decoration that relies primarily on the emotional qualities of aesthetics. It might be considered the reverse of the dictum "form follows function," because after a "style" has been created that is judged to be acceptable, the functional elements may be modified or fitted to it. The engineer should avoid styling his designs, and he must be able to combat the influences of styling in the development of new or existing products.

aesthetic elements for engineering design

There are several basic elements that can be used to create an aesthetically satisfying design. Some of these, line, mass, space, balance, proportion, contrast, and color, will be discussed here. These elements might be compared to the individual components of a mathematical formula. In this sense, aesthetics might be considered as the formula and the aesthetic elements might be considered as the components of the formula. One must be careful in carrying this analogy too far, however, because it might be misunderstood to imply that there *is* a formula for aesthetics, which is not the case. Again we should restate the point: there is no magic formula or prescription, no assured way to create aesthetic pleasure.

Line

The basic element in the creation of a form is the *line*. This is particularly true of two-dimensional respresentations of form, the

4-33
Line personalities.[1]

BROKEN LINE

QUIET LINE

SAD LINE

PLAYFUL LINE

FURIOUS LINE

4-34
Traditionally defined line.

A

B

shorthand of design. The instant that a designer creates a line, he visually alters the environment where the line appears. The line is a symbol that defines where one form ends and another begins. It has many characteristics that may appeal to the intellectual aspect of aesthetics, because it can be measured and quantified. For example, a line may be curved or it may be straight. It has length and thickness (sometimes referred to as *weight*), and it has orientation [4-32].

These characteristics are measurable, and in this sense their effect can be compared with similar characteristics on other forms. If the linear characteristics contributed to the desired aesthetic effect, then intellectual fulfillment has probably been achieved.

In addition to the measurable characteristics, a line also may possess emotive or subjective characteristics. These characteristics are equally important, but it is often difficult to measure them or to agree on the effect created [4-33]. The gentle curve, the strong line, undecided, delicate, lively, weak, bold, or harsh lines are some of the many expressions that may be used to describe the emotive characteristics of lines. A straight line suggests honesty, directness, precision, simplicity, strength. A curved line is free, flexible, gentle, graceful, elegant. Thin lines are delicate, small, or frail, whereas thick lines are bold, forceful, vigorous, strong. Appropriate use of line in a design will contribute to its market appeal aesthetically by emphasizing the intended function, as discussed earlier.

Traditionally, to the engineer the line has been a simple connection between two points in space. Although this definition is technically correct, the engineer must recognize that a line also defines the separation between two dissimilar objects or conditions. Under this stipulation, two colors, different textures, dissimilar materials, varia-

[1]C. W. Valentine, *The Experimental Psychology of Beauty*, London: Methuen, 1962.

4-35
Patterns are the result of change. Change is wrought by action. Action occurs as a result of a force in motion. But it takes a change in energy to beget such a result. Nature accomplishes this complex chain of events simply and directly, as is evidenced here in the cracking and partitioning of drying mud to produce a condition of perfect equilibrium.

4-36
Patterns are also formed by lines of greatest economy—of least effort. Such lines are rarely, if ever, straight lines. Rather, they are smooth curves representing the most economical patterns of flow.

4-37
In man-made designs, patterns often emerge as a result of man's imperfect understanding of natural phenomena, rather than of perfect designs born of honest simplicity. Gears are man-made designs. There are no gears in nature, yet gears currently are among the most efficient of devices for transmitting power. Has man really been able to improve on nature?

4-38
A. Color
B. Texture
C. Material

COLOR
A

TEXTURE
B

MATERIAL
C

tions in space, or any other elements that have a visual contrast also can be used to define a line.

It should be apparent then that the line is a basic and powerful design element that can be used in the application of aesthetics to objects, and the designer who can effectively utilize the emotional as well as the intellectual qualities of a line will be able to create a design with strong aesthetic appeal.

Mass

Mass is that aspect of aesthetics that imparts a sense of weight or heaviness to an object—a sense of solidity. It is the positive three-dimensional expression of a form. The existence of an object is best demonstrated through its visible mass. An object not only exhibits a unified mass in the total form, but the smaller elements within the form also can have a mass independent of the total form. The designer needs to be aware of the relationship of such elements so that he can effect aesthetically pleasing arrangements of the individual masses. This is necessary to ensure that they will be in harmony with the function of the object as well as its form. As an example, in a tensile testing machine, the visual masses of the parts must be in balance and concentrated as near the floor as possible [4-39]. This relation not only enhances the functional operations of the machine, but also gives the operator a feeling of safety, sturdiness, and reliability. These feelings result in general operator confidence and improved performance.

As new materials are developed and applied in the design of new products, the difficulties caused by stereotypes become apparent. Many of us have said "that just doesn't look strong enough," or "I wonder if that will last?" These feelings are often related to one's emotional assessment of the product based on *traditional* expectations of the mass of the materials or of the elements used. For example, what might appear to be flimsy or fragile if made of pot metal may appear to be adequately strong if made of stainless steel. And a new lightweight material could be even more desirable than stainless steel from strength considerations alone.

4-39
A tensile testing machine.

4-40
The Picturephone—
an example
of the use of
positive and
negative space.

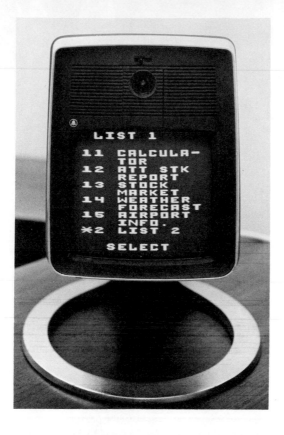

Space

To the designer *space* refers not only to the infinite reaches beyond the atmosphere of Earth, but also to the real environment that exists within his visual field. It is the total environment in which he perceives an object to exist. The psychologists have defined space as having a *figure–ground* relationship. The figure is the object, three dimensional or two dimensional, that attracts and holds one's attention. It is viewed relative to the environment that surrounds it, which is referred to as the *ground*. For the engineer, the figure is often a solid mass occupying a positive space. The remaining, encompassing space is the ground. It may be referred to as a *negative space*. Space when considered in this manner becomes manageable, and is as responsive to the concepts of aesthetics as any other element. The visually contrasting edge between positive and negative space defines a line. Negative areas, such as holes, apertures, and voids, are as much a part of design as the positive masses of material.

The effective apportionment of space is a difficult and sometimes confusing matter because the elements of a figure–ground relationship, particularly in two dimensions, can sometimes interchange their relative positions [4-41]. Of course, with a three-dimensional object it is impossible for such an exchange of space to physically

4-41
A famous figure-ground ambiguity.

Is it a chalice . . .
or . . .
is it two profiles?

4-42
When a person's visual perceptions are distorted through the use of prisms, lenses, or other optical devices, his "position sense" adapts to accord with what he sees. Thus, he learns to locate an object where he sees it, rather than vice versa, as has been supposed.

occur, but if the engineer does not consider the object in relation to its surrounding environment, a visual translation could occur [4-42]. For example, camouflage is the intentional use of visual translation. Imagine the problems that might develop if an operator of a high speed router were not visually certain of the figure–ground relationship of the cutting blade and the working surface.

Balance

Balance is a manifestation of equilibrium, and its existence provides the observer with a sense of comfort and security. To the average person, balance is simply the process of equating the two sides of a scale. In engineering analysis, if the sum of the forces (weights) on each side of an equality sign is the same as the sum of the forces (weights) on the other side, the system is considered to be balanced. Basically, the same is true in aesthetic design. However, weight has another emotional meaning here. For example, a square that encloses a dark color appears to be heavier than a light

4-43
The small dark square can "balance" the larger light square.

4-44
Relative position affects visual balance.

one [4-43]. As a result, a dark-colored square might be made noticeably smaller than a light-colored square in the same frame of reference and still achieve an emotionally satisfying balance.

The relative positions of elements also influence visual balance [4-44].

Balance is an important consideration in design. There are two types of balance, symmetrical and asymmetrical. Symmetrical balance is the more easily understood, and it can be measured to some extent. Symmetry is the balance of mirror figures about a point, line, or plane [4-45]. It is a simple matter for one to measure the length, width, and other pertinent dimensions on one side of the center line of a design and to repeat the measurements on the other side. By using this technique, one is assured of achieving a symmetrically balanced design of the object [4-46]. The usual emotional response to symmetrical balance is "stability" or "satisfaction with the status quo."

Asymmetrical balance, sometimes referred to as *occult balance*, is much more subtle but it usually stimulates a dynamic and emo-

4-46
The Apollo space capsule—a symmetrically balanced design.

tional response. Acceptable asymmetric balance depends largely on the emotional qualities of aesthetics and the personalities of the designer and the viewer. Occult balance is somewhat like the concept of *torque* or *moment effect* in physics. The difference is that varying centers of interest are involved instead of varying forces (weights) and lengths of moment arms [4-47]. A form may be in equilibrium, but the elements that will contribute to the feeling of "equilibrium"

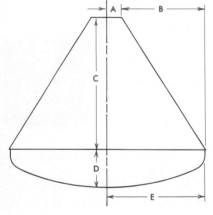

4-45
Symmetrical balance.

Asymmetrical balance.   **4-47**   **4-48**

are not always easy to identify or understand. The examples using the relative position and differences in color are indicative of elements that one might encounter when developing an asymmetrical design [4-48].

It is important for the engineer to be able to achieve asymmetrical balance in a design, because the development of a new product or technique is not always compatible with the concept of symmetrical balance. The sewing machine, the engine lathe, and the sporting rifle are examples of products that have effectively created a sense of equilibrium and of form through asymmetrical balance [4-49 and 4-50].

4-50
An asymmetrical design in wood and steel.

147

4-51

Good engineering design recognizes the value of modular construction without excess. Invite enough variety, however, to thwart boredom.

. . . if we are conscious of a law of proportion, and then slightly deviate from it, to avoid its precision, we shall produce a more beautiful effect.

SIR HERBERT READ
Art and Industry, 1953

4-52

Proportion

Proportion relates the overall dimensions to the dimensions of smaller elements or parts within the form. In the simplest sense, it is the ratios of the parts to the whole. Proportions are one of the most effective elements for achieving aesthetical balance and the concept of unity. The simplest proportions to use and control are regular geometric figures, such as circles, equilateral triangles, and squares. However, these shapes are monotonous if they are used exclusively. Variety helps.

Complete systems of aesthetics have been developed around the mathematical relationships that exist between the length and width dimensions of rectangles. One of the most popular and effective concepts using rectangles is *modular construction*. It is used in architecture, particularly mass housing, in electronics, such as computer circuitry, and in machine design involving component subassemblies [4-51].

A system of proportions is a common means of developing an aesthetically pleasing design, as well as a functionally efficient one. Since the days of Pythagoras and Plato, and perhaps even before, man has tried to establish a universally acceptable proportioning system. One of the popular systems to produce an orderly relationship between parts is believed to have been used in building the Greek Parthenon. This system has been called the *divine proportion, golden ratio,* or *golden rectangle.* This ratio is believed by some to be the most pleasing visual arrangement for a rectangle, and several systems for proportioning form have evolved using it as the base. It is a rectangle whose proportions are such that when a square is removed from either end, the remaining rectangle will be proportional to the original rectangle [4-53]. Mathematically, the formation of such a relationship may be expressed as

4-53

The divine proportion.

$$\frac{a + b}{a} = \frac{a}{b} = \frac{1.618}{1} \qquad [4\text{-}54]$$

It was discovered long ago, perhaps by Pythagoras' Egyptian predecessors, that this pleasing ratio plays a very important role in the morphology of the natural world, both organic and inorganic. Forms of crystals, shells, plants, and even parts of the human body seem to follow this proportion closely.

Other systems of proportioning have also found enthusiastic followers. A number of these systems are based upon the premise that, in nature, the growth of things into particular shapes results because of forces that act in accordance with well-defined laws of mathematics and physics. The honeybee's comb is an example of this logic [4-55].

Other plants and animal forms also assume mathematically defina-

4-54

1.000

1.618

Each cell in a honeycomb is a close approach to a perfect mathematical figure—or rather to an uncompleted perfect mathematical figure, for one end is left open. In the technical language of mathematics it is a hexagonal prism with one open or unfinished end, and one trihedral apex of a rhombic dodecahedron. And further, this form is not only the strongest possible structure for a mass of adjacent cells, but theoretically it is also the most economical, the one which requires the least possible amount of labor and wax.

SIR HERBERT READ
Education Through Art, 1957

4-56
Many creatures of nature are formed in geometric designs.

4-57
One of the most beautiful of mathematical curves is the logarithmic spiral, such as is evidenced in this computer design, The Snail. Spirals such as this occur commonly in nature, although their beauty is transient and eventually dies. The day dawns when the chambered nautilus is no more. The rainbow fades, the flower withers, the mountain crumbles—even the star, in time, grows cold. Not so with beauty in mathematics, which endures as long as man has eyes to see and breath to give expression to his pleasure.

4-58
This radiograph of the *chambered nautilus* (a sea shell) shows clearly the logarithmic spiral pattern of growth of the successive chambers. As the shell grows the chamber sizes increase, but their shape remains unchanged.

152

4-59

ble configurations, for example, the lens of a water beetle's eye, snowflakes, and sea shells [4-56]. These latter "children of nature" follow curvilinear rather than rectangular growth patterns with the logarithmic spiral being the most common [4-57 and 4-58].

Another system of proportioning is based on the *pear shape* [4-59]. This shape occurs in nature when there is a balance between the forces of gravity and surface tension.

The engineer may be tempted to adapt a system such as one of these to satisfy the aesthetic requirements of a particular design and by so doing believe that he has made an object that will be judged to be beautiful. This is a false premise and such temptations should be shunned. If a proportioning system is needed in a design, the engineer is advised to establish a system based on the concepts of function, form, and unity as it applies to the object that he is developing, rather than to adopt arbitrarily some "so-called" established system.

Contrast

The fact that you are able to read this book is due in part to the aesthetic element of *contrast*. The contrast between the black letters and the white page improves the legibility of the text. Con-

This is the ship of pearl, which, poets feign,
   Sails the unshadowed main—
The venturous bark that flings
   On the sweet summer wind its purpled wings
In gulfs enchanted, where the siren sings,
   And coral reefs lie bare,
Where the cold sea-maids rise to sun their streaming
   hair.

Build thee more stately mansions, O my soul,
   As the swift seasons roll!
Leave thy low-vaulted past!
   Let each new temple, nobler than the last,
Shut thee from heaven with a dome more vast
   Till thou at last art free,
Leaving thine outgrown shell by life's unresting sea.
          OLIVER WENDELL HOLMES
          The Chambered Nautilus, 1858

4-60
In design there is an appropriate time and place for the use of contrast, such as used on this control board.

If . . . we propose to create beauty in our own handiwork, it is a fair conclusion that we should not forget those same divergencies from mathematical exactitude which the Greeks were so careful to recognize in the lines and columns of the Parthenon; and we should realize that one great factor in the beauty of art and of Nature consists in those same subtle variations which have molded vital forms since life began.

THEODORE ANDREA COOK
The Curves of Life, 1914

There is a very significant characteristic of the application of the spiral to organic forms; that application invariably results in the discovery that nothing which is alive is ever simply mathematical. In other words, there is in every organic object a factor which baffles mathematics—a factor which we can only describe as Life. The nautilus is perhaps the natural object which most closely approximates to a logarithmic spiral; but it is only an approximation; the nautilus is alive and, therefore, it cannot be exactly expressed by any simple mathematical conception; we may in the future be able to define a given nautilus in the terms of its differences from a given logarithmic spiral; and it is these differences which are one characteristic of life.

THEODORE ANDREA COOK
The Curves of Life, 1914

The Bower birds of Australia and New Guinea build bowers for courtship with brightly coloured fruits or flowers which are not eaten but left for display and replaced when they wither. . . . They stick to a particular colour scheme. Thus, a bird using blue flowers will throw away a yellow flower inserted by the experimenter, while a bird using yellow flowers will not tolerate a blue one.

W. H. THORPE
Science, Man and Morals

trast is the same quality as difference: difference in color, line, mass, or some other element.

Contrast, as a design element, is useful for drawing attention to or emphasizing a component or combination of components within a design. Conversely, reducing visual contrast may diminish an unsightly or distracting aspect of a design. Many machines have specific areas for the control mechanisms, such as start–stop buttons, levers, and wheels. By applying the principle of contrast, the engineer draws attention to the location of the controls and thereby increases safety and efficiency [4-60].

Reducing the contrast is particularly desirable when conditions exist that are beyond the control of the engineer. If it is too expensive to enclose exposed pipes and ductwork in factory offices, they can be painted the same color as the ceiling.

Color

Color is probably the element that is most commonly associated with aesthetics, and its use readily demonstrates the two qualities of aesthetic appreciation, intellectual and emotional. Intellectually, colors are described as those sensations that are produced in the brain as the result of light waves impinging on the retina of the eye. The visible spectrum [4-61] consists of electromagnetic radiation with wavelengths between 380 millimicrons[2] (violet) and 760 millimi-

[2]One millimicron is 10^{-9} meter, about 1 ten-millionth of $\frac{1}{4}$ inch.

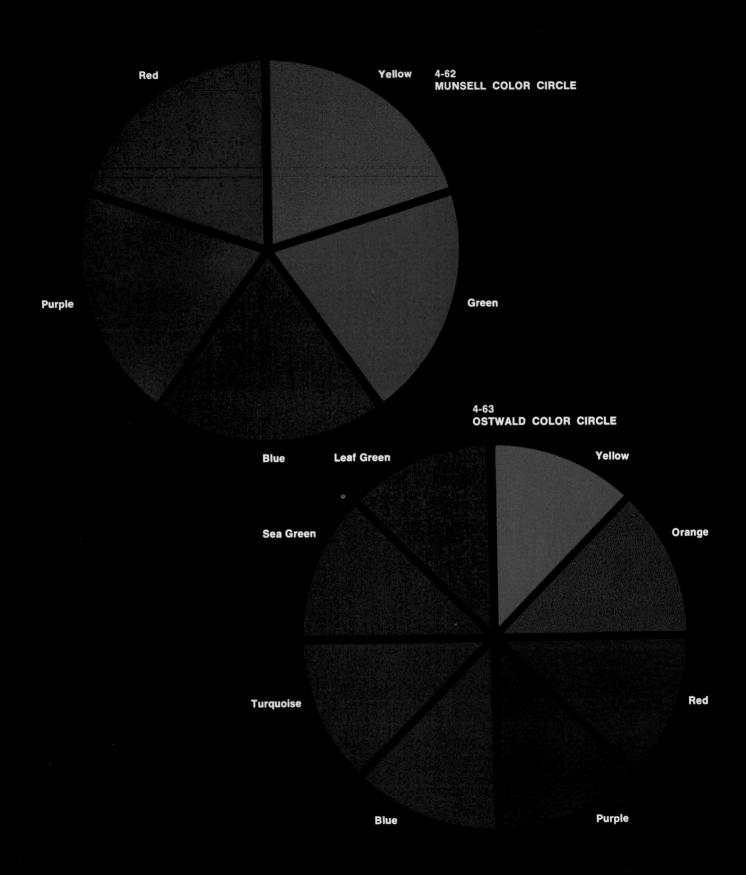

Red

Yellow   4-62
MUNSELL COLOR CIRCLE

Purple

Green

Blue   Leaf Green

4-63
OSTWALD COLOR CIRCLE

Yellow

Sea Green

Orange

Turquoise

Red

Blue

Purple

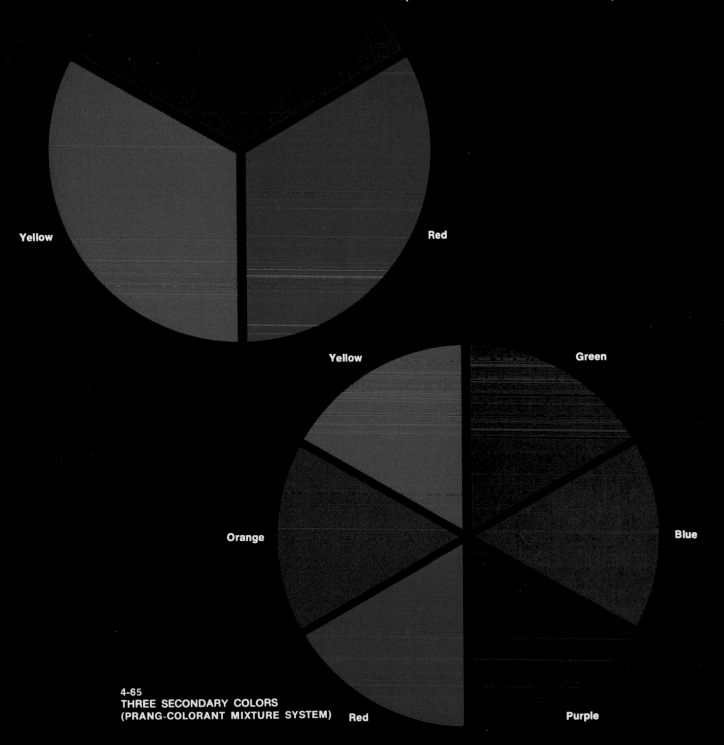

Blue

4-64
THREE PRIMARY COLORS
(PRANG-COLORANT MIXTURE SYSTEM)

Yellow

Red

Yellow

Green

Orange

Blue

4-65
THREE SECONDARY COLORS
(PRANG-COLORANT MIXTURE SYSTEM)

Red

Purple

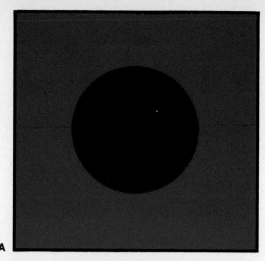

A

4-66
CLOSELY ASSOCIATED HUES

B

C

crons (red). Within this rather limited range, it is estimated that the human eye can distinguish 10 million different colors. We are, therefore, quite sensitive to color (see also [9-13]).

Color and its various attributes have been the subject of considerable investigation and theorizing. Sir Isaac Newton was one of the earlier investigators of color, and he proposed the first color circle. His color circle was based on the seven colors that he considered to be primary to the spectrum. Others followed him, and several color theories presently exist. Two of the more important are the Munsell theory [4-62], based on colored light, and the Ostwald theory [4-63], based on colored pigments.

The distinction between light and pigment is important to these theories. Munsell's theory, based on light, assumes that color is additive and that all colors of the spectrum, when mixed together, produce white light, the common example being daylight. Ostwald's theory, based on pigments, assumes that color is subtractive and that all colors mixed together produce black. In other words, the pigment of a color absorbs (subtracts) all the wavelengths of light except that which we perceive. Both theories are accepted and may be used by the engineer in the selection of colors.

Color theories, like those developed by Newton, Ostwald, and Munsell, are useful to the artist and engineer for two important reasons. One is that they provide a means whereby one can identify and describe colors. In a sense, they serve as a dictionary of colors. Recall the difficulty that one has in trying to describe a specific color to a friend or associate. In many instances it is necessary to resort to the use of references, such as "green like grass" or "about the same color as your shirt." Such comparisons are subject to considerable variation in interpretation. The color theories provide a means of identifying selected colors.

The second important use of color theories is that they provide a means of manipulating colors in a consistent manner. One of the simplest color theories (but the least accurate) is the Prang color theory. It is based on three primary colors—red, yellow, and blue [4-64]. Under this theory, mixing any two of the primary colors produces a secondary color, specifically orange, green, and violet [4-65]. These secondary colors are located directly opposite their complementary primary color in the color circle and between the two primary colors from which they are produced. Tertiary colors are produced by mixing any pair of secondary colors together. These tertiary colors such as olive, russet, and slate are not exhibited on the color circle. When one mixes adjacent primary and secondary colors in equal amounts, he creates an intermediate color such as yellow-green, blue-green, and blue-violet. Theoretically, mixing opposite or complementary colors produces a neutral gray. Unfortunately, the complementary colors in this system are not well defined so that in practice the grays produced by different complementary

4-67
Ten step value scale.

colors must be supplemented (usually with white or black pigments) to be truly neutral.

Any given color has three important attributes: hue, saturation, and value. These terms vary with each system, but the attributes they represent are fairly constant. *Hue* is the property that distinguishes one color from another, that is, red from yellow from blue. Yellow, red, and blue are hues. *Saturation* refers to the intensity of the hue. The purity of the color and the absence or lack of gray are aspects of saturation. In the preceding color systems, the hues are assumed to be at their most saturated condition. Finally, *value*

4-68
Colors have an emotional quality, a psychological effect.

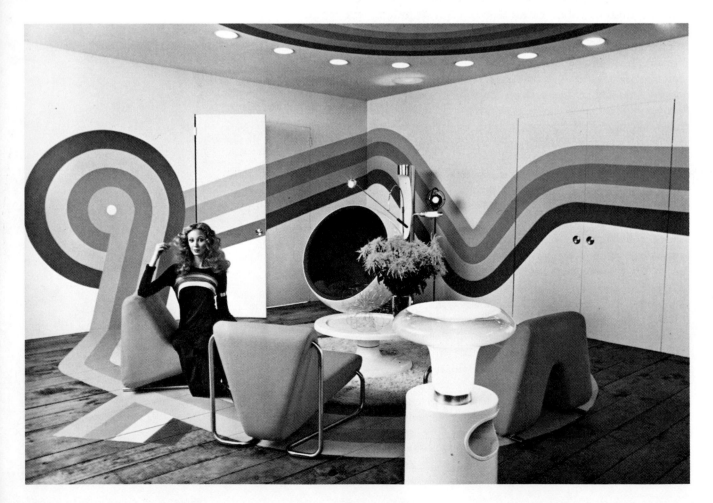

is used to describe the lightness or darkness of a hue. The degree of lightness or darkness of the color is related to a white-through-black value scale. Using red as an example, pink would be the high value and rose red would be the low value. A color with a low-value background will appear to have a higher value than it actually has, or would have, if displayed against a high-value background.

In discussing the characteristics of color, there are two other terms that are useful to the engineer: chromatic color and achromatic color. Chromatic colors are all the hues that fall in the visible spectrum of electromagnetic radiations. Achromatic colors are white through all shades of grey to black, as on the value scale [4-67].

Colors have an emotional quality, a psychological effect [4-68]. Properly applied, these effects can greatly enhance the appearance as well as the functional suitability of an object. Artists have been aware of many of these effects and have used them successfully for many centuries. Since it is difficult to measure or explain some of these effects technically, some examples of the more commonly known color effects will be discussed.

Some hues have predictable emotional effects. Yellow is considered to be friendly, happy, warm, cheerful, sunny, and is associated with the spring season. Orange tends to be gay, warm, vivacious, and outgoing. Red is exciting, arresting, and lively. Orange and red are normally related to the autumn season. Green is relaxed, pastoral, earthly, reposed, and reflects the spring and summer seasons. Serene, cool, and melancholy are effects stimulated with blue hues. Blue hues are often associated with the sea and the winter season. Violet is royal, splendid, elegant.

Color can influence our emotions rather dramatically. A space such as a room or production facility that is painted blue may initially appear cool and welcoming. Some people, if forced to remain in this environment too long, would become uncomfortable, uneasy, and even depressed. A large amount of red in our visual environment at first excites and invites us, but in a short time the excitement becomes nervousness and we attempt to escape from the tension created in a predominately red environment. Yellow and green, on the other hand, have been found to be relaxing for long periods of time and are often used in many institutional applications. Small amounts of brilliant colors—red, orange, blue, and others—will attract people to an otherwise unused area. They also are effectively used as contrasting elements to reduce the monotony of a predominate single hue.

We frequently hear references to the *warmness* or *coolness* of colors, the red and blue sides of the color spectrum, respectively. But we are less likely to be aware that a warm color appears to be "advancing" from a picture or object, while the cool colors tend to "recede." This effect has interesting applications, particularly in the design of display advertising and trademarks.

4-69

(a) Product seems to be top heavy due to dark color.

(b) A more stable appearing product results with proper value relation.

4-70

(a) Color tends to destroy the concept of the form.

(b) Color enhances the concept of the form.

Differences in education are mainly responsible for differences in taste.

H. E. HUNTLEY
The Divine Proportion

Also, closely associated hues will affect each other. If a hue, for example orange, is displayed on a yellow background, it will tend to appear to be more red; turquoise will appear more blue on a green background, or more green on a blue background. In other words, the hue of the figure will tend to appear in the opposite direction of the background hue in any color system. These relationships, when understood and applied, can create many desirable effects and increase a design's acceptability [4-66].

Colors also exhibit sensations of weight; darker hues and values generally appear to be heavier [4-69].

The appearance of the design form may be enhanced by a proper application of color. In general, one should avoid excess in the number of colors applied to a design. Too many colors on a product can create a garish and offensive impression. However, colors can accentuate the form of a product. Misapplied color can do much to destroy an otherwise successful design [4-70].

Product sales, especially those oriented to the general public, are much influenced by color. All too often colors are chosen because of personal whims or what *seems* to be popular in the market.

the aesthetic engineer—a summary

Aesthetics is a critical part of any engineering design, and there are several basic principles that one should understand. This is similar to the mastery of any scientific endeavor; however, in addition, aesthetics includes the important quality of intuitive judgment, which can be developed by the individual by being sensitive to and aware of the variables. The concepts, components, and elements that have been discussed in this chapter are basic and are generally accepted by professional designers and artists. If we could isolate these components, we would be able to logically apply their influences to an aesthetic solution. There are two reasons why this cannot be accomplished. First and most important, all the qualities of aesthetics are not known to us, particularly the emotional qualities. Second, logic, although useful to the engineer in making certain functional decisions, is not totally effective in achieving a beautiful object. Thus, a successful application of design principles in one product cannot assure success in a second design. The elements of aesthetics are so interrelated and interdependent that it is difficult to determine what concepts or elements exert the most influence. If one element is changed, all are affected. Considerable effort has been devoted to the logical application of design principles in the creation of form. In some instances the designs that have resulted from these efforts are characterized by rigid formality and mechanistic contrivance, often entirely devoid of any human quality. For this reason, if no other, concepts and elements discussed here should not be taken as *rules* to create aesthetically satisfying designs.

The engineer is responsible for much of our physical world. It is his responsibility to develop and construct the forms of our society. One does not expect him to become an expert in aesthetic considerations of design, but it is essential to the development of meaningful products that the engineer be aware of the aesthetic implications of the designs that he creates and that he be able to react to this understanding. He must develop the intuitive judgments that determine many of his decisions about the unknown qualities of human response and appreciation. There is no known way to *guarantee* the creation of a beautiful design, but there are certain aesthetic considerations that, if taken into account, will greatly enhance this possibility.

You may not, cannot, appropriate beauty. It is the wealth of the eye, and a cat may gaze upon the king.
THEODORE PARKER

a portfolio of successful designs

The designs [4-71] through [4-85] picture a number of items that are in many respects quite different one from the other. Yet, they share a commonality—their acknowledged acceptance. Each has survived within a competitive environment. Study each design carefully. What has been the secret of its success, the ability to satisfy an expressed human need? Has the primary quality been one of uniqueness, simplicity, beauty, cost, effectiveness—or perhaps some other? What role, if any, do you believe that aesthetics played? What design modifications might have been made to improve the aesthetic qualities of each design? Compare your opinions with those of your colleagues.

Beauty, like supreme dominion, Is but supported by opinion.
BENJAMIN FRANKLIN
Poor Richard's Almanack, 1741

4-71
1905 Raleigh Roadster. Designer: Frank Bowden.

4-72A

4-72B

SKF self-aligning ball bearing.
First sketch made in 1907.

4-73
1908 Luger pistol.
Designers: R. Borchardt and
G. Leuger.

4-74
1908 Model-T Ford. Designer: Henry Ford.

4-75
1929 Barcelona chair.
Designer: Mies Van
der Rohe.

4-76
1932 Zippo lighter. Designer: George Blaisdell.

4-77
1937 Luxo lamp.
Designer: Jac
Jacobson.

4-78
1938 Victor Mouse
Trap. Designer: L. L.
Victor.

4-79
1941 Chemex
Coffee Maker.
Designer: Dr.
Peter
Schlumbum.

4-80
1941 Willys Jeep. Designer: Barney Roos.

4-81
1947 Eames plywood chair. Designer: Charles Eames.

4-82
Los Angeles International Theme Center. Designer: Wm. L. Pereira.

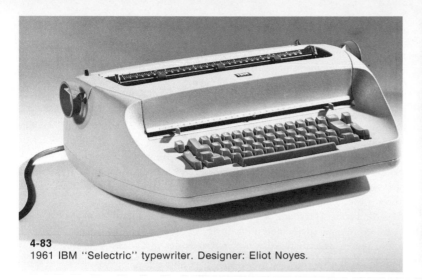

4-83
1961 IBM "Selectric" typewriter. Designer: Eliot Noyes.

4-84
1963 Cummins diesel engine. Designer: Eliot Noyes.

4-85
1969 Porsche 911. Designer: Dr. Fernanand Porsche.

exercises in aesthetics

4-1. Briefly describe an outstanding aesthetic experience that you had during the past year. Why do you consider the experience to be aesthetic?

4-2. Name five products or engineering designs that are aesthetically appealing to you on an intellectual basis; name five that appeal to you on an emotional basis.

4-3. What are three social influences that have contributed to your aesthetic appreciation? Why have they influenced you?

4-4. What are three attitudes about aesthetics that you have been taught? Who was responsible for teaching them to you—your parents, teacher, or relatives? Are these attitudes appropriate for today's environment?

4-5. From a recent engineering design magazine or trade journal, select three examples of what you consider good functional design. Be prepared to discuss the reasons for your choice. Do the three examples satisfy all the requirements of aesthetics?

4-6. From any popular magazine or advertising literature, select three examples of what you consider as styling. Do you see any relationship between your choices and current fads in color, shape, patterns, and other design elements? What are these relationships?

4-7. Using an inexpensive camera with black and white film, photograph five patterns or groups of objects on the campus that demonstrate the concept of unity. Photograph five more examples that demonstrate monotony or dissimilar components.

4-8. Draw a line, whose total length is at least 4 inches, that exemplifies any six of the following emotional reactions:

anger	joy	outrage	disappointment
melancholy	dismay	timidity	surprise
mirth	frustration	pity	frivolity

4-9. Repeat Exercise 4-8, but make each line convey a masculine character as well. Produce a second group that is feminine in character.

4-10. Using a series of lines, not longer than $\frac{1}{2}$ inch, create an illusion of accelerating movement from the upper left-hand corner to the lower right-hand corner of a 3- by 5-inch card.

4-11. Through the technique of varying line weight and spacing, create an illusion of receding and advancing "posts" using lines no longer than 1 inch. On a 3- by 5-inch card arrange the "posts" so that they would appear as an "S" in top view.

4-12. Cut three proportional shapes from four 10-inch squares of cardboard. Discard any excess material. Create an asymmetrically balanced arrangement within an $8\frac{1}{2}$- by 11-inch sheet of unruled paper using the three proportionate pieces.

4-13. From styrofoam or cardboard cut five pieces any size you desire. Arrange four of these pieces on or above an 8- by 8-inch square. Balance these pieces asymmetrically or symmetrically in at least three views.

4-14. Using parallel lines of various lengths and allowing no connection between lines, create a circular form on a 3- by 5-inch card.

4-15. Create a monotonous pattern using geometric shapes.

4-16. Using the pattern created in Problem 4-15, interject interest through altered or different geometric shapes.

4-17. Using the pattern created in Problem 4-15, destroy the unity of the pattern with a variety of geometric or other shapes.

4-18. From your personal possessions, select objects to demonstrate symmetrical balance in a single plane, in two planes, in three planes.

4-19. Select two advertisements from your favorite magazine. One should demonstrate clearly a high contrast between the figure and the background of the ad and the other low contrast.

4-20. Find photographs, sketches, or drawings of three products that have their visual mass below their vertical midpoint. Find three in which this visual mass is above their vertical midpoint.

4-21. Point out at least three areas on any product of your choice that might be considered negative spaces. Explain the reasons for your selections.

4-22. Using paint color chips, select three intermediate colors in the "warm" spectrum of the color circle. Select three intermediate "cool" colors. Arrange these six colors in receding order.

4-23. Select three paint color chips, preferably adjacent intermediates, from your local paint-supply store. Cut these color chips into 3- by 3-inch squares. Choose one additional color, such as a primary or secondary of the Prang color system, and cut three 1-inch circles. Glue one circle in the center of each 3-inch square. Arrange the three completed squares side by side and report any apparent changes in the hue of the circles, the surrounding squares, or both.

4-24. From your local art-supply store, obtain the three primary colors of the Prang system or a near equivalent. Be sure these colors are on a transparent paper or plastic film. Cut a 3-inch circle from each sheet of colored film. Arrange the circles in a way such that you produce the three secondary colors by overlapping the primaries. Are these secondary colors of as high a saturation as the primaries?

4-25. Select 18 paint chips that cover the full visible spectrum of light.

Arrange these chips in order, with infrared on the left and ultraviolet on the right. Be sure to select your hues so that there appears to be an equal color spacing from left to right.

4-26. Select a color chip that best conveys the meaning of the following:

sweet	tense	relaxed
sad	enraged	ugly
jolly	smooth	sour

bibliography

ALEXANDER, CHRISTOPHER, *Notes on the Synthesis of Form*, Cambridge: Harvard University Press, 1964.

ARNHEIM, RUDOLF, *Art and Visual Perception*, Berkeley: University of California Press, 1960.

ASHFORD, F. C., *Designing for Industry*, New York: Philosophical Library, 1955.

BILL, MAX, *Form*, Switzerland: Karl Werner, 1952.

BRONOWSKI, J., *Science and Human Values*, New York: Harper & Row, 1965.

CARRITT, E. F., *Philosophies of Beauty*, London: Oxford University Press, 1931.

COOK, T. A., *The Curves of Life*, London: Constable and Company, 1914.

GRILLO, P. J., *What Is Design?* Chicago: Paul Theobald, 1960.

HUNTLEY, H. E., *The Divine Proportion*, New York: Dover, 1970.

KEPES, GYORGY, *Language of Vision*, Chicago: Paul Theobald, 1944.

KRANZ, STEWART, and ROBERT FISHER, *The Design Continuum*, New York: Van Nostrand Reinhold, 1966.

LIPPINCOTT, J. G., *Design for Business*, Chicago: Paul Theobald, 1947.

MAYALL, W. H., *Industrial Design for Engineers*, London: Iliffe Books, Ltd., 1967.

McHARG, I. L., *Design With Nature*, Garden City, N.Y.: Natural History Press, 1969.

NELSON, GEORGE, *Problems of Design*, New York: Whitney Publications, 1957.

READ, HERBERT, *Art and Industry*, Bloomington, Ind.: Indiana University Press, 1953.

SMITH, J. K., *A Manual of Design*, New York: Van Nostrand Reinhold, 1949.

TEAGUE, W. D., *Design This Day*, New York: Harcourt Brace, 1949.

THOMPSON, D'ARCY W., *On Growth and Form*, 2 vols., New York: Cambridge University Press, 1959.

THORPE, W. H., *Science, Man and Morals*, Scientific Book Club, p. 88.

VALENTINE, C. W., *The Experimental Psychology of Beauty*, London: Methuen, 1962.

part two

design

The melt was responsible for this rather arbitrary configuration whose surfaces, originally smooth, now exhibit typical skeleton formations. ε-caprolactam is the monomeric first stage whose polymerization product has attained worldwide fame as nylon or Perlon.

much of the history of man has been influenced by developments in engineering, science, and technology. When progress in these fields was impeded, the culture of the era tended to stagnate and decline; the converse was also true. Although many definitions have been given of *engineering*, it is generally agreed that *the basic purpose of the engineering profession is to develop technical devices, services, and systems for the use and benefit of man*. The engineer's design is, in a sense, a bridge across the unknown between the resources available and the needs of mankind.

Regardless of his field of specialization or the complexity of the problem, the method by which the engineer does his work is known as the *engineering design process*. This process, which will be described in some detail in Chapter 6, is a creative and iterative approach to problem solving. It is creative because it brings into being new ideas and combinations of ideas that did not exist before. It is iterative because it brings into play the cyclic process of problem solving, applied over and over again as the scope of a problem becomes more completely defined and better understood. In solving complex engineering problems the engineering design process is applied in several distinct *phases*. What these phases are and how they are used is the subject of this chapter. But first, a word about the characteristics of designers.

A design engineer must be a creative person—an idea man—and he must be able to try one idea after another without becoming discouraged. In general, he learns more from his failures than from his successes, and his final designs usually will be compromises and departures from the "ideal" that he would like to achieve.

A final engineering design usually is the product of the inspired and organized efforts of more than one person. The personalities of

. . . the process of design, the process of inventing physical things which display new physical order, organization, form, in response to function.
CHRISTOPHER ALEXANDER
Notes on the Synthesis of Form

A scientist can discover a new star but he cannot make one. He would have to ask an engineer to do it for him.
GORDON L. GLEGG
The Design of Design, 1969

5-1

Resources Available   Engineering Design   Needs of Mankind

The Unknown

good designers vary, but certain characteristics are strikingly similar. Among these are

1. Technical competence.
2. Understanding of nature.
3. Empathy for the requirements of his fellowmen.
4. Active curiosity.
5. Ability to observe with discernment.
6. Initiative.
7. Motivation to design for the pleasure of accomplishment.
8. Confidence.
9. Integrity.
10. Willingness to take a calculated risk and assume responsibility.
11. Capacity to synthesize.
12. Persistence and sense of purpose.

Certain design precepts and methods can be learned by study, but the ability to design cannot be gained solely by reading or studying. The engineer also must grapple with real problems and apply his knowledge and abilities to finding solutions. Just as an athlete needs rigorous practice, so an engineer needs practice on design problems as he attempts to gain proficiency in his art. Such experience must necessarily be gained over a period of years, but now is a good time to begin acquiring some of the requisite fundamentals.

phases of engineering design

Most engineering designs go through three distinct phases:

1. The feasibility study.
2. The preliminary design.
3. The detail design.

In general, a design project will proceed through the various phases in the sequence indicated. The amount of time spent on any phase

5-2

THE DESIGN PHASES

FEASIBILITY   PRELIMINARY   DETAIL

GENERAL   SPECIFIC   5-3

A city that outdistances Man's walking powers is a trap for Man. It threatens to become a prison from which he cannot escape unless he has mechanical means of transport, the thoroughfares for carrying these, and the purchasing power for commanding the use of artificial means of communication.

ARNOLD TOYNBEE
Has Man's Metropolitan Environment Any Precedents?
December, 1966

is a function of the complexity of the problem and the restrictions placed upon the engineer—time, money, or performance characteristics.

The Feasibility Study

The feasibility study is concerned with

1. Definition of the problem.
2. Identification of the factors that limit the scope of the design.
3. Evaluation of the difficulties that can be anticipated.
4. Consideration of the consequences of the design.

The objectives of the feasibility study are to discover possible solutions and to determine which of these appear to have promise and which are not feasible, and why.

Let us see how this might work in a situation in which you, as the chief engineer of an aircraft company, have been asked to diversify the company's product line by designing a small, low-power passenger vehicle for town driving with substantially less pollution than present cars.

What are the elements of the problem; what factors limit its scope? Where and by whom will such vehicles be used? Are they to carry people individually and randomly to and from work, school, shopping areas, or places of amusement like the present car, or are they to be links in a more comprehensive transportation system? Are they to be privately or publicly owned? If privately owned, perhaps the emphasis should be on low cost, simple upkeep, and ease of parking.

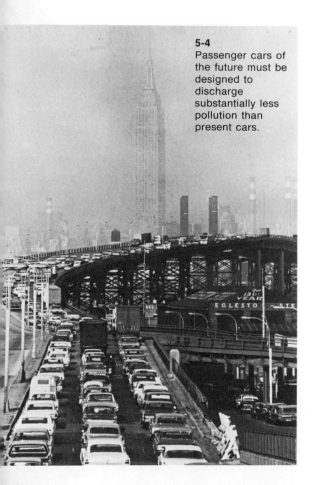

5-4
Passenger cars of the future must be designed to discharge substantially less pollution than present cars.

5-5
". . . emphasis . . . on ease of parking."

THE PHASES OF DESIGN

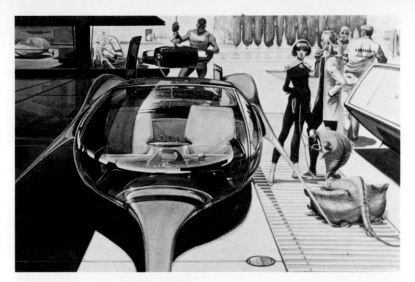

5-6
Vehicles of the future may assume entirely new shapes.

If publicly owned—a car which a licensed driver can pick up at one parking place and leave at another—then ease of handling, reliable operation, and long life might be the major considerations. You will want to know how fast it is to go, how far between fuelings, and how many people it is to carry.

Assume that it is decided to design a vehicle for public ownership. What difficulties can be anticipated? Probably the major ones will have to do with people and what they might do. How do you make such a vehicle safe and nearly foolproof? People must be prevented from driving it too far and from abandoning it anywhere except at designated parking places. Provision must be made to redistribute the vehicles if for some reason—a ball game, a sale, a happening—too many people converge into one area or if there is an unusually high demand for cars, as on a rainy day. Maintenance and repair will present many problems.

Assuming that such a vehicle can be built and sold to cities, what would be the consequences? Some of the desirable ones are obvious: less traffic, lower air pollution, fewer parking problems, and more efficient vehicle utilization. But what about the uncertainty of finding a car when and where you want it, particularly on a wet, cold night or during the rush hour; the new rules and regulations that would have to be devised; the risk of nonacceptance by the public? These would be some of the early considerations during such a feasibility study.

The ideas and possibilities generated in early discussions should be checked for

1. Acceptability in meeting the specifications.
2. Compatibility with known principles of science and engineering.
3. Compatibility with the environment.

4. Compatibility of the properties of the design with other parts of the system.
5. Comparison of the design with other known solutions to the problem.

Each alternative is examined to see whether it can, in fact, be built, whether its potential benefits will exceed its cost, and whether it can be sold at a profit. The feasibility study is, in effect, a *pilot* effort whose primary purpose is to seek information pertinent to all possible solutions to the problem. After the information has been collected and evaluated, and after the undesirable design possibilities have been discarded, the engineer still may have several alternatives to consider—all of which may be acceptable.

During the generation of ideas, the engineer has intentionally avoided making any final selection so as to leave his mind open to all possibilities and to give free rein to his thoughts. Now he must reduce this number of ideas to a few—those most likely to be successful, those that will compete for the final solution. How many ideas he keeps will depend on the complexity of ideas and the amount of time and manpower that he can afford to spend during the preliminary design phase. In most design situations the number of ideas remaining at the end of the feasibility study will vary from two to six.

At this point no objective evaluations are available; the discarding of ideas must depend to a large extent upon experience and judgment. There are few substitutes for experience, but there are ways in which judgment can be improved. For example, decision processes based on the theory of probability can be employed effectively.

fill this higher later

Analog and digital computer simulations are particularly useful to the engineer in this early comparison of alternatives.

In some instances it will be more convenient for the engineer to compare the expected performance of the component parts of one design with the counterpart performances of another design. When this is done, he must be very careful to consider if the component parts create the optimum effect in the overall design. Frequently, it is true that a simple combination of seemingly ideal parts will not produce an optimum condition. It is not too difficult to list the advantages and disadvantages of each alternative, but the proper evaluation of such lists may require the wisdom of Solomon.

The consideration of *value* is very important in the early selection process. From whose point of view should a particular alternative be appraised? Performance characteristics that may be advantageous in one situation may be equally disadvantageous in another. As an example, automatic redistribution of cars would increase the efficiency of the public car system and save driver cost. However, such an automatic system would almost surely not be possible on public streets, and the cost of extra rights-of-way may make it prohibitive. How does one select the location of parking places? How far should people be asked to walk, and how many parking places can be serviced effectively? How does one select the maximum speed of the cars and reconcile the conflicting demands of safety and service? When danger to human life is a possibility, the measurement of value becomes exceedingly difficult. There is great reluctance to place a "cost" or value on the life of a human being. If the engineer assumes an infinite cost penalty, the design may be impossible, but to ignore this factor would effectively assign a cost factor of zero to a life. The engineer must face his responsibilities with honesty and realism.[1]

Engineers engaged in a feasibility study must be able to project the future effectiveness of the alternative designs. In many cases, the preliminary-design stage of a product will precede its manufacture by several years. Conditions change with time, and these changes must be anticipated by the engineer. Many companies have become eminently successful because of the accuracy of their projections, whereas others have been forced into bankruptcy.

The Preliminary-Design Phase

With alternatives narrowed to a few, the engineer must select the design he wishes to develop in detail. The choice is easy if only one of the proposed designs fulfills all requirements. More often, several of the concepts appear to meet the specifications equally well. The choice then must be made on such factors as economics, novelty, reliability, and the number and severity of unsolved problems.

[1] By assigning financial damages to a family whose breadwinner has lost his life in an industrial accident, the courts have effectively placed a monetary value on human life. Damages as high as $250,000 have been awarded.

5-8
"The proper evaluation . . . may require the wisdom of Solomon."

5-9
Jute preparation in Korea?

From whose point of view should an alternative be appraised?

5-10
A mechanized reaper in the United States?

Since it is difficult to make such comparisons in one's head without introducing personal bias, it is useful to prepare an evaluation table. All the important design criteria are listed, and each is assigned an importance factor. There always will be both positive and negative criteria. Then each design is rated as to how well it meets each criterion. This rating should be done by somebody who is not aware of the value assigned to each importance factor, so that he is not unduly influenced.

Let us apply this procedure to our city transportation problem, and particularly to the selection of the propulsion system. Let us assume that the ordinary automobile engine has already been discarded because it is unable to meet air-pollution requirements, and that the choice has narrowed to one of three types of engines: the gas turbine, the electric motor, and the steam engine. We shall then enter these as Designs 1, 2, and 3 in a table and assign values to the various positive and negative design criteria [Table 5-1]. For

A great many people think they are thinking when they are really rearranging their prejudices.

EDWARD R. MURROW

Table 5-1 Evaluation of Propulsion Systems

Design Criteria	Importance I	Design (1) Gas Turbine		Design (2) Electric		Design (3) Steam	
		R	$R \times I$	R	$R \times I$	R	$R \times I$
Positive:							
A. Novelty		0		1		3	
B. Practicability		1		3		2	
C. Reliability		2		3		1	
D. Life expectancy		2		2		2	
E. Probability of meeting specifications		2		3		2	
*F. Adaptability to company expertise (research, sales, etc.)		1		1		1	
*G. Suitability to human use							
*H. Other:							
TOTAL POSITIVE SCORE							
Negative:							
A. Number and severity of unresolved problems		1		2		3	
B. Production cost		3		1		2	
C. Maintenance cost		1		1		2	
D. Time to perfect		1		1		3	
*E. Environmental effects		1		0		1	
*F. Other:							
TOTAL NEGATIVE SCORE							
NET SCORE							

Importance (I) varies from 1 (small importance) to 5 (extreme importance). Rating (R) values are 3 (high), 2 (medium), 1 (low), and 0 (none).
* Such factors may not always be pertinent.

Table 5-2 Evaluation of Propulsion Systems

Design Criteria	Importance I
Positive:	
A. Novelty	2
B. Practicability	5
C. Reliability	5
D. Life expectancy	3
E. Probability of meeting specifications	4
*F. Adaptability to company expertise (research, sales, etc.)	3
*G. Suitability to human use	N.A.
*H. Other:	
TOTAL POSITIVE SCORE	
Negative:	
A. Number and severity of unresolved problems	3
B. Production cost	4
C. Maintenance cost	4
D. Time to perfect	4
*E. Environmental effects	4
*F. Other:	
TOTAL NEGATIVE SCORE	
NET SCORE	

Importance (*I*) varies from 1 (small importance) to 5 (extreme importance). Rating (R) values are 3 (high), 2 (medium), 1 (low), and 0 (none).
* Such factors may not always be pertinent.

example, the gas turbine and electric motor rate low on *novelty* for they are well developed, but an automobile steam engine could rate high if it uses modern thermodynamic principles. On *practicability* the electric motor rates higher than the others, for it requires the least service and provides the easiest and safest way to power a small vehicle. This table is completed to the best ability of the engineer for each of the criteria.

Then the engineer "blanks out" the ratings and assigns *importance factors* to each of the criteria [Table 5-2]. For example, he may rate practicability much higher than novelty.

Finally, the ratings and importance factors are multiplied and added, yielding a final rating for the three systems [Table 5-3], which, in this case, favors the electric-motor drive. Although others may come up with different ratings, the method minimizes personal bias.

After selecting the best alternative to pursue, the engineer should

Table 5-3 Evaluation of Propulsion Systems

Design Criteria	Importance I	Design (1) Gas Turbine		Design (2) Electric		Design (3) Steam	
		R	$R \times I$	R	$R \times I$	R	$R \times I$
Positive:							
A. Novelty	2	0	0	1	2	3	6
B. Practicability	5	1	5	3	15	2	10
C. Reliability	5	2	10	3	15	1	5
D. Life expectancy	3	2	6	2	6	2	6
E. Probability of meeting specifications	4	2	8	3	12	2	8
*F. Adaptability to company expertise (research, sales, etc.)	3	1	3	1	3	1	3
*G. Suitability to human use	N.A.						
*H. Other:							
TOTAL POSITIVE SCORE			32		53		38
Negative:							
A. Number and severity of unresolved problems	3	1	3	2	6	3	9
B. Production cost	4	3	12	1	4	2	8
C. Maintenance cost	4	1	4	1	4	2	8
D. Time to perfect	4	1	4	1	4	3	12
*E. Environmental effects	4	1	4	0	0	1	4
*F. Other:							
TOTAL NEGATIVE SCORE			27		18		41
NET SCORE			+5		+35		−3

Importance (I) varies from 1 (small importance) to 5 (extreme importance). Rating (R) values are 3 (high), 2 (medium), 1 (low), and 0 (none).
* Such factors may not always be pertinent.

make every effort to refine the chosen concept into its most elementary form. Simplicity in design has long been recognized as a hallmark of quality. Simple solutions are the most difficult to achieve, but the engineer should work to this end. He should also learn that such timeless ideas as the lever, the wedge, the inclined plane, the screw, the pulley, and the wheel are still basic tools of good design.

In terms of the electric-drive vehicle, this means that initially he will strive for a single motor, directly driving the rear wheels, and a battery that can be recharged in each parking area. He may later find that a smaller motor at each wheel is preferable, that a geared-down, high-speed motor is more efficient than a direct-drive motor, or that an on-board electric generator is preferable to a rechargeable battery. He will start with the simplest ideas.

Once the design concept has been selected, the engineer must consider all the component parts—their sizes, relationships, and

5-11
". . . not only pleasing to the eye but economical to build." This model is a prize-winning design of an exhibition hall. All steel members in the roof are of equal length to save cost.

materials. In selecting materials, he must consider their strengths, dimensions, and the loads to which they will be exposed. In this sense, he is analogous to the painter who has just chosen his subject and now must select his colors, shapes, and brushstrokes and put them together in a pleasing and harmonious arrangement. The engineer, having selected a design concept that fulfills the desired functions, must organize his components to produce a device that is not only pleasing to the eye but economical to build and operate.

The engineer must make sure that his design does not interfere with or disturb the environment, that it agrees with man and nature. We are especially reminded of these responsibilities when we encounter foul air, polluted streams, and eroded watersheds. Environmental effects are increasingly important criteria in the design of engineering structures, as evidenced by the voluble concern about such projects as the trans-Alaska pipeline, the supersonic jet transport, and facilities for the disposal or reclamation of industrial and human waste. As the earth's natural resources are depleted, the engineer will be under increasing pressure to provide technical assurances that no harm is done to the environment.

The designer must consider such factors as heat, noise, light, vibration, acceleration, air supply, and humidity, and their effects upon the physical and mental well-being of the user. For example, although it would be desirable to accelerate to top speed as quickly as possible, there are human comfort limits on acceleration that should not be exceeded. Controls must respond rapidly, have the right "feel," and not tire the driver. The suspension system must be "soft" for a comfortable ride, but stiff enough for good performance on curves. Automatic heating and air conditioning probably will be required in most parts of the country.

By now the picture of the vehicle has become clearer, and the chief engineer can delegate the preliminary design of components to various people in his organization. Someone will be working on the drive train, another on the wheels and suspension, a third on the battery. Then there are the speed-control system, the interior layout, and perhaps three or four other components, such as safety devices, recharging facilities, and systems for redistributing the cars, that must be developed.

The Detail-design Phase

Detailed design begins after determination of the overall functions and dimensions of the major members, the forces and allowable deflections of load-carrying members, the speed and power requirements of rotating parts, the pressures and flow rates of moving fluids, the aesthetic proportions, and the needs of the operation—in short, after the principal requirements are determined. The models that were devised during the preliminary selection process should be refined and studied under a considerably wider range of parameters than was possible originally. The designer is interested not only in normal operation, but also in what happens during start-up and shutdown, during malfunctions, and in emergencies. He will study the range of the loads that act on his design and how these loads are transmitted through its parts as stresses and strains. He will look at the effects of temperature, wind, and weather, of vibrations and chemical attack. In short, he will determine the range of operating conditions for each component of the design and for the entire device.

He must have an understanding of the mechanisms of engineering: the levers, linkages, and screw threads that transfer and transform linear and rotating motion; the shafts, gears, belts, and chain drives that transmit power; the electrical power generating systems and their electronic control circuits. With today's wide range of available materials, shapes, and manufacturing techniques, with the growing array of prefabricated devices and parts, the choices for the design engineer are vast indeed. How should he start? What guide lines are available if he wants to produce the best possible design?

It is usually wise to begin investigating that part or component which is thought to be most critical in the overall design—perhaps the one that must withstand the greatest variation of loads or other environmental influences, the one that is likely to be most expensive to make, or the most critical in operation.

At this stage the designer will encounter many conflicting requirements. One consideration tells him that he needs more power, another that the motor must be smaller and lighter. Springs should be stiff to minimize road clearance; they should be soft to give a comfortable ride. Windows should be large for good visibility, but small for safety and high body strength. The way to resolve this type of conflict is called *optimization*. It is accomplished by assigning values to all requirements and selecting that design which maximizes (optimizes) the total value.

Materials and stock subassemblies are commercially available in

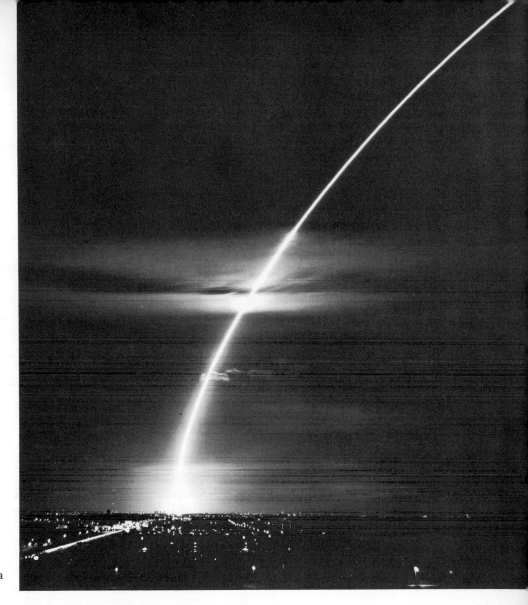

5-13
". . . let us consider the design of a
meteorological rocket."

a specific range of sizes.[2] Sheet steel is commonly available in certain
thicknesses (gages), electric motors in certain horsepower ratings, and
pipe in a limited range of diameters and wall thicknesses. Generally,
the engineer should specify commonly available items; only rarely
will the design justify the cost of a special mill run with off-standard
dimensions or specifications. When available sizes are substantially
different from the desired optimum size, the engineer may have to
revise his optimization procedure.

To illustrate, let us consider the design of a meteorological rocket.
At an earlier point in the design process the fuel for this rocket will

[2] See, for example, *Manual of Steel Construction*, New York: American Institute
of Steel Construction, Inc.

"... strong enough to withstand the pressure and temperature of the burning fuel."

have been chosen. Let us assume that it is a solid fuel, a material that looks and feels like rubber, burns without air, and, when ignited, produces high-temperature high-pressure gases that are expelled through the nozzle to propel the rocket. The rocket consists principally of the payload (the meteorological instruments that are to be carried aloft), the nose cone that houses the instruments, the fuel, the fuel casing, and the nozzle. If we can estimate the weight of the rocket and how high it is to ascend, we can calculate the requirements.

The most critical design part is the fuel casing, that is, the cylindrical shell which must contain the rocket fuel while it burns. It must be strong enough to withstand the pressure and temperature of the burning fuel without bulging or bursting, and strong enough to transmit the thrust from the nozzle to the nose cone without buckling and without vibrating. The shell must also be light. If the casing weighs more than had been estimated originally, more fuel will be needed to propel the rocket. More fuel will produce higher pressures and higher temperatures inside the casing. This, in turn, will require a stronger casing and even more weight. This additional weight requires still more fuel, and so it goes.

Let us assume that we decided to use a high-strength high-temperature-resistant steel for our casing. Our calculations indicate its wall thickness to be not less than 0.22 inches. Our steel catalog may tell us that this steel is generally available in sheet form only in thicknesses of 0.25 and 0.1875 inch. If we use the thicker sheet, the casing weight will increase by 14 per cent; then we must re-calculate the amount of fuel required, the pressures and stresses in the casing, and consequent changes in the dimensions of the rocket. Will the 0.25-inch material withstand the resultant higher stresses? Can we improve its strength by heat treating? If we choose the thinner material, must we provide the casing with extra stiffeners (rings that will reduce the stresses in the casing shell)? In either case, the original design must be altered until the stresses, weights, pressures, and dimensions are satisfactory.

Similar design procedures will be followed in designing the nose cone, the nozzle, and the launching gear for the rocket.

It is important to understand that this example is typical of the design process. Design is not a simple straightforward process, but a procedure of *trial and error and compromise* until a well matched combination of components has been found. The more the engineer knows about materials and about ways of reducing or redistributing stresses (in short, the more alternatives he has), the better the design is likely to be.

Consider, as another example, that the engineer has been asked to design the gearshift lever for a racing automobile. The gearbox has already been designed, so he knows how far the shifting fork (the end that actually moves the gears in the gearbox) must travel

5-15
". . . he may find that a bent lever is more convenient . . . ."

in all directions. He also knows how much force will be required at the fork under normal and abnormal driving conditions. He will need to refer to *anthropometric*[3] *data* to learn how much force the healthy driver can provide forward, backward, and sideways, and what his reach can be without distracting his eye from the road. With all this information he can choose the location of the ball joint, the fulcrum of the gearshift lever, and the length of each arm of the lever. He may decide to use a straight stick or he may find that a bent lever is more convenient for the driver. Before he finalizes this decision he may build a mock-up and make experiments to determine the most convenient location. Next he must select the material and the cross-sectional shape and area of the lever. Since it is likely to be loaded evenly in all directions, he may find that a circular or a cruciform cross section is most suitable. He must decide between a lever of constant thickness and a lighter, tapered stick (with the greater strength where it is needed—near the joint) which is more costly to manufacture.

Next he will consider the design of the ball joint, which transmits the motion smoothly to the gearbox and provides vibration isolation so that the hand of the driver does not shake. It is difficult to find just the right amount of isolation that will retain for the driver the "feel" so essential during a race. The engineer needs a complete understanding of lubricated ball joints and proficiency in testing a series of possible designs.

[3] Anthropometry—the measurement of the size and proportions of the human body (*Random House Dictionary*). See also Chapter 9.

The final component in this design is the handle itself, which should be attractive to look at and comfortable to grip. Here again anthropometric data can tell him much, yet he will be well advised to make several mock-ups and to have them tested for "feel" by experienced drivers.

During the design process, the engineer will have made a series of sketches to illustrate to himself the relative position of the parts that he is designing. Now he or his draftsman will use these sketches to make a finished drawing. This will consist of a separate detail drawing for each individually machined item showing all dimensions, the material from which it is to be made, the type of work to be performed, and the finish to be provided. There also will be subassembly and assembly drawings showing how these parts are to be put together.

The detail-design phase will include the completion of an operating physical model or prototype (a model having the correct layout and physical appearance but constructed by custom non-production-line techniques), which may have been started in an earlier design phase. The first prototype will usually be incomplete, and modifications and alterations will be necessary. This is to be expected. Problems theretofore unanticipated may be identified, undesirable characteristics may be eliminated, and performance under design conditions may be observed for the first time. This part of the design process is always a time of excitement for everyone, especially the engineer.

The final phase of design involves the checking of every detail, every component, and every subsystem. All must be compatible. Much testing may be necessary to prove theoretical calculations or to discover unsuspected consequences. Assumptions made in the earlier design phases should be reexamined and viewed with suspicion. Are they still valid? Would other assumptions now be more realistic? If so, what changes would be called for in the design?

As one moves through the design phases—from feasibility study to detail design—the tasks to be accomplished become less and less abstract and consequently more closely defined. In the earlier phases, the engineer worked with the design of systems, subsystems, and components. In the detail-design phase he works with the design of the parts and elementary pieces that will be assembled to form the components.

In the previous phase of engineering design, a large majority of the people involved were engineers. In the detail phase this is not necessarily the case. Many people—metallurgists, chemists, tool designers, detailers, draftsmen, technicians, checkers, estimators, manufacturing and shop personnel—will work together under the direction of engineers. These technically trained support people probably will outnumber the engineers. The engineer who works in this phase of design must be a good manager in addition to his technical respon-

5-16
"Much testing may be necessary to prove theoretical calculations . . . ."

sibilities, and his successes may be measured largely by his ability to bring forth the best efforts of many people.

The engineer should strive to produce a design that is the "obvious" answer to everyone who sees it, *once it is complete.* Such designs, simple and pleasing in appearance, are in a sense as beautiful as any painting, piece of sculpture, or poem penned by the hand of man . . . and they are frequently considerably more useful to his well-being.

design philosophy

Design philosophy is an important factor with many industries, companies, and consulting firms. The aircraft industry, for example, generally would support a design philosophy that includes

The question "Who ought to be boss?" is like asking "Who ought to be the tenor in the quartet?" Obviously, the man who can sing tenor.

HENRY FORD

187

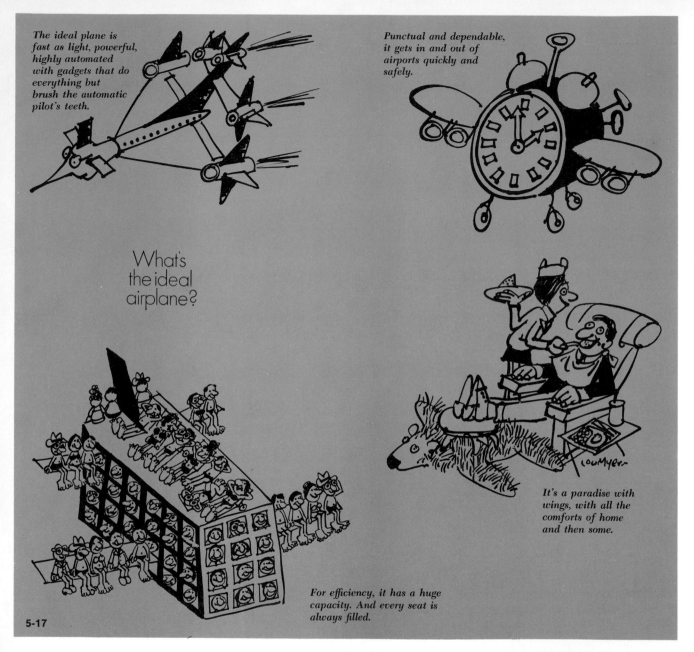

The ideal plane is fast as light, powerful, highly automated with gadgets that do everything but brush the automatic pilot's teeth.

Punctual and dependable, it gets in and out of airports quickly and safely.

What's the ideal airplane?

For efficiency, it has a huge capacity. And every seat is always filled.

It's a paradise with wings, with all the comforts of home and then some.

5-17

(1) lightweight components, (2) safety, (3) limited service life, (4) a wide range of loading conditions and temperature extremes, and (5) concern about vibration and fatigue. The automobile industry, on the other hand, would be more likely to support a design philosophy that stresses (1) consumer price consciousness, (2) minimum service and maintenance, (3) customer appeal, (4) safety for the occupants, and (5) design for mass production.

188

5-18
You oaf! You misread the scale. I wanted a toy!
What could we ever do with something this big?

Some companies are concerned that their products have a "family-like" image and that a responsiveness to customer appeal be designed into all their products. In some instances the image is safety, in some efficiency, in some quality. Public relations should be an important factor with all companies, and the engineer should not be insensitive to the effects that his design will have upon the total company image. The appearance of the product is particularly important in consumer-oriented industries. In such cases, the engineer must take this into account in all phases of his design.

Any engineering design is but *one* answer to an identified problem. For this reason few designs have withstood the test of time without undergoing substantial revisions. One need but look at the continuous parade of modifications, alterations, changes, and complete redesigns that have taken place within the automobile industry to see how the product of a single industry has been changed thousands and thousands of times. Each change, it was believed at the time, was an improvement over the existing model, even if in appearance only. In some instances this assumption proved to be false, and other modifications were quickly made (compare [10-7]).

Usually, the engineer is under pressure for a quick and low-cost solution. He is paid to create new things that are better, less costly, and more efficient than those that exist. Occasionally, the pressures may be unrealistically high. He may feel that he cannot produce a good engineering design in the time permitted and at the desired cost. Yet he alone is responsible for the engineering performance of his solution. In the long run he is judged by the acceptability of his design, whether it is efficient, safe, attractive, and durable. Sometimes the price constraints may be such that an acceptable solution cannot be found. In that case the engineer, as a professional, must so report to his client or employer as soon as possible, for no one

An engineer is an unordinary person who can do for one dollar what any ordinary person can do for two dollars.

189

is served by producing an unacceptable engineering product or by a good design that is too expensive to be sold. Facing such facts squarely, and reporting the truth as he sees it, is a part of professionalism. It is a characteristic demanded of engineers as it is demanded of physicians, attorneys, and architects.

problems

5-1. List the tasks to be accomplished in making a feasibility study for
(a) a sleepy-driver alarm
(b) a method for locating lost contact lenses
(c) a credit card protection system
(d) a portable traffic light
(e) a miles-per-gallon meter for cars
(f) a way to bolt all outside doors of a house from a central location
(g) a low-friction support for an intercity transit system—not using wheels

5-2. Make a list of at least five desirable properties (e.g., low cost, light weight, low maintenance, etc.) for the projects in Problem 5-1. Indicate the way these properties are to be measured, and establish a value scale that allows you to compare the total values of solutions to these problems.

5-3. Suggest at least three different solutions for the projects in Problem 5-1, and evaluate them by means of the value criteria developed in Problem 5-2.

5-4. Prepare a detail design (including material specifications, manufacturing and assembly techniques) for the following items:
(a) a doghouse for a German shepherd dog
(b) your favorite three-course dinner
(c) a book case for a wall 10 feet wide by 8 feet high
(d) a schnorkel-type underwater breathing device

5-5. Your friend's house can be reached by two routes: Route A uses the freeway, is 8.8 miles long, and you can drive it with a maximum average speed of 60 miles per hour. Route B is 6.2 miles and permits a maximum average speed of 35 miles per hour. The cost of driving your car is $0.005 \times V^2$ cents/mile, where V is the driving speed in miles per hour. Choose the cheapest route to your friend's house if
(a) time is worth 5¢/minute
(b) you are late and time is worth $1/minute to you
(c) a special friend is with you and the longer the ride takes, the better you like it
Show all your calculations

5-6. A furniture manufacturer has in his warehouse 1 ton of hardwood worth 10¢ a pound and $\frac{3}{4}$ ton of softwood worth 5¢ a pound. He can make chairs and tables. A chair takes 5 pounds of hardwood and 10 pounds of softwood, and when sold for $25.00 brings a profit of $4.00. A table takes 25 pounds of hardwood, 15 pounds of softwood, and brings a profit of $10.00 when sold for $50.00. How many chairs and tables should he manufacture to maximize his profit? (*Suggestion:* Calculate profit for various possible chair–table combinations and plot the data.)

5-7. A local industry produces 1 pound of sulfur dioxide (SO_2, an air pollutant) for every 1 pound of product made. (The product sells for

50¢/pound of which 5¢ is profit for a return of 20% on the investment.) Now all the SO_2 is dumped into the air. The local air pollution agency has decided to tax SO_2 emission and needs your advice on how high to set the tax rate. They have found out that available removal equipment costs $2.5X^3$ cents/pound of total SO_2 produced, where X is the fraction of SO_2 removed. How many cents/pound of SO_2 emitted should the agency charge to cause a reduction of 50, 60, 70, 80, 90, or 100 per cent? How much can they charge before profits have been reduced to 3¢/pound, and what is the fraction of SO_2 removed, i.e., what is X? How could this fraction change if technology changed the equipment cost to $2.0X^3$ cents/pound but the tax rate remained the same?

The following problems are in the nature of short, competitive projects to develop the creativity of students. Each is a difficult and unusual task and should be evaluated on the basis of a predetermined value scale. The method is illustrated by the first two problems, which are given in detail. Additional projects are given by title only.

5-8. Design and build a system capable of deflecting a compass needle from its usual N–S alignment. The grade on the project will be based on the logarithm of a design value V, which is calculated from the following formula:

$$V = \frac{\phi D^2}{WC^2}$$

where ϕ = angle of deflection, degrees

D = distance between the device and the compass, centimeters

W = total weight of the device, grams

C = cost of the device, dollars

Cost is actual total cost, except for nonpurchased items, where the fair market value of the nearest equivalent item must be used. In any case, it is the responsibility of each student to verify his own cost figures. During the evaluation testing, the compass will be furnished by the instructor, as will an electrical power source (50 volts, 250 milliamperes dc maximum).

5-9. Devise a method of transferring water a distance of 6 feet into a narrow-neck beaker. The beaker will be set into the center of two concentric circles, one 4 feet, the other 12 feet in diameter. You will be given 250 cubic centimeters of water and are to transfer as much of this as possible into the beaker as quickly as you can. A part of your transfer device may touch the ground inside the 4-foot circle but not between the two circles. No part of your body may project into the 12-foot circle. Time, weight of apparatus, and amount of water transferred are important factors. The cost of material must not exceed $0.80. A suitable evaluation formula is

$$\text{grade} = \frac{50V}{T^2(W + 5)}$$

where V = volume transferred, cubic centimeters

T = time, seconds

W = weight of apparatus, grams

5-10. From a distance of 12 feet light a match stuck into the top of a pole.

5-11. Devise a small low-cost light-weight container for an egg that will permit the egg to drop from a third-floor window onto a concrete landing without breaking.

5-12. Thread a standard sewing needle from a distance of 50 feet.

5-13. Place a Coke bottle at ground level and fill it from the third floor.

5-14. Start a fire without friction.

5-15. Design a device that will allow a person to open a can of soda with one hand only.

5-16. Design a device that will turn the pages of a book.

5-17. Tie two pieces of string together from 20 feet away.

5-18. Drive a nail into a board at a distance of 12 feet.

bibliography

BEAKLEY, G. C., and H. W. LEACH, *Engineering: An Introduction to a Creative Profession*, New York: Macmillan, 1972.

EDEL, D. H., JR., *Introduction to Creative Design*, Englewood Cliffs, N.J.: Prentice-Hall, 1967.

GLEGG, G. L., *The Design of Design*. Cambridge: The University Press, 1969.

HARRISBERGER, L., *Engineersmanship, A Philosophy of Design*, Belmont, Calif: Brooks-Cole Publishing Co., 1966.

HILL, P. H., *The Science of Engineering Design*, New York: Holt, Rinehart and Winston, 1970.

JONES, J. C., *Design Methods*, London: Wiley-Interscience, 1970.

KRICK, E. V., *An Introduction to Engineering and Engineering Design*. New York: Wiley, 1969.

MATOUSEK, ROBERT, *Engineering Design*, London: Blackie, 1963.

VIDOSIC, J. C., *Elements of Design Engineering*, New York: Ronald, 1969.

WOODSON, T. T., *Introduction to Engineering Design*, New York: McGraw-Hill, 1966.

Photomicrograph of diatom enlarged 5,000×.

to many people engineering design means the making of engineering drawings, putting on paper ideas that have been developed by others, and perhaps supervising the construction of a working model. Although engineers should possess the capability to do these things, the process of engineering design includes much more: the *formulation* of problems, the *development* of ideas, their *evaluation* and *testing* through the use of models and analysis, and the *description* of the design and its function in proposals and reports.

An engineering problem may appear in any size or complexity. It may be so small that an engineer can complete it in one day, or so large that it will take a team of engineers many years to complete. It may call for the design of a tiny gear in a big machine, perhaps the whole machine, or an entire plant or process, which would include the machine as one of its components. When the design project gets so big that its individual components can no longer be stored in one man's head, special techniques are required to catalog all the details and to ensure that the components of the system work harmoniously as a coherent unit. The techniques that have been developed to ensure such coordination are called *systems design.*

Regardless of the complexity of a problem that might arise, the method for solving it follows a pattern similar to that represented in [6-3]. Each part of this cyclic process will be described in more detail, but first, two general characteristics of the process should be recognized:

1. Although the process conventionally moves in a circular direction, there is continuous feedback within the cycle.

   The concept of *feedback* is not new. Feedback is used by all of us to evaluate the results of actions that we have taken. The eye sees something bright that appears desirable and the brain sends a command to the hand and fingers to grasp it. If the bright object is also hot to the touch, the nerves in the fingers feed back information to the brain with the message that contact with this object will be injurious, and pain is registered to emphasize this fact. The brain reacts to this new information and sends another command to the fingers to release the object. Upon completion of the feedback loop, the fingers release the object.

   Another example is a thermostat. As part of a heating or cooling system, it is a feedback device. A change in temperature produces a response from the thermostat to alter the heating or cooling rate.

2. The method of solution is a repetitious process that may be continuously refined through any desired number of cycles.

The rate at which one proceeds through the problem-solving cycle is a function of many factors, and these factors change with each

6-1

The engineer may be responsible for preparing a design of sm[...] size, such as this integrated-circuit television-color demodulator.

6-2

. . . or he may direct the activities of many people, such as in the building of the Nagarjunasagar Dam on the Krishna River in India, the world's largest masonry gravity dam.

IDENTIFY
PROBLEM

GATHER
DATA

CREATE
IDEAS

N E E D S

FEEDBACK SYSTEM

EXPERIMENT

PREPARE
MODEL

ANALYZE and
EVALUATE

6-3
The design process.

THE ENGINEERING METHOD

PROBLEM

SOLUTION

FEEDBACK

REPETITION

6-4

Reach   **Pain**   **Release**

6-5

6-6   SWITCH   THERMOSTAT

POWER   HEATER
OR
COOLER   AIR

FEEDBACK SIGNAL

6-7
To the engineer, a graph *without scales* is as
fraught with danger as a serpent *with scales.*

problem. Considerable time or very little time may be spent at any
point within the cycle, depending upon the situation.

Thus the problem-solving process is a dynamic and constantly
changing process that provides allowances for the individuality and
capability of the user.

The *design process* is used in each phase of design that was described in Chapter 5. Each phase starts with the identification of
the problem and ends with a report. Some parts of the loop are more
important in one phase than another. For example, the search for
ideas is most important during the feasibility study; analysis and
experimentation tend to predominate in the preliminary- and detail-
design phases. The *solution* of one phase often leads directly to the
problem formulation for the next phase.

identification of the problem

One of the biggest surprises that awaits the newly graduated engineer
is the discovery that there is a significant difference between the
classroom problems that he solved in school and the real-life problems that he is now asked to solve. Problems in real life are poorly
defined. The individuals (whether they be commercial clients or the
engineer's employer) who have the problems rarely know or specify
exactly what is wanted, and the engineer must decide for himself
what information he needs to secure in order to solve the problem.
In the classroom he was confronted with well-defined problems, and
he usually was given in the problem statements all the facts necessary
to solve them. Now he finds that he has available insufficient data
in some areas and an overabundance of data in others. In short, he
must first find out what the problem *really* is. In this sense he is
no different from the physician who must diagnose an illness or the

DESIGN

The engineer's first problem in any design situation is to discover what the problem really is.

The mere formulation of a problem is far more often essential than its solution, which may be merely a matter of mathematical or experimental skill. To raise new questions, new possibilities, to regard old problems from a new angle requires creative imagination and marks real advances in science.

ALBERT EINSTEIN

6-8
An overabundance of data does not necessarily guarantee that the engineer's task will be simplified.

attorney who must research a case before he appears in court. In fact, problem formulation is one of the most interesting and difficult tasks that the engineer faces. It is a necessary task, for one can arrive at a good and satisfactory solution only if the problem is fully understood. Many poor designs are the result of inadequate problem statements.

The ideal client who hires a designer to solve a problem will know what he wants the designer to accomplish; that is, he knows his problem. He will set up a list of limitations or restrictions that must be observed by the designer. He will know that an *absolute* design rarely exists—a *yes-or-no* type of situation—and that the designer usually has a number of choices available. The client can specify the most appropriate criteria on which the final selection (among these choices) should be based. These criteria might be cost, or reliability, or beauty, or any of a number of other desirable results.

The engineer must determine many other basic components of the problem statement for himself. He must understand not only the task that the design is required to perform, but what its range of performance characteristics is, how long it is expected to last in the job, and what demands will be placed on it 1, 2, or 5 years in the future. He must know the kind of environment in which the design is to operate. Does it operate continuously or intermittently? Is it subject to high temperatures, or moisture, or corrosive chemicals? Does it create noise or fumes? Does it vibrate? In short, what type of design is best suited for the job?

For example, let us assume that the engineer has been asked by a physician to design a flow meter for blood. What does he need to know before he can begin his design? Of course he should know something about the quantity of blood flow that will be involved. Does the physician want to measure the flow in a vein or in an artery? Does he want to measure the flow in the very small blood vessels near the skin or in one of the major blood vessels leading to or from the heart? Does he want to measure the average flow of blood or

6-9
Engineering frequently finds its way into the operating room.

BLOOD FLOW

TO VOLTMETER

ELECTROMAGNET

6-10
Electromagnetic blood flow meter.

the way in which the blood flow varies with every pulse beat? How easy will it be to have access to the blood vessels to be tested? Will it be better to measure the blood flow without entering the vessel itself, or may a device be inserted directly into the vessel? One major problem in inserting any kind of material into the blood stream is a strong tendency to produce blood clots. In case an instrument can be inserted into the vessel, how small must it be so that it does not disturb the flow which it is to measure? How long a section of blood vessel is available, and how does the diameter of the blood vessel vary along its length and during the measurement? These and many more components of the problem statement must be determined by the engineer before an effective solution can be designed.

Another example of the importance and difficulty of problem definition is the urban-transportation problem. Designers have proposed bigger and faster subways, monorails, and other technical devices, because the problem was assumed to be simply one of

6-11
The design of rapid transportation systems of the future must be carefully coordinated with the design of the city.

transporting people faster from the suburbs into the city. In many cases, it was not questioned whether the problem that they were solving was *really* the problem that needed a solution.

Surely the suburbanite needs a rapid transportation system to get into the city, but the rapid transport train is not enough. He must also have short-haul devices to take him from the train to his home or to his work with a minimum of walking and delay. Consequently, the typical rapid-transit system must be coordinated with a city-wide network of slower and shorter-distance transportation that permits the traveler to exit near his job, wherever it may be. For the suburbanite, speed is not nearly as important as frequent, convenient service on which he can rely and for which he need not wait.

Urbanites, particularly the poor who generally live far from the places where they might find work, are also in need of better transportation. For these people, high speed again is not nearly as important as low cost, and transportation routes and vehicles that provide access to the job market. Instead of placing emphasis on bigger and faster trains, designers should consider the *wants* and *needs* of the people they are trying to serve and determine what these wants and needs really are.

How does the engineer find out? How does he define his problem and know that his definition is in fact what is needed? Of course, the first step is to find out what is already known. He must study the literature. He must become thoroughly familiar with the problem, with the environments in which it operates, with similar machines or devices built elsewhere, and with peculiarities of the situation and the operators. *He must ask questions.*

After evaluating the available information, it may be that the engineer will be convinced that the problem statement is unsatisfactory—just as today's statement of the transportation problem appears to be unsatisfactory. In that case he may suggest or perform additional studies—studies that involve simulation models of the situation and the environment in which the machine is to be built. They may include experiments with these models to show how this environment would react to various solutions of the problem.

The design engineer must work with many types of people. Some will be knowledgeable in engineering—others will not. His design considerations will involve many areas other than engineering, particularly during problem formulation. He must learn to work with

6-12
The engineer's work is frequently worldwide in its scope. Consequently, he must be adaptive to new and unusual physical environments and be able to work with many types of people.

physicists and physicians, with architects and attorneys, with plumbers and politicians—in short, with all those who may contribute useful information to a problem. He will find that these men have a technical vocabulary different from his. They look at the world through different eyes and approach the solution of problems in a different way. It is important for the engineer to have the experience of working with such people before he accepts a position in industry. What better opportunity is there than to make their acquaintance during his college years? With the manifold problems that tomorrow's engineer will face—problems that involve human values as well as purely technical values—collaboration between the engineer and other professional people becomes increasingly important.

collection of information

We can have facts without thinking but we cannot have thinking without facts.

JOHN DEWEY

The amount of technical information available to today's scientists and engineers is prodigious and increasing daily. Two hundred years ago, during the time of Jefferson and Franklin, it was possible for an individual to have a fair grounding in all the social and physical sciences then known, including geography, history, medicine, physics, and chemistry, and to be an authority in several of these. Since the Industrial Revolution, or about the middle of the last century, the amount of knowledge in all the sciences has grown at such a rapid rate that no one can keep fully abreast of one major field, let alone more than one. It has been estimated that if a person, trained in speed reading, devoted 20 hours a day, 7 days a week to nothing but the study of the literature in a relatively specialized field, such as mechanical engineering, he would barely keep up with the current literature. He would not have time to go backwards in time to study what has been published before or to consider developments in other fields of engineering. How then may one be able to find information that is available, or know what has been done concerning the solution of a particular problem? The answer is twofold: know *where* the information resources are located, and know *how* to retrieve information from a vast resource.

A typical technical library may contain from 10,000 to 200,000 books. It may subscribe to as many as 500 technical and scientific magazines, as well as a large store of technical reports published at irregular intervals by government agencies, universities, research institutes, and professional and industrial organizations. The problem then is principally one of finding the proper books or articles.

Libraries have become quite efficient at cataloging books and major reports in their general catalog file. Usually these catalogs are arranged into three groups, one by author, one by title, and one by subject matter. Although the library catalog is an excellent source of book references, it does not contain any of the thousands of articles in magazines, technical journals, and special reports.

One's direction to these journal articles and special reports is through the reference section in the library. Here the abstract journals and books devoted to collecting and ordering all publications in a particular field are housed. For engineers, two of the most useful of these are the *Engineering Index* and the *Applied Science and Technology Index*. They appear annually and contain short abstracts of most important articles appearing in the engineering field. Articles are organized according to subject headings, so that all articles on a similar subject appear together. By looking under the appropriate heading, the researcher can discover the references of greatest interest to him, or related headings where other references might be found. After satisfying himself that he has the correct references, the researcher then goes to the appropriate periodicals to find the full articles. There are many other indexes besides the two mentioned above, some more, some less specialized. Those most important for the engineer are listed at the end of this chapter.

As an example, assume that we are concerned with the design of a pipeline to transport solid refuse (garbage) from the center of a large city to a disposal site where it may be processed, incinerated, or buried. Let us follow and observe an engineer making the required library search.

Genius may conceive, but patient labor must consummate.

HORACE MANN

6-14

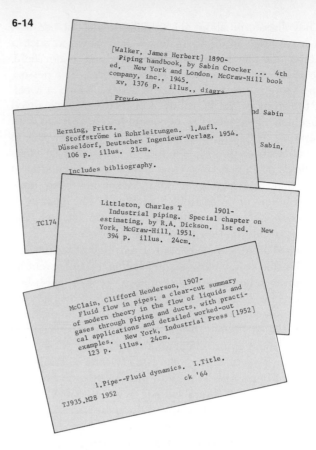

```
[Walker, James Herbert] 1890-
    Piping handbook, by Sabin Crocker ... 4th
ed.  New York and London, McGraw-Hill book
company, inc., 1945.
    xv, 1376 p.  illus., diagrs
```

```
Herning, Fritz.
    Stoffströme in Rohrleitungen.  1.Aufl.
Düsseldorf, Deutscher Ingenieur-Verlag, 1954.
    106 p.  illus.  21cm.

    Includes bibliography.
```

```
    Littleton, Charles T        1901-
        Industrial piping.  Special chapter on
    estimating, by R.A. Dickson.  1st ed.   New
    York, McGraw-Hill, 1951.
        394 p.  illus.  24cm.
```

```
McClain, Clifford Henderson, 1907-
    Fluid flow in pipes; a clear-cut summary
of modern theory in the flow of liquids and
gases through piping and ducts, with practi-
cal applications and detailed worked-out
examples.  New York, Industrial Press [1952]
    123 p.  illus.  24cm.


    1.Pipe--Fluid dynamics.  I.Title.
                                ck '64
TJ935.M28 1952
```

6-15

REFUSE DISPOSAL
See Also Coal Mines and Mining—Waste Disposal; Coal Preparation—Refuse Disposal; Industrial Wastes.

TRANSPORTATION
See also Air Transportation; City Planning; Coal Transportation;
Highway Engineering—Research; Highway Systems—Planning; In-
dustrial Plants—Location; Mines and Mining—Surface Transporta-
tion; Motor Bus Transportation; Motor Truck Transportation;
Noise—Control; Operations Research; Power Plant Equipment—
Transportation; Railroads; Rapid Transit; Street Traffic Control;
Traffic Surveys; Vehicles—Ground Effect; Waterway Transporta-
tion.

COAL HANDLING
See also Bins; Coal Transportation.

Hydraulic. See also Materials Handling—Pipe Lines; Ore Handling
—Hydraulic; Pipe, Plastic.

MATERIALS HANDLING
See also Air Transportation; Aircraft Carriers; Barges; Bins;
Bottle Caps; Cableways; Cargo Handling; Cement Handling; Chemi-
cals—Transportation; Coal Handling; Construction Equipment; Con-
tainers; Conveyors; Cranes; Elevators; Flour Mills; Food Pro-
ducts—Packaging; Foundry Practice—Cleaning; Freight Handling;
Furniture Manufacture—Finishing; Grinding Mills; Hoists; Indus-
trial Engineering; Industrial Trucks; Logging; Machine Tools; Mail
Handling; Mines and Mining—Surface Transportation; Nuclear Fuels
—Safe Handling; Ore Handling; Packaging; Packaging Machines;
Packaging Materials; Production Planning and Control; Rivers—
Revetments; Salt—Storage; Scales and Weighing; Silos; Systems
Engineering; Transportation; Warehouses.

Literature Search on "Pipelining of Refuse"

(The following "capsule narrative" indicates what actually happened during a quick noncomprehensive search conducted in an
afternoon at a typical university library, and it is typical of the kind
of search that an engineer might make for a brief study.)

Going first to the subject section of the catalog file, I could think of
only three headings to look under: Refuse, Garbage, and Pipelines. There
were eight entries under "Refuse and Refuse Disposal." Some dealt with
conveyors and trucking but none with pipelining (not surprisingly since
this is not a common way to convey garbage). I copied some of the titles
and reference numbers because they might help to give me some idea of
the composition and consistency of garbage and of the shredders and other
devices used to make refuse more uniform in size and more capable of
being transported in a pipeline.

The card under "Garbage" referred me right back to "Refuse and Refuse
Disposal," a dead end.

Under "Pipe" there were some 70 entries under 16 different subheadings
from "Pipe-Asbestos, Cement" to "Pipe-Welding." I copied the titles and
numbers shown in [6-14].

I wasn't satisfied that I had exhausted the subject file but could not think

Research Can Take Guesswork out of Bulk Handling, H.COLIJN. Matl Handling Eng v 23 n 3 Mar 1968 p 105-7. Characteristics of bulk materials include particle size, size consist, abrasiveness, angles of friction, particle shape; bulk handling in mining, primary metals, chemicals, railroading; report of European research at Hanover and Braunschweig.

Konzentrationsprofile beim hydraulischen Transport feinkoerniger Feststoffe, E.KRIEGEL. VDI Zeit-Fortschritt-Berichte pt 13 n 9 Dec 1967 51 p. Concentration profile during hydraulic transport of fine grain solids; dimensionless concentration profiles were calculated for uniform grain mixture and compared to published data; calculated grain distributions were compared with photographic records for coke-water mixture; relationship between profiles and precipitation velocity, suitability of equations for multigrain mixtures, as well as effect of most important physical magnitudes were studied. 11 refs. In German.

Pipeline Flow of Paste Slugs—2, R.A.S.BROWN, E.J.JENSEN. Can J Chem Eng v 46 n 3 June 1968 p 157-61. Pressure gradients and velocities of trains of slugs; measurements were taken in 70-ft long, closed-loop line made from 0.95 in. bore, rigid plastic tubing; flow in line could be switched to maintain continuous movement of train of slugs; tests were made with slugs of 80 to 20 (w/w) coal—water paste which was extruded through 0.775-in. die, and also with slugs which were stabilized by addition of agar to water used for making slugs; oil used as carrier fluid was light mineral oil which was circulated through pipe line loop at velocities ranging from 1.0 to 10.0 fps. 11 refs.

Pipeline Transportation of Solids—Theoretical and Practical Considerations, D.ANDERSON, P.R.PERKINS. ICHCA J v 1 n 10 Oct 1967 p 9-13 (French résumé p 41, 43). For many years it has been known that number of bulk solid materials can be transported by mixing them with suitable liquid and handling them as slurries using conventional pumps, pipes or open channels; as empirical knowledge has accumulated proposed uses of slurry pipelines have greatly increased in size and scope; problems are rapidly being overcome to make solids pipelines serious competitors for transportation of bulk materials.

Considerations in Selection of Pneumatic Conveying System, E.A.VITUNAC. Min Eng v 20 n 5 May 1968 p 83-7. Emerging importance of pneumatic conveying systems for bulk materials is largely due to economic advantages such systems frequently exhibit when compared to alternate methods; basically, there are three types of pneumatic systems—mechanical-pneumatic solids pumps, air slides, and pneumatic systems; choice of pneumatic conveying system should be based on economic, operational and maintenance variables; review of typical industrial systems reveals progress made in recent years in design of systems and their component parts.

Gesetzmaessigkeiten beim hydraulischen und pneumatischen Feststofftransport durch waagerechte Rohre, E.KRIEGEL. Verfahrenstechnik v 2 n 4 Apr 1968 p 170-7. Laws of hydraulic and pneumatic handling of solids in horizontal pipes; these laws are investigated separately because large difference of ratio, density of solids to conveying medium, influences handling mechanism; during pneumatic handling grains hit wall of pipe, while they are carried by forces of flow during hydraulic handling; law of resistance and distribution of solids during hydraulic handling can be determined as concept of turbulent mass exchange in flow of liquid; in case of pneumatic handling only individual explanations can be used; comparison of resistance laws for both types of handling emphasizes fundamental differences. 20 ref. In German.

Optimization of Pipelines Transporting Solids, W.A.HUNT, L.C.HOFFMAN. ASCE—Proc v 94 (J Pipeline Div) n PL1 Oct 1968 paper 6179 p 89-106. Method is presented for optimizing economic model of nonclosed network of pipe lines transporting mixtures of wood chips and water; cost function for single pipe is developed as polynomial expression in terms of concentration of solids and pipe diameter; characteristic response surface generated by this polynomial provides method for reducing pipe diameters; optimization of multiple-pipe networks utilizes cost function of single pipes and requires that continuity of flow of mixture is satisfied at junctions; summaries of numerical examples of three-line network are given; costs of pipe line transport of woodchips are compared with those of truck and rail for existing area.

6-16

of any other pertinent headings. So I went next to the reference library and sat down in front of the shelf with the *Engineering Index*. The latest complete year was 1968. Looking under the headings like "Pipeline" and "Refuse Disposal" I paid particular attention to "See also" lists (see [6-15]) and these eventually led me to a veritable gold mine of references under "Materials Handling." A few of these are shown in [6-16]. Notice that two of the most interesting articles are in German. If I find them, I will have to have them translated.

Now that I know some of the best headings, I can look through other years' editions of the *Index* and also study other indexes. I can also go back to the subject catalog and look under the headings that have been productive in the *Index*, headings like "Materials Handling," of which I did not think the first time.

In this way, in a short afternoon, one can assemble a reasonably good reference list on any subject he needs to study.

Reason can answer questions, but imagination has to ask them.

Getting an idea should be like sitting down on a pin; it should make you jump up and do something.
E. L. SIMPSON

A first rate soup is more creative than a second rate painting.
ABRAHAM MASLOW
Creativity in Self-actualizing People

"I can't believe that," said Alice. "Can't you?" the Queen said in a pitying tone. "Try again; draw a long breath and shut your eyes." Alice laughed. "There's no use trying," she said, "one can't believe impossible things."

"I daresay you haven't had much practice," said the Queen. "When I was younger, I always did it for half an hour a day. Why, sometimes I've believed as many as six impossible things before breakfast."
LEWIS CARROLL

Next I have to obtain copies of those articles that I want to study in their entirety. If I found them as books in the subject catalog, I can ask for them or look for them myself in the stacks. For articles which have appeared in magazines, like the references from the *Engineering Index*, I first have to find out whether these references are available in the library and, if so, I'll find the appropriate order number and borrow them from the library. If they are particularly interesting, I may have the library make me a photostatic copy so that I can have a permanent record of the article.

If it is important for the searcher to find the very latest work done in his subject, the library will not be of much help. There is a time delay between the performance of a piece of research, its publication, and its appearance in any of the abstract journals. This delay is usually 3 years or more. The only source for the very latest materials is the expert himself. If one has made an exhaustive literature survey, he has usually found one or more researchers who are specialists and have published extensively in the field under investigation. These people are also the ones who probably can provide the latest technical information in the field. Often these men are happy to share their knowledge with the searcher in the field. However, it is customary to offer them a consultant's remuneration if a substantial amount of their time is required for this service.

generation of ideas

Of all the steps in the design process none is more difficult to describe, or less likely to follow a set routine, than the generation of ideas that may solve the problem. The more difficult the problem, the more elusive the process and the fewer the engineers capable of generating a desirable answer.

Many engineering problems, once they are properly understood, can be solved by the application of known engineering facts and theories, a knowledge of materials, manufacturing techniques, and economics. Other problems require far more imaginative ideas and inventions for their solution.

To bridge a waterway [6-17] may be a monumental engineering task and demand a great deal of know-how by many engineers, but it does not require the creative and innovative thought needed to design an entirely new concept, such as bridging the gap between the earth and the moon [6-18].

Since there is always a great demand for creative and innovative ideas, many attempts have been made to develop procedures for stimulating them. Certain of these procedures will work satisfactorily in one situation, yet at other times different methods may be needed.

There are many methods of stimulating ideas that are used in industry today:

6-17
To bridge a waterway . . .

. . . or the gap between the earth and the moon.

6-18

1. The use of checklists and attribute lists.
2. Reviewing of properties and alternatives.
3. Systematically searching design parameters.
4. Brainstorming.
5. Syneotios.

These methods will be discussed briefly.

Checklists and Attribute Lists

One of the simplest ways for an individual to originate a number of new ideas in a minimum amount of time is to make use of prepared lists of general questions to apply to the problem under consideration. It supposes that a solution or an idea for a solution exists already. Then a typical list of such questions might be:

1. In what ways can the solution or idea be improved in quality, performance, and appearance?
2. To what other uses can the solution be put? Can it be modified, enlarged, or minified?
3. Can some other solution be substituted? Can it be combined with another idea?
4. What are the solution's advantages and disadvantages? Can the disadvantages be overcome? Can the advantages be improved?
5. What is the particular scientific basis for the idea? Are there other scientific bases that might work equally well?

The present generation of students will still be employed in the year 2000. But long before then their degrees and diplomas, at any rate in science, technology and the social sciences, will have become obsolete. The only students who can be sure of escaping obsolescence are those very few who will themselves become innovators.

SIR ERIC ASHBY
Master of Clare College at Cambridge

Watch your step when you immediately know the one way to do anything. Nine times out of ten, there are several better ways.

W. B. GIVEN, JR.

Use logic to decide between alternatives, not to initiate them.

6. What are the least desirable features of the solution? The most desirable?

Attribute listing (also called *value analysis*) is a technique of idea stimulation that has been most effective in improving products. It is based upon the assumption that most ideas are merely extensions or combinations of previously recognized observations. Attribute listing involves

1. Listing the key elements or parts of the product.
2. Listing the main features, functions, or significant attributes of the product and of each of its key elements or parts.
3. Systematically modifying, changing, or eliminating each feature, quality, or attribute so that the *original purpose* is better satisfied, or perhaps a new need is fulfilled.

Checklists and attribute lists are merely stimulators and are not intended to replace original and intelligent thinking. Rather, like a wrench that extends the power or leverage of a man's hand, these ideation tools extend the power and effectiveness of the mind.

Reviewing of Properties and Alternatives

Another rather common procedure, somewhat similar to attribute listing, is to consider how all the various properties or qualities of a particular design might be changed, modified, or eliminated. This method lists the modifiable properties, such as weight, size, color, odor, taste, shape, and texture. Attributes that are desirable for the item's intended use may also be listed: automatic, strong, durable, or lightweight. After developing these lists, the engineer can consider and modify each property or function individually.

Imagine redesigning a lawn mower. The listed properties might include (1) metal, (2) two-cycle gasoline powered, (3) four wheels, (4) rotary blade, (5) medium weight, (6) manually propelled, (7) chain-driven, and (8) green in color. In beginning the design of an improved lawn mower, the engineer might first consider other possibilities for each property. What other materials could be used? Can the engine be improved—what about using electrical power? Should the mower operate automatically? Should the type of blade motion be changed? Questions like these may suggest how the design *could* be improved. The properties of lawn mowers have been changed many times, and these changes have presumably made lawn mowers more efficient and easier to use.

Besides considering the product's various properties, the engineer must question, observe, and associate its functions. Can these functions be modified, rearranged, or combined? Can the product serve other functions or be adapted to other uses? Can we change the shape (magnify or minify parts of the design)? With this type of questioning we can stimulate ideas that will bring design improvements to the product.

Systematic Search of Design Parameters

Frequently, it is advisable to investigate alternatives more thoroughly. A systematic search considers all possible combinations of given conditions or design parameters. This type of search is frequently called a *matrix analysis* or a *morphological synthesis* of alternatives.[1,2] Its success in stimulating ideas depends upon the engineer's ability to identify the significant parameters that affect the design. The necessary steps for implementing this type of idea search are the following:

1. *Describe the problem.* This description should be broad and general, so that it will not exclude possible solutions.
2. *Select the major independent-variable conditions* required to describe the characteristics and functions of the problem.
3. *List the alternative methods* that satisfy each of the independent-variable conditions selected.
4. *Establish a matrix* with each of the independent-variable conditions as one axis of a rectangular array. Where more than three conditions are shown, the display can be presented in parallel columns.[3]

Let us consider a specific example to see how this method can be applied.

1. *Problem statement:* A continuous source of uncontaminated water is needed.
2. *Independent-variable conditions:*
   (a) Energy
   (b) Source
   (c) Process
3. *Methods of satisfying each condition:*
   (a) *Types of energy:*
      1. Solar
      2. Electrical
      3. Fossil
      4. Atomic
      5. Mechanical

[1] K. W. Norris, "The Morphological Approach to Engineering Design," in J. Christopher Jones (ed.), *Conference on Design Methods*, New York: Macmillan, 1963, p. 116.
[2] M. S. Allen, *Morphological Synthesis* Englewood Cliffs, N.J.: Prentice-Hall, 1962.
[3] M. S. Allen, *Morphological Synthesis*, Englewood Cliffs, N.J.: Prentice-Hall, 1962.

6-19

(b) *Types of source:*
  1. Underground
  2. Atmosphere
  3. Surface supply
(c) *Types of process:*
  1. Distillation
  2. Transport
  3. Manufacture
4. *The matrix* [6-19].
5. *Combinations.*

This particular matrix may be represented as an orderly arrangement of 45 small blocks stacked to form a rectangular box. Every block will be labeled with the designations selected previously. Thus, block X in our preceding example suggests obtaining pure water by distilling a surface supply with a solar-energy power source, block Y means transporting water from an underground source by some mechanical means, and block Z recommends manufacturing water from the atmosphere using atomic power. Obviously, some of the blocks represent well-known solutions, and others suggest absurd or impractical possibilities. But some represent untried combinations that deserve investigation.

When more than three variables are involved, a method that has been developed by Myron S. Allen might be implemented:

STEP 1. Get the feel of the general problem area. Read all available material concerning the problem, marking or otherwise identifying all ideas that appear to be of any possible significance—without any immediate evaluation. Talk with as many people as possible who are parts of the problem in any way. Take careful notes.

STEP 2. Type all of the ideas collected in step 1 on 2.5 by 3-inch cards, with the 3-inch side horizontal.

STEP 3. Lay the cards on a table in blocks of twelve—three cards wide and four cards high. Leave about one quarter of an inch between individual cards, and one inch between blocks of cards. This arrangement has worked out to be the best of many different plans.

STEP 4. Read the cards over four or five times, as quickly as you can. All of the ideas presented will be retained in your mind permanently, most of them in your subconscious. We shall make intuitive use of these "submerged" ideas during the process of setting up the total problem.

STEP 5. Go away from the cards for at least half an hour, taking great pains to occupy your conscious mind so completely that it will not be thinking about the cards. Your subconscious mind will continue to work diligently on the problem, and with much higher efficiency than it could if your conscious mind simultaneously is criticizing every new idea proposed by your intuition.

STEP 6. Return to the cards and again study them. You will now notice that certain of the cards appear to be friendly to one another—just friendly—and may easily be collected into congenial groups. If you had started with 500 cards you might wind up with from 20 to 30 of these friendly groups. Now write a descriptive title card for each group (use a distinctive color) and place a rubber band around the group.

STEP 7. Treating each of the groups of cards now as a single element, continue combining the groups into a still smaller number of groups until you finally come to no more than seven groups. Again write a descriptive card for each of these final groups. These are the fundamental elements of the problem, which are commonly called parameters. (This number seven was not an arbitrary assumption, but is in recognition of the proven psychological fact that seven elements is the maximum that the human mind can consider efficiently at one time in a single group.)

STEP 8. Analyze the cards of each parameter and divide them into not more than seven subgroups, called components. The original groupings as found in step 6 will often turn out to be components, but sometimes other arrangements will appear more suitable.

STEP 9. Type the parameters, and their components, in columns.

STEP 10. Cut the pages into strips of one parameter each. Then paste the strips on pieces of thin cardboard of the same size as the paper strips. Make a simple device to hold the slides. You are now ready to take a look at the real, the total, problem.[4]

In matrix analysis electronic computers may be used to excellent advantage. After the matrix has been programmed, the computer can print a list of all the alternative combinations. Use of the computer is especially helpful when considering a large number of parameters.

The preceding techniques of stimulating new design concepts are particularly useful for the individual engineer. But often several designers may be searching jointly for imaginative ideas about some particular product. Then it is advantageous to use brainstorming or synectics.

Brainstorming

The term *brainstorming* was coined by Alex F. Osborn[5] to describe an organized group effort aimed at solving a problem. The technique involves compiling all the ideas that the group can contribute and deferring judgment concerning their worth. This is accomplished (1) by releasing the imagination of the participants from restraints such as fear, conformity, and judgment, and (2) by providing a method to improve and combine ideas the moment an idea has been

[4]M. S. Allen, *Morphological Synthesis*, Englewood Cliffs, N.J.: Prentice-Hall, 1962, p. 182.
[5]A. F. Osborn, *Applied Imagination*, New York: Scribner's, 1963, p. 151.

Depend upon it, sir, when a man knows he is to be hanged in a fortnight, it concentrates his mind wonderfully.

SAMUEL JOHNSON
September 19, 1777

Necessity may be the mother of invention but imagination is its father.

Were it not for imagination, Sir, a man would be as happy in the arms of a chambermaid as of a Duchess.
SAMUEL JOHNSON
Boswell's Life, May 9, 1778

Whatever one man is capable of conceiving, other men will be able to achieve.

JULES VERNE

More ways of killing a cat than choking her with cream.
CHARLES KINGSLEY
Westward Ho, 1855

Originality is just a fresh pair of eyes.

W. WILSON

It is obvious that invention or discovery, be it in mathematics or anywhere else, takes place by combining ideas.
JACQUES HADAMARD
An Essay on the Physchology of Invention in the Mathematical Fields

The person who is capable of producing a large number of ideas per unit of time, other things being equal, has a greater chance of having significant ideas.

J. P. GUILFORD

He that answereth a matter before he heareth it, it is folly and shame unto him.

PROVERBS 18:13
The Holy Bible

expressed. Osborn points out that this collaborative group effort does not replace individual ideative effort. Group brainstorming is used solely to supplement individual idea production and works very effectively for finding a large volume of alternative solutions or novel design approaches. It has been particularly useful for stimulating imaginative ideas for new products. It is not recommended when the problem solution will depend primarily on judgment or when the problem is vast, complex, vague, or controversial. A group of six to twelve persons of similar age and position seems to be best for stimulating ideas with this method. However, the US Armed Forces have used a hundred or more participants effectively. The typical brainstorming session has only two officials: a chairman and a recorder. The chairman's responsibility is to provide each panel member with a brief statement of the problem, preferably 24 hours prior to the meeting. He should make every effort to describe the problem in clear, concise terms. It should be *specific*, rather than *general*, in nature. Some examples of ideas that satisfy the problem statement may be included with the statement. Before beginning the session, the chairman should review the rules of brainstorming with the panel. These principles, although few, are very important and are summarized as follows:

1. *All ideas that come to mind are to be recorded.* No idea should be stifled. As Osborn says, "The wilder the idea, the better; it is easier to tame down than to think up." He recommends recording ideas on a chalkboard as they are suggested. Sometimes a tape recorder can be very valuable, especially when panel members· suggest several different ideas in rapid succession.
2. *Suggested ideas must not be criticized or evaluated.* Judgments, whether adverse or laudatory, *must be withheld* until after the brainstorming session, because many ideas that are normally inhibited because of fear of ridicule and criticism are then brought out into the open. In many instances, ideas that would normally have been omitted turn out to be the best ideas.
3. *Combine, modify, alter, or add to ideas as they are suggested.* Participants should consciously attempt to improve on other people's ideas, as well as contributing their own imaginative ideas. Modifying a previously suggested idea will often lead to other entirely new ideas.
4. *The group should be encouraged to think up a large quantity of ideas.* Research at the State University of New York at Buffalo[6] seems to indicate that when a brainstorming session produces more ideas, it will also produce higher-quality ideas.

[6]S. J. Parnes and Arnold Meadow, "Effects of Brain-storming Instructions on Creative Problem Solving by Trained and Untrained Subjects," *Journal of Educational Psychology*, Vol. 50, No. 4 (1959), p. 176.

The brainstorming chairman must always be alert to keep *evaluations* and *judgments* from creeping into the meeting. The spirit of enthusiasm that will permeate the group meeting is also very important to the success of the brainstorming session. The entire period should be conducted in a free and informal manner. It is most important to maintain, throughout the period, an environment in which the group members are not afraid of seeming foolish. Both the speed of producing and recording ideas and the number of ideas produced help create this environment. Each panel member should bring to the meeting a list of new ideas that he has generated from the problem statement. These ideas help to get the session started. In general, the entire brainstorming period should not last more than 30 minutes to 1 hour.

The recorder keeps a stenographic account of all ideas presented and, after the session, lists them by type of solution without reference to their source. Team members may add ideas to the accumulated list for a 24-hour period. Later, the entire list of ideas should be rigorously evaluated, either by the original brainstorming group or, preferably, by a completely new team. Many of the ideas will be discarded quickly—others after some deliberation. Still others will likely show promise of success or at least suggest how the product can be improved.

Some specialists recommend that the brainstorming team include a few persons who are broadly educated and alert but who are amateurs in the particular topic to be discussed. Thus new points of view usually emerge for later consideration. Usually, executives or other people mostly concerned with evaluation and judgment do not make good panel members. As suggested previously, particular care should be taken to confine the problem statement within a narrow or limited range to ensure that all team members direct their ideas toward a common target. It should be recognized that the objective of brainstorming is to stimulate ideas—not to generate a complete solution for a given problem.

William J. J. Gordon[7] has described a somewhat similar method of group therapy for stimulating imaginative ideas, which he calls *synectics*.

Synectics

This group effort is particularly useful to the engineer in eliciting a radically new idea or in improving products or developing new products. Unlike brainstorming, this technique does not aim at producing a large number of ideas. Rather, it attempts to bring about one or more solutions to a problem by drawing seemingly unrelated ideas together and forcing them to complement each other. The synectics participant tries to *imagine* himself as the "personality"

No idea is so outlandish that it should not be considered with a searching but at the same time with a steady eye.
WINSTON CHURCHILL

---

[7] W. J. J. Gordon, *Synectics*, New York: Harper & Row, 1961.

6-20

of the inanimate object: "What would be my reaction *if I were that gear* (or drop of paint, or tank, or electron)?" Thus familiar objects take on strange appearances and actions, and strange concepts often become more comprehensible. A key part of this technique lies in the group leader's ability to make the team members "force-fit" or combine seemingly unrelated ideas into a new and useful solution. This is a difficult and time-consuming process. Synectics emphasizes the conscious, preconscious, and subconscious psychological states that are involved in all creative acts. In beginning, the group chairman leads the members to understand the problem and explore its *broad* aspects. For example, if a synectics group is seeking a better roofing material for traditional structures, the leader might begin a discussion on "coverings." He could also explore how the colors of coverings might enhance the overall efficiency (white in summer, black in winter). This might lead to a discussion of how colors are changed in nature. The group leader could then focus the group on more detailed discussion of how roofing materials could be made to change color automatically to correspond to different light intensities—like the biological action of a chameleon or a flounder. Similarly, the leader might approach the problem of devising a new type of can opener by first leading a group discussion of the word "opening," or he could begin considering a new type of lawn mower by first discussing the word "separation."

In general, synectics recommends viewing problems from various analogous situations. Paint that will not adhere to a surface might be viewed as analogous to water running off a duck's back. The earth's crust might be seen as analogous to the peel of an orange. The problem of enabling army tanks to cross a 40-foot-wide bottomless crevass might be made analogous to the problem that two ants have in crossing chasms wider than their individual lengths.

Synectics has been used quite successfully in problem-solving situations in such diverse fields as military defense, the theatre, manufacturing, public administration, and education. Whereas most members of the brainstorming team are very knowledgeable about the problem field, synectics frequently draws the team members from diverse fields of learning, so that the group spans many areas of knowledge. Philosophers, artists, psychologists, machinists, physicists, geologists, biologists, as well as engineers, might all serve equally well in a synectics group. Synectics assumes that someone who is imaginative but not experienced in that field may produce as many creative ideas as one who *is* experienced in that field. Unlike the expert, the novice can stretch his imagination. He approaches the problem with fewer preconceived ideas or theories, and he is thus freer from binding mental restrictions. (Obviously, this will not be true when the problem requires analysis or evaluation, and when experience is a vital factor.) There is always present in the synectics conference an expert in the particular problem field. The expert can use his superior

New things are made familiar, and familiar things are made new.

SAMUEL JOHNSON
Lives of the Poets, 1781

technical knowledge to give the team missing facts, or he may even assume the role of "devil's advocate," pointing out the weaknesses of an idea the group is considering. *All* synectics sessions are tape recorded for later review and to provide a permanent record.

Many believe that brainstorming comes to grips with the problem too abruptly, whereas synectics delays too long. However, industry is using both methods successfully today.

preparation of a model

Seek simplicity, and distrust it.
ALFRED NORTH WHITEHEAD

Psychologists and others who study the workings of the human mind tell us that we can think effectively only about simple problems and small bits of information. They tell us that those who master complicated problems do so by reducing them to a series of simple problems that can be solved and synthesized to a final solution. They form a mental picture of the entire problem, and then simplify and alter this picture until it can be taken apart into manageable components. These components must be simple and similar to concepts with which we are already familiar, to situations that we know. Such mental pictures are called *models*.

We are all familiar with models of sorts—with maps as models for road systems; with catalogs of merchandise as models of what is offered for sale. We have a model in our mind of the food we eat, the clothes we buy, and of the person we want to marry.

We often form judgments and make decisions on the basis of the model, even though the model may not be entirely appropriate. Thus the color of an apple may or may not be a sign of its ripeness, no more than the girl's apple-blossom cheeks and tip-tilted nose are the sign of a desirable girl friend.

Some engineering models are similar to sports diagrams composed of circles, squares, triangles, curved and straight lines, and other similar symbols used to represent a play in a football or basketball game. Such geometrical models are limited because they are two-dimensional and do not allow for the strengths, weaknesses, and imaginative decisions of the individual athletes. Their use, however, has proved to be quite valuable in simulating a brief action in the game and in suggesting the best strategy for the player should he find himself in a similar situation [6-22; 6-23].

A *model* may emphasize some overall aspects of the whole of a system and not represent closely the behavior of its components; or it may be designed to represent the action of only some part of the system. Its function is to make visualization, analysis, and testing more practical. The engineer thereby limits the complexity of a problem so that he can apply known principles in its solution. The solutions developed for the model are then limited by the extent to which the model represents the real system; their validity depends

A damsel of high lineage and a brow
May-blossom, and a cheek of apple-blossom
Hawk-eyes; and lightly her slender nose
Tip-tilted like the petal of a flower.

TENNYSON

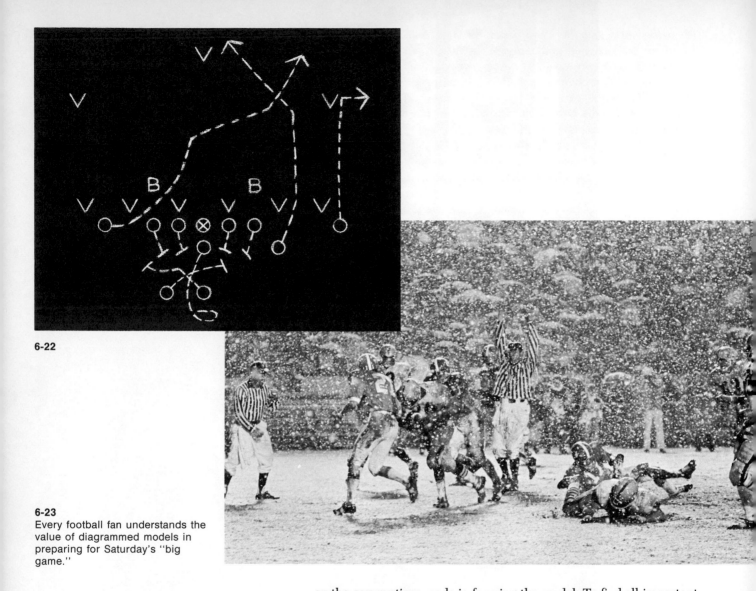

6-22

6-23
Every football fan understands the value of diagrammed models in preparing for Saturday's "big game."

on the *assumptions* made in forming the model. To find all important aspects of a system, several different models may be needed, each with its own set of assumptions, each illuminating a different component or mode of action of the system.

The usefulness of the models to predict the action of the real system must be verified. This is accomplished by experimentation and testing. Refinement of the model and verification by experimentation are continued until an acceptable model has been obtained.

Two characteristics, more than any others, determine an engineer's competence. The first is his ability to devise simple, meaningful models; the second is the breadth of his knowledge and experience with examples with which he can compare his models. The simpler his models are, and the more generally applicable, the easier it is to predict the behavior and compute the performance of the design. *Yet models have value only to the engineer who can analyze them.* The beauty and simplicity of a model of the atom will appeal to someone familiar with astronomy [6-26]. The free-body diagram of a wheelbarrow handle has meaning only to someone who knows how such a diagram can be used to find the strength of the handle [6-27].

Aside from models for "things," we can make models of situations, environments, and events. The football or baseball diagram is such a model. Another familiar model of this type is the weather map,

6-24

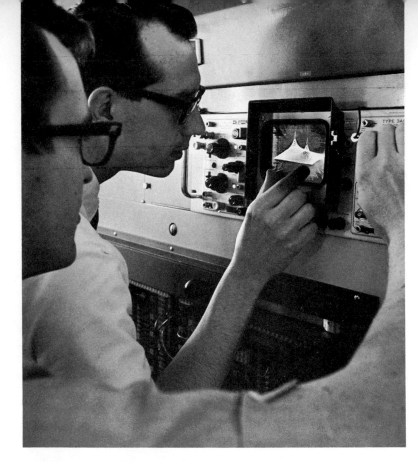

6-25
A computerized model of water-pollution effects.

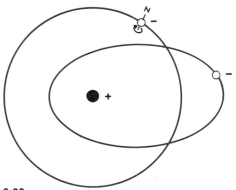

6-26
Modified Bohr–Sommerfeldt model of the atom.

which depicts high- and low-pressure regions and other weather phenomena traveling across the country. Any meteorologist will tell you that the weather map is a very crude model for predicting weather, but that its simplicity makes the explanation of current weather trends more understandable for the layman. Models of situations and environmental conditions are particularly important in the analysis of large systems, because they aid in predicting and analyzing the performance of the system before its actual implementation.

6-27

6-28

Such models have been prepared for economic, military, and political situations, and their preparation and testing is a science all its own. Models are such an important part of engineering that all of Chapter 7 is devoted to their generation and use.

Analysis

One of the principal purposes of a model is to simplify the problem so that we can calculate the behavior, strength, and performance of the design. This calculation process is *analysis*.

Analysis is a mental process and, like any useful mental process, requires a store of basic knowledge and the ability to apply that knowledge. Since the amount of knowledge he possesses and his ability to use it are the major measures of a capable engineer, more time is spent at the university in studying analysis than any other subject. Just as one cannot solve a crossword puzzle without a knowledge of words, or make a medical diagnosis without a knowledge of the human body and its functions, so one cannot produce an acceptable engineering design without a basic knowledge of mathematics, physics, chemistry, and their engineering relatives: stress analysis, heat transfer, electric network theory, vibration, etc. Nor can the engineer work effectively without an understanding of how his work affects man and his environment.

Analysis allows the engineer to "experiment on paper." For example, if he is concerned with the behavior of a wheel on a vehicle,

6-29   6-30

his model might be a *rigid, perfectly round* wheel rolling on a *flat unyielding* surface [6-29]. (Words in italics indicate the assumptions made in the model.)

The motion of each point on the rim of the model wheel can be expressed by a well-known mathematical relationship called the *cycloid.* By knowing this motion, the engineer can calculate the velocity of each point and determine how it varies with time [6-30]. These calculations will enable him to solve for the centrifugal force on the wheel rim and to learn how fast the point makes contact with the ground.

This elementary problem illustrates two important restrictions of engineering analysis: First, an equation usually describes only a very limited part or function of the design, even in the case of a simple design such as a wheel. Second, an equation usually cannot describe *exactly* the action that takes place in the model. For example, we make the assumption that the wheel is perfectly rigid. This implies that it does not deform when it touches the ground. Such an assumption may be reasonably accurate in the case of a steel train wheel rolling on a steel rail, but it is probably a poor assumption to make for the rubber-tired wheels of an automobile.

Just as a carpenter's toolbox may contain several different saws, chisels, and hammers, so the tools of analysis can be divided into several categories, such as the following:

Mathematical tools	Mathematics
	Statistics
	Computer operations
Material tools	Chemistry
	Materials and metallurgy
Physical tools	Solid mechanics
	Fluid mechanics
	Electricity
	Thermodynamics
Environmental tools	Physical limitations of man
	Economics
	Social sciences
	Ecological sciences

It is obvious that we cannot describe all these subjects in this text. Many books have been written about each of them. However, some have been discussed earlier and others will be considered here.

the mathematical tools

The language of engineering is *mathematics* and to be an effective engineer one must learn to use its language. Although in theory one can describe everything with words of the English language, English is, in fact, cumbersome and frequently ill adapted to express *precisely* the "physics" of a situation, as can be done with a mathematical equation. Consider, for example, a ball resting on a flat horizontal surface [6-31]. Its weight under the force of gravity (W) acts downward and the surface resists upward on the ball (N) so that it does not move. In this case the English language is adequate to describe that the two forces act along the same line and are of equal magnitude. However, consider the same ball resting on an incline against a stop that prevents its moving down the incline [6-32]. Here we must consider the action of three forces: the force of gravity pulling down (W), the normal force from the incline (F_1), and the resisting force from the stop (F_2). Since the ball is not moving, we know that these three forces must somehow balance, and that to do so the magnitudes of the supporting forces will vary depending on the angle of the incline with the horizontal (θ). We can say in general terms that if this angle becomes larger, the force from the plane (F_1) decreases, and the force on the stop (F_2) increases, but just exactly how they are related to one another would be most difficult to describe with words alone. Yet in mathematical terms the relationship between these forces can be expressed simply and easily [6-33].

This very simple problem is taken from the field of *statics*, because it deals with forces at rest. When bodies are in motion, when discussing the flow of liquids, gases, heat, or electricity, we enter the field of *dynamics*. The mathematics describing such phenomena is the mathematics of *change*, the realm of calculus. Since there are many excellent texts on the calculus and students engaged in technical studies become familiar with it early, there is no need for us to cover it here.

Mathematical analysis is rarely if ever able to depict exactly the physical behavior of *real* materials and devices. In fact, even if it were, such exactitude would be of little value to the engineer, since each piece of material differs from all others (even if these differences are only microscopic); and at best one can talk only about *statistical average behavior* and attempt to estimate how much any one sample may vary from this average.

Statistics relates experiment to analysis. It furnishes the numbers used in the analysis and tells how reliable they are. If, for example, a large number of "pull tests" have shown that the average failure load for the samples tested was 100,000 pounds, and the failures were distributed as shown [6-34], then we can expect 10 samples in 100 to fail at as low a load as 75,000 pounds and 10 to survive a load of 125,000 pounds.

> Mathematics is the queen of the sciences.
> CARL FRIEDRICH GAUSS

6-31

6-32

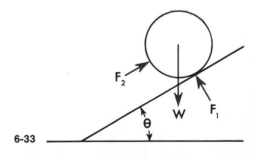

6-33

$$F_1 \cos\theta + F_2 \sin\theta = W$$

$$F_1 \sin\theta = F_2 \cos\theta$$

6-34

PERCENT FAILED

100
80
60
40
20

0   50   100   150   200

TEST LOAD (1,000 lbs.)

Statistics are no substitute for judgment.

HENRY CLAY

The computer is the most significant of human inventions because it complements the human brain in precisely the two ways which limit the brain—slowness and boredom. . . . It has added speed to the complexity of the brain . . . and the capability to solve many problems which would never be attempted because of the tedium involved.

COLIN PITTENDRIGH

"Can you do addition?" the White Queen said. "What's one and one and one and one and one and one and one and one and one and one?" "I don't know," said Alice. "I lost count." "She can't do addition," the Red Queen interrupted.

LEWIS CARROLL

The engineer, who can rarely ask that every production item be tested, must decide what kind of failure rate he can tolerate and proceed with his design accordingly. For unimportant items, easily replaced, he may well accept a 1 or 2 per cent failure rate. However, if failure of the part were to endanger human life, he would want to make sure that its *probability* of failure is very low and that it is tested to full load and beyond before it leaves the factory.

Computers

Any discussion of mathematics for the engineer would not be complete without a brief review of what a *digital computer* is and how it is used. The digital computer has become an almost indispensible tool for today's engineer. But what can a computer do that makes it so valuable to the engineer? Is it some type of ultra-fast adding machine or perhaps a mysterious device that answers questions that are put to it? It is really neither of these—although it is frequently used for both of these purposes. If one looks beyond the dazzle of flashing lights and whirling tapes, he can identify four primary attributes in any modern computer:

1. The ability to store thousands of numbers and to recall them rapidly from storage when needed. The storage is appropriately called *memory*. The memory not only stores the numbers on which the computer operates and the results of its calculations, but also stores the *program* that tells it what kind of calculations to perform. Therefore, the same program can be used again and again with different data, without having to repeat the original instructions to the machine.

2. An *arithmetic* center that works much like a desk calculator, primarily by adding (or subtracting) numbers. It can do this so rapidly—an addition may take as little as a few millionths of a second—that even very lengthy calculations are made in an extremely short time. The process of multiplication is accomplished by repeated addition; division by repeated subtraction.

3. The capability of comparing two numbers and of making a *decision* based upon the outcome. This is one of the most important attributes of the computer. How this works will be demonstrated in the example below.

4. Communication or *input–output* facilities that allow one to "talk" to the computer, to give it instructions, to feed it numbers with which to compute, and to receive its answers in readable form.

Since the computer works only with numbers, the instructions in the program (such as "add number x to number y") must also be translated into appropriate numbers. In the early days of computers, the programmer was required to accomplish these translations himself. To do so he had to know the internal computer language. Today, computers are able to accomplish their own translation, provided that the program is written in a "standard" language. These standard languages are easy to learn because they are written in almost the same way that one would normally express the steps of the program in written English. Among the most frequently used standard languages are FORTRAN, ALGOL, and BASIC.

Let us examine how a typical computer program would work on this problem (reportedly more than 1,500 years old).[8]

According to an Arabic legend, the game of chess was invented by a Brahmin to show his student, the heir to the throne, that the king is no stronger than his subjects. Invited to name a reward, the Brahmin asked only for grains of rice: one grain on the first square of the chess board, two on the second, four on the third, and so on, always doubling until the sixty-fourth square is reached. Since this request appeared to be modest, it was granted. *Yet all the rice in India could not satisfy this simple request.*

How many grains would there be on each square? How many altogether? Of course one could calculate it easily, *but laboriously.* (Note that the total is one less than twice the amount of the last square.) Here is the computer program[9] [6-37] that will evaluate the

[8] Translated from *Grand Larousse encyclopédique*, Librairie Larousse, Paris, 1961, Vol. 4, p. 321.
[9] The computer language used is BASIC.

6-36
. . . the game of chess.

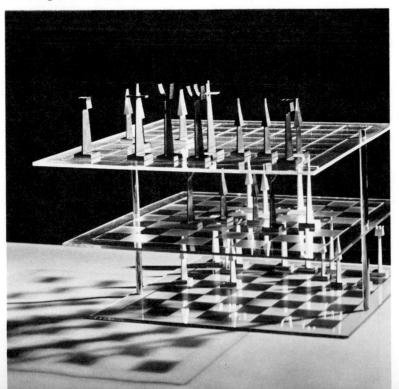

ARITHMETIC	$+$, $-$
BIOLOGY	♀ , ♂
ARISTOTLE	*either ⌣ or*
DESCARTES	x , y
HAMLET	"To be or not to be"
CHESS	P·K4 , P·Q3
PHOTOGRAPHY	▣ ▢
LIGHT BULB	💡 💡
AVIATION	flaps up , flaps down
BASEBALL	**strike** , **ball**
ACCOUNTING	CREDIT , DEBIT
STOCK MARKET	*Bull* , *Bear*
CRAP TABLE	come , no come
BOWLING	☒ ▢
SWITCH	ON ⌐ OFF
ASTRONAUT	go · no go
TEST ANSWER	true , false
COURSE GRADE	P , F
MARRIAGE	Yes , NO
COMPUTER LANGUAGE	1 , 0

6-35

It's a Barnum and Binary World
Just as ideatic as it can be,
But it would only be make-believe
If it wasn't for you and me.

6-37

```
1 LET X=N=1
2 PRINT N,X
3 IF N=64 THEN 7
4 LET N=N+1
5 LET X=2*X
6 GO TO 2
7 LET X=2*X-1
8 PRINT "TOTAL=";X
9 STOP
```

1	1
2	2
3	4
4	8
5	16
6	32
7	64
8	128
9	256
10	512
11	1024
12	2048
13	4096
14	8192
15	16384
16	32768
17	65536
18	131072
19	262144
20	524288
21	1048576
22	2097152
23	4194304
24	8388608
25	16777216
26	33554432
27	67108864
28	134217728
29	268435456
30	536870912
31	1.07374E+09
32	2.14748E+09
33	4.29497E+09
34	8.58993E+09
35	1.71799E+10
36	3.43597E+10
37	6.87195E+10
38	1.37439E+11
39	2.74878E+11
40	5.49756E+11
41	1.09951E+12
42	2.19902E+12
43	4.39805E+12
44	8.79609E+12
45	1.75922E+13
46	3.51844E+13
47	7.03687E+13
48	1.40737E+14
49	2.81475E+14
50	5.62950E+14
51	1.12590E+15
52	2.25180E+15
53	4.50360E+15
54	9.00720E+15
55	1.80144E+16
56	3.60288E+16
57	7.20576E+16
58	1.44115E+17
59	2.88230E+17
60	5.76461E+17
61	1.15292E+18
62	2.30584E+18
63	4.61169E+18
64	9.22337E+18

TOTAL = 1.84467E+19

desired result. There are nine *statements,* each one numbered for reference. N stands for the number of the square (from 1 to 64), X for the number of grains of rice on that square. Although the statements beginning with LET look like equations, they are more properly called *assignments,* for we ask the computer to calculate the right-hand side and to *assign* the resultant number to the symbol on the left. For example, in statement 4, the computer adds 1 to the present value of N and then assigns this sum to N. The asterisk (*) is used as the symbol for multiplication. Note the decision statement 3. It tells the computer to compare the present value of N with the number 64. If N is equal to 64, then the program switches to statement 7; if not, it goes on to the next statement in line. When it gets to statement 6, the computer is told to go next to statement 2 and then to proceed accordingly.

The result is shown in [6-38]. It took a medium-sized computer 7 seconds to calculate all these values, and about 2 minutes to print them. Note that this particular computer does not keep track of more than nine digits. From square 31 on, the numbers are rounded off and expressed as decimals, with an *exponential* added. For example, square 31 (which should actually be 1,073,741,824) becomes 1.07374×10^9 or, in computer terms, 1.07374E+09.

the material tools

The materials and processes that are of most general use to the engineer are discussed in some detail in Chapter 8.

the physical tools

The engineering curriculum contains more courses in physics and in subjects derived from physics than any of the other pure sciences. Usually it begins with *static mechanics* or statics—the science of bodies at rest and in equilibrium and the forces necessary to keep them there. Buildings, bridges, dams could not be designed without the fundamental principles of statics, nor could an automobile, a railroad, or an airplane. For even though they are moving, they are in *equilibrium* when they are moving at constant speed along a straight course. It is only when they make turns, speed up, or slow down that one must call on the theories of *dynamics.* Dynamics, therefore, covers motion, particularly uneven motion, such as acceleration, rotation, vibration, and impact. No real bodies are truly rigid—they all deform under load, some materials more so than others. It is logical to next study the statics and dynamics of *deformable bodies,* often called *strength of materials,* for it is concerned not only with how much such bodies change shape but also when and how they break. Of course, a knowledge of the properties of various materials is essential for the practical use of strength of materials.

The most easily deformable bodies are liquids and gases (often combined under the name *fluids*). They are so easily deformable, so different from rigid bodies, that entire new theories are needed to describe their behavior. These theories are usually combined in *fluid dynamics*. A special offshoot of fluid dynamics is *aerodynamics* or *gas-dynamics*, which, as the name implies, deals with gases only.

All these courses are applications of the area of physics called *mechanics*. Two other areas have had a vast influence on engineering. These are *heat* and *electricity*. Heat is the subject of *thermodynamics*, the study, particularly, of the conversion of heat to mechanical work and vice versa. It is the background for almost all our power generation, whether from coal or oil or gas, whether in a power plant or an automobile engine. Closely related to thermodynamics is the

Physics—the science that deals with matter and energy in terms of motion and force.
Random House Dictionary, 1967

When Newton saw an apple fall, he found . . .
A mode of proving that the earth turn'd round
In a most natural whirl, called "gravitation"
And thus is the sole mortal who could grapple,
Since Adam, with a fall or with an apple.
LORD GEORGE GORDON BYRON
Don Juan, 1788–1824

6-39
The principles of mechanics are useful in analyzing bodies in motion.

A man who has tried to play Mozart and failed, through that vain effort comes into position better to understand the man who tried to paint the Sistine Madonna, and did.

GERALD WHITE JOHNSON
A Little Night Music, 1937

6-40
Model of the proposed accelerometer.

subject of *heat transfer,* which teaches how heat flows between fluids, and from fluids to solids.

Engineering courses in electricity usually start with an understanding of *direct* and *alternating current circuits,* with the elements of current, voltage, and charge, and how resistances, capacitances, and inductances affect them. Inseparable from electric-circuit theory is an understanding of *magnetic theory.* From here electricity leads either to the field of *electric power* generation, transmission, and use, or into *communication,* the large field that has created the telephone, radio, TV, radar, sonar, and countless other devices.

To illustrate how an engineer might use some of these theories and to show why an understanding of them is important, let us show how an engineer might deal with a particular problem. (A related, and more sophisticated problem,[10] is given in Appendix VIII.)

The problem is not difficult, and our discussion of it may therefore appear to be unduly long. Our purpose is to make clear not only what an engineer might do at each stage of the solution, but why he might do it.

We shall suppose that the engineer is faced with the task of analyzing a form of accelerometer, which an inventor has proposed for use in an automobile, and making a recommendation concerning its development. The inventor has submitted a model [6-40] to demonstrate his proposal. The device is a glass tube bent into a rectangular U shape and containing colored liquid. It is to be mounted in the automobile with the lower part of the tube fore and aft and the side parts vertical. The inventor says that, if the car moves at constant velocity, the liquid in each of the two vertical arms has the same height; if the car is accelerating, the liquid rises in one arm and falls in the other; if the brakes are applied and the car decelerates, there is again a difference of levels, but the direction of the change is reversed. The change of level in one vertical tube as read against a scale gives the amount of acceleration or deceleration. Thus, the proposed instrument should be useful in testing the ability of a vehicle to accelerate or the capacity of its brakes to stop it. There is a rubber connection across the top of the U with a clamp to impede the air flow when the levels are changing, for the purpose of damping out the oscillations that occur when the acceleration changes suddenly and that interfere with the reading of the instrument. The inventor believes that making the bottom horizontal tube larger than the vertical ones makes the instrument more sensitive; that is, it gives a greater change of level for a given acceleration.

The engineer wishes to determine whether the device is operable in the way that the inventor claims. We shall suppose that he has neither seen nor heard of such a device before, but, in the basic

[10]Both problems adapted from D. W. Ver Planck and B. R. Teare, Jr., *Engineering Analysis,* New York: Wiley, 1954, by permission.

science and engineering of his education, he has studied principles that will be useful in handling the problem. One characteristic of this problem *that is typical* is that numerical data are not given to the engineer, but he himself must supply what he needs.

To come to grips with the situation, the engineer thinks about the physical implications of the inventor's claims, and as his thoughts develop he jots them down somewhat as follows:

Evidently the device is responsive to acceleration, for if it is accelerated horizontally the liquid certainly will tend to back up into the rear tube and out of the forward one, thus giving a difference in liquid levels that might be read against a scale. Such a difference in level, however, could also result from other influences:

1. Tilting of the base.
2. Difference in capillarity in the two side tubes.
3. Difference in air pressures on the two free surfaces.

For a first analysis assume that these influences are not present. That is, assume that

1. Base remains horizontal and the acceleration is horizontal. Vertical tubes identical so that surface-tension effects cancel.
2. The air pressures above the two sides have equalized.

With these assumptions the problem is: How is difference in the liquid levels related to acceleration?

Now let us pause to see what the engineer has accomplished so far. In the first place, he has reduced vague wonderings such as "Is the device any good?" or "How does it work?" to a single definite question capable of a specific answer, which will be just what he needs to know. Second, by making simplifying assumptions he has stripped away all but what he believes are the determining factors. This does not mean that he intends to ignore the other factors; rather he is reserving them for consideration after focusing his whole attention on what seems to him at this stage to be the essential problem. He has built the first conceptual model. Using this model, the engineer goes on organizing his thoughts and writing them down to keep them straight:

Consider the horizontal portion of the liquid when the car is accelerating. If there were no net force on it, there would be no acceleration and the car would move away from the liquid, which would back up into the rear vertical tube. Evidently, this creates a greater pressure at the rear end of the tube and provides the unbalanced force to keep the liquid accelerating with the car. To find how this force depends on acceleration, apply Newton's law $f = ma$ to the liquid in the horizontal tube.

The engineer is mindful that Newton's law in this form applies not only to rigid bodies but also to liquids, provided the acceleration is that of the center of mass.

Continuing his planning, the engineer writes

Since the liquid is at rest relative to the tube, there will be no shearing forces between it and the glass surfaces. Also, the pressure acting across these surfaces gives no resultant horizontal force on the liquid, because the axis of the tube is horizontal and its cross section is uniform. Thus the only horizontal forces acting on the liquid mass are those supplied by the pressures at the ends.

The engineer now begins to carry out his plan for solution by sketching the diagram of [6-41], showing the liquid in the horizontal tube as a free body and the horizontal forces acting on it. This is the second model.

In doing this he is confronted with the desirability for another simplification, and he makes it:

Neglect the effects of the corners of the tube by treating the liquid body as a cylinder extending between the center lines of the vertical tubes.

Now he is ready to state explicitly how Newton's law of motion applies, and he writes

The difference of the forces at the two ends of the liquid, which result from the columns of liquid in the vertical arms, is equal to the product of the mass of the liquid in the horizontal tube by its acceleration, which is the acceleration of the instrument.

Referring to this statement of Newton's law as applied to his particular case and aided by the free-body diagram, the engineer writes an equation[11] in mathematical form:

$$f_1 - f_2 = ma \hspace{3cm} \text{Equation A}$$

f_1 = force on left end of the liquid, positive when exerted to the right (pounds).
f_2 = force on right end, positive to the left (pounds).
m = mass of the liquid in the horizontal tube (slugs).
a = acceleration of the liquid (same as that of tube), positive to the right (feet per second^2).

Notice that in starting to execute his plan for solving the problem the engineer did not try immediately to write a mathematical equation. Instead he proceeded in two distinct steps. First he constructed

6-41
Free-body diagram of the liquid in the horizontal tube.

[11] In this example we have assumed that the reader is familiar with a few basic physical principles, such as Newton's law, the pressure of a fluid on its container, and the units of mass and force.

the model. To it he then applied the physical law by writing a clear statement in words using the free-body diagram to help him visualize. Then with the physical truth clearly set down before him, he translated it into a mathematical equation, carefully defining the symbols and positive directions. A formulation in mathematical terms involves two different functions: applying a physical law and using arbitrarily defined symbols and coordinates. When both these functions are performed together, there is far greater chance for confusion and consequent error than when they are separated. Particularly in a problem that taxes your capacity to the limit, the complexity of doing these two things at once may make the difference between success and failure. Accordingly, good professional engineering method demands separation of the two functions. Application of physical law is accomplished by making a statement in precise English telling exactly what the chosen principle implies in the particular case at hand. Definition of symbols and arbitrary choice of coordinates is then made a separate matter, and the final translation into mathematics is relatively easy.

Having established equation A the engineer considers how he can put it in a useful form. He wishes to express the differences in forces $f_1 - f_2$ in terms of difference in height of the vertical columns of liquid. To do this he writes

The force is average pressure times area, therefore,

$$f_1 = p_1 A$$
$$f_2 = p_2 A$$

Equation B

A = cross-sectional area of the horizontal tube (square feet).
p_1 = average pressure over the cross section at the left end of the tube (pounds per square foot).
p_2 = (similarly) the pressure at the right end.
Thus

$$f_1 - f_2 = (p_1 - p_2)A$$

Equation C

But the difference in pressures at the two ends $(p_1 - p_2)$ is proportional to the difference in heights of the two vertical liquid columns; that is,

$$p_1 - p_2 = \rho g H$$

Equation D

ρ = mass density of the liquid (slugs per cubic foot).
g = acceleration of gravity (feet per second²).
H = difference in height (feet) shown in the sketch [6-42], the difference being taken between corresponding points on the meniscuses.

6-42

Here the engineer has neglected, perfectly properly, the pressure differential associated with the air column of height H in the right-hand tube. Going on with his work, he combines equations C and D with equation A and writes

$$\rho g H A = ma \qquad \text{Equation E}$$

but the mass m is density ρ times volume of the horizontal tube; thus

$$m = \rho A L \qquad \text{Equation F}$$

L = length of the lower tube (feet).

The engineer also defines L on his sketch [6-42], and going on he substitutes equation F into equation E and solves for H:

$$H = \frac{\rho A L}{\rho g A}\, a$$

$$= L \frac{a}{g} \qquad \text{Equation G}$$

Since the vertical tubes have been assumed identical in section, the rise of liquid in one will equal the fall in the other, and each will equal $H/2$. Then

$$h = \frac{La}{2g} \qquad \text{Equation H}$$

where h is the rise of the liquid in the left-hand tube above its level when the acceleration is zero.

The left member of equation H represents a change of level on one of the scales of the instrument, and, according to the equation, is proportional to the acceleration as the inventor claims. The engineer, however, does not stop here, for in his analysis he deliberately ignored various factors that may affect the final conclusion significantly. Moreover, at this point he is not yet sure that there may not be errors in his analysis of even the simplified case which he has treated. So he goes on with his thinking and writing.

The result checks dimensionally.

By this he means that the terms of the equation each measure the same kind of physical quantity, in this case length. The term on the left is defined as a length; the right member is a length L multiplied by an acceleration a and divided by another acceleration g, and hence also has the dimensions of length. Thus the equation is dimensionally homogeneous, as it should be.

The result (equation H) says that if a is zero, h will be zero, and as a increases h also increases as it should.

If L is zero, h is zero no matter what the value of acceleration. This is correct because with $L =$ zero there would be no horizontal body of liquid to accelerate, hence no difference in heights would be brought about.

In each of these checks the result agrees in a special case with what is concluded by direct physical reasoning for the special case. These checks and the test for dimensional homogeneity are powerful means for detecting such errors as the misplacement or omission of factors. The engineer is aware, however, that he has not positively established that his result is correct. For example, is the numerical factor $\frac{1}{2}$ in equation H correct? To assure himself on this and similar points, he reviews all his analysis, carefully going over it step by step from the beginning.

As the engineer reexamines his work, he collects the simplifying assumptions he has made and keeps alert to detect any additional assumptions that may be implied in his analysis. He jots down his assumptions with remarks about their effects.

1. Base and lower tube are horizontal. This is not an important limitation because the instrument can be mounted to permit leveling, or, if necessary, the analysis can be redone for the case in which the instrument is not horizontal.
2. Vertical tubes identical. This assumption was introduced so that the effects of capillarity would balance, but, since the reading of the instrument can be made on one scale as the difference in two positions of the meniscus, the assumption need not have been made. If, however, the tubes are of unequal area, the rise of liquid in one would not equal the fall in the other, but the analysis could be modified to take this into account if necessary.
3. Transient effects have been neglected. The analysis assumes the acceleration to be constant or to be changing very slowly. Actually, there would be transient effects such as there are in many measuring devices. Whether or not these effects would be serious in this case would require further study.
4. The horizontal tube is assumed uniform in section and straight throughout its length, but its section need not be the same as that of the vertical tubes. This analysis does not hold if the horizontal tube is of nonuniform section between the planes where the vertical tubes join it.

By this systematic examination of what he has done, the engineer not only has gained further assurance that his analysis is sound but he has also checked to see what limitations are imposed by his assumptions. Also, he has learned a good deal about the significance of his result in relation to what he is trying to find out. He is now in a position to draw his analysis to a conclusion, and does so by writing the following general statements.

Change in height of either vertical liquid column is directly proportional to acceleration as the inventor claims.

In addition to the change in height, only two other quantities need be known to determine the acceleration: the horizontal distance between the vertical tubes, and g.

The result is independent of density of the fluid, although density may influence the transient response.

Contrary to the inventor's opinion, the sensitivity is independent of the diameter of the horizontal tube.

With this generalization by the engineer, let us turn from the study of the accelerometer to a study of the main features of his method of analysis. In the first place it should be pointed out that there are other more sophisticated ways of analyzing the U-tube accelerometer that may seem to arrive at a solution more quickly or precisely. Judgment, taste, and the engineer's background will determine which he chooses. We have chosen the particular approach here because it employs very elementary principles. This possibility of alternative schemes of approach is typical of most engineering problems.

An important characteristic of the work is the completeness with which the engineer wrote out his thoughts about the problem and his analysis of it. This writing is not a report to communicate the findings to someone else; it is a careful record of the analysis that the engineer made for himself as he went along to keep his thinking consistent and orderly.

We can summarize by saying that the analysis of this problem proceeded in five distinct stages: defining the problem, planning a way to solve it, executing the plan, checking the work, and, finally, learning and generalizing from what was done. These five stages characterize the professional method. They are illustrated further in Appendix VIII by a more difficult example of the design of an electrical accelerometer.

testing

The construction of a model and its analysis are based on assumptions, and these assumptions have to be verified.

One way in which the engineer can accomplish this is by the use of experiments. Experiments do not necessarily require construction of the entire design but only those portions of it that are important for the evaluation of the particular assumption. Components of a design are frequently tested instead of testing the entire design. If, in the design of a pipeline, the strength of the pipe is questionable, the engineer could obtain short sections of the pipe for testing. In the laboratory, liquid of appropriate density and pressure could be pumped through these sections of pipe to simulate the flowing fluid in the line. By measuring how much the pipe expands under the pressure and observing whether the results check with the calcula-

6-43
The strength of materials used in the design may be verified by pulling a sample to destruction.

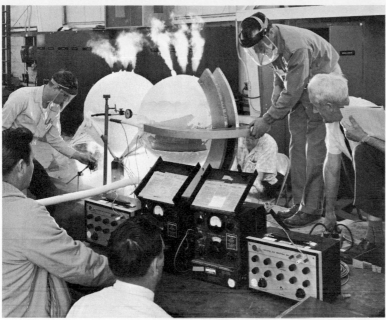

6-44
". . . a model, a testing facility, and an arrangement of instruments . . . ."

tions of his model, the engineer can verify if he has selected the proper pipe for his design.

It is important to remember that the value of the experiment is in the checking of the validity of the assumptions, not in checking the accuracy of the algebra. There is no need to run a rigid wheel on a rigid flat surface to prove the validity of the cycloidal motion of a point on the rim. If, however, the equation is to show the motion of a rubber-tired vehicle, it may be well to run a rubber-tired wheel over a rigid surface to see how closely the cycloid does describe the motion of the nonrigid wheel.

For testing, one needs a model, a testing facility, and an arrangement of instruments suitable to measure what occurs during the test. Above all, one needs a test plan, just as a traveler needs direction to get to a desired destination. There is no sense in beginning a test without an objective and a plan for achieving the results necessary to satisfy that objective.

To test a completed design, the engineer should specify the characteristics that are most important and the instruments to be used for measuring these characteristics. In selecting the instruments the engineer must ask himself the question: "Does it provide the accuracy I need?" There being no such thing as *absolute* accuracy, the engineer must also know the tolerable error in the measurement. Only if that accuracy is greater than his allowable error is the instrument suitable. He is concerned also with the effect of the measurement on the performance itself. This is very important in the case of small, intricate devices requiring great accuracy. According to

If you can measure that of which you speak, and can express it by a number, you know something of your subject; but if you cannot measure it, your knowledge is meager and unsatisfactory.

LORD KELVIN

There is no experiment to which a man will not resort to avoid the real labor of thinking.

SIR JOSHUA REYNOLDS

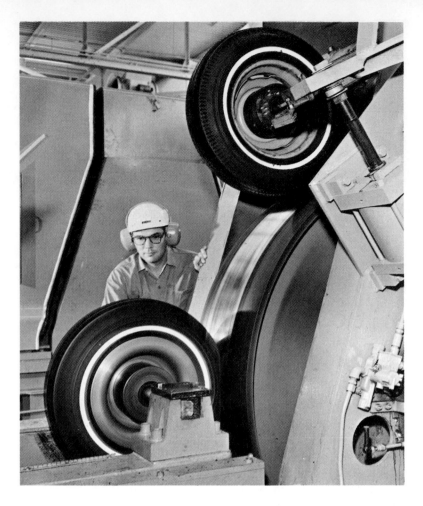

6-45
A rubber tire deforms when running.

We must never make experiments to confirm our ideas, but simply to control them.

CLAUD BERNARD
Bulletin of New York Academy of Medicine, 1928

Heisenberg,[12] we cannot measure any characteristic without affecting the system. (We all know this to be true from our experience in a physician's office. Our pulse rate and blood pressure quite often change as soon as the doctor starts to measure them. Whether this is psychologically or physically conditioned does not really matter; the fact is the measurement *does* influence the performance.)

The conditions under which tests are to be conducted must be defined; these must include all the important conditions of the design. A list of characteristics that might be tested include start-up and shutdown conditions, operation under partial and full load,[13] opera-

[12]W. K. Heisenberg (German physicist, 1901–) showed that, since observation must always necessarily affect the event being observed, this interference will lead to a fundamental limit on the accuracy of the observation. *Encyclopedia of Science,* New York: Harper & Row, 1967.

[13]Whenever we talk about *load,* we mean this in the general sense to include such things as force, pressure, voltage, vibration, amplitude, temperature, and corrosive effects.

6-46
Prototype testing of a helicopter rotor.

tion under the failure of auxiliary equipment, operator errors, material selection, and many, many others.

There are five frequently used objectives for engineering tests. These objectives determine

1. Quality assurance of materials and subassemblies.
2. Performance.
3. Life, endurance, and safety.
4. Human acceptance.
5. Effects of the environment.[14]

Some tests are required on every design and, in certain cases, all the tests are needed. In general, when the analysis has been com-

[14] The effects that the design or process has *on* the environment, whether or not it pollutes air, water, or soil, has been a major concern for engineers only in the last few years. Pollution effects are described in Chapter 1 and beginning on page 245 in this chapter.

6-47
Subassembly testing on a computer module.

pleted, a prototype model of the design will be constructed. Usually this model is subjected to all the necessary tests. Once the prototype has passed the tests and the design has gone into the production stage, each final product may be subjected to selected tests. In this case, the tests are primarily for the purpose of assuring product uniformity and reliability.

Prototype testing generally applies only to products that go into mass production, such as the automobile wheel. When the design is for a one-of-a-kind item, such as a pipeline, one will make as many tests as possible on raw materials and subassemblies to detect design errors before construction is completed. However, final tests on the complete design still will be necessary to *ensure* its safety and acceptability.

Quality Assurance Tests

Anyone who has selected wood at a lumberyard knows that the quality of raw material varies substantially from one piece to the next. It is less well known that such variations occur also in other materials, such as metals, ceramics, and polymers. Variation in these materials may be as great as the variation between the pieces of wood at the lumber yard and, just as the lumberman will provide more uniform wood at a higher price, so one can get a more uniform steel, aluminum oxide, or plexiglas at a higher price (to pay for preselection by the manufacturer). Typical variations in the strength of metals are shown in Appendix III.

The competent designer should account for this type of variation—either by designing the part so that it will perform satisfactorily with the least desirable (weakest) material or by prescribing tests that would ensure that only premium materials be used. Both approaches add to the cost. The conservative design may require more material and more weight, the testing process may require the use of more expensive material, or the extra cost may result from the testing and the discarding of unusable pieces.

Manufacturers, like lumber dealers, have realized the need for uniformity in engineering materials. For this reason, materials with more uniform properties than standard, or with guaranteed minimum properties are available (at higher prices). For example, one can buy electrical carbon resistors in three ranges: the first grade, indicated by a gold band, varies a maximum of 5 per cent from its indicated value; the second grade (silver band) may vary as much as 10 per cent; and the standard product (no band) may vary as much as 20 per cent. Typically, a silver-band resistor will cost twice as much as the standard, and the gold four times as much. Quality assurance includes the checking of dimensions of completed parts (a type of inspection routine in most modern machine shops), tests on the quality of joints between two members, whether welded, brazed, soldered, riveted, or glued, and the continuity of electrical circuits.

What has been said about raw materials is also true for components and subassemblies that the designer may wish to include in his design. Electric motors, pumps, amplifiers, heat exchangers, pressure vessels, and similar items are designed to certain manufacturing standards. The products will usually be constructed at least as well as the manufacturer claims. However, if the quality of the total design depends critically upon the specifications of a subassembly, it is best to inspect and test that subassembly separately before it is included in the construction. This is particularly true for one-of-a-kind designs, such as space capsules. Since the performance of the capsule is critically dependent upon that of its components, the designer must specify a series of tests that will be made at the manufacturers' plants to assure acceptability. He may, in fact, personally supervise the testing.

Performance Tests

A performance test simply shows whether a design does what it is supposed to do. It measures the skill of the engineer and the validity of the assumptions made in his analyses.

Performance testing generally does not wait until the design is completed. It follows step by step with the design. For example, the heat shield of the space capsule is tested in the supersonic wind tunnel to see if it can withstand the aerodynamic heating for which it was designed; the parachute is tested to see if it supports the capsule at just the right speed; structural members are tested for strength and stiffness; and instruments are checked to show if they indicate what they are supposed to measure.

6-48
All new products, such as this improved golf club, should be tested in use and their performance measured.

6-49
"Life" testing on a vibration table.

6-50

Performance tests may require special testing apparatus, such as supersonic wind tunnels and space-simulation chambers. They always need careful planning and instrumentation to assure that the tests measure what is really needed—a proof of the validity of the design.

Life, Endurance, and Safety Tests

We know that machines, like people, age. One of the most important and most difficult tests from which to gain meaningful data is the life test, a test that tells how long a product will survive in service and whether it can take excessive loads, misoperations, and other punishment without failure. It is rarely possible to carry out life tests accurately, for one seldom has the time to subject the prototype to the same period of aging that the real part will experience in actual service. In some instances, accelerated life tests are used. Paints and other surface protections may be exposed to the actions of sunlight, wind, rain, snow, or saltwater spray for months or even years. In this way a body of knowledge relating to the life of these surface finishes slowly develops. Since an engineer cannot always wait for the results of life tests under real loads, these tests must be accelerated, and the engineer does so by increasing the load, by applying the load more rapidly, or by subjecting the design to a more severe environment. However, he is never quite sure how accurately these short term life tests *really* represent the effect of the aging conditions and how their results should be interpreted. Usually, this is done (in the case of mechanical tests) by making tests on several specimens, each at a different degree of overload. The length of life of each part tested is then plotted as a function of the applied load, and the resulting curve is extrapolated to the maximum load that the part is expected to endure in real life.

If different types of loading are applied to the part, such as pressure, temperature, and vibration, it may be necessary to make separate tests with overloads in each one of these areas to see how they extrapolate to "true life." It may be desirable to use overloads in combination and observe if the combined effect is different from the sum of the effects of the individual loads. Very often two combined loads have a much more serious effect on the part than the arithmetic sum of the separate effects of the two loads. This is called *synergistic behavior.*

We again use the automobile wheel for an example of life testing. It is reasonable to assume that a good automobile tire and wheel should survive without failure at least 50,000 miles under normal loads, at speeds of 50 miles per hour. This means that the tire must be tested at that load for at least 1,000 hours—a period in excess of 40 days of uninterrupted testing. Such a test may indeed be possible and, in fact, is often performed on new tire designs. But the designer will want to know also the effects of overload, of speeds higher than 50 miles per hour, of curves, rough roads, under- and over inflation, and of the effect of very high or very low temperatures. It is easy to see that one needs a battery of testing machines and testing times much shorter than 40 days to find out all he will want to know within a reasonable period of time.

Even though the test part may pass the predicted life during the test without failure, the test is usually not terminated, but is continued until the part actually fails. This then becomes an endurance test, and it determines the excess life of the part. Since the life of each part is likely to differ, and since not every part can be life tested, it is essential to know the excess life of the average part. Since there is a statistical variability between parts, the engineer will want to know not only the *average* excess life but also the range in *variation* in this lifetime.

Instead of measuring the endurance of a part under a constant load, the engineer may decide to increase the load until the part fails. This failure load will be higher than the design load if the part is properly designed. The ratio between the failure load and the design load is called the *factor of safety*. Factors of safety may be quite low when parts are very carefully manufactured, when excessive weight is undesirable, or when their failure causes no serious hardship. However, when human life is at stake, factors of safety must be so chosen that no variation in materials or workmanship, or simplified assumption in the designer's calculations, can possibly make the part unsafe and cause failure under normal operating loads.

Because the engineer has the responsibility to see that no one is injured as a consequence of his design, he must also consider the possibility of accidental or thoughtless misoperation. For example, the automobile tire may be underinflated, it may be operated under too heavy a load, at too high a speed, or on a rough road, and yet it should not fail catastrophically.

6-51
Impact testing of automotive safety devices.

6-52
A newly designed windshield "header" will provide additional protection for front-seat passengers.

Human Acceptance Tests

For a long time the designers of consumer goods have been concerned with the appearance and acceptability of their product to the buyer. It is unfortunate that in many instances they have appealed more often to the buyer's baser instincts, such as pride, greed, and desire for status, rather than to his sense of quality and beauty. Engineers, on the other hand, have been concerned too little with the interaction of their designs with the people who buy or use them. They have often failed to ask themselves whether the physical, mental, and emotional needs and limitations of the human being permit him to operate the machine in the *best* possible way. In the past engineers have all too often assumed that the human body is sufficiently adaptable to operate any kind of control lever or wheel. Although the adaptability of people is truly astonishing, we now know that for maximum efficiency levers and wheels must be carefully designed, that the forces necessary to operate them must be neither too large nor too small, that the operator should be able to "feel" the effect that he is producing, and that the use of the device or design should not tire him physically. A new design, then, should be tested with real people. Such tests usually cannot be performed by an engineer alone, but require the aid of others, such as industrial psychologists and/or human factors engineers.

Those who have studied mental processes have found that a man's attention span is short, that he cannot be asked continually to peer at a gage or work piece unless things are "happening" to it. It is also known that warnings are better heeded if they are audible than if they are visual. If they are visual, a bright red light or a blinking

6-53
". . . our emotions are influenced . . . by our opinion of the design."

light that draws the operator's attention is much better than the movement of a dial to some position that has been marked "unacceptable." In recent years we have learned that our emotional responses play a major part in our daily lives, that elation or depression can affect the quality of our work and the attention we give to the instruments we are asked to observe, or the levers we are asked to operate. In turn, our emotions are influenced by color, beauty, or attractive design—in short, by our opinion of the design.

The purpose of acceptability testing is to see whether the design meets the physical, mental, and emotional requirements of the average person for whom it is designed. Since the "average" person can never be found, it is essential that a series of tests be made by and with different people, and that these observations be used to make whatever changes are necessary to make the device as acceptable as possible within the technical and economical constraints.

Environmental Tests

The environment is the aggregate of all conditions that surround the design under operating conditions. It may be air, wind, and weather; it may be the soil in which it is buried or the chemicals in which it is immersed; it may be the vacuum of outer space or an intense field of nuclear or electromagnetic radiation. In general, the operating environment is different from the normal environment in the laboratory in which the tests are made. Sometimes the effects of the environment are not important, but more frequently the environment can strongly affect the functioning and life of the part.

6-54
Rocket engine testing in a cold chamber.

Therefore, environmental testing has become an important part of the final testing of most new products.

We have already mentioned how paints and other surface finishes are exposed to sun, wind, and rain for long periods of time, thereby developing a considerable body of knowledge concerning how such surface finishes behave under both normal and unusual weather conditions. Similarly, an extensive body of knowledge exists on how chemicals deteriorate or corrode construction materials. These and other environmental factors are under continuing study. Therefore, unless the engineer is faced with an unusual environment, he can often (but not always) find pertinent information in the literature to predict how a particular environment is going to affect his design.

However, there are many instances when additional tests are needed. Tests are particularly important if two or more environmental effects work together, such as moisture and heat, or chemicals and vibrations. The result of such effects may not be predictable from either of the individual effects acting by themselves. Thus we know that a vibrating environment in a salt-spray atmosphere can cause corrosion fatigue at a rate far higher than that which might have been predicted from either the vibration or the saltwater corrosion taken independently.

With the advent of space travel, one of the most intensively studied types of environment is *space*. When away from the earth's atmosphere, a body in space will be in a nearly complete vacuum, but it will be exposed to a variety of types of radiation and to meteoric dust from which things on earth are normally protected by the earth's atmosphere. The radiation effects may be severe enough to seriously attack electronic circuits and cause deterioration of transistors and other electronic devices. The meteoric dust, though generally quite fine, travels with speeds of 10,000 to 70,000 miles per hour and has sufficient energy to penetrate some of the strongest materials. Within the last few years some ways have been found to simulate in the laboratory both the high radiation and the presence of meteoric dust, and to subject space equipment to these kinds of attack.

the engineer and the environment

We described at some length how the environment—wind, weather, sun—affects engineering design and how to test for these effects. Now we should consider how our engineering designs will affect the environment: the air we breathe, the water we drink, and the land on which we live and grow our food.

Until a few years ago it was assumed generally that air, water, and land were inexhaustible and self-cleansing. It was common practice to throw our wastes into the air or water. As a people we seemed

The engineer, more than any other professional group, is involved with the form and quality of the urban environment, with the condition of our lakes and rivers, with transportation and communications, with water and soil and air pollution, with urban blight, and with the character of man's physical environment as it is rapidly being evolved.

JOHN A. LOGAN

245

Let us not look back in anger, nor forward in fear, but around in awareness.

JAMES THURBER

to care only that such wastes would not spoil our immediate neighborhood. Therefore, we carefully build high smokestacks and injected our effluent into the rivers downstream of our drinking-water intakes. Little did we concern ourselves with what might happen 10 or 100 miles downwind or downstream; little, that is, until our eyes began to smart, our lungs to congest, our rivers to stink and burn, and the land around our cities to be littered with garbage. In addition, our ears are increasingly assaulted by loud and undesired noises, from jackhammers and hot rods, sonic booms and tractors.

All too often the engineer is blamed for bringing about this situation, but such blame is neither justified nor effective. Until recently he was no more aware of the ultimate consequences of industrial pollution than the rest of the population, and even if he had been, his employers were not committed to pay the cost of treating effluents and reducing noise. After all, such malpractices as sweatshops and child labor were accepted conditions until public conscience and legislative action forced their discontinuance. The public outcry about despoiling the environment is now bringing governmental action to force industry to "clean up."

What can the engineer do to help? Is the solution to be found in eliminating technology and industry and returning to a rural existence? We believe not; and not just because we have become accustomed to the comforts and conveniences of a modern technical society, *but because a primitive rural society would mean ultimate*

6-55	6-56
The problem.	A solution.

starvation for most of mankind. No, the solution lies in the creation of innovative and sensible technology, and in engineers who learn to recognize the most frequent causes of pollution and understand how to remove them or make them harmless. Finally, it requires that people be more interested in preserving the quality of their world than in making a quick profit.

Dust and Smoke

The smoke from an open fire or a drive along a dusty road reminds us that our lungs are accustomed to clean air and that they cannot tolerate much dust or smoke. Dust and smoke consist of small solid particles or liquid droplets suspended in the air. The hazard to human health depends not only on the concentration of the particles (the number of units/cubic foot of air) but also on their size and composition. Physicians tell us that the nose is a reasonably effective filter for particles larger than about 2 to 3 microns,[15] but that smaller particles pass through the nose and into the lungs. There they can be absorbed by the blood, react with the lung tissue, or simply irritate the lung. Such tiny particles are difficult to see and hard to measure. They not only are more harmful than the larger, readily visible particles, but they also stay in the air longer than larger ones, which tend to float to the ground and settle out.[16] This has led some air pollution researchers to say, "It's what you cannot see that hurts you." It is now recognized that the engineer must find out not only how much dust or smoke his process produces but also the *size distribution* and the effects on human health if these particles are inhaled. Particle size measurement is a special technology still under development.

How can the engineer remove fine particles or droplets from the air? Of course the best solution is to avoid putting them into the air in the first place. This is possible more often than a first glance might indicate. Lead particles are best removed from automobile exhaust by using lead-free gasoline; some electric power companies can more economically change from coal to oil or natural gas than remove the fly ash from their stacks; some copper smelters are turning to new smokeless electric refining techniques rather than trying to remove sulfur dioxide and particulates from their stack gases.

If we cannot alter the process to make it smoke or dust free, we must trap most of the particles before they leave the plant. This means, first, that the process equipment must be airtight. All the exhaust must be passed through one or more dust-removel devices before it can be let out into the stack. These devices range in complexity from a simple bag filter (similar to the air bag used on most

---

[15]One micron = 10^{-6} meter $\simeq 4 \times 10^{-5}$ inch.

[16]Air suspensions of very fine particles that take a long time to settle out often are called *aerosols*.

6-57
Air pollutants (typical of many a city's atmosphere) are shown here magnified 400 times, where they have been captured on strands of cloth mesh in an air filter.

". . . quite frankly Johnston when I asked you to solve the emission problem from that stack I expected a somewhat more sophisticated solution. . ."

6-58

vacuum cleaners) to electrostatic precipitators in which particles are charged electrically and then attracted to oppositely charged plates, where they settle out. Just which technique would be best depends on the number and size of particles and on how contaminate free the exhaust must be.

Combustion Gases

Man uses energy at ever-increasing rates. Over the last 50 years, global energy consumption has doubled every 10 years, and the leveling off is not in sight. Most of this energy comes from the combusion of fossil fuel[17]—coal, oil, and gas. Only a very small percentage is water power or nuclear (see p. 30). Fossil fuels are hydrocarbons, that is, a mixture of chemical compounds consisting primarily of carbon and hydrogen atoms. (Other chemical elements, notably sulfur, may be present also.) Perfect combustion in air would transform all carbon to carbon dioxide (CO_2) and all hydrogen to water (H_2O). Unfortunately, perfect combustion is not easy to achieve, particularly in internal combustion engines,[18] and some carbon may burn incompletely to form carbon monoxide (CO), while some hydrocarbon may not burn at all. Any sulfur in the fuel will turn into sulfur dioxide (SO_2). Furthermore, high combustion temperatures cause some of the nitrogen in the air to combine with oxygen to form nitric oxide (NO). Therefore, the exhaust of a typical

[17]Fossil—the remains of an animal or plant of a former geological age.
[18]In an internal combustion engine the fuel is burned inside the power cylinder, in contrast to steam engines or gas turbines in which fuel is burned in a separate combustion chamber.

automobile engine contains not only CO_2 and water, but also CO, unburned hydrocarbons, and NO. (It contains little or no SO_2 since gasoline sold in the United States contains practically no sulfur.) A coal-burning power station, on the other hand, usually will emit NO and SO_2 in addition to CO_2 and water, but little CO or unburned hydrocarbon, because these plants usually burn their fuel efficiently and completely.

Generally, water and CO_2 are considered harmless effluents, although there is some concern that a sizable increase of CO_2 in the atmosphere of the earth will cause the earth to heat up more (see p. 16). Yet CO_2 has no direct adverse effect on people, animals, or plants. However, all the other combustion gases are harmful. CO deprives the blood of oxygen; SO_2 forms sulfurous and sulfuric acids that deteriorate lung tissue, plants, and paint—particularly if accompanied by small particulates; NO and the hydrocarbons combine in sunlight to form the eye- and throat-irritating smog first found in Los Angeles and now observed in every big city around the world.

Only partial solutions are known for these problems today. For fixed power plants, sulfur-free fuel could eliminate SO_2. Also, there are chemical processes that will extract SO_2 from the stack gases and convert it to sulfuric acid or elemental sulfur. But these are costly, particularly if there is little SO_2. Lower flame temperatures can suppress NO formation, albeit at the cost of less efficient heat use. For internal combustion engines, in particular for private cars, the first step is enforced maintenance to assure that they will burn the gasoline as efficiently as possible. This not only cuts down on CO and hydrocarbon emissions, but also it will save gas. The next step may be carburetor improvements, the addition of an exhaust reactor to remove NO and/or hydrocarbons, or even the installation of an external combustion engine.

Sewage

For centuries rivers, lakes, and oceans have served man as depositories for his liquid wastes. And indeed the waters of the world have a remarkably large capacity to absorb wastes and to purify themselves. But this capacity is not infinite. When populations started to grow and industry added its oily, acid, or alkaline waste to streams, the waters could not carry these away without severe pollution, as noted in Chapter 1.

Laws against pollution of waterways date back to the beginning of the century. However, they have not been enforced until recently, when the people began to realize that they were irretrievably losing their rivers and lakes as places for swimming or fishing—or even boating.

Industrial liquid pollutants are so numerous that it is difficult to classify them. But they include oily waste from refineries and dilute acids and alkalines from many industrial processes. Conventional

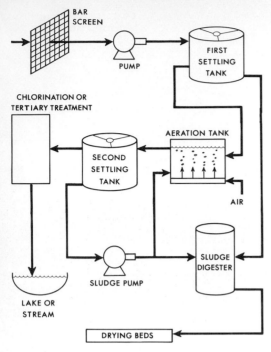

6-59
A sewage treatment system.

techniques for dealing with these effluents are well known. They can all be concentrated and reused—but concentration techniques are costly, and, unless required by law, they will not be undertaken if it is cheaper to dump these wastes into the nearest water way.

Domestic sewage—and some industrial wastes—can be and are treated effectively in modern sewage-treatment plants. The sewage is first filtered to remove the coarser solids. Remaining solids are then allowed to settle out in large settling tanks. The remaining liquid now contains about 1 per cent of organic material, which, if pumped into a lake or river, would cause severe eutrophication (see Chapter 1), that is, growth of plants and algae. This same property is made use of to remove the organics in the *activated-sludge* process. Here a small amount of bacteria is pumped into the sewage (after solids are settled out) and at the same time air is bubbled through the liquid. The combination of air and organic nutrient is readily consumed by the bacteria. At the same time they multiply profusely, and, in doing so, they form clusters big enough to settle out in a second settling tank. Some of the bacteria are thrown away with the solids from the first settling tank; a small amount is recycled to feast on a new load in the aeration tank. The water emerging from the second settling tank is usually chlorinated to kill any remaining bacteria. It is clean enough to use for agricultural purposes or to be discharged into most waterways. It still contains most of the inorganic materials—phosphates, nitrates, and ammonium salts, for example—that originate in detergents, fertilizers, etc. These chemicals may be useful to the farmer, but they make this water unfit for human consumption and also appear to accelerate plant growth if the water is discharged into a lake. A third step (tertiary treatment) is possible to remove even these chemicals and to produce water of drinking quality. It involves the use of activated charcoal filters and more than doubles the cost of sewage treatment. But it is effective in producing water as pure as that of a mountain stream.

Recently, man has become aware that some poisons, notably heavy metals like mercury and cadmium, and certain pesticides like DDT concentrate in the marine food chains. They are taken up from polluted waters by algae and other elementary organisms. From these they go to the small fishes or crustaceans (shrimps, mussels, or sea shells) who live on algae. Larger fish who eat the small ones further concentrate these poisons. Finally, man (or birds who eat these larger fish) can become seriously ill from these concentrated poisons. There is no known method to combat this "chain of action" short of stopping it at the source and preventing the dumping of metallic residues and the use of persistent pesticides.

Solid Waste

Whatever fancy name we may give it, solid waste is garbage. And Americans produced it at a rate of about 5 pounds per person per day in 1970—expected to rise to 8 pounds by 1980. To understand the meaning of this, consider a four-lane freeway between Los Angeles and San Francisco, a distance of about 400 miles. If all the garbage produced in California in 1 year were dumped on this freeway, it would cover the entire 400 miles of roadway to a depth of about 35 feet. Household garbage is about 50 per cent paper and some 25 to 30 per cent food remnants and garden clippings. The rest is plastics, cans, bottles, and other waste.

The world will little note nor long remember what we say here; but it can never forget what they did here. . . .
ABRAHAM LINCOLN
Address at Gettysburg, 1863

6-61
As larger and larger numbers of people move to the cities, unplanned congestion will be the result unless . . .

6-62
. . . we implement carefully designed systems of multiple housing. . .

6-63
. . . to cope with the unique problems that exist . . .

6-64

. . . such as is evidenced in this design for the future

The practice of open-dump burning is rapidly disappearing, for it has contributed greatly to the air pollution problem. Modern disposal practices use either burning in a carefully controlled, municipal incinerator or burying in a sanitary landfill, where alternate layers of garbage and dirt are placed on top of one another. The resultant *fill* has proved to be stable enough to permit the construction of parks and golf courses.

In the vicinities of large cities, landfill sites are becoming scarce and the choice is narrowing to incineration, shipping to distant fills, or recycling the garbage. Recycling means sorting and reusing—the paper for pulp to make more paper, metal and glass for remelting, organic matter for compost and fertilizer. Of course, recycling would conserve raw materials and land best of all. Unfortunately, the cost is still excessive.

Engineering possibilities are only now becoming apparent. Better ways of collecting and moving garbage from centers of population, methods for reclaiming the various components of garbage efficiently and cheaply, and good ways of disposing of those parts that cannot be reclaimed are badly needed, and only engineers can produce them.

Noise

The causes of noise pollution, and its most obvious effect, loss of hearing ability, were discussed in Chapter 1. Not so obvious are psychological problems suspected to be caused or aggravated by noise—and not only audible noise but high-frequency noise beyond the range of hearing.[19] Research concerning such effects is as yet insufficiently conclusive to tell us exactly what noises to permit and which to prohibit and prevent. But, as with so many of man's changes to the environment, we find more and more unsuspected effects—and few of them are beneficial.

Noise is best cured at its source. Examples are the design of better mufflers for cars and motorcycles, the use of rubber-tired wheels for subways (underground railways) in place of steel wheels, and the aerodynamic design of air ducts to minimize sharp corners around which the air can whistle. If the source itself cannot be removed, the next step is to enclose it in a sound-absorbing box or enclosure, so that little of the noise can escape, or to deflect the noise in a direction (such as up) where it will cause no harm. This technique is used in turbine and compressor installations, in test cells for aircraft engines, and along the road through towns with new rapid transit systems.[20] Least effective, although sometimes the only alternative, is to surround the noise recipients, the public, with sound-absorbing

[19] A. Glorig, "Non-auditory Effects of Noise Exposure," *Sound and Vibration*, Vol. 5, No. 5 (May, 1971), p. 28.

[20] V. Salmon, "Noise in Mass Transit Systems," *Stanford Research Institute Journal*, No. 16 (September, 1967), pp. 2–7.

walls or other sound-protection devices. This is done with the control rooms in noisy machine shops, with earmuffs for airplane mechanics, and with soundproofing in houses, apartments, and office buildings in our noisy cities. Acoustically satisfactory building construction is now possible, though it is practiced all too rarely. Occasionally, a harmless but objectionable noise that cannot be silenced can be "hidden" by another, pleasing sound, like that of a splashing water fountain. However, this practice is not recommended unless all else fails.

The Weather

Not all environmental problems are man-made; nature with its typhoons, tornadoes, thunderstorms, hail, and drought causes its share of misery. However, up to now "everyone talks about the weather

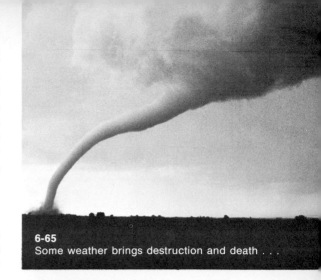

6-65
Some weather brings destruction and death . . .

6-66
. . . while other weather brings the moisture necessary for life.

He gave it for his opinion, that whoever could make two ears of corn or two blades of grass to grow upon a spot of ground where only one grew before, would deserve better of mankind, and do more essential service to his country than the whole race of politicians put together.

JONATHAN SWIFT
Gullivers Travels, 1726

Forewarned is forearmed; to be prepared is half the victory.

MIGUEL DE CERVANTES SAAVEDRA
Don Quixote, 1547-1616

Ich weiss, dass Sie glauben zu verstehen, was Sie denken, dass ich gesagt habe, aber ich bin mir nicht sicher, dass Sie sich klar sind, dass das, was Sie gehört haben, nicht das ist, was ich gemeint habe.

Je sais que vous pensez comprendre ce que vous croyez que j'ai dit, mais je ne suis pas sûr que vous vous rendez compte que ce que vous avez entendu n'est pas ce que je voulais dire.

Sé que crees entiendes lo que piensas que dije, pero no estoy seguro te das cuenta que lo que oíste no es lo que quise decir.

I know you believe you understand what you think I said, but I'm not sure you realize that what you heard is not what I meant.

but nobody does anything about it," as Mark Twain is said to have quipped. This may be changing because of the discoveries of modern *meteorology*. We are beginning to understand how tornadoes form, why some clouds bring rain and others do not. So far this knowledge has helped primarily in predicting the weather. Of enormous help have been the weather satellites, which observe the movement of great air masses over the globe, follow tornadoes in their courses, and give the weathermen an overview they have never had in the past. Beyond predicting, scientists claim considerable success with cloud seeding to produce rain. Understandably, they cannot make rain where there are no clouds, but they have shown that, under certain conditions, they can cause a cloud to shed its water long before it would have done so on its own. The success of these techniques has led to studies on how to bring more water to arid lands. For example, if more precipitation can be caused over the southwestern parts of the Rocky Mountains, there will be more water in the Colorado River, which is the main water source for Arizona, southern California, and parts of northern Mexico.[21]

the report

Now that the engineer has made his model, completed his analysis, tested assumptions and performance, and related his design to the environment in which it must operate, he is ready to report on his activities. Reporting is the process of information transfer. For the engineer the ability to write and speak clearly is most essential, for however good he may be as an analyst or experimenter, if he cannot convey his ideas clearly, concisely, and interestingly to others, then he is like a stranger in a foreign country whose people cannot understand him. The transmittal of information includes writing, drawing, and speaking. Particular attention will be given in this chapter to the preparation of technical papers and to the oral presentation of ideas. Chapters 12 to 17 describe the details of graphics.

Written Reports

There may have been a time when engineers were not required to write reports, that is, when most of them worked with small groups of people and they could let their ideas be known by word of mouth or by circulating an occasional sketch or drawing. These times are gone for all but a very few engineers. Most engineers today work in large organizations. They cannot be "heard" unless their ideas are written down in proposals and their findings are recorded in reports. This does not mean that the spoken word and the drawing

[21]See A. L. Hammond, "Weather Modification: A Technology Coming of Age," *Science*, Vol. 172 (May 7, 1971) p. 548.

or sketch have lost their importance, but rather that they must be supplemented by the written word. Therefore, it is important for the engineer to know how best to communicate his ideas to a reader; how to put his best foot forward with a client whom he may never see, or with the company vice-president to whom he will report.

Although the engineer's writing is often directed toward other engineers, occasionally he may be called upon to write for an audience unfamiliar with technical terms. Then he must be able to express his thoughts in terminology that can be understood by an intelligent layman. During the years to come when engineers must solve the problems of society, such as the urban crisis, air and water pollution, transportation, etc., the need for cooperation between technical and nontechnical persons becomes increasingly important. The engineer must learn to communicate with people of all types of background, and he must be able to state his views clearly and concisely.

So many books have been written about the art of writing, about grammar, syntax, and style, that it would be presumptuous to try here to summarize them in a few words. However, we would like to quote a few phrases from a small but exceedingly valuable book on style.[22] These authors recommend some 21 rules, among which are the following:

Place yourself in the background. Write in a way that draws the reader's attention to the sense and substance of the writing.

Write in a way that comes naturally. But do not assume that because you have acted naturally, your product is without flaws.

Write with nouns and verbs, not with adjectives and adverbs.

Revise and rewrite.

Do not overstate, because it causes your reader to lose confidence in your judgment.

If we can assume that one knows how to write, how to express one's thoughts in words and sentences that are clear to the reader, one still needs to know how to organize one's ideas. Organization is important to the writer so that his ideas will be presented in a logical sequence and to assure that the important things are included in his writing. Organization is important to the reader so that he can follow the presentation and conclusions of the author easily, so that he need not jump back and forth in his thoughts (a tiring exercise for any reader).

Over the years certain minimum conventions (standards) have been established concerning the writing of engineering reports and proposals, conventions that are not binding but have proven to be useful guidelines for technical writers. Let us look at the typical organization of such a report.

[22] William Strunk, Jr., and E. B. White, *The Elements of Style*, New York: Macmillan, 1959.

Organization of a Technical Report

The essential features of the technical report are shown in *color*. The other items *may* appear in the report if appropriate.

Although it appears first in the report, the *abstract* is usually the last item to be written. It is a summary of the summary, containing in less than a page a statement of the problem, the way in which it was solved, and the results and conclusions that were drawn from the work. One may well ask, "Why repeat the contents of the report first in the summary and then again in the abstract?" One reason is the variation in the interest of the readers. One man may have only a general interest in the report and is satisfied with a well-written abstract; the second, wanting to go somewhat deeper, may wish to read the summary and conclusions, and only a few (those particularly interested in the subject) may be sufficiently interested to read the entire report. Yet it is important that all these readers obtain a clear picture of why it was done and what was accomplished. Another reason is the need for some repetition in communication. This attitude is exemplified in the philosophy of the successful southern preacher who, when asked why his sermons were so successful, answered, "Well, first Ah tells 'em what Ah's goin' to tell 'em—then Ah tells 'em—then Ah tell's 'em what Ah done told 'em."

The *Introduction* tells what the problem is and why it was studied. It will discuss the *background* for the study, the literature that pertains to the subject, the solutions that have been tried before, and why these are not adequate for the present investigation. It is here that the majority of the literature references are mentioned. If there are three or less, it may be adequate to list them in footnotes. However, when there are more than three references, it is common practice to list them together in a reference section at the end of the report.

The *body of the report* may have any of a number of titles and may, in fact, consist of several chapters with different titles. The author has considerable latitude here, and he should make use of the titles that appear to him to be appropriate. For example, if the work was essentially analytical in nature, he may wish to entitle the section "Analysis," or he may wish to be more specific and to discuss first the assumptions that were made, then the construction of the model, the pertinent equations, and finally the solution of the equations. If the report contains information on experiments, the writer may wish to discuss the experimental apparatus, the construction of the test model, and the performance and organization of the test. He may then follow it up with a chapter discussing the test results.

The preparation of the body of the report requires considerable judgment. The engineer must provide enough information to give the reader a very clear picture of what was done and to allow him to arrive at the *conclusions* of the report. On the other hand, it is essential that the reader not be bored by unnecessary detail. Many writers find it appropriate to give only the major outline of their work in the body of the report and to relegate all minor details to appendixes at the end of the report even if they are important. This technique gives a report a highly desirable conciseness.

Young engineers often feel impelled to write their reports in the same chronological sequence in which the work was accomplished. This is both unnecessary and undesirable, for very rarely does one proceed in a straight line from the beginning to the finish of his work. Rather one detours down side roads and retraces one's steps. If the report follows the same path of procedures, it will be very difficult to follow. It is much more important to present the data in the sequence that the engineer would have used in his work if he had been knowledgeable of all the difficulties and errors in the beginning. The actual chronological sequence of the study is of little interest to anyone but the author.

It is usually expedient to illustrate the body of the report with tables, charts, graphs, sketches, drawings, and photographs. The old adage that "one picture is worth a thousand words" is often true, but care should be taken to avoid unnecessary illustrations.

Since it is customary to limit the body of the report to facts, the *discussion* section permits a review of the author's opinion. It is as if he were able to stand back and look at the work and say why this or that was done, to speculate on why the results are the way they are and what they might have been if the experiment had been done differently. The discussion sections should anticipate the type of questions the listener would ask and attempt to answer them as forthrightly and honestly as possible.

The *summary and conclusion* is, as the name implies, a concise statement of the work done—including goals, background, analysis, experiment, and a review of the work accomplished. The concise statement of the conclusions reached is most important. For the reader, the conclusions should be the "pot of gold" at the end of

Great is the art of beginning, but greater the art of ending. . . .

HENRY WADSWORTH LONGFELLOW
Elegiac Verse, 1879

Men are more apt to be mistaken in their generalizations than in their particular observations.

NICCOLÓ MACHIAVELLI
Discourses on Livy, 1469-1527

the rainbow, the information that will be directly useful to him. Therefore, the development of meaningful conclusions, well stated, is one of the most important parts in writing a report. They should include all that is new and important, and yet they should be so stated that they leave no question in the reader's mind as to what is incontrovertible fact and what is opinion. Wherever possible the writer should make estimates of the accuracy and repeatability of his results. It is often useful to number the conclusions much as a patent attorney will number the claims in a patent application.

After the conclusions have been written, the author should write the abstract as if it were a summary of the summary and conclusions just finished. Only the most important conclusions need be included in the abstract.

A note on the convention for *references*. In most engineering reports, it is now customary to list the last name of the senior author first, followed by his initials, and followed by initials and names of coauthors. The names are then followed by the title of the report and this by the name of the journal in which it was published, or the publisher and year, in case it is a book. Typical references are as follows:

> Smith, A. B., and T. D. Jones, "Air Pollution at the North Pole," *J. Arctic Society,* Vol. 15, No. 6 (1964), pp. 317–320.
> Beakley, G. C., and H. W. Leach, *Careers in Engineering and Technology.* New York: Macmillan, 1969.

The Proposal

The formal report of a feasibility study may often be in the form of a proposal that suggests how the problem should be pursued. There are many similarities between an engineering report and a proposal, but their purposes are quite different. The report exists to present the results of a study and to present them so clearly and completely that other engineers can use them as stepping stones in the further development of engineering knowledge and use. The proposal, on the other hand, proposes to sell an idea—tries to convince a client or a superior to make funds available for the preliminary design. Thus, whereas the report is written for a general audience, not necessarily all engineers, the proposal is always written for just one person or organization. A proposal is an attempt to sell an idea. Therefore, what is good advice for the salesman is also good advice for the proposal writer: *try to put yourself in the position of the client.* Find out what his needs and wants are and see to what extent your idea meets these needs. Find out who else competes for the funds that might be used to further your idea, and emphasize those special points that make your idea or talents superior to that of others.

There is no general format for the organization of a proposal, but the following order is frequently used.

Typical Organization of a Technical Proposal

Technical Part
    Introduction
    Objectives
    Background
    Method of Approach
    Qualifications
Management Part
    Statement of Work
    Schedule and Reporting
    Cost Estimate
    (Other special paragraphs, for example
        Rights to inventions
        Security provisions
        Time at which work can begin
        Time limit on proposal acceptance)

The proposal is often split into a technical part that discusses the technical aspects and a management part that considers the financial and legal aspects. The first part of the technical portion introduces the reason for the proposed work and clarifies why its solution should be of importance to the potential client. The introduction is followed by a brief statement of the objectives, that is, what the author hopes to be able to achieve by performing the work. This may be followed, if appropriate, by a study of background information, such as the literature surveyed, to indicate that the author is well informed on the subject. Following this, a plan or method of approach is suggested which shows the client that the author has a well-thought-out plan of how he is going to proceed with the work. The method of approach should indicate not only what the author wishes to do, but also what results he expects to obtain from the various portions of his program, what he is going to do if the outcome of the results is as expected, and what if it is not. In conclusion, the technical part of the proposal should include the qualifications of the author or his organization to perform the work.

The management part of the proposal starts with a precise specification of the work. This is followed by the schedule for the work, including the time and type of reports to be presented, and by a cost estimate.

Although many young engineers may believe that fancy covers and big words can sell proposals, it is a fact that the most successful proposals are those that convince the reader of the sincerity and expertise of the writer and his ability to accomplish the objective.

Success depends on three things: who says it, what he says, how he says it; and of these three things, what he says is the least important.

JOHN, VISCOUNT MORLEY of Blackburn
Recollections, 1917

There are three things to aim at in public speaking: first to get into your subject, then to get your subject into yourself, and lastly, to get your subject into your hearers.

GREGG

No man pleases by silence; many please by speaking briefly.

DECIMUS MAGNUS AUSONIUS
Epistolae, 4th century A.D.

Blessed is the man who, having nothing to say, abstains from giving in words evidence of the fact.

GEORGE ELIOT
Impressions of Theophrastus, 1879

Oral Communication

Though most engineers like to talk, too few enjoy speaking. Talking is casual, random, and unrehearsed, but speaking requires a plan, an organization, and practice. Public speaking, like writing, is an art of increasing necessity for the successful engineer, an art that he must perfect if he is to succeed in his profession and his society. In his professional life the engineer will be called upon to present his ideas clearly and concisely to his peers, his supervisors, or the board of directors of the company for which he is working. If he has conducted research or development, he may wish to present the results at a meeting of his professional society. As an effective member of civic, social, and religious organizations, he will want to express his opinions clearly and convincingly.

There is an appreciable difference between effective written and spoken words. The reader can proceed as quickly or as slowly as he wishes, or retrace his steps, and in this way absorb difficult and complicated thoughts. The listener, on the other hand, cannot control the speed of the speaker nor can he retrace his step if he has lost the thread of the remarks. It is important, therefore, for the speaker to retain the interest of his listeners by the conviction of his presentation and by the presentation of a forthright, orderly, and logical sequence of thoughts. The most effective speakers do not try to present more than two or three important ideas in one speech, and they get these ideas across by using clear logic, simple illustrations, and by similes or analogies, knowing that different listeners have different ways of seeing things.

In preparing a speech or oral presentation, first make an outline of the principal ideas that you wish to project. Place them in a logical sequence and prepare your illustrations and similes, but do not attempt to write every word of your speech. Few things are more likely to put an audience to sleep than a speaker who reads his speech. If you tend to be nervous, memorize the first sentence or two, which will get you started, and then use notes only as reminders for the sequence of your talk and to make sure that you have said everything that you wanted to say. Since an audience can best follow simple ideas, it is rarely advisable to present mathematical developments in a speech unless it is to an audience of mathematicians. Nor is it often useful or desirable to delve into the circuitous routes that were used during the development of the idea or the research that is being presented. *The audience is interested in the results and in the usefulness of the results for their own purposes.* All of us are interested primarily in our own life and work, and the better a speaker can convince us that his findings are useful to us, the more successful we believe him to be. Therefore, in preparing a speech, first, find out to whom you will be speaking, and then ask yourself what it is that you can give to the audience that is useful to them. What will they remember after you have stopped speaking?

6-67
Communication is complex. An idea may be transmitted and acknowledged between earth and moon in a matter of seconds, while a similar transmission and acknowledgment between individuals standing within arms length may take years.

6-68
''. . . different listeners have different ways of seeing things.''

6-69
The oral presentation should be well illustrated with model, charts, and pictures.

Short words are best and the old words when short are best of all.

SIR WINSTON SPENCER CHURCHILL

The successful speech, like a successful athletic contest, requires practice and rehearsal. In practicing, use a "sparring partner"—a person not afraid to criticize or interrupt and ask questions when something is not clear. Go over a speech with your "sparring partner" again and again, until you are sure that you could present it even if you lost all your notes.

problems

6-1. List the criteria for an urban transportation system in your town. Assign relative values to each of the criteria.

6-2. It has been found that for comfort train passengers should not be exposed to accelerations or decelerations greater than about 4.5 feet/second^2 in the direction of motion. For urban rapid-transit trains, which must stop every 2 miles, this restriction (and not top speed) sets the limit on how long it takes to get from station to station. So says Mr. L. K. Edwards, president of Tube-Transit, Inc. He proposes instead to dig inclined tunnels and allow gravity to speed up (and slow down) the trains [6-70]. He says he can achieve much greater real accelerations without the passengers' feeling any acceleration at all. He proposes that the slope be about 15°.

6-70

Evaluate the merits of his scheme and find the time it would take between stations 2 miles apart for Edwards' train as against a regular, aboveground train.

6-3. Make a check list and attribute list for each of the following:
(a) house telephone   (d) shower faucet
(b) ironing board   (e) can opener
(c) light switch

6-4.[23] It is proposed to increase the sensitivity of the liquid-level accelerometer discussed on pages 228 to 234 by replacing the air in the upper part with a second liquid having a density less than that of the liquid in the lower part. The two liquids would not mix, for example, kerosene and water, and they would have different colors. It is believed that the sensitivity would be particularly high if the densities of the two liquids were nearly equal. In this modified design the upper horizontal tube would have no constriction, but would be a smooth cylindrical glass tube like the bottom one. Constrictions, if necessary to provide damping, could be put at the tops of the vertical tubes.

Study this proposal and make a recommendation.

[23] Problems reprinted by permission from *Engineering Analysis* by D. W. Ver Planck and B. R. Teare, Jr., New York: Wiley, 1954.

6-5.[24] A modification of the liquid-level accelerometer on pages 228 to 234 has been produced commercially in which one of the vertical tubes has a diameter about ten times that of the other. Is there any advantage in this design?

6-6. Design a new mechanism to deploy the Lunar antenna shown in [6-71].

6-7. Make a literature search and prepare a written and oral report on the following subjects:

(a) Packaging of a TV tube for shipment
(b) Transmission of electric power to a high-speed train
(c) Automatic bicycle transmissions
(d) A speed reduction device (gearbox) with at least 10:1 reduction
(e) Nonslip highway surfacing
(f) Solar-powered refrigeration

6-8. Prepare a two- or three-dimensional matrix of the independent conditions for the problems in (6-7) and show how at least six of the possible combinations might be used.

6-9. (Note to the instructor: The following problems are related. They are intentionally vague and ill defined like most real-life problems. Their purpose is to stimulate creativity and imaginative solutions, to permit students to find out for themselves, make assumptions, test them, compare ideas, build models, and prepare reports—written or oral—to convince a nontechnical audience. Give only as much aid or additional information as you believe to be absolutely essential. Additional problems for this setting may suggest themselves.)

You are a Peace-Corps volunteer (or a small team) about to be sent to a village of about 500 people in a primitive, underdeveloped country. The village lies 3,000 feet below a steep escarpment in a valley through which a raging river flows. The river is about 80 feet wide, 4 to 8 feet deep, and too fast to wade or swim across. On your side of the river there is the village of mud huts in a clearing of the hardwood forest. The trees are no more than 40 feet tall. At the foot of the escarpment there is broken rock. Across the river there is another village, which cannot be reached except by a very long path and a difficult river crossing upstream. There are other villages on top of the escarpment. The people are small, few over 5 feet 6 inches tall. They live mostly by hunting, gathering, and fishing, though they could trade to their benefit with the people across the river and on the escarpment if communication were easier.

Before you leave for your assignment, you should try to find solutions to one or more of the following problems:

(a) How to improve communication, trade, and social contact between the two villages on each side of the river.
(b) How to transport goods easily up and down the escarpment. There is a path up the escarpment, but it is steep, dangerous, and almost useless as a trade route.
(c) Suggest a better way of hunting than the bow and arrows now used. A crossbow has been suggested to be more powerful, easier to aim, and more accurate. Evaluate these claims and provide design criteria.

---

[24]Problems reprinted by permission from *Engineering Analysis* by D. W. Ver Planck and B. R. Teare, Jr., New York: Wiley, 1954.

6-71

(d) Provide for lighting of the huts. The villagers now use wicks dipped in open bowls of tallow. Can you improve their lamps so that they burn brighter, smoke less, and don't get blown out in the wind?

For each of these problems, select criteria for evaluating ideas. Choose several different solutions, check them against the criteria, and pick the best one; develop this idea by analysis and testing until you know how it will work. All the while, keep track of and test your assumptions whenever possible. Finally, prepare a way to convince the villagers of the value of your idea.

bibliography

BLUM, J. J., *Introduction to Analog Computation*, New York: Harcourt Brace, 1968.

STEIN, P. K., *Measurement Engineering*, Phoenix: Stein Engineering Services, 1964.

STRUNK, W., and E. B. WHITE, *The Elements of Style*, New York: Macmillan, 1959.

TOWN, H. C., and R. COLEBOURNE, *Engineering Inspection, Measurement and Testing*, London: Odham Press, 1957.

VER PLANCK, D. W., and B. R. TEARE, JR., *Engineering Analysis*, New York: Wiley, 1954.

WEISS, E. A. (ed.), *Computer Usage Fundamentals*, New York: McGraw-Hill, 1969.

Abstract Journals (a partial listing)

Air Pollution Control Association (APCA) Abstracts
Applied Mechanics Reviews
Applied Science and Technology Index
ASM Review of Metal Literature
British Technology Index
Building Science Abstracts
Chemical Abstracts
Computer Abstracts
Corrosion Abstracts
Current Literature in Traffic and Transportation
Electrical and Electronic Abstracts
Engineering Index
Fuel Abstracts and Current Titles
Highway Research Abstracts
International Aerospace Abstracts
Mathematical Reviews
Nuclear Science Abstracts
Physics Abstracts
Science Citation Index
Scientific and Technical Aerospace Reports (STAR)
Solid State Abstracts Journal
Technical Book Review Index
Water Pollution Abstracts

Concentric hexagonal etch pits in cadmium sulfide, a widely used semiconductor, express the symmetry of the crystal. This photomicrograph was made as part of a study of how dislocations affect electronic properties of compound semiconductors. (Interference of reflected light produced the colors.) Dislocations were found to increase or decrease conductivity of cadmium sulfide by 1000 to 100,000 times. Pyramidal pits are formed by the preferential attack of very dilute hydrochloric acid on the crystal surface, and they mark defects in the crystalline structure of the metal. Etch pits with the most hexagons are the deepest ones—but still are only a few thousand atomic layers deep.

models are simplified, idealized versions of complex systems. Models are used because the human mind works best with simple systems. The mind has great difficulty in analyzing a complex situation and in handling a large number of different influences at the same time. The art of making a model consists in selecting the most appropriate degree of simplification and in assessing the importance of the effects that have been neglected in making the simplification. If important influences are neglected, the model may be misleading; if unimportant matters are included, the model may be unnecessarily complicated and confusing. For example, politicians often oversimplify complex social and economic problems of the nation in order to explain them to the voters. If the models presented are too simple and neglect vitally important ingredients of the problem, then it is likely the remedies proposed will be ineffective or even negative in their effect. Often the incomplete (and sometimes distorted) pictures or models that two nations have of one another can lead them to war. Peace, rather than war, is most likely to prevail in an environment where all parties have realistic models of one another.

Until about 1940, suspension bridges were designed using imperfect models of bridge behavior when they were buffeted by strong winds. Although the presence of wind forces in general had been

When we mean to build, we first survey the plot, then draw the model; and when we see the figure of the house, then must we rate the cost of the erection.
WILLIAM SHAKESPEARE
King Henry IV, Part II, Act I, Sc. 3, Line 41

Seek simplicity, and distrust it.
ALFRED NORTH WHITEHEAD

The battle of Waterloo was won on the playing fields of Eton.
ARTHUR WELLESLEY, DUKE OF WELLINGTON
From Fraser, *Words on Wellington*, 1889

7-1
Models are simplified versions of complex systems.

7-2
Model of a complex chemical molecule.

Moment of failure of the Tacoma Narrows Bridge.

recognized, their *dynamic effects* had not been considered. These effects, however, led to the failure of the Tacoma Narrows Bridge in Washington [7-3] and pointed out the need for research concerning improved methods of bridge design.

scale and test models

Among the most useful and easily understood models are physical or *scale models*, which are used for visualization and experiments. For example, after the failure of the Tacoma Narrows Bridge, scale models of the bridge (and of other suspension bridges) were tested in wind tunnels to find out why and how it failed, to predict which other bridges, if any, were in danger of failure, and to learn how to properly design new ones. The results of these tests showed that the Golden Gate Bridge near San Francisco, which had been built on similar principles as the Tacoma Narrows Bridge, was in fact stable, because it was wider in relation to its length than the Tacoma Narrows Bridge. This was very fortunate indeed, because the rebuilding of that bridge would have been very costly.

There can be considerable differences between wind tunnel models—even between models for the same design, such as an aircraft—depending upon the purpose of the model. There are aerodynamic models to predict the lift, drag, side forces, and turning moment exerted by the air on the aircraft in different flight maneuvers. Such a model can be made of any materials, such as wood,

7-4
Some models are successful . . .

7-5
. . . other models fail.

plastic, or metal, provided only that its shape is correct and that the surface is appropriately smooth. Structural models, used to predict the flexibility or stiffness of wings, tail surfaces, and controls, cannot be made of arbitrary materials but must be constructed carefully so that each model simulates the deflections and vibrations of the real part. Often it is sufficient to simulate only a wing or tail surface in such a test, rather than to make a model of the entire aircraft as is done for aerodynamic models.

When planning a new circuit, electrical engineers often will build a *breadboard* model [7-10], so called because the early radio and telegraphy circuits were fastened to a wooden board. Here tubes and transistors, capacitors and coils, fixed resistors and potentiometers can be displayed in a fashion that simplifies testing and alteration. The initial layout of components is likely to be quite different from the final arrangement, which may need to be as compact and light as possible, vibration and moisture resistant, tamper proof, or perhaps completely "potted" in plastic. Breadboard models assume that the

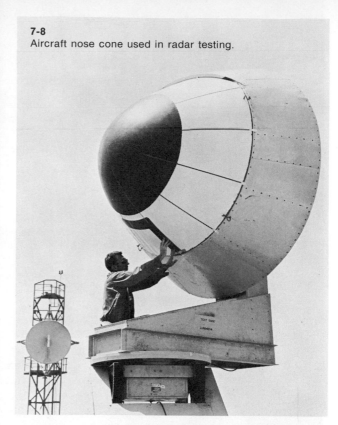

7-8
Aircraft nose cone used in radar testing.

7-7
Aerodynamic model of supersonic aircraft.

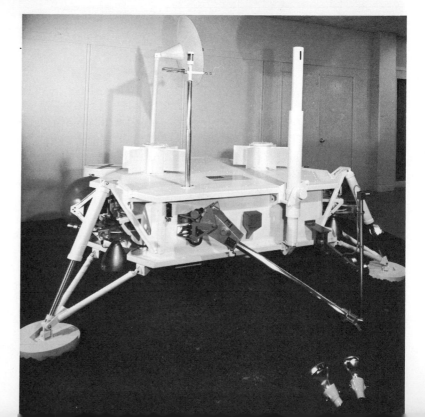

7-9
Model of a Mars landing craft.

272

7-10
Breadboard models.

physical location of the components has little or no influence on the performance of the circuit—a reasonably valid assumption for radios and other low-frequency apparatus—but of questionable validity for high-frequency circuits such as microwave or radar devices.

Scale models of complex plants and factories, such as those used in chemical industries, refineries, and aircraft or automobile manufacturing and assembly plants, are helpful in visualizing how all the pipes, process equipment, conveyor belts, and machines are located with respect to one another. Unless one can "see" the plant in three dimensions, it is difficult to avoid interference between the various pieces of equipment and to assure that there is sufficient working space, that valves and other controls are readily accessible, and that the work or product flows through the plant rapidly and without obstruction. Although scale models, such as the one for the chemical plant [7-11], are costly, they can save many times their costs in

7-11
Scale model of a chemical plant.

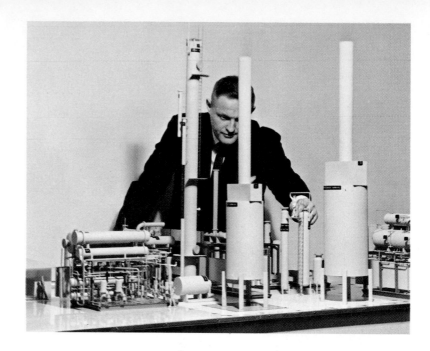

7-12
A spotlight and plastic "cornstalks" can be used effectively to determine optimum spacing of plants.

preventing subsequent corrections in the full-scale plant. The models shown may be made of any convenient material as long as the outside dimensions of all pieces of equipment are made to scale and are in their proper relative location. However, pipes and storage vessels need not be hollow, valves need not work, nor conveyor belts operate. Scale models can be used for many purposes, such as studies in agriculture [7-12].

A quite different type of model, often used in the chemical and petroleum industry, is the *pilot plant*. This model simulates each step of the manufacturing process and actually produces small amounts of the product. Here it is important not that the outside dimensions of pipes, reactors, and storage vessels be manufactured to scale, but rather that the quantities of chemicals used, their respective flow rates, and corresponding temperatures and pressures be scaled properly so that their total effect on product quality and quantity can be measured and evaluated. In addition, the product that is manufactured in a pilot plant often is used to test the consumer market by providing samples to potential customers. Customer reaction then can be used as a guide to predict the size of the full-scale plant.

models for analysis

One of the principal purposes of a model is *to idealize and simplify the problem* so that we can predict the performance of the design. This process is analysis (see p. 221). Analysis requires a simple, yet meaningful, model of the problem to which certain physical laws apply. Often the analysis is expressed in mathematical equations, tables of numbers, or graphical performance curves that express the behavior of the model and make it possible to draw conclusions about the behavior of the real thing, provided the assumptions made in selecting the model were realistic.[1]

A famous historical example has been selected to illustrate this point.[2] Early in the eighteenth century the city of Königsberg, Germany, included seven bridges over the Pregel River [7-13]. A favorite pastime on pleasant Sunday afternoons was to start at some point in the city and see if one could walk in such a path as to cross *each bridge just once*. One could start at any point and end at any point.

In 1736, Leonhard Euler[3] spoiled the future Sunday afternoons of the Königsbergers by answering the question with a simple model —which solved the problem not only for Königsberg but for other localities with any number of bridges. To understand his solution, we should first consider the map of bridge locations. There is an island (marked region C), two sides of the main river (B and D), and a region (A) located between the two sections of the river after it divided.

Euler's solution of the problem becomes obvious if we draw a line model of the real problem [7-14]. In this diagram, each vertex represents a region (A, B, C, or D), and the seven lines represent the bridges. Travel over a bridge *once* is represented by one traversal of a line in the diagram.

Thus, the model [7-14] is simply another way of showing the arrangement of the seven bridges (with each line representing one bridge).

We should determine what property this diagram must have if we are allowed to travel over each bridge once and only once. Suppose that we are asked to follow such a path. Beginning at vertex A, we might proceed first to vertex B. We would then be entering B on one line but would need to leave it on another line. A continuation of this process from vertex to vertex would lead us to conclude that *each time that we desire to pass through a vertex, there must be at least two lines connected to that vertex.*

Since we are not required to start and end at the same point, we

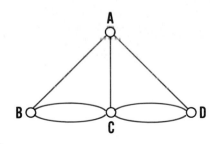

7-13
Seven bridges of Königsberg.

7-14
Line model of 7-13.

---

[1] Often engineers refer to "mathematical models" or "graphical models" when really they mean mathematical or graphical representations of a physical model. This difference may seem to be splitting hairs, but it is preferred that one think of the model as a simplified picture of the real thing—in effect a picture that retains a physical resemblance to reality. Sometimes a mathematical model is called an *algorithm*.

[2] Drawn from *The Man-Made World*, E. E. David, Jr. and J. G. Truxall (eds.), McGraw-Hill, 1971, by permission.

[3] Famous Swiss mathematician, who published an enormous number of articles on all phases of mathematics and physics.

might not necessarily pass through two of the vertices—but rather we could begin at one and end at another. This leads us to the only possible exception to the conclusion previously drawn—*that the starting vertex and the ending vertex may have an odd number of lines connected to them.*[4]

Thus a closed path traversing all bridges is possible only if

1. Every vertex has an even number of lines connected to it (then one would start and end at the same point), or
2. Exactly two vertices have an odd number of lines connected to them (then one would start at one of these and end at the other).

Inspection of [7-14] reveals that the vertices have the following number of lines:

A	3	C	5
B	3	D	3

All four numbers are odd; hence there is no hope of walking over each Königsberg bridge only once, no matter where we start and end and no matter what route we follow.

If one additional bridge were built (or perhaps if we were permitted to swim across the river), the graph would be changed by adding a new link or path between two regions. If the new bridge were built from A to C, a model could be drawn as shown in [7-15]. Now the problem can be solved. (Euler also showed this part of the solution.) In this case only vertices B and D are odd; hence we can start from B, traverse all bridges, and end at D.

Few persons today would be concerned with the crossing of bridges, but there are many contemporary problems of great interest that lend themselves to solution by similar techniques of modeling. For example, you might want to consider the problem of selecting an optimum route from your place of work to your home. It would be impractical to try all possible routes or to hover overhead in a helicopter and view the routes in operation. However, by modeling the problem, a number of alternatives could be examined. The shortest route might be preferred if you were low on gasoline, the quickest route if guests had been invited for an early dinner, the most direct route (fewest stops) if your car's brake linings are badly worn, and the safest route if it is necessary for you to drop by nursery school to pick up your little daughter Sara. Such is the versatility of the modeling process.

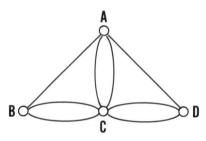

7-15
Königsberg with one additional bridge.

[4]If one starts and ends at the same vertex, every vertex must possess an even number of lines.

7-16

THE DOW-JONES INDUSTRIAL AVERAGES

charts and graphs

Charts and graphs are convenient ways to illustrate the behavior of models and the relationships among several variables affecting a model. We have all seen charts of the fluctuations of the stock market averages in the newspaper from day to day, or you may have had your parents plot your growth up the closet door. In these examples, *time* is one of the variables. The others, in the examples above, are the average value of the stock in dollars and your height in feet and inches, respectively. A chart or graph is not necessarily a model but presents facts in a readily understandable manner. *It becomes a model only when used to predict, project, or draw generalized conclusions* about a certain set of conditions.

Consider the following example of how facts can be used to develop a model and a graphical chart. An engineer wants to test a pump and determine how much water it can deliver to different heights [7-17]. Calibrated reservoirs are placed at several different elevations, and the engineer can direct the flow of water to any of these reservoirs by opening or closing the appropriate valves. Using a stopwatch, he measures the amount of water pumped to the different heights in a given time. See if you can identify the assumptions made. How important are they in understanding the performance of the pump?

His test results are plotted as crosses on a chart [7-18]. So far, the chart is nothing more than a convenient way to represent his test results. Only when the engineer makes the assumption that the plotted points represent the typical performance of this or another pump under similar conditions can the chart be considered to represent a model of the pump. Once this assumption is made, he can

7-17

7-18

HEIGHT OF RESERVOIR

A PLOT OF
TEST DATA

AMOUNT OF WATER PUMPED PER MINUTE

7-19

HEIGHT OF RESERVOIR

A GRAPHICAL
MODEL

AMOUNT OF WATER PUMPED PER MINUTE

draw a smooth curve through the points. With this performance curve as a model, the engineer can predict that if he put additional reservoirs between the actual ones, they would produce results like that shown by the circle [7-19]. He makes this assumption based on his experience that pumps generally behave in a predictable way, and that curves representing phenomena in nature generally are smooth and continuous—for example, the rate at which one's height increases. The stock market, on the other hand, is not a natural phenomenon, and its behavior is anything but smooth.

diagrams

A convenient way to visualize a model is the *diagram*. Typical forms are *block, flow,* and *energy diagrams,* the *circuit diagram* in electrical engineering, and the *free-body diagram* in mechanics.

The *block diagram* is a generalized approach for examining the whole problem, for identifying the main components and describing their relationships and interdependencies. This type of diagram is particularly useful in the early stages of design work when representation by mathematical equations would be difficult to accomplish. Figure [7-20] is an example of a block diagram in which components are drawn as blocks, and the connecting lines between blocks indicate the flow of information or product in the whole assembly. This type of presentation is widely used to lay out large or complicated systems—such as computers, communication or navigation systems, chemical processes, or manufacturing plants. No attempt is made on the drawing to detail any of the components pictured. They are simply shown as a box with a label that tells their function—such as "amplifier," "distillation column," "drill press." They are the origin of the term *black boxes* for components whose function we know, but whose details are not yet designed.

7-20
The relations of component parts of a transistorized telemetering system are best shown by means of a block diagram.

Closely related to the block diagram is the *flow diagram*, often used by chemical engineers and exemplified by [7-21]. Here the blocks are replaced by *unit operations* symbols representative of such equipment as heat exchangers, pumps, distillation columns, and storage vessels. The lines connecting these unit operations represent the flow of liquids and gases. In the example, the heavy line is the main product flow, the others are by-products, auxiliary fluids, or waste. Flow diagrams are also useful in the control room of a chemical or power plant to show the operator visually and quickly where trouble is located when it occurs [7-22].

The *energy diagram* [7-23] is a special diagram used in the study of thermodynamic systems involving mass and energy flow.

Circuit diagrams are representations or models in symbolic language of an electrical assembly. Figure [7-24] shows a circuit diagram

Energy is most usable where it is most concentrated—for example, in highly structured chemical bonds (gasoline, sugar) or at high temperature (steam, incoming sunlight). Since the second law of thermodynamics says that the *overall* tendency in all processes is away from concentration, away from high temperature, it is saying that, overall, more and more energy is becoming less and less usable.

PAUL AND ANNE EHRLICH
Population, Resource, Environment: Issues in Human Ecology, 1970

7-21
Flow diagram of a helium plant.

7-22
Flow diagrams are also used in the control house of a power plant.

7-23
An energy diagram.

7-24
A simple photoelectric-tube relay circuit.

of a photoelectric tube that operates a relay. The diagram details only the essential parts to provide a clear picture of the electrical continuity. A resistance is represented by a zigzag line, the relay by a coiled curve and appropriate contact points, a capacitor by two parallel lines. The arrow across the capacitor indicates that it is adjustable.

The *free-body diagram* is a diagrammatical representation of a physical system that has been removed from all surrounding bodies or systems for purposes of examination. It may represent a complete system or any smaller part of it. This form of idealized model is most useful in showing the effects of forces that can act upon a system.

Figure [7-25] shows a ship moving through the water. It is not necessary that the model of the ship be drawn to scale since the shape of the idealized model is only an imaginary concept.

There are four external forces acting on the model: a forward thrust, which acts at the ship's propeller; a friction drag, which acts so as to retard motion; a buoyant force, which keeps the ship afloat; and the ship's weight, which in simplification may be considered to be acting through the center of gravity (c.g.) of the ship [7-26]. The

7-25
The situation.

7-26
The free-body diagram.

7-27
Actual and idealized designs.

STORAGE WAREHOUSE

ACTUAL

IDEALIZED

BRIDGE

ACTUAL

INDUSTRIAL COMPLEX

ACTUAL

PRAYER TOWER

IDEALIZED

ACTUAL

IDEALIZED

CHURCH

ACTUAL

IDEALIZED

HIGH VOLTAGE TOWER

ACTUAL

IDEALIZED

WAREHOUSE

ACTUAL

IDEALIZED

IDEALIZED

IDEALIZED

symbol ✪ is used to denote the location of the c.g. A coordinate system is very useful for purposes of orientation. The one shown here is horizontal and vertical, and centered on the c.g.

The diagram would make possible an analysis of the relationships between the weight and buoyant force and between the thrust and drag. It would not be useful for determining the loads on the ship's engine mounts. Another free-body diagram of the engine alone would be required for that purpose.

analog models

Analogs and similes are used to compare something that is unfamiliar to something else that is very familiar. Writers and teachers have found the *simile* to be a very effective way to describe an idea. For example, how are you to explain the elementary concepts of electricity when you can neither see nor hear an electric current? You can compare it with the flow of water flowing from one reservoir to another on a lower level. The difference in height (h) corresponds to the voltage difference (E) across the circuit, the rate of flow of water (Q) to the electric current (i), and the function of the valve to the resistance (R) [7-28]. This simile is useful in understanding some simple electric circuits, but, for a number of reasons,[5] the water system is not a good analog of the electric circuit.

Analogs must provide more than a descriptive picture of what one wants to study; their action should correspond closely with the real thing. They should be *mathematically* similar to it; that is, the same type of mathematical expressions must describe well the actions of both systems, the real and the analog [7-29].

A vibrating string is an analog of an organ pipe because the sound in an organ pipe behaves quite a bit like the waves traveling along a vibrating string. Under certain assumptions, similar mathematical equations can describe both systems. In other words, one can compare the corresponding actions of the *model* of the organ pipe with a *model* of the vibrating string. It is the *models* that behave exactly alike, *not the real systems*. If these models are good models, then, under certain conditions, one can perform experiments with the string and draw valid conclusions concerning how the organ pipe would behave. Since one system may be much easier to experiment with than the other, one can work with the easier system and obtain results that are applicable to both.

An example of the use of a very successful analog is the electrical network that forms an analog for complete gas pipeline systems [7-31

I often find, in wrestling with a problem, that analogy helps to change my viewpoint and to draw upon the wisdom of others. Used with caution, analogy can provide a new model and frequently it leads to questions and answers that I have not seen before.

JACK MORTON
Innovation, May 1969

7-28

---

[5] For example, the flow of water through a valve is not truly analogous to the flow of current through a resistor.

7-29
An analog computer uses electrical circuits to stimulate mechanical or chemical phenomena.

7-31
A compressor station.

7-30

7-32
Analog of one of the compressor cylinders in [7-31].

and 7-32]. Using such a model, one can predict just what would happen if a lot of gas were suddenly needed at one point along the system. Experiments with the actual pipeline would be very costly and might disrupt service. The electrical network analog provides the answers faster, cheaper, and without disturbing anyone.

assumptions

If we were able to study and analyze every physical system exactly as it is, or if every model were identical with the real thing, then we would not need to make assumptions. The assumptions are the *differences* between reality and the model. They are the simplifications we introduce to make the model manageable. Usually, the greater the simplification, the more sweeping the assumptions, and the more the model differs from reality. The art of modeling is the art of making the widest possible assumptions that will not violate or obscure the important aspects of the problem.

Sometimes the simplifications in the model are obvious—particularly in hindsight. To replace the bridges of Königsberg with lines, and to represent each land area they connected by a single point at the end of the lines seems obviously permissible, and this simplification leads to the right solution of the problem. Not so obvious was Niels Bohr's model of the atom (p. 220). In fact, the validity of its assumptions were widely disputed by physicists for decades. Today we know from hundreds of experiments which aspects of atomic physics are explainable by the model and which ones are not.

Experiments often are needed to validate assumptions. If a mock-up of the Tacoma bridge had been tested in the wind tunnel before the real bridge was built, the engineers would have found out that wind cannot always be assumed to act like a constant, steady force. All too often we make assumptions out of habit or without questioning, only to find them invalid later on. Who has not measured

Experience is the name everyone gives to their mistakes.
Oscar Fingal O'Flahertie Wills Wilde
1854–1900

and cut a set of shelves for a closet or laid floor tiles on the assumption that the walls were straight and square? Experience, the great teacher, helps us in selecting assumptions, in engineering as well as tile laying. However, reliance on experience alone is not good enough. All assumptions must be scrutinized and tested.

If we can state clearly all the assumptions made, that is, all the ways in which the model differs from reality, then and only then can we devise tests to check their validity or importance. For example, in the pump test model [7-17] we may have assumed that friction in the pipes could be neglected. This assumption can be checked by changing the pipe diameter. If friction was not important, a change in pipe size should not alter the test results significantly.

This raises the new problem of *"what is significant?"* Obviously, a pipe diameter change will cause *some* difference in results. Unless we have first decided what a significant error is, we cannot tell whether it is important or not. The importance of accuracy varies from problem to problem. In an interplanetary rocket, where every ounce of weight and every watt of power is important, accuracy requirements will be much higher than with a manufacturing plant, where a bit of extra weight or power is relatively unimportant. Accuracy is usually expressed as a percentage of the measured variable. If the accuracy was specified as ± 5 per cent and the measured pump *head*[6] was 100 feet, then a change due to friction of less than 5 feet would be acceptable.

The closer the accuracy tolerance, the more accurate must be the measuring instruments, the more carefully each part must be checked, and the fewer the assumptions that can be permitted. Therefore, close accuracy is costly in tests, in analysis, and in design. It should be no surprise that equipment for a moon rocket may be 10 to 100 times as expensive as equipment used for comparable purposes in a chemical plant.

Sometimes it is useful to make many sweeping assumptions at first and then to relax them, that is, to test and/or remove them one by one. In this way the engineer can obtain a rough "first solution" quickly and then refine it until he has obtained the accuracy desired. For example, when designing an air pollution control system for an automobile, the engineer may base his first calculations on a perfectly tuned engine, operating at normal temperature on standard fuel. Later, he takes into account different gasolines, climatic variations, and a poorly tuned engine. It is very tempting to claim success for one's design if it works under ideal conditions, but the prudent designer waits with his judgment until *all* assumptions have been checked out thoroughly.

[6]*Head* is the height of a column of water and is used as a measure of the pressure at the bottom of the column. (For example, a column of water 100 feet high has a pressure at the base of 6,240 pounds/square foot.)

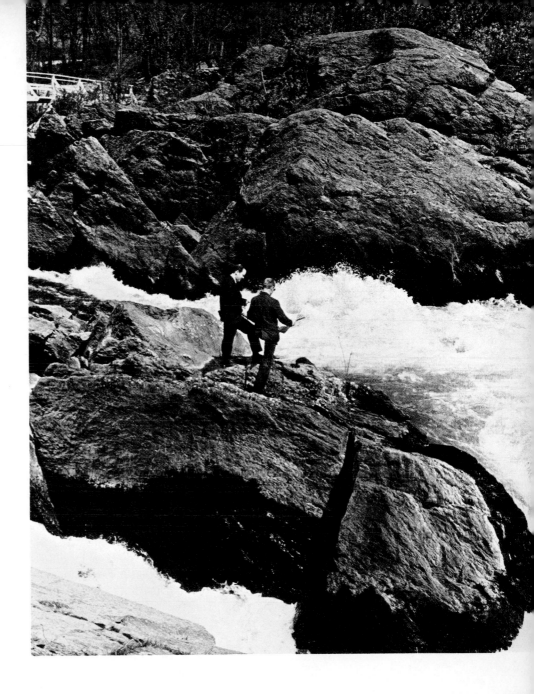

7-33
Frequently the engineer is called upon to make on-the-spot calculations.

rough estimating

An engineer often is called upon to make quick decisions that must be based on rough estimates, on simple and incomplete models of the situation. His ability to do this depends to a large degree on experience—on knowledge of similar situations. The young engineer cannot start too early to practice correct estimating. If later he

A little experience often upsets a lot of theory.

CADMAN

checks his estimates with reliable calculations and sees where he erred, he can improve his technique steadily.

Here are some sample situations in which quick estimates are needed:

A civil engineer high in the mountains may be required to estimate the effectiveness of a proposed storage dam to generate power. He has only a pencil and a scrap of paper with him. Let us assume that he has measured the size of the proposed reservoir and finds that it would contain about 100 billion gallons of water, that the river which flows into it supplies enough water to permit him to withdraw twice the contents of the reservoir every year, and that the average vertical drop to the proposed power house is 1,000 feet. He remembers that 1 gallon of water weighs about 8 pounds.[7] He writes

Facts and Data

Reservoir content 100×10^9 gal
1 gal water ≈ 8 lb

Usable quantity $= 2 \times$ content/yr

1 yr $\approx 3 \times 10^7$ sec

750 lb ft/sec ≈ 1 kW

Calculations

$\therefore$ Reservoir content $= 8 \times 100 \times 10^9$ lb
Potential energy $= 8 \times 100 \times 10^9$ lb $\times 1,000$ ft
$= 8 \times 10^{14}$ lb ft
Usable energy $= 2 \times 8 \times 10^{14}$ lb ft/yr

16×10^{14} lb ft/yr $\times \dfrac{1 \text{ yr}}{3 \times 10^7 \text{ sec}} \approx 5 \times 10^7$ lb ft/sec

5×10^7 ft/sec $\times \dfrac{1 \text{ kW}}{750 \text{ lb ft/sec}} \approx 6.5 \times 10^4$ kW

This means that the maximum energy that could be withdrawn from the reservoir is about 65,000 kW. His experience may tell him that his pipes, turbines, and generators when working together will be no more than 80 per cent efficient in converting this power into electricity, so that he can expect a power output of $0.80 \times 65,000$, or about 50,000 kilowatts. Notice that wherever the engineer rounded off a number he did so in a safe or "conservative" way to make sure that his estimates would be on the safe side; that is, they would, if anything, underestimate the power that could be generated. This type of conservatism is good engineering practice.

Another example deals with a highway engineer who is asked to estimate the maximum safe speed on a highway curve with a 300-foot radius. He considers two major causes of accident: sliding and overturning. His model is the free-body diagram of the car shown in [7-34]. The major forces acting on the car as it goes around the curve are the centrifugal force, its own weight, and the friction between road and tires. Now he needs some basic laws of mechanics (physics) to tell him how to compute the centrifugal force and the friction, and how to compute overturning moments. Let us call the weight

7-34

$$C.F. = \frac{W v^2}{g R}$$

[7]The actual weight of water is 8.33 pounds/gallon. At this point, the engineer is interested in approximate numbers, not great accuracy.

of the car W(pounds), its speed V(feet/second) (note that 30 miles per hour = 44 feet/second); let R be the radius of the curve in feet, f the coefficient of friction[8] between road and tire, and g the acceleration (the "pull") of gravity (32.2 feet/second²). To prevent sliding, Wf must be larger than WV^2/gR, the centrifugal force. This means that V must be less than $\sqrt{gRf}$.

His experience (or a good handbook) tells the engineer that, under bad weather conditions, f may be as low as 0.5. Hence the velocity at which sliding might start is about $\sqrt{32.2 \times 300 \times 0.5} = \sqrt{4,830} = 69.5$ feet/second or 47.5 miles per hour.

Another calculation (not shown here) indicates to him that most cars are more likely to slide than to overturn; that is, they would have to travel faster than 47.5 miles per hour before they would overturn. Although his calculations indicate 47.5 to be the maximum speed, he knows he must set the speed limit much lower than that to allow for the assumptions of his model, for cars with extra smooth tires, or drivers who don't take the curves smoothly or use their brakes in the curve. How much tolerance to allow for these factors is a matter of experience alone.

problems

7-1. A police beat covers four city blocks as shown. If a policeman is to start at precinct headquarters (H.Q.), cover every street at least once, and return to H.Q., what is the minimum number of street sections (such as 2nd St. between Elm and Oak) he must cover twice? What route would you recommend?

7-35

[8]The coefficient of friction is the ratio of the frictional force to the load on the surface where the friction is. Therefore, the friction force at the tire is $W \times f$.

Pulling a barrel
over a curb

7-36

A ladder resting against
a frictionless wall

60°

7-37

B   7-38

60°

A

45°

15.8 ft.

705 lb.

C

P

13.0

28°

0.74

7-39

1.52

1.41

7-2. The following problems are to be solved by building and testing a model. Design and build the test model, discuss the assumptions used, make the test, and prepare a report on your findings.

(a) The friction coefficient of automobile tires on dry and wet roads (use tire samples from a junk yard).

(b) The strength of commercial glues to be used to glue sheets of aluminum together.

(c) The rate at which heat is transferred in a heat exchanger. [*Note:* In a heat exchanger a group of tubes containing one fluid (liquid or gas) is immersed in another fluid. One fluid is used to heat (or cool) the other. The fluids may be at rest or moving past the tube wall. Two thermometers and a stopwatch will be furnished by the instructor.]

7-3. Prepare a flow diagram of the water system in your house.

7-4. Draw a block or flow diagram for each of the following systems:

(a) The passage of a bill through the State legislature.

(b) The water cycle in nature (beginning with water evaporating from the ocean).

(c) The manufacturing process of any item manufactured in your community.

7-5. Draw a circuit diagram for

(a) Your car, including battery, generator, starter, key switch, ignition system, and front lights only.

(b) An automatic sprinkler system that, in turn, operates three sprinkler valves one after the other on an adjustable time schedule.

(c) An electric washing machine (for clothes).

(d) The electrical wiring in your home.

7-6. Draw a free-body diagram, showing *all* forces acting on

(a) A see-saw with one light and one heavy child in balance.

(b) A lawn roller being pulled over a curb, as in [7-36].

(c) A ladder resting on a frictionless wall and supporting a man two thirds of the way up [7-37].

(d) The arm *BC* of the hoist shown in [7-38].

(e) The hammer pulling out a nail, as shown in [7-39].

bibliography

ALLEN, J., *Scale Models in Hydraulic Engineering*, London: Longmans, Green, 1952.

Dartmouth College Writing Group, *Modern Mathematical Methods and Models*, Vol. I, Mathematical Association of America, 1958.

DAVID, E. E., JR., and J. G. TRUXAL (eds.), *The Man Made World*, New York: McGraw-Hill, 1971.

HOOKE, ROBERT, and DOUGLAS SHAFFER, *Math and Aftermath*, New York: Walker & Co., 1965.

OLSON, H. F., *Solutions of Engineering Problems by Dynamic Analysis*, New York: Van Nostrand Reinhold, 1966.

An optical microscope photograph of carbon, magnified 250 times, permits careful study of its structure. This is used in connection with research on pyrolytic graphite, a ceramic material that withstands temperatures above 3,000 degrees Fahrenheit, where it has the highest strength-to-weight ratio of any high temperature material now under consideration for practical use.

Whatever an engineer builds, whether it be a space ship, an electronic circuit, or a suspension bridge, he uses materials of construction. Therefore, he must know something about material properties and the ways that materials can be shaped into the specific forms that he may require. Different applications demand different types of properties—perhaps high strength and rigidity in one case or suppleness and flexibility in another. There can be no universal material. Therefore, the engineer uses variously metals and plastics, concrete and rubber, wood and ceramics, and special combinations of these.

In this chapter we shall describe some of the more common engineering materials; how, where, and why they are used; and how they are formed, machined, and joined together to make useful engineering products. Finally, some of the most common of these engineering products, such as nuts and bolts, gears and bearings, cables and I-beams, will be described. In this discussion the student will be guided on a quick tour through foundries, mills, and machine shops, stopping only long enough to get some idea of what goes on there and why. A more complete understanding must be reserved for later courses in the engineering curriculum.

A civilization is both developed and limited by the materials at its disposal. . . .

SIR GEORGE PAGET THOMSON

8-1
"Whatever an engineer builds . . . he uses materials of construction." The Great Pyramid of Egypt is an example of the durability of properly chosen building materials.

8-2
"Different applications demand different types of
properties . . . ." However, good engineering
design can do much to overcome inherent
limitations of engineering materials. Who would
believe, for example, that a bridge of paper and
cardboard could be designed to be strong enough
to withstand the load of a large truck, as is shown
here?

materials for the engineer

The most important materials for the engineer are the *metals*. They
exhibit strength, toughness, ductility, resistance to both high and low
temperatures, and good conductivity to heat and electricity. They
can be formed, shaped, and joined into a great variety of shapes
and, by suitable treatment, they can be made resistant to the attack
of most chemicals. The most important primary metals for the engineer are iron,[1] copper, and aluminum, together with auxiliary metals
such as nickel, zinc, tin, cobalt, lead, and manganese. During recent
years, some of the scarce metals such as titanium, tantalum, vana-
dium, beryllium, and columbium (also called niobium) have gained
importance for special applications.

With very few exceptions, metals are not found pure in nature
but as minerals, combinations of the metal with such chemical elements as oxygen, sulfur, and carbon—in the form of oxides, sulfates,
sulfides, and carbonates. The process of separating the metal from
the other constituents is called smelting, beneficiation, reduction, or
refining. One way to accomplish this is by heating in the presence
of other chemicals that have a greater affinity or attractive power
than metal for the undesired chemical. Another way is electrolyti-
cally, that is, by melting the original compound or dissolving it in
a liquid and applying an electrical current through two electrodes
in such a way that the valuable metal portion of the compound is
attracted by one of the electrodes and the less desirable chemical

[1] Although pure iron is seldom used, it is the main constituent of cast iron and
steel.

8-3
Stirring the melt with a mechanical crust breaker
in an aluminum smelter.

by the other. The metal resulting from these refining methods is cast
into ingots or bars called *pigs,* or left in a molten state for later
modification. With the notable exception of copper,[2] the pure metal
is rarely useful as an engineering material. Pig iron,[3] for example,
is weak and brittle, and pig aluminum is too soft and ductile for
most engineering uses.

Metals become most useful to the engineer when they are combined with other constituents that give them the qualities of strength
and toughness for which they are prized. Only when they are combined with other metals and elements to form what is known as *alloys*

[2]One of the principal uses for copper is as a conductor of electricity. The purer
the copper, the higher its electrical conductivity (i.e., the lower its resistance to the
flow of electrical current).
[3]Pig iron is not pure iron but contains many impurities.

do the base metals—iron, copper, and aluminum—become useful as engineering construction materials. *Metallurgy,* the science that deals with the improvement of metal properties, is probably the oldest science known to man. Long before man had fires hot enough to work iron, he combined copper and tin to make bronze, a material stronger than either copper or tin alone.

When man learned to make coal fires, he obtained not only a temperature high enough to melt iron but also the carbon that is so essential to lend iron its strength. The coarse iron produced by early man contained a great many impurities, which made it weak and brittle. Grey cast iron—used even today where tensile strength is not too important—is quite similar to man's early iron utensils. Only by further refining—by removing or reducing to a minimum undesirable impurities such as sulfur and phosphorus, by adding strengthening components such as silicon and manganese, and by close control over the amount of carbon—can iron be turned into steel. By varying the constituents (alloying) and the way in which the steel is heated and cooled (heat treatment) an enormous range of properties can be obtained—high or low strength, brittleness or ductility, ease of machining or toughness—and, with the metallurgist's help, the engineer has learned to take advantage of these properties.

Among the most useful of the steel alloys are those using nickel and chromium to produce stainless steels, and those containing cobalt, manganese, nickel, and other elements to achieve high strength. The production of steel in a modern steel mill is shown in [8-4]. The raw iron ore—a form of iron oxide—is fed into a blast furnace along with limestone and coke[4] in alternate layers. Here the iron oxide is reduced to iron, which then combines with carbon. The resulting pig iron is then further refined in an open-hearth furnace, a basic oxygen-process converter, or an electric-arc furnace, where its final composition can be closely controlled. The molten metal is poured into *ingot molds,* where it cools and solidifies to await further treatment in the *rolling mill.*

Just as the alloying of iron with other elements forms steels of great strength, so also can copper and aluminum be strengthened by alloying. Alloys of copper and tin are called *bronze* and alloys of copper and zinc are called *brass*—both are stronger than either of their constituents. An *aluminum bronze* can be made by alloying a few per cent of aluminum with copper. If, on the other hand, the alloy contains mostly aluminum and only a few per cent copper, it is called an *aluminum alloy* (the British call it *duralumin*). The "aluminum" products and utensils we see about us every day are almost all made from such aluminum alloys, although they usually contain many other alloying elements besides copper.

[4]Coke is the pure carbon residue of coal, formed by heating coal in an airtight furnace and removing the impurities as a gas.

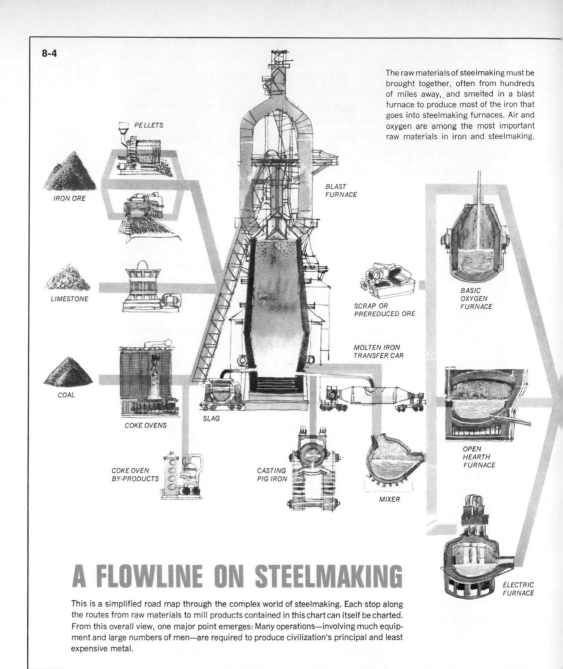

8-4

The raw materials of steelmaking must be brought together, often from hundreds of miles away, and smelted in a blast furnace to produce most of the iron that goes into steelmaking furnaces. Air and oxygen are among the most important raw materials in iron and steelmaking.

PELLETS

IRON ORE

LIMESTONE

COAL

COKE OVENS

COKE OVEN BY-PRODUCTS

SLAG

CASTING PIG IRON

MIXER

BLAST FURNACE

SCRAP OR PREREDUCED ORE

MOLTEN IRON TRANSFER CAR

BASIC OXYGEN FURNACE

OPEN HEARTH FURNACE

ELECTRIC FURNACE

A FLOWLINE ON STEELMAKING

This is a simplified road map through the complex world of steelmaking. Each stop along the routes from raw materials to mill products contained in this chart can itself be charted. From this overall view, one major point emerges: Many operations—involving much equipment and large numbers of men—are required to produce civilization's principal and least expensive metal.

Aluminum was once a precious metal.

JULES VERNE
From the Earth to the Moon, 1865

A list of the most common metals and alloys and some of their properties are shown in Appendix III.

Next to the metals the most useful engineering materials are found among the *rubbers* and *plastics*. Whereas metals are strong, heavy, and relatively inflexible, the rubbers and plastics are relatively weak, light in weight, and pliable. With the single exception of natural

Molten steel must solidify before it can be made into finished products by the industry's rolling mills and forging presses. The metal is usually formed first at high temperature, after which it may be cold-formed into additional products.

FORGING PRESS

INGOT TEEMING

BILLETS

COLD-DRAWN BARS

BARS

WIRE

TUBE ROUNDS

SEAMLESS PIPE

INGOTS

SOAKING PIT

ROUGHING MILL

BLOOMS

STRUCTURAL SHAPES

RAILS

HOT-ROLLED SHEET & STRIP

COLD-ROLLED SHEET & STRIP

TIN MILL PRODUCTS

CONTINUOUS CASTING

SLABS

SKELP

WELDED PIPE & TUBING

LARGE-DIAMETER PIPE

PLATES

rubber, they do not occur in nature and are the products of modern chemistry (even natural rubber must be carefully compounded with other chemicals to make it into a useful material). Metals have a history going back to the beginnings of human history; plastics, however, are an invention of this century.

Rubbers and plastics are long-chain hydrocarbon *polymers;* that

8-5
Feeding a steel furnace—basic oxygen process.

is, they are produced by linking together large numbers of relatively simple molecules—called *monomers*. This linking process is called *polymerization*. Some monomers will polymerize with moderate heat (a few hundred degrees Fahrenheit) alone; more often a catalyst[5] is required. The long chain molecules of a polymer can be visualized as long, elastic, coiled springs randomly distributed in the polymer. They are interconnected here and there, and it is the degree of or number of interconnections that determines the rigidity and strength of the polymer. In rubbers there are few interconnections; in rigid plastics there are many. In some plastics the interconnections can be broken by moderate heat so that the plastic can be reformed by heating. When cooled, the links are reestablished. Such plastics are called *thermoplastic*. In other plastics the links are permanent and cannot be broken without destroying the material. Such plastics are known as *thermosetting*. A list of typical rubbers and plastics and their properties are included in Appendix III.

Glass, prized primarily for its transparency and its resistance to most chemicals, is one of the strongest materials known to man. Unfortunately, it is also very brittle when exposed to air and moisture. Therefore, its strength can best be used when the glass is protected, for example, when it is embedded in plastic. Glass-fiber-reinforced plastics gain their high strength from thousands of fine glass fibers that are surrounded and held together by plastics. The production process is costly and lends itself primarily to simple shapes, such as fishing rods, corrugated roof panels, fuel tanks, boat hulls, and rocket casings.

The idea of combining two different materials and using the good qualities of each to make a superior product is much older than the glass-reinforced plastics. An earlier example is reinforced *concrete* in which the strength of steel and the rigidity of concrete are used to make superior structural members.

Concrete itself is a mixture of sand, gravel, and cement, each of which is of relatively little practical importance alone. *Cement*, also called Portland cement, is a roasted (calcined) mixture of clay and limestone that combines readily with water to form a rigid, stable solid. Hardened cement is very durable and can resist not only heat and cold and other variations in climate, but also a large number of chemicals. However, it is very brittle and has little physical strength. In concrete, strength is provided by adding the sand and gravel, which are then held together by the cement binder. Concrete, which is very strong when compressed, offers much less resistance to tension. Here is where the use of steel reinforcing becomes important. Steel rods, embedded in the concrete, can lend strength in tension. For example, imagine a concrete beam acting as a bridge

[5] A catalyst may be compared to a marriage broker; its presence is essential for the reaction, but it does not end up in the final product.

8-6
Structural shape emerging from a rolling mill.

8-7
Glass fibers in plastic. (Micrograph taken on scanning electron microscope.)

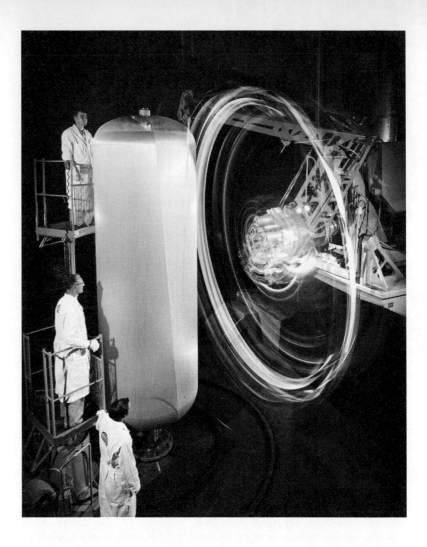

8-8
Winding glass fibers to make a rocket fuel tank.

over a canyon. When a heavy truck travels over this bridge, the beam will bend downward, with the roadway (or top surface of the beam) being pushed together or compressed, and the bottom part of the beam (the part nearest the canyon) being pulled apart in tension. Since concrete is much stronger in compression than in tension, steel reinforcing bars are cast into the bottom part of the beam to bring its tension strength up to that of the top (compression) side.

Typical concrete consists of 13 parts of cement, 33 parts of sand, and 46 parts of gravel together with 8 parts of water by weight. The strength of concrete depends upon how completely the cement

8-9
Steel reinforcing bars are used in abundance in concrete construction to improve its strength.

and water have reacted. If maximum strength is desired, it is important to keep the structure moist for several days after it has been poured.

The cement–water reaction—called *hydration*—develops heat. In most structures this heat is readily dissipated by the surrounding air. However, in large thick sections of concrete, such as dams, special water cooling pipes are often inserted to make sure that this heat can be removed and will not cause damage to the structure.

For extremely high temperature use (close to or above the melting point of metals where few of the metals have any strength left), refractories (a form of *ceramics*) are used. They resemble cement in that they are generally simple, inorganic chemical compounds.[6] Among the most common ceramics are the oxides, nitrides, carbides, and borides of metals such as aluminum, beryllium, titanium, tantalum, and many others. Appendix III lists some of the most useful ceramics. Prior to molding, ceramic compounds usually exist in powder form. They can be shaped into useful engineering products by pressing the powder into a suitable mold, at elevated temperature, enough interparticle bonds are formed to maintain the shape. The powder can be mixed with water or another liquid to form a pliable clay that is shaped and allowed to dry. However formed, these shapes are then heated to a very high temperature at which the grains fuse together and form a dense, strong body highly resistant to heat and abrasion. One of the most common ceramics is porcelain. It is made of sand (silicon oxide) and alumina (aluminum oxide).

Ceramics are used in the nozzles of rocket engines, in gas turbine combustors, on the nose cones of missiles, in the heat shield for reentry space vehicles, in furnaces, or wherever extremely high temperature resistance is required. Like concrete, ceramics tend to have much greater strength in compression (being pushed together) than in tension (being pulled apart). To increase their strength in tension, ceramics have been embedded with fine fibers of metal such as tungsten or boron, with results comparable to glass-fiber-reinforced plastics or steel-reinforced concrete.

Graphite is usually included among the ceramics because of its high temperature resistance. Although not strictly a ceramic, graphite is pure carbon in a form that permits it to be sintered and worked much like ceramics. Although its strength is not high, graphite retains its strength at temperatures even higher than most ceramics, thus

[6]Organic compounds contain carbon and hydrogen and can form very large and complicated molecules, such as the rubbers and plastics mentioned above. They are so called because most living organisms, such as plants, animals, and men, are made of compounds containing carbon and hydrogen. Even petroleum and natural gas, the raw material of today's organic chemical industry, come from long-decayed plants and animals. Inorganic compounds are a combination of other chemical elements. These may contain either carbon or hydrogen, but usually not both. Normally, inorganic molecules are smaller and simpler than the organic molecules.

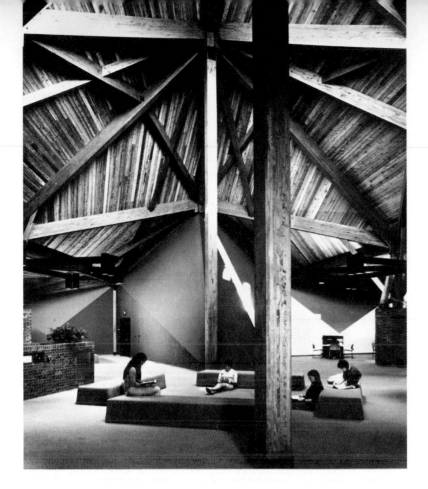

8-10
Wood construction is versatile.

becoming very useful for very high temperature applications, such as electrodes for electric arc furnaces.

Wood, once one of the most widely used engineering materials, is used very little in engineering today, partly because of its scarcity, and partly because, as a product of nature, its properties vary from batch to batch. We talk about softwoods and hardwoods. Softwoods, such as pines and firs, are relatively plentiful, grow fairly rapidly, and are not too costly. However, their strength is low and they tend to warp easily; consequently, they are used today primarily for housing construction and for the production of paper. About their only engineering use is in making forms for concrete, and even here the use of metal is rapidly replacing wood. Hardwoods, such as oak, ash, walnut, and others from the tropics, have become so scarce and costly that they are used almost exclusively for decorative effects or for the production of beautiful and costly furniture. One remaining engineering use is the production of patterns for few-of-a-kind castings. We can expect to see the use of wood curtailed more and more as our forests become depleted. The forests that remain are needed more and more for recreation and for the preservation of watersheds.

the properties of materials

With so many materials to choose from, how does the engineer select the best materials for his design? How can he find his way through a number of basic metals and hundreds of alloys? The answer lies in acquiring an understanding of the properties of the materials and how they will affect the behavior of the part, that is, performance, cost, appearance, and life. The types of properties that the engineer is most concerned with are

1. *Mechanical* properties such as strength, toughness, flexibility and hardness.
2. *Physical* properties such as specific weight, melting point, ability to conduct heat and electricity, and amount of expansion when heated.
3. *Chemical* properties such as the resistance to air, water, and other fluids, its toxicity (particularly if used in medical applications or food preparation), and how each material will combine with others.
4. Availability in suitable shapes or the difficulty of forming and molding it into some desired shape.
5. Cost—both of the raw material and of the process to get it into the desired shape.

Appendix III shows some of the properties of a selected few of the most common materials. More specific details and data for other materials can be found in the references at the end of this chapter.

8-11
The grainy structure of metal is seen here magnified by a metallograph.

8-12

forming

The forming of a useful product is a vital part of the manufacturing process, often the most costly portion of the final product. It is here that the engineer's knowledge and ingenuity can be most effective in saving time, materials, and labor that often spell the difference between a failure and a success in the competitive market.

Materials are formed basically by five general techniques:

1. Pouring or forcing the material as a liquid into a form or mold and causing it to harden in the desired shape. These techniques are called *casting* or *molding*.
2. Shaping the solid material by force into the desired form with presses, hammers, or brakes. Such methods are usually called *working*.
3. Severing material by shearing and punching.
4. Removing material by cutting, drilling, grinding, etc. This is known as *machining*.

5. *Joining* pieces together. This includes welding, brazing, soldering, and the use of adhesives. Screws, bolts, nails, and rivets also may be used to join or assemble parts.

We shall take a brief look at these techniques, particularly as they refer to metals.

Casting or Molding

After metal has been refined and combined with its alloying elements, it is usually a hot liquid. What could be simpler than to pour this liquid into a preformed hollow form, a mold, which allows the liquid metal to solidify and cool to some desired shape? Such a technique is called *casting* or *molding*. It is the oldest metal-forming technique known. Historically, the earliest metal parts were made by casting into depressions dug in the ground. Later, man learned that certain fine sands made particularly good molds and that a wooden *pattern* could be used to advantage to form the *cavity* in the sand. Today the sand is placed in a box or *flask* and tamped around the pattern. The flask is split so that the pattern can be removed. Special passages, called *sprues* and *runners*, lead to the cavity. The metal is poured into the sprue, and, after the cavity is filled, excess metal remains in the sprue or flows into *risers*. The sprue (and the riser, if one is used) provides some space liquid metal that is available to make up for metal shrinkage during cooling. Hollow castings can be made by using a hard sand *core* in the mold. After the metal has solidified and cooled, the mold can be broken open and the *casting* removed.

Since a sand mold is not reusable, it is broken up to facilitate removal of the finished product after the metal has solidified and cooled. The main advantages of cast products are that (1) they can be formed in the most intricate of shapes, and (2) there is almost no limit to their size. On the other hand, sand castings tend to have rougher surfaces and to be weaker and more brittle than items that have been produced by other methods. It is difficult to hold dimensions precisely and to make sure that the item does not warp during the cooling process. Finally, sand casting does not always lend itself well for the making of mass-produced items. However, in the last 50 years the art of casting has been substantially improved. Special steels have been developed that, when cast, are no longer brittle and weak but strong and tough; and there are now reusable metal molds and continuous casting methods that lend themselves well to mass-production practices. The engine block in your car, its pump housing, and the carburetor body are all made from castings.

Many special casting techniques have been developed. *Investment* castings, using ceramic molds, are used for castings with smooth surfaces and close dimensional tolerances. In *centrifugal* casting the mold is rotated rapidly so that centrifugal force helps to fill every

8-13
A typical sand mold.

8-14
There is almost no limit to the size of castings. Shown here are the cast-steel sprocket and treads of a large mining shovel.

8-15
A piston forces the liquid metal into a mold in the submerged plunger die casting process.

PRESSURE
CYLINDER

DIE (CLOSED)

PLUNGER

GOOSE-
NECK

POT

BURNER

EJECTOR

8-16
Die casting is a mass-production technique. After the aluminum die casting is removed from the machine, it will be trimmed.

corner of the mold and produce a denser and more uniform casting. In *die casting* the liquid metal is forced by a piston into a metal mold. The mold is then cooled, opened, the casting is ejected, and the mold is closed for the next cycle. Die casting is a rapid mass-production technique, particularly useful with relatively low-melting-point metals, such as aluminum, copper, and zinc alloys.

Most plastics are formed by a process similar to die casting known as *injection molding*. Plastic granules are softened to a viscous state by heat. The viscous liquid is forced under pressure into very accurately machined metal molds where the plastic polymerizes. These molds produce plastic parts of precise dimensions and excellent surface finish. The same mold can be used for hundreds of thousands of parts. We all are aware of the innumerable household products and items of modern life produced from molded plastics. Though an original mold may be costly, the cost of each part produced may

The "House of the Future," built in Disneyland, was planned for family living and conformed to all Los Angeles building codes. The structure consisted of thin (0.3 inch) curved projecting shells of molded glass fiber reinforced polyesters. Floor slabs were of the same material bonded as sandwich facings to a honeycomb core. The parts were fastened with epoxy adhesives, and joints were sealed with polysulfides. In ten years, about 20 million people tramped through the house. It withstood high winds and several mild to moderate earthquakes.

LLOYD W. DUNLAP, JR.
Chemical & Engineering News, March 11, 1968

8-17
Die castings can be formed in the most intricate of shapes, such as illustrated here by the aluminum die castings for an automobile transmission.

8-18
"The viscous liquid is forced under pressure into the mold."

Hammer the iron when it is glowing hot.
PUBLILIUS SYRUS
Maxims, 1st Century B.C.

8-19
A workman adjusts the position of a large raw-steel billet prior to drop-hammer forging.

be remarkably low if the price of the mold can be distributed over hundreds of thousands of parts. This is why picnic forks, ball-point pens, and pocket combs are inexpensive.

The most common procedure used in making *concrete* structures is closely related to sand casting. When the shapes of the structure are simple and straight (such as building walls and driveways), wooden molds are used. For more intricate shapes (such as the pillars on highway bridges and the curbing and gutters for sidewalks), reusable metal molds or *forms* are most common. Where needed, reinforcing steel is placed into the cavity and secured to the forms before the concrete mixture is poured in. *Strongback* clamps are used to hold the forms in place until the concrete has set.

Hot and Cold Working

We do not know who first discovered that the strength and resilience of steel could be improved appreciably by hammering when hot, but we do know that for thousands of years swords, horseshoes, and ax heads have been produced by hammering or forging. However, the forge of old has now been replaced by huge drop hammers or forging presses and by the rolling mill.

Under the drop hammer the hot piece of metal is impacted repeatedly in a formed cavity called a *die* until it has been formed into its desired shape. Forging presses squeeze the hot metal into a die in one movement. Some gigantic presses, creating loads as high as 50,000 to 100,000 tons, have been built.

Although steel makers sell ingots as they are poured from the furnaces, by far the largest quantity of steel is processed by the steel makers themselves in the *rolling mill* (see Figure 8-6) and sold in shapes such as plate and sheet; round, square, or hexagonal bars; wire; or structural shapes such as I-beams, channels, and angles. In the rolling mill the reheated ingot is passed through one set of heavy rolls after another until it is squeezed into the desired shape. The rolling process works the steel to the same strength and toughness as can be achieved by a forge. Its final shapes are convenient for the manufacture of automobiles, bridges, kitchen appliances, and countless other products.

Extrusion is another hot-working technique. The metal is heated until it is plastic and pliable but not liquid. It is then forced through a die, much as a baker presses frosting through a form to decorate a cake. The resultant shapes may be very simple forms, such as bars, rods, and hollow tubes, or more complex forms, such as window and door moldings. Extrusion is a rapid and low-cost process, but it is limited to materials that lend themselves readily to plastic deformation at moderate temperatures, e.g., copper, aluminum, and thermoplastics.

Cold working depends on the *ductility* of material, that is, its ability to deform plastically at room temperatures. Sheet-metal parts, such as air conditioning ducts, automobile fenders and bodies, and aluminum pots, are cold-formed from flat sheet metal. The principal tools used for cold forming are brakes, presses, wire-drawing dies, and impact extruders. Brakes are used extensively for bending operations in sheet-metal shops. To cold form a contour in metal pieces requires a set of hard metal dies between which the *blank* is pressed or *drawn* into the desired shape [8-22]. Obviously, dies are costly and justified only when many parts can be made in the same die. Typical cold-formed parts are automobile body panels. *Coining*—the forming of a design onto a metal blank, such as on pennies, nickels, dimes, and quarters—is a cold-pressing operation. Various diameters of wire are formed by pulling rods through successively smaller openings in *wire-drawing* dies. *Impact extrusion* is used primarily to form soft and ductile materials into tubular shapes. The plunger descends with great speed on to a *slug* (disc) of metal in the die. The metal in the slug, trying to flow out of the way, can only flow up along the sides of the plunger, thus forming a tube with a closed end. Aluminum containers of various shapes and sizes are commonly made in this way.

Most cold-formed materials show some elastic *springback;* that is, they won't remain in exactly the shape into which the brake or die forced them once the pressure is released. Therefore, a properly operated brake and a well-designed die will overform the metal just enough so that elastic springback will result in the desired shape. This requires not only careful calculation and design, but also close control over the metallurgy and the forming process that produced

8-20
The extruding press operates "much as a baker presses frosting through a form to decorate a cake."

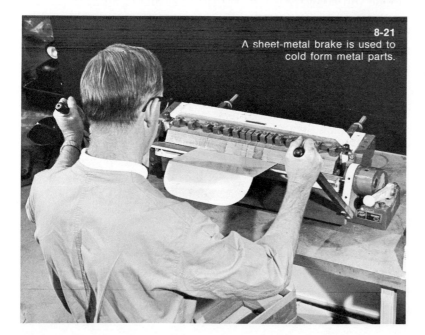

8-21
A sheet-metal brake is used to cold form metal parts.

8-22
Deep drawing a metal pan.

8-23
A punch and die for making holes in sheet metal.

8-24
Cutting tools—for a lathe (foreground), milling machine (center), drill press (upper right), and broach (upper left).

the blanks to make sure that the springback is as predicted and the same for all parts.

Shearing and Punching

Punches are used principally to cut thin metal sections, primarily sheet metal. The punch is always accompanied by a die, which has one or more cutouts. The punch fits snugly into these cutouts. When a piece of sheet metal is laid over the die and the punch lowered swiftly, it shears the metal at the edge of the cutouts. With sharp, well beveled, and well adjusted punches, the metal cuts clean and does not warp. The punching operation is closely related to cold working, such as coining. Although the cost of a punch and die set may be high, since it is made from high-strength steel with close tolerances, thousands of parts can be made rapidly on one set; so punching is one of the least costly manufacturing operations and should be considered whenever a large quantity of parts is to be made.

Machining and Material Removing

Except in special circumstances, castings, forgings, and hot- or cold-formed shapes cannot be used without some *machining*, whether it be by milling, drilling, grinding, turning, shaping, or by some other means. Most machining techniques use single- or multiple-point *cutting tools*. The sharp-edged points of these tools are made of a material harder than the metal to be cut. Ordinary steel will cut brass or aluminum, hardened steel will cut ordinary steel, tungsten carbide will cut hardened steel; but what will cut tungsten carbide or other superhard materials?[7] Single-edge cutting tools are used on *lathes* and *boring mills* for shaping round parts, and on *shapers* and *planers* for making flat surfaces. Multiple-edge tools are used in *saws*, on *drills* and *reamers*, and on *broaching* and *milling* machines. The *grinding* wheel can be thought of as the ultimate in multiple-edge tools, because each grain of abrasive on the wheel becomes a small cutting tool.

Machine tools differ not only by the number of cutting edges, but also in the way that the tool and work pieces are moved with respect to each other. In some machines[8] (shapers, drill presses, milling machines, grinders) the work piece remains motionless and the tool moves. In others (planers, lathes, boring mills) the tool stands still and the work piece moves. The size of the work piece and the type

[7] Such materials are usually cast by special techniques into as near the finished shape as possible. They are often finished by grinding with wheels containing small particles of diamonds, the hardest material known to man.

[8] Here we refer only to the primary high-speed cutting motion between tool and work piece. The much slower movement (called *feed*), which presents the tool with a fresh surface to be cut, is a secondary motion.

of cut that is to be made should dictate the proper machine to be used. Let us now look at some of these machines in more detail.

Saws. Metals can be sawed in much the same way that wood is sawed, by circular saws, band (contour) saws, or reciprocating saws (hacksaws). The teeth of a metal saw are smaller and more numerous, and each takes a much smaller "bite" than does the tooth of a wood saw. Also, the saw must be pressed hard against the metal to be cut and must be moved more slowly than the wood saw to prevent overheating. Often a cooling liquid is used to keep blade and work piece cool.

Saws make a fairly coarse cut. Therefore, they are used to *rough cut* the material. (Steel can also be cut with an oxyacetylene torch—see welding. This is faster than sawing but usually makes a very coarse cut.)

Shapers, Planers, Lathes, and Boring Mills. These machines all use a single-point tool, a tool that is relatively inexpensive and easy to sharpen and to adjust. Shapers cut in straight lines by a reciprocating (to-and-fro) motion. The work piece is clamped and is moved sideways or up only a tiny amount after each stroke of the tool, to present the tool with a fresh surface to cut. The tool is fastened to a tool holder (clapper box), which is hinged to the reciprocating ram, so that on the return stroke the tool slides freely over the work piece without gouging. Shapers are used to make surfaces flat.

Planers are similar to shapers in that they make a straight-line cut. However, in most planers the tools stand still and the work piece

8-25
Feed and cutting motions of various machine tools.

8-26
Shaper.

8-27
Planer.

HEADSTOCK

SPINDLE

BED

TOOL POST

COMPOUND REST

CROSS SLIDE

TAILSTOCK

GEAR BOX

FEED ROD

LEAD SCREW

CARRIAGE

8-28
Lathe.

8-29
Precision turning on a lathe.

8-30
Lathe cutting tools.

STRAIGHT SHANK LATHE TOOL HOLDER

UNGROUND TOOL BIT

R.H. TURNING TOOL

L.H. TURNING TOOL

R.H. FACING TOOL

CUT-OFF TOOL

BORING TOOL

THREADING TOOL

8-31
Modern turret lathes are operated by an electronic computer. An operator is required only to make adjustments and replace dull tools.

moves past them. Planers are used to "true up" very large castings or forgings.

On lathes and boring mills the work piece rotates and the tool advances slowly to make a fresh cut on each revolution of the work piece. Lathes handle pieces up to 2 or 3 feet in diameter, which rotate about a horizontal axis. Boring mills handle very large diameter pieces, which are generally rotated about a vertical axis. Besides removing metal uniformly so as to make shafts, tubes, and other cylindrical shapes, lathes are also used to form conical and spherical shapes, to drill and bore out the inside of a work piece, and to cut threads. When many operations must be performed on one part on the lathe, and many parts of the same type must be made, as many as six different tools can be arranged on a many-sided tool holder, or *turret*. Each time the work of one tool is finished, the turret is turned and the next tool is ready for its cut. In modern automatic lathes, not only is the turret turned automatically, but the finished work piece is automatically ejected and a new one put in its place ready for machining. An operator need only make the initial adjustment and see that there is enough new material and cutting fluid. Therefore, one man can handle several of these automatic *screw machines*.

CROSS RAIL

TOOL HEADS

TABLE

8-32
Vertical boring mill.

8-33
Radial-arm
drill press.

COLUMN

SPINDLE

TABLE OR
KNEE

8-35

8-34

ALL SPINDLES
ROTATE AND
FEED
SIMULTANEOUSLY

Many holes can be drilled at the same time
using a multispindle drilling machine.

8-36
Horizontal milling machine.

OVERARM

TABLE

SADDLE

SPINDLE
ARBOR

COLUMN

KNEE

8-37
A small
horizontal
milling
machine
can perform a
great variety
of tasks.

Drilling, Milling, and Grinding. These operations require rotating tools with more than one cutting edge, thereby making more but finer cuts. Drills normally have two cutting edges; milling cutters have anywhere from two to twenty, or even more; grinders have thousands of tiny abrasive grains, each of which may be considered as a cutting edge.

Drills, of course, make circular holes, one at a time on a single-spindle drill press, or a whole series at once on a multispindle one. Milling machines come in a wide variety of types and sizes—vertical or horizontal, according to the arrangement of the main shaft or spindle holding the milling cutter. Normally, this shaft stays in one place and the work piece is moved past it. Milling cutters form contours; cut slots, gears, and threads; and machine parallel surfaces and square corners. Milling machines are the most versatile tools in the average machine shop.

Grinding wheels have thousands of tiny cutting edges. Each grain does not remove much material but thousands taken together may cut quite fast. Grinding wheels are used primarily to make very smooth uniform cuts and to produce a smooth finish on rough-machined surfaces. The abrasives most commonly used to make grinding wheels are aluminum oxide and silicon carbide. The size

8-38
Vertical milling machine.

SPINDLE

TABLE

SADDLE

KNEE

8-39
A slot is out in a large steel block by a computer-controlled vertical mill.

STRAIGHT
TOOTH

HELICAL MILL
(LIGHT DUTY)

HELICAL MILL
(HEAVY DUTY)

HELICAL MILL
(ARBOR TYPE)

SPIRAL MILL WITH
INSERTED BLADES

CARBIDE-TIPPED PLAN MILL
WITH CAST BODY

HELICAL MILL (SHANK TYPE)

PLAIN MILLING
CUTTERS

STYLE A

STYLE B
ALTERNATE GASH PLAIN MILLS

INSIDE CONE TYPE

OUTSIDE CONE TYPE

CHANNELING
CUTTER

INTEGRAL-TOOTH

SHELL END MILL

"SHEAR CLEAR" CUTTER
FACE MILLING CUTTERS WITH INSERTED BLADES

HERRINGBONE TYPE

INTEGRAL-TOOTH SIDE MILLS

INSERTED BLADE
SIDE MILLING CUTTERS

INTERLOCKING
SIDE MILL

INSERTED BLADE
STAGGERED-TOOTH
SIDE MILLS

HALF SIDE MILLS

SET-UP FOR STRADDLE MILLING

SOLID FACE MILL WITH
BRAZED CARBIDE TIPS

INSERTED BLADE COMBINATION
FACE AND END MILL
FACE AND END MILLS

8-40
Milling cutters come in a great variety of shapes and sizes. They can cut
both flat and curved surfaces, slots, and holes.

8-41
Surface grinder.

8-42
A special fluid is used to cool the part and the grinding wheel of the surface grinder, and to carry away the cuttings.

and spacing of the abrasive grains and the material that bonds the grains together determine the roughness of the cut and the speed of metal removal. The smoother the finish, the less metal will be removed by the wheel.

In a well-maintained machine shop, parts can be machined easily to tolerances (accuracy) of 1 one-thousandth of an inch (25 microns), and, with great care and extra time, to one tenth of this amount. Greater accuracy than this becomes very costly and usually requires special machines that must be operated in air-conditioned and temperature-controlled rooms.

There are many other machining techniques, such as *broaching* (for high-volume production of noncircular holes and contoured surfaces), and *honing* and *lapping* (to make extra-fine surface finishes), whose description is beyond the scope of this text. We refer the interested reader to the references at the end of this chapter.

Joining

Often we wish to join two or more pieces of material together, either because the product consists of a group of simple elements, like a steel bridge or a transmission tower or because the product is too large to be made from one piece, like a ship's hull or because it is far too complicated to be made in one piece, like an aircraft engine. There are three basically different joining techniques: adhesives, welds, and fasteners.

Household experiences have made us familiar with many kinds of glues or *adhesives* that can join broken pieces of furniture, dishes,

8-43

In centerless grinding the part is held in place by the rotating grinding wheels.

8-44
Oxyacetylene welding.

or paper. Adhesives are easy to apply; they can join dissimilar materials; they usually demand little or no heat; they are good electrical and thermal insulators; and they can be remarkably strong (as witness some of the epoxy adhesives), though rarely as strong as the materials they are asked to join. Adhesives are usually stronger in *shear* than in direct tension. Since most modern adhesives are hydrocarbon compounds, just as the plastics, they cannot be used at high temperature. Despite these drawbacks, adhesives are used more and more often in joining metal parts, and in attaching metals to nonmetals.

Where the strength of the joint must be as high as that of the parent metal, *welding* is used. In welding, the parts that are to be joined are fused together to form one solid body, almost as if the two pieces had never been apart. To do this, the parts must be heated in the vicinity of the joint, so that the atoms of one part can intermingle with those of the other. Sometimes not only heat but pressure is required; in fact, when pressure is used the heat may not need to be as high. (Under extreme pressure, metal parts can weld without heat.) Sometimes a *filler* is used, a material that readily welds to both parts, particularly if the main parts may not easily weld to one another or if additional material is needed to fill the joint.

8-45
A welder at work.

8-46
Arc welding.

ELECTRODE HOLDER

FLUX- COATED
ELECTRODE

POWER
SOURCE

GROUND CLAMP

There are several ways to heat metal quickly and effectively: a hot flame (such as an oxyacetylene torch), an electric arc, a heavy electric current passed through the joint, a beam of electrons, or induction from a high-frequency alternating current. A good welder controls his heat carefully, just enough to get a good strong weld but not so much that the metal structure is weakened. Arc and torch welding are common processes in every blacksmith and machine shop. They are simple and easily controlled by hand. The other welding techniques lend themselves best to automatic manufacturing operations when many duplicate parts must be welded.

In addition to proper heating, cleanliness (the absence of impurities in the weld) is the most important criterion. These impurities may come from the surface of the metal, from the alloys in it, or from the atmosphere around it. If they are not removed or neutralized, they may cause a weak weld or prevent welding altogether. For this reason, *fluxes* are used. Fluxes are chemicals that attract some of the impurities and neutralize them. When impurities in the air cannot be tolerated, the weld is either surrounded by a special inert atmosphere, such as argon, or the welding is done in a vacuum chamber.

Although welded joints can be as strong as the parent metal, the heating and cooling tends to distort the metal near the joint and may even affect its metallurgical properties. Therefore, additional machining and/or heat treating is often needed after welding to reestablish the proper dimensions and properties.

Not all metals can be welded. As a general rule, the more alloying elements present, the less weldable a material is. For example, ordinary low-carbon steels are more easily welded than most of the high-strength alloy steels. Few dissimilar metals can be welded together satisfactorily.

A compromise between the strength and heat resistance of welding and the convenience of adhesives is offered by *brazing* and *soldering*. These methods use as fillers metallic alloys having lower melting points than those of the materials being joined, and are used for joining dissimilar metals, for joints that do not require the strength of the parent metal, and where distortion must be avoided. Brazing is by far the strongest of these processes. In brazing or silver solder-

8-47
Electron-beam welding is used where strength and precision are paramount factors. Here a thin high-alloy steel shell is inspected after electron-beam welding.

PRESSURE

MOVABLE
ELECTRODE

AC
POWER
SOURCE

STATIONARY
ELECTRODE

8-48
Spot welding is one type of electric resistance welding.

319

8-49
Brazing a laboratory vessel.

8-50
A single-riveted lap joint.

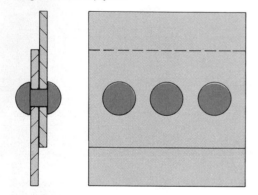

8-51
A single-riveted butt joint.

ing, a copper or silver alloy is used, which melts above 800°F (for welding, the temperature of steel is usually well above 1,500°F). The parent metal is heated to the melting point of the brazing compound, which then bonds to the surfaces of the mating parts to form a strong joint, though not as strong as a welded joint.

Lead–tin solder is used primarily for electrical connections where strength is not important. Solder melts at temperatures well below 800°F and forms a weak joint, but one which conducts heat and electricity well.

To obtain high joint strength without the use of heat and without distortion, one must use mechanical *fasteners,* such as *rivets, screws,* or *bolts* (see also Appendix IV). Their use requires careful aligning of the parts and the drilling or punching of holes. Rivets are usually heated before they are inserted in the hole and then deformed by hammering so as to fill the hole completely and to create a head on each side of the joined parts to hold them together. As the rivet cools, it contracts and tightens the joint. Newer riveting processes use mechanical or explosive means to deform the rivet after placement in the hole.

Of all joining methods discussed here, the only one that can be

BOLT   SCREW   STUD

8-52
A bolt mates with a nut; a screw finds its mating thread in the part being secured; a stud has two threaded ends—one for the part and one for a nut.

opened or disconnected to facilitate repair and adjustment is the screwed or bolted connection. Just as in riveting, bolting requires drilling and careful aligning, usually on an assembly guide or *jig*. Screws and bolts usually allow a small amount of relative movement of the parts for final alignment if required. A *stud* is a bolt without head. It is threaded at each end.

surface treatment

It is the surface of the metal that, like your skin, is in contact with the environment and must be protected against mechanical and chemical attack. Since most failures begin at the surface, many special techniques have been developed to harden and toughen the surface and to make it more resistant to the environment in which it operates. Among the surface-hardening techniques are carburizing, cyaniding, and nitriding—all methods in which the surface is chemically altered; quench hardening and shot peening, in which the crystal structure of the surface metal is altered; and galvanizing with zinc or plating or cladding with chromium, nickel, or cadmium, which protect the surface from chemical attack by adding a corrosion-resistant coating.

Painting is familiar to all of us. It can provide an attractive as well as a protective coating on parts. If a paint coat is to last, the part must be prepared by cleaning and priming to provide a surface to which the paint can bond. Paint can be applied by dipping, spraying, or brushing, assisted in some cases by electrostatic attraction. The drying of paint coats is often hastened and made more durable by heating (baking). Automobile body parts, such as fenders and doors, are first passed through a vapor degreaser to remove grease and then dipped in a chemical solution to create a phosphate coating on the surface to resist rust and provide a good bond for the paint coats. Next the parts are primed with a base coat, wet sanded, and then finished with several coats of enamel, which are baked to provide the long-lasting attractive surface we all know.

8-53
Automobile engine valves can withstand heat and wear much better if they are coated with a very hard material, such as stellite.

To minimize deterioration, metal can be sprayed with a protective coating.

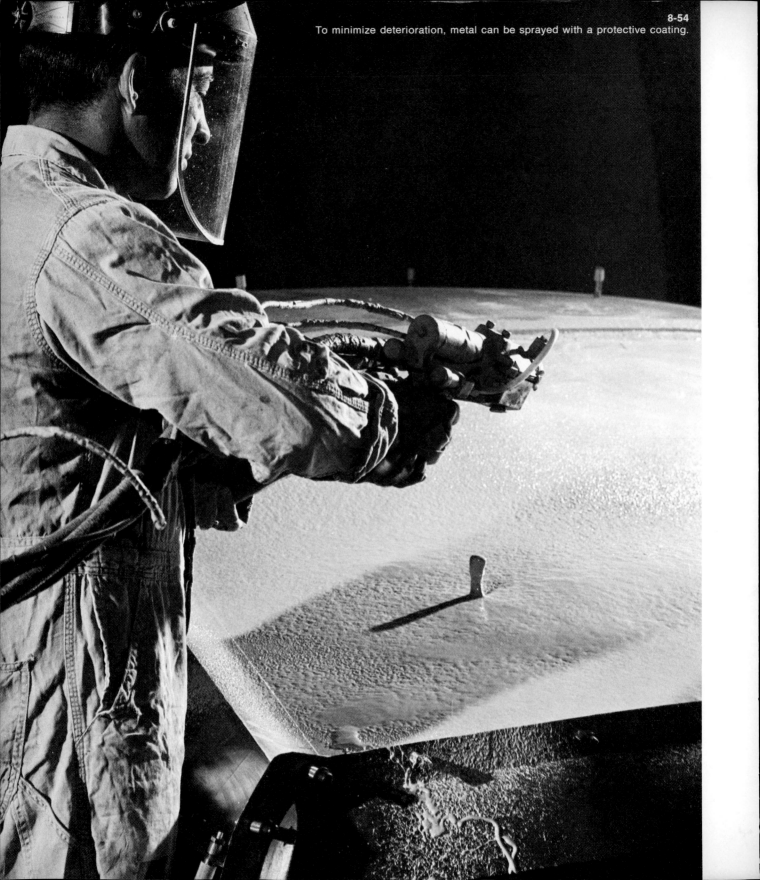

8-55
The first "automatic" dishwasher required a number of unusual components!

THE PROFESSOR TURNS ON HIS THINK-FAUCET AND DOPES OUT A MACHINE FOR WASHING DISHES WHILE YOU ARE AT THE MOVIES.

WHEN SPOILED TOMCAT (A) DISCOVERS HE IS ALONE HE LETS OUT A YELL WHICH SCARES MOUSE (B) INTO JUMPING INTO BASKET (C), CAUSING LEVER END (D) TO RISE AND PULL STRING (E) WHICH SNAPS AUTOMATIC CIGAR LIGHTER (F). FLAME (G) STARTS FIRE SPRINKLER (H). WATER RUNS ON DISHES (I) AND DRIPS INTO SINK (J). TURTLE (K), THINKING HE HEARS BABBLING BROOK BABBLING, AND HAVING NO SENSE OF DIRECTION, STARTS WRONG WAY AND PULLS STRING (L), WHICH TURNS ON SWITCH (M) THAT STARTS ELECTRIC GLOW HEATER (N). HEAT RAY (O) DRIES THE DISHES.

IF THE CAT AND THE TURTLE GET ON TO YOUR SCHEME AND REFUSE TO COOPERATE, SIMPLY PUT THE DISHES ON THE FRONT PORCH AND PRAY FOR RAIN.

components

Many standard parts and components occur again and again in engineering practice. These include such items as levers, linkages and screw threads, belts and gears, bearings and shaft seals, coil springs and leaf springs, and cables and I-beams. They are as necessary to the engineer as the common nail and 2 by 4 lumber are to the carpenter, the button and zipper to the tailor, and paint and canvas to the artist. These components have been developed to a high degree of efficiency, and their performance has been calculated, tested, and documented in handbooks. Therefore, the engineer can use them with confidence. In fact, many engineering designs are merely ingenious combinations of these elementary components. There are, for example, a number of mechanical toys that have fascinated men for centuries, in an era much less technically oriented than ours. Even in our time, the artist (and pseudo-engineer), Rube Goldberg, became famous for his whimsical and intricate combinations of mechanical components to perform essentially simple tasks.

Levers, Linkages, and Screw Threads

The lever is said to be the oldest mechanical tool known to man. The first ancestor who picked up a stick and used it to pry fruit off a tree or a stone off the ground was utilizing the principle of the lever, *mechanical advantage*. Mechanical advantage is the replacement of a large force by a small force to do work. Of course, to create the large force the smaller force must be moved a greater distance. All of us have observed that if a small child and a heavy adult are balanced on a seesaw, the adult moves up and down only a short distance, while the child bounces high into the air. You can think of many other examples of mechanical advantage, such as the bicycle transmission, the block and tackle, the nutcracker, and the hydraulic jack.

Give me a lever long enough, and a fulcrum strong enough, and singlehanded I can move the world.
ARCHIMEDES
circa 220 B.C.

8-56

8-57
The slider-crank mechanism converts the back-and-forth motion of the piston into rotation of the crankshaft.

A lever need not always be straight like a seesaw. If it is bent into a *bell crank*, it can be used to translate motion in one direction into motion in another direction. One lever can be made to act upon another lever by linking them together at the ends. Two or more such levers linked together are called a *linkage*. Linkages are used to create special kinds of motion, such as the motion of a front-wheel suspension of a racing car, the magnification of a drawing by a pantograph, or the translation from linear to rotary motion by a slider-crank mechanism.

The *slider-crank* mechanism is, of course, the mechanism used in all reciprocating engines, the mechanism that converts the back-and-forth motion of the piston into the rotation of the crankshaft, and eventually to the wheels. Notice that with a single piston, the force trying to turn the crankshaft around—the *torque*—changes from a maximum, when the crank is near or at right angles with the piston rod, to zero, when the crank and piston rod are in line. This is one of the reasons why more than one piston is necessary to achieve a smooth-running engine. Each crank is fixed to the crankshaft at a different angle so that when one piston goes through its zero torque position, another exerts its maximum torque. Of course, the slider-crank mechanism can also be used in reverse, that is, to convert a rotating motion into a straight-line or reciprocating motion. The electric-motor-driven air compressor or pump are typical examples.

Another mechanism that converts rotational into straight-line motion at a great mechanical advantage is the *screw thread*. We all know that if one wants to get to the top of a mountain, it is usually a lot easier to wind his way around the mountain on a gentle incline than to climb straight up. The work that we have to do to get up the mountain is the same in either case. The mechanical advantage (that is, the ratio of the forces that we have to expend) is just the inverse of the ratio of the distances that we must travel. The same is true with a screw thread. An American standard 1-inch bolt has eight threads per inch and a pitch diameter[9] of 0.919 inch. This means that once around the bolt the nut travels $\pi \times 0.919$, or 2.89 inches, to advance one eighth of an inch. Hence, the mechanical advantage is 2.89 times 8, or 23.1. To provide the engineer with a variety of choices, bolt manufacturers also provide fine and extra-fine threads. For example, the 1-inch fine thread has a pitch diameter of 0.946 inch and 12 threads per inch, giving a mechanical advantage of 35.7. The extra-fine thread has 20 threads per inch, a pitch diameter of 0.9675 inch, giving a mechanical advantage of 60.9. Because of friction, a screw thread usually cannot be used in reverse, that is, to translate a linear motion into a rotating motion. Since friction has the same mechanical advantage in loosening that you possess

[9]The pitch diameter is the "effective" diameter, the diameter of the "middle of the road" on the thread that is cut into the bolt.

in tightening the bolt, the friction does not have to be very large to prevent any motion of the nut. The lock washer used under a nut operates on the principle of increasing the friction to the point where, even under vibration, the nut has little chance to become loose.

Rotation and Its Transmission

The use of rotation to generate and transmit power and to move objects is entirely an invention of man; it has no counterpart in nature.[10] The rotating *shaft* or *axle* is fundamental to rotating machinery. Shafts are normally straight, usually round, and may be solid or hollow. To keep them rotating in place, they are supported in *bearings*. The simplest and least expensive bearings are *sleeve* bearings in which the metal shaft is separated from the stationary bearing by an oil or air film. The material of the shaft and that of the bearing must be different, so that they will not bind or weld together even when the film disappears. Normally, the bearing material is made of a softer material than the shaft so that abrasion will occur on the part that can be replaced most easily. In the last few years, the advent of certain very strong plastics, such as nylon and Teflon, has made unlubricated bearings possible for light loads.

Where exact alignment and minimum friction are essential, the engineer uses *ball* or *roller* bearings. Ball and roller bearings must be lubricated. In some instances it may be perfectly satisfactory to let the lubricating oil or grease run out of the bearing and into a sump from which it is pumped back into the bearing. In many applications, however, such as with domestic appliances, this would be impractical. Therefore, bearings for these applications are provided with oil seals that keep the oil or grease inside the bearings.

A rotating shaft alone is of very little use unless it can transmit its rotation to *wheels, pulleys,* or *gears.* The standard way of attaching these to the shaft is by *splines, keys,* or *set screws.* The illustrations in the margin show how these devices work. Where high

8-59
The sleeve bearing is the simplest type of bearing.

---

[10] A possible exception is the rotational movement of the celestial bodies, such as the planets about the sun or the moon around the earth.

8-60
A roller bearing has very low friction and can support heavy loads at high speeds.

8-61
The three most common ways to fasten a wheel to a shaft are the spline, the key, and the set screw.

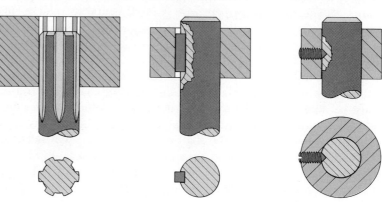

torques are involved, the spline is stronger than the key, and the key is stronger than the set screw; and, as one might expect, the stronger they are, the more costly and difficult they are to manufacture.

There are four fundamentally different ways of transmitting power (torque and motion) from one shaft to another: belt and chain drives, gears, universal joints, and clutches. Belts and chains are used principally when the shafts are parallel, when the shafts are a considerable distance apart, or when it may be necessary to adjust their distance. The flat leather belt (which was used for so many years in industry) has been replaced almost completely by the V-belt (e.g., the fan belt in your automobile). There are two reasons for this: the V-belt has a much better grip and a smaller tendency to slip off the pulley.

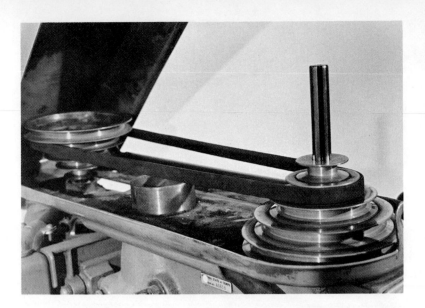

Chain drives—similar to that on a bicycle—are used when slippage cannot be tolerated at all. They are more costly than belt drives and require more lubrication. Chain belts are used primarily at low speeds, such as for conveyors that move a manufactured article from one place to the next in the assembly line.

Since the *drive* pulley or sprocket and the *driven* one need not be of the same diameter, we can obtain a mechanical advantage in a chain or belt drive. In a bicycle the driving sprocket (at the pedals) is usually bigger than the driven sprocket (at the rear wheel). This produces a mechanical advantage of less than 1, so that the rear wheel will turn faster than the pedals, but the torque required at the pedals is larger than at the rear wheels. This is done because the torque required to move your bicycle at a steady speed over flat roads is smaller than that which you can reasonably exert on the pedals with your feet.[11]

When driving and driven shafts can be put close together, *gears* are the preferred way of translating power. With gears there is no concern about slippage; they can be made to transmit high torques; and they can run at much higher speeds than belts or chains. Gears of a sort have been known to men since at least the Middle Ages. Leonardo da Vinci in his sketches of machines of war shows some crude uses of geared wheels; and the old wind- or water-driven flour mills used huge wooden geared wheels to transmit the power to the grindstone. The perfection of the mechanical clock has probably done more to develop fine gears and gear teeth than any other

[11]If you have an adjustable transmission in the hub of your rear wheel, you can increase your mechanical advantage by shifting to lower gears.

8-63
Chain drives are used most often where slippage must be eliminated.

8-64
The millstone, in the mills of olden days, was driven with
wooden gears such as these.

8-65
Modern gears are cut on machines, such as the vertical gear
shaper shown here cutting a herringbone gear.

8-66
Gears can be very large, such as the one driving
this ball mill stone crusher.

mechanical device. The teeth on the modern *spur* gear are not straight but are very carefully shaped so that the teeth of mating gears roll over each other and so that the next tooth has already picked up the load before the first tooth has quite relinquished it. This produces a quiet running gear and a relatively smooth power transmission. For even greater smoothness, one can use *helical* gears. *Bevel* gears are used when the two shafts are not parallel.

The mechanical advantage of a pair of spur gears rarely exceeds 10—much the same as in belt or chain drives. When a larger mechanical advantage is desired, a *worm* gear can be used. This is very much like a screw thread that has been fitted to engage a gear rather than a nut. It has the large mechanical advantage typical of screw threads, but similarly cannot run in the reverse direction because friction prevents the gear from driving the worm.

Springs

Springs are used to store mechanical energy temporarily. When you wind your watch, you store energy in a spiral spring. This energy is used to run the watch for the next 24 hours. When you cock your rifle, the energy you expend on the cocking lever is stored in a spring to be released when you pull the trigger to drive the bolt forward. When a bump in the road pushes a wheel on your car upward, the work done by the bump is stored in the suspension spring, which later uses that energy to push the wheel back into position.

Springs come in a large variety of shapes and sizes, including the familiar coil spring used in countless mechanical devices, flat leaf springs, and spiral springs, such as the spring in most watches. Springs are made from metals with good elasticity or springback, such as alloy steels or phosphor bronzes, and materials that do not weaken with time.

problems

8-1. You are the manager of a production department. This means that you must specify raw material purchases, and, in detail, the type and order in which parts are manufactured. You receive the following sketches from the engineering department. Prepare the raw materials list and each production step in detail. Indicate the machine tools needed.

(a) Locking pins [8-67]
(b) Concrete beam [8-68]
(c) Piping assembly [8-69]
(d) Engine mount [8-70]

8-67

LOCKING PIN
SCALE: FULL
MATERIAL: AISI 1040 STEEL
HEAT TREAT AFTER MACHINING
TOLERANCE: ±.005"

8-68

8-69

CONCRETE BEAM
MATERIAL: CONCRETE
STEEL REINFORCED - #8 BAR
TOLERANCE: ± 0.25"

FOUR 1" RE-BARS
ON 4" CENTERS

SCALE: 1"= 1'-0"

PIPING ASSEMBLY
MATERIAL: ASTM A53B STEEL
SCALE: 1'=4"

8-70

ENGINE MOUNT
MATERIAL: C.R. STEEL
TOLERANCE: ±.005

SCALE : FULL

8-2. Your 10-year-old sister has been after you to build her a swing. To do so you must fix a horizontal bar between two branches 3 feet apart. The local hardware store can sell you a $\frac{1}{2}$-inch-diameter steel rod at $0.35/pound, a $\frac{3}{4}$-inch-diameter aluminum rod at $0.60/pound, or a 2-inch-diameter hardwood dowel for $0.25/foot. You check with a friend who is 2 years ahead of you in engineering. He doesn't have time to make the calculations for you, but he looks up some formulas and tells you that the maximum stress in pounds/square inch (which shouldn't be over one-fourth the ultimate tensile strength) is about $30.5\ L/D^3$ pounds/square inch, where L is the load in pounds and D is the bar diameter in inches. Which of the three bars would you choose, and why? How would you fasten the bar to the tree so that it is secure and does not injure the tree?

8-3. The table on page 705 in Appendix III gives, among other data, the coefficient of thermal expansion of various metals.

(a) How would you define this coefficient to a freshman high school student?

(b) Often thermometers are made by cementing together two strips of different metals. Why does this work? What metals would you choose for an outdoor thermometer useful anywhere in the United States? Show the criteria on which your selection is based.

(c) Pick the dimensions in (b) so that a temperature change of 100°F will give a $\frac{1}{8}$-inch deflection.

Note: The deflection is about $l^2/2r$ where l is the length of the strips and r is given by the equation

$$r = t\ \frac{1 + \dfrac{(E_1 + E_2)^2}{12\ E_1\ E_2}}{(\alpha_1 + \alpha_2)\ \Delta T}$$

provided the layers are equally thick.

Here: E_1 and E_2 are the moduli of elasticity of the two metals:

α_1 and α_2 are their coefficients of thermal expansion:

t   is the thickness of each layer; and

ΔT is the temperature change.

Make sure that you choose matching dimensions.

8-71

DESIGN

8-72

8-73

8-74

8-75 **8-76**

(d) Select the construction method for the element and lay out a step-by-step production flow chart.
(e) If facilities are available, build a prototype and test it.
8-4. Select materials and develop a complete production schedule for
(a) One thousand ornamental wall shelf brackets [8-72]
(b) Fifty frying pans
(c) Ten thousand hollow plastic balls (PVC)—each to support 10 pounds of fishing net
(d) Forty thousand safety bolts for doors [8-73]
(e) One million metallic screw bases for electric light bulbs
8-5. What is the mechanical advantage of
(a) The hammer shown in [8-74]
(b) A block and tackle as shown [8-75]
(c) A block and tackle similar to that in (b) except that the rope makes two loops (runs twice over each set of pulleys) [8-76]
(d) A 26-inch bicycle—between the push at your pedals and the propulsion force on the road (take your own measurements)
8-6. Study one of the following methods of metal treating in the references cited and in others at your library (for "how" see Chapter 6). Then report in writing and/or orally about what it accomplishes, how it is done, its limitations, and applications.
(a) Nitriding
(b) Cyaniding
(c) Flame hardening
(d) Shot peening
(e) Chromizing
8-7. Some standard mechanisms, more complex than levers, gears, etc., are made up of these simple components. Find out what the following mechanisms are and report in writing and/or orally how they are built and used.
(a) Four-bar linkage
(b) Scotch yoke
(c) Planetary gear transmission
(d) Differential gear transmission
(e) Continually adjustable V-belt drive

bibliography

BAUMEISTER, T., and L. S. MARKS (eds.), *Standard Handbook for Mechanical Engineers*, (7th ed.), New York: McGraw-Hill, 1967.
DEGARINO, E. P., *Materials and Processes in Manufacturing*, New York: Macmillan, 1957.
MARIN, J., *Mechanical Behavior of Engineering Materials*, Englewood Cliffs, N.J.: Prentice-Hall, 1962.
NIEBEL, B. W., and E. N. BALDWIN, *Designing for Production*, Homewood, Ill.: Irwin, 1963.
OBERG, E., and F. D. JONES (eds.), *Machinery's Handbook*, New York: Industrial Press, Inc., 1968.
PARKER, E. R., *Materials Data Book*, New York: McGraw-Hill, 1967.
Plastics Engineering Handbook, New York: Van Nostrand Reinhold, 1960.

design for human satisfaction

9

A giant's fingerprint at first glance, these lines were produced by reflecting a laser light from a photographic plate whose emulsion was under study. The reflected rays produced on a second piece of film these interference lines —an interferogram. It was made to study how variations in the plate's emulsion thickness cause errors when lasers are used in precision metrology. By studying the interference patterns, researchers can calculate the emulsion thickness at various points on the plate. They have determined that for maximum accuracy the emulsion must be extremely flat— with a radius of curvature of no less than one mile—and have devised a technique that corrects for variations in emulsion thickness.

333

Man is not the largest of the animals nor are his vision, his hearing or his sense of smell the most acute; he is not the strongest of animals, the most fleet of foot nor even the longest-lived; but he is superlative in the quality of his central nervous system and he possesses a hand which does its bidding.

J. C. BOILEAU GRANT
Method of Anatomy, 1952

Man is the only animal that eats when he is not hungry, drinks when he is not thirsty, and makes love at all seasons.

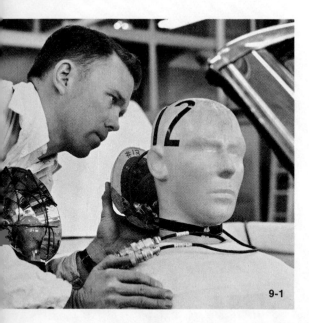
9-1

the engineer's only client is man. Everything the engineer designs, builds, modifies, or analyzes is for ultimate use and consumption by man. The engineer should be knowledgeable and understanding concerning man's needs and desires, and his social, cultural, and physical limitations. Before the engineer can adopt the motto of his profession, "applying science to the needs of man," he must know and understand the needs of man—and he must be able to describe them to others. In this chapter we shall look at man and see what conditions meet his needs and desires.

Four important areas should be considered:

1. Human factors engineering—the discipline that is concerned with man–machine[1] relationships.
2. Physical and biological limitations of man—the operating ranges of man.
3. Social limitations of man—the effects of social, cultural, and emotional influences on man.
4. The future and man—the role of engineering in man's future.

human factors engineering

World War II spawned a science known as human factors engineering, a hybrid offspring of engineering and experimental psychology. It has evolved from an attitude of "it's only common sense" to an organized and analytical engineering science—called variously biotechnology, human engineering, ergonomics, or human factors. Its purpose is to optimize the total man–machine system—the combination of the human and the nonhuman.

Human factors engineers study man in all types of environments. They are knowledgeable in physiology, anatomy, systems analysis, physical anthropology, and engineering. One important contribution of these engineers has been the development of anthropometric data (the "factory specifications" for all current models of men, women, and children).

There are many designs in use today that have disregarded the needs and comforts of the human who uses them. It is important that all engineers have a fundamental understanding of human factors so that they can participate effectively as team members in the design of highly complicated man–machine systems. The engineer should design instruments that give clear signals and make possible rapid and accurate decisions in a comfortable environment.

A man–machine system is subject to a complex mixture of influ-

[1] Man–machine systems are those combinations of men and machines (including tools and equipment) that work in concert toward the achievement of a common objective.

ences that originate from the *physical* and *operational* environments [9-4]. These influences have effects on the design and the performance. The design, in turn, influences environment, ecology, and society. A detailed examination of these influences should be made for every design. For example, a motorcycle can be attractively designed, but its price must be within a man's ability to purchase it. It can be designed economically for maximum horsepower, but it must also meet important biological and social specifications, such as those relating to excessive noise and exhaust pollution. The seat must have rigidity, strength, and wearability, yet it must be comfortable to sit on.

In developing a *systems approach* to a man–machine system, the engineer must investigate the origin of all the influences of the physical and the operational environments that will affect the final man–machine system.

The physical environment relates to the measurable physical world. It is the realm of *mass, length, time, electrical charge,* and their derived quantities. If it relates to the application of the physical sciences, it acquires the label of *engineering;* if it relates to the realm of living things it involves the *biological sciences.* Because the physical environment is measurable and repeatable, it is considered to be *static.*

The operational environment by contrast is *dynamic.* It changes from situation to situation—even from moment to moment at the

9-2

The right formulation of the relationship between man and machines is not one of competition, but of cooperation.

WARD EDWARDS
Innovation, 1969

9-3

9-4

MAN

biological influences

social influences

physical environment

operational environment

engineering influences

economic influences

MACHINE

9-5

same location. The many influences that arise from this changing environment, for example, job stress and safety hazards, are measured in different units and involve different concepts than the influences of the physical environment.

The influences that are directed toward the "machine side" of the system are measured in terms of time and money—those directed toward the "man side" are measured by safety, comfort, status, or mobility. This chapter is concerned with the biological and social influences on design, since the physical and economic influences are discussed elsewhere in the text.

physical and biological limitations of man

The physical and biological influences and limitations of the man–machine system are the direct result of the design constraints of the physical environment. Size, strength, and the biological tolerances of man are particularly important considerations. However, these influences are measured in different types of units. Size is measured in units of length, strength in terms of the force that the body can apply, etc. Much of man's surrounding environment can be measured in units of length—for example, desk and counter heights, doorway and passageway widths, and arm and hand working spaces. It is apparent that one should not design small, closely spaced pedals for use by populations with wide feet (Turks and Italians, for example), nor small drawer pulls to be used by people wearing thick gloves (such as bakers), nor to require women to perform a task that is difficult and dangerous to them (such as handling a 10-pound casting at arm's length). Most design problems are dependent on the dimensions of the human body, such as the reach and strength of its limbs, its endurance, and the range of these factors relative to sex and age. Therefore, the designer must have at his disposal a complete "data bank" when his design is to be used by humans. The study of the shapes, weights, and measurements of people is called *anthropometry*. The most complete and accurate anthropometric studies done in this country are those by Hertzberger and his group at Wright-Patterson Air Force Base.[2] Selected parts of this work are included in Appendix V.

It is important to recognize that humans, unlike machinery, are not standardized, and it would be a fallacy of the greatest magnitude to assume that all designs should accommodate the "average" man.

[2]H. T. E. Hertzberg, G. S. Daniels, and E. Churchill, *Anthropometry of Flying Personnel—1950*, WADC Technical Report 52-321, USAF, Wright Air Development Center, Wright-Patterson AFB, Ohio, September, 1954.

Unfortunately, there is no "average" man. Hertzberg has reported an interesting example of this fact.[3]

A few years ago, a study was made by Daniels and Churchill[4] to test the assumptions of the concept of the "average" man. They examined the records of more than 4,000 United States Air Force flying personnel to find how many men could be average in 10 dimensions useful in clothing design. Instead of using the exact average, the authors make a very generous allowance of plus and minus 15 per cent from the exact average. This is the middle 30 per cent of the sample for each dimension. This they called

[3]H. T. E. Hertzberg, "Some Contributions of Applied Physical Anthropology to Human Engineering," *Annals of the New York Academy of Sciences*, Vol. 63, Art. 4 (November 28, 1955), p. 617.

[4]G. S. Daniels, and E. Churchill. The "Average" Man? Technical Note WCRD 53-7, USAF, Wright Air Development Center, Air Research and Development Command, Wright-Patterson AFB, Ohio, December, 1952.

9-6

9-7

9-8

9-9

9-10

Isn't it a fortunate circumstance that all people aren't *average?*

the "approximate average." These investigators used these approximate averages of each of the dimensions as hurdles in a step-by-step elimination.

The following passage is quoted from their report. Only the percentage table has been added.

	Per cent of original sample
(1) Of the original 4063 men, 1055 were of approximately average *stature*	25.9
(2) Of these 1055 men, 302 were also of approximately average *chest circumference*	7.4
(3) Of these 302 men, 143 were also of approximately average *sleeve length*	3.5
(4) Of these 143 men, 73 were also of approximately average *crotch height*	1.8
(5) Of these 73 men, 28 were also of approximately average *torso circumference*	0.69
(6) Of these 28 men, 12 were also of approximately average *hip circumference*	0.29
(7) Of these 12 men, 6 were also of approximately average *neck circumference*	0.14
(8) Of these 6 men, 3 were also of approximately average *waist circumference*	0.07
(9) Of these 3 men, 2 were also of approximately average *thigh circumference*	0.04
(10) Of these 2 men, 0 were also of approximately average *crotch length*	0.00

The percentages show that by the third hurdle the number of "approximately average" men had shrunk to an insignificant 3.5 per cent and at only the fourth, the relative number, 1.8 per cent, is for practical purposes at the vanishing point.

The fact that these figures represent an exceedingly generous middle 30 per cent of the population for each dimension makes the demonstration even more convincing. Nor are these dimensions chosen for this purpose. Any other set would have shown the same results.

Thus it must be clear that the assumptions of the "average man" concept are fundamentally incorrect because no such creature exists.

Since the concept of "average" is untenable as a standard for the design engineer, it is necessary that an intelligent choice be made of design limits for the range of body size for each population to be accommodated. For this reason the tables in Appendix V give data for the 1st, 5th, 50th, 95th, and 99th percentiles.

Sensing and The Internal Communication Systems

The human has two internal communication systems, the nervous system and the circulatory system. The nervous system is composed of nerve fibers and brain cells. It has a very rapid response (measured in milliseconds) somewhat similar to that of an electrical circuit. The circulatory system is composed of all the blood-filled channels and

I have heard Dr. William Harvey say that after his book of the Circulation of the Blood came out, that he fell mightly in his practice, and that 'twas believed by the vulgar that he was crackbrained.

JOHN AUBREY
Brief Lives, 1626–1697

Everyone complains of his memory, but no one complains of his judgment.
Duc de la Rochefoucauld
Reflections, 1678

Brain. An apparatus with which we think that we think.
Ambrose Bierce
The Devil's Dictionary

9-12

tubes of the body, and it is similar to a system of rivers and tributaries. Its communication time is comparatively slow (a matter of hours or even days), and it is concerned mainly with the regulation of our internal chemical environment.

The nervous system is divided into three main subsections. The first is the *motor system*. It is composed of involuntary and voluntary elements. The involuntary elements are concerned with the control of muscles and body functions without resort to decision processes of the human himself, e.g., heartbeat, breathing, blinking of eyes, and digestion. The voluntary elements act on call and include all the motor muscles of the body. The second subsection is the *sensory* system, which interprets for the body the effects of the environment. Finally, the psyche or *intellect system* stores knowledge, makes decisions, and in general forms the personality and intelligence of the individual.

The nervous system communicates over a network of nerve fibers located throughout the body. As suggested above, some of the messages sent over this network are automatic and involuntary (like the heartbeat) and some are voluntary (like kicking a football). The sensory elements of the body, the eyes, nose, ears, fingertips, balance mechanism, etc., furnish input signals to the nervous system. The purpose of these sensors is to detect, recognize, and measure external and internal information and to relay it to the brain. It is through these incoming signals that we become aware of the influences and effects of our environment. The internal sensing mechanism contains a number of back-up, or secondary *circuits,* to protect us in case false or misleading signals have been received. This safety feature is especially important when (through injury or disease) we lose a particular component of the system.

Our circulatory system provides one means of reacting to the influences of our environment. (This explanation is perhaps oversimplified, but it does provide one with a rationale for decision making in design.) The circulatory system consists of a pump and a set of conduits, a major circulation network, and a minor circulation network. The major circulation system operates under relatively high pressure (the average healthy arterial pressure is about 100 millimeters of mercury), and it supplies blood to all the muscles and organs of the body. The minor circulation system operates under a low pressure (about 20 millimeters of mercury) and is concerned with continuously exchanging oxygen for carbon dioxide by passing the blood through the lungs.

Vision and Illumination

Man gains 80 per cent of his knowledge through his sight. For this reason it is easy to understand the anthropologist's claim that man's culture is *vision based*. The organ of vision is the eye; it enables us to perceive form, color, brightness, and motion. In terms of

WAVELENGTH IN METERS

GAMMA RAYS | X-RAYS | ULTRA-VIOLET RAYS | INFRA-RED RAYS | RADAR | RADIO WAVES — FM TV SW BC | A C CIRCUITS

VISIBLE SPECTRUM

VIOLET | BLUE | GREEN | YELLOW | ORANGE | RED

400   500   600   700

WAVELENGTH IN MILLIMICRONS

9-13
Visible portion of the electromagnetic spectrum.[5]

physics, the eyes are sensitive to a narrow wavelength band from slightly less than 4,000 to over 7,000 angstroms (Å)[6]. This is that part of the electromagnetic radiation (EMR) spectrum that we call *light* [9-13].

There are a number of factors that influence the actual process of seeing—some of which can be controlled:

1. *Visual acuity* is how well the eye can see, its resolving power. Normal acuity is considered to be 20/20 vision or a "normal" condition. Someone with exceptionally good vision may, for example, have a visual acuity of 20/12. This means that the "exceptional" person can see an object clearly while standing 20 feet away from it, whereas another man with "normal" vision would have to move up to 12 feet from the object to see it with equal clarity. In the acuity fractional index, the numerator is always 20. This is because 20 feet has been assumed to be the distance at which the eye interprets light rays from a single source as being essentially parallel. Those individuals who have fair or poor visual acuity can usually improve their condition by using glasses.

2. *Movement*. Although we cannot see the spokes of a rapidly revolving wheel, we can usually "sense" the motion. This is true of other types of motion as well. Discrimination improves as viewing time increases. In addition, the eyes "sense" the uprightness of the body position and help to maintain equilibrium. This function is aided by the inertial guidance mechanism that is built into the inner ear.

[5] Adapted from Air Force Systems Command Manual 80-3, Wright Patterson AFB, Dayton, Ohio, October 15, 1966, p. A5-4.

[6] $1,000 \text{ Å} = \dfrac{1}{100,000} \text{ centimeter} \simeq \dfrac{4}{1,000,000} \text{ inch.}$

9-14

343

Color	Percentage of Reflected Light
White	85
Light	
cream	75
gray	75
ivory	75
yellow	75
buff	70
green	65
blue	50
Medium	
yellow	65
gray	65
buff	63
green	52
blue	35
orange	23
Dark	
gray	30
purple	15
red	13
black	10
brown	10
blue	8
green	7
Wood finish	
maple	42
satinwood	34
English oak	17
walnut	16
mahogany	12

3. *Color* is the variations in wavelengths in the visual EMR spectrum. Color plays a very important role in design, and its value cannot be overemphasized. Chapter 4 addresses itself specifically to this point.

4. *Brightness contrast* is the difference in light intensity between the "task" (object being viewed) and the "background." This relationship may be expressed as

$$\text{contrast} = \frac{B_1 - B_2}{B_1}$$

where B_1 is a brighter, lighter, or greater percentage of reflectance, B_2 is the darker of the two surfaces, or lesser percentage of reflectance. B_1 and B_2 are expressed either in quantity of reflected light (that is, in lamberts[7], foot-lamberts, millilamberts, etc.) or as a percentage of reflectance (percentage of ambient illumination reflected).

For example, if we were to paint a dark green X on a light green background, we could calculate the contrast between the two colors:

$$\text{contrast} = \frac{65 - 7}{65} = 89\%$$

Similarly, if we used a purple X on a white background, the contrast could be calculated as

$$\text{contrast} = \frac{85 - 15}{85} = 82\%$$

What brightness contrast do you calculate for the type on this page?

5. *Illumination* is the measurement of light for human environments. Originally, the standard light source was a sperm whale oil candle and its intensity was equated to "one candle." Today we use a more reproducible standard unit of luminous intensity and we call it the *candela* (c). Its intensity is about the same as the old sperm whale oil candle that it replaced.

6. *Glare* is light reflected directly from a solid flat surface. If the reflecting surface is a horizontal plane, the resulting horizontal orientation of light waves tends to hide the properties of the material behind a "veil of light." We have all experienced this "veil" when looking at the strong reflections of light from water and snow. If one can reduce the glare by some means, such as by using polarized glasses, he effectively improves the contrast.

[7]A measure of brightness or luminance of light is the lambert (L), which is equal to $1/\pi$ candela per square centimeter.

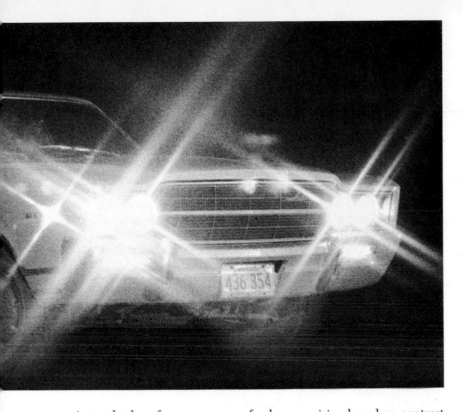

9-15
Glare is a common highway hazard.

A standard performance curve for human vision based on contrast (as calculated in the equation on p. 344) and illumination is shown in [9-16]. The area above the curve is the acceptable visual environment. Any lighting system that produces an environmental range below the curve is considered to be substandard. Assume that a task is to be performed and its visual environment corresponds to the small circle. This condition is below the standard performance curve—which indicates that the task is too difficult visually. To reach an acceptable environmental level, we can either increase the contrast value (vertical arrow) or increase the illumination (horizontal arrow), or some combination of both. The resultant ease of seeing in any case would be approximately the same. We can see that improvement of task–background contrast is likely to be the easier approach from an engineering point of view. An increase in the candlepower of the lighting system means an increase in power and heat. This means increased costs.

9-16
Performance of human vision.[8]

Hearing and Sound

Noise is unwanted sound. The effects of noise and the control of sound have become of increasing importance to the well-being of

[8] Adapted from H. Richard Blackwell, "Visual Benefits of Polarized Light," *Journal of the American Institute of Architects*, November, 1963. (A foot candle is the illumination 1 ft away from a light source of 1 candela.)

The crescendo of noise—whether it comes from truck or jackhammer, siren or airplane—is more than an irritating nuisance. It intrudes on privacy, shatters serenity and can inflict pain. We dare not be complacent about this ever mounting volume of noise. In the years ahead, it can bring even more discomfort—and worse—to the lives of people.

LYNDON BAINES JOHNSON

Unnecessary noise is the most cruel absence of care which can be inflicted either on sick or well.

FLORENCE NIGHTINGALE
1860

Nature has given man one tongue and two ears, that we may hear twice as much as we speak.

EPICTETUS
Fragments, 90 A.D.

Psychologists have found that music does things to you whether you like it or not. Fast tempos invariably raise your pulse, respiration, and blood pressure; slow music lowers them.

DORON K. ANTRIM

man. Today, the public is concerned not only about air and water pollution but about noise pollution as well. For the engineer, the goals of good acoustic design are control of noise, improvement of acoustics, and the introduction of pleasant background sound.

Next to the eye, the ear is man's most important sense organ. The ear has a very wide sensitivity range for sounds. It can distinguish pressures as low as 0.0002 dyne per square centimeter, and, for short periods of time, can tolerate pressures as high as 20,000 dynes per square centimeter—a range of 100,000,000:1. This extreme range makes the use of a linear scale for measurement purposes impractical. The difficulty of doing so would be somewhat analogous to finding a "ruler" that could be used to measure any distance from 1 inch to 16,000 miles. For this reason, a logarithmic or *decibel* scale is used to indicate the intensity of sound pressures. On this scale, zero decibel (dB) sound pressure is equivalent to a pressure of 0.0002 dyne/square centimeter, 60 dB is equivalent to 0.2 dyne/square centimeter, 100 dB is equivalent to 20 dyne/square centimeter, and 160 dB is equivalent to 20,000 dyne/square centimeter.

The primary effects of noise exposure are on the hearing organs and on the hearing functions. Depending upon the duration and intensity of the noise, temporary or permanent impairment of hear-

9-17   9-18

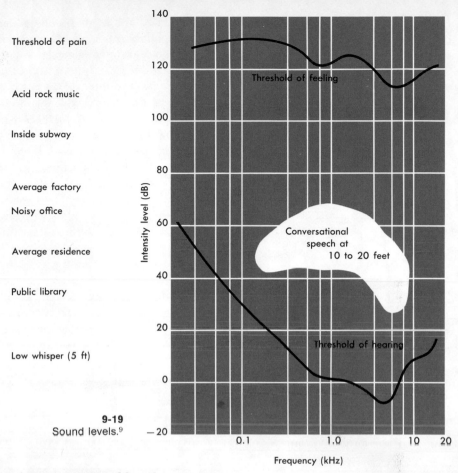

Threshold of pain

Acid rock music

Inside subway

Average factory

Noisy office

Average residence

Public library

Low whisper (5 ft)

9-19
Sound levels.[9]

ing may result. Investigation of the industrial noise problem has shown that prolonged exposure to noise can cause progressive loss of hearing in all ranges, starting with high-frequency sound perception. In addition to measurable loss of hearing ability, exposure to intense and constant types of noise has adverse effects on the personality, such as increasing irritability and causing psychoses and neuroses. Blood vessels also can be affected, and stomach ulcers and allergies can be aggravated.

Sometimes we must communicate verbally against a background of noise. Since our speech communication is really a signal, we must generate a signal that is loud enough, clear enough, and distinct enough to be understood over the background noise [9-19]. Although one may shout in a boiler factory and whisper in a library, the ratio between the verbal signal and the background noise (in decibels) may be nearly identical in each case. This is an example of the *signal-to-noise-ratio*.

Men trust their ears less than their eyes.

HERODOTUS
ca.485–ca.425 B.C.

[9] Adapted from W. E. Woodson and D. W. Conover, *Human Engineering Guide for Equipment Designers*, Berkeley: University of California Press, 1964, pp. 4–10.

9-20
Anechoic (anti-echo) chambers are used to test sound reflective characteristics of materials.

The designer of buildings tries to collect the noisy rooms into a single area, and then uses hallways, closets, or other structures to provide *buffers* between areas of different noise levels. Acoustical improvements can be achieved through the use of structural configurations and the sound absorption or reflection characteristics of construction materials.

Sound can also be used in indicating or warning systems. Auditory displays (such as bells, horns, and speakers) should be considered for use under the following conditions:

1. When the eyes are busy.
2. When light levels are low.
3. For emergencies.

One would not use an auditory display in high-noise environments or when the environmental noise is similar to the display signal.

Auditory displays for emergencies are commonly called *alarm systems*. Because of their importance in design, they deserve special mention. Alarm systems must have an independent power source, and they must be distinctive so that they are discernible over the normal prevailing sound field; just as a mother can hear her baby crying in the next room—while listening to a loud radio in an apartment next to the airport. The U.S. Air Force recently has used a recorded feminine voice for a warning system on one of its operational jet aircraft.

Taste and Smell

Taste and smell are affective senses, and their main purpose is to differentiate between the pleasurable and the nonpleasurable. For something to be detected by smell it must be volatile, part water soluble, and part *lipid* (composed of fats) soluble. Otherwise, its odor will not penetrate the smell nerve hair-cells (*olfactory organs*) that are located at the top of the nasal cavity. Smell is stimulated by air circulation, and its sensitivity depends on one's mental state. Smells influence the emotions, which explains the value of perfumes and incense. Smell is not the most highly developed of man's senses, but there are some vapors that can be detected in dilutions of less than one part per million parts of air. The organs of smell tire easily, and, in fact, grow insensitive to a continuous scent, while maintaining a sensitivity for a new scent. Some smells are composed of "feelings" since there are organs of feeling in the lower part of the nasal lining. For example, the camphor *smell* is also a feeling of *cold*, and the sharp odor of ammonia is part *pain*. There is no consistent way to classify odors. One system uses six categories: spicy, flowery, fruity, resinous, putrid, and burnt.

The sense of taste is more easily categorized into blends of four reactions—sweet, sour, salty, and bitter. Many "tastes" are actually

None is so deaf as who will not hear.
THOMAS INGELAND
Disobedient Child, 1560

349

9-21   9-22

combinations of tastes and smells, and it is very difficult to differentiate between them. For example, if one holds his nose, he may
find it very difficult to tell the difference between a bite of apple
and a bite of onion. The nerve cells of taste, *taste buds,* are located
primarily on the tongue. Different areas of the tongue are sensitive
to different tastes. The reaction of the taste buds to a particular
substance is closely connected with the organs of feeling in the mouth

Let onion atoms lurk
within the bowl
And, half suspected,
animate the whole.

SIDNEY SMITH
Lady Holland's Memoir Recipe for Salad Dressing

9-23

and with the organs of smell. For this reason it is difficult to distinguish tastes if the nose is congested, for example with a bad cold. Also, some sensations that are commonly attributed to taste are really sensations of feeling (*pain*), not taste, such as the distinction between a crisp dry cracker and a soft soggy cracker. Similarly, a sharp, biting taste sensation is usually due to a feeling of pain. Like smell, the sense of taste is also very sensitive and can distinguish the bitter sensation caused by one part of quinine dissolved in 2 million parts of water.

Pain

Pain is a protective mechanism for the body set into motion by the response of tiny nerve endings located at almost every point on the skin. Some of these nerves are stimulated by sensations of discomfort; others respond to touch, heat, and cold. When stimulated, they carry impulses to the brain that "the body is being hurt." Pain, itch, and tickle are similar sensations except in degree of intensity.

Some individuals are more sensitive to pain than others. In addition to pain sensed through nerve endings in the skin, we can feel pain in our bones, blood vessels, and in various organs of the body. Pain can also be caused by mental disturbances, when no nerve endings are affected. The feeling of pain can be reduced in severity by the application of certain drugs and by changes in attitude of mind.

Temperature

Man lives and works in a broad environmental range from the frigid arctic to the torrid desert. In cold climates, man tries to minimize heat loss and maximize heat production by utilizing heavy, insulated clothing and a diet high in calories. In the tropics, the situation is reversed. The critical variable in each case is exposure time to the surrounding elements.

The engineer should endeavor to design his machines so that the operator will stay within a specified comfort zone or "envelope"

Taste is the intermediate faculty which connects the active with the passive powers of our nature, the intellect with the senses; and its appointed function is to elevate the *images* of the latter, while it realizes the *ideas* of the former.

SAMUEL TAYLOR COLERIDGE
On the Principles of Genial Criticism, 1813

It would be a great thing to understand pain in all its meanings.

PETER MERE LATHAM
Collected Works, 1849

St. Agnes' Eve—Ah, bitter chill it was!
The owl, for all his feathers, was a-cold;
The hare limp'd trembling through the frozen grass,
And silent was the flock in woolly fold.

JOHN KEATS
The Eve of St. Agnes

"Heat, ma'am," I said; "it was so dreadful here, that I found there was nothing left for it but to take off my flesh and sit in my bones."

SIDNEY SMITH
Lady Holland's Memoir, 1771-1845

9-24

There are places and times where the "comfort zone" is synonymous with the "life zone."

9-26
Comfort zone.[10]

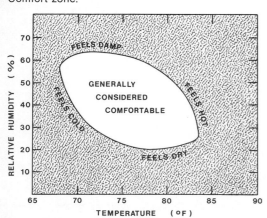

[9-26]. This zone includes the most desirable combinations of temperature and relative humidity. The types of heat loss (conduction, convection, or radiation) may be important, as is the *heat of vaporization*. As an example, in Arizona, where the humidity is low (7 to 10 per cent), little children should not swim until the *ambient* temperature reaches 90°F, because rapid evaporation of water from the skin in a low-humidity environment produces severe and rapid chilling. Factors such as this should be taken into account when designing an inland amusement park.

[10] W. E. Woodson and D. W. Conover, *Human Engineering Guide for Equipment Designers,* Berkeley: University of California Press, 1964, pp. 2–227.

9-27
When subjected to high "g" forces, the body must be given additional support.

Accelerations

There are four classes of acceleration that affect man. These are vibration, impact, sustained accelerations, and subgravity. Since future engineers will be increasingly involved in problems concerned with acceleration, it is essential that they be familiar with the biological constraints germane to this area.

In most high-performance transportation systems some *vibration or oscillation* is expected. Vibration experiments on humans are inherently dangerous. For this reason the precise comfort range for vibrations is not as well known as it is for other environmental influences. The resonant or natural frequency of a seated man is between 3 and 10 hertz (cycles per second), depending upon the man's body build, leanness, muscularity, and so on. This vibration range should be avoided, since damage to body structures and undesirable functional changes are likely to occur.

Impacts are short-term accelerations caused by sudden stops. If the stopping time is less than 0.1 second, the human body behaves like a solid viscous mass with no displacement of internal organs or body fluids. However, such impacts are rare. The majority of impacts involving humans are of longer (0.1 to 1.0-second) duration. The harmful effects of an impact result from the mechanical displacement of organs, or from shearing and direct trauma to body structures. *Man's tolerance to high g[11] forces (as in crash impact or*

[11] g forces relate to those forces that act on a body due to the acceleration of gravity. A body on the earth's surface is pressed toward the center of the earth by a "pull" of 1 g.

WHAT EXPOSURE TO RADIATION CAN DO[12]

LOCAL INJURY

erythema   depilation   vesiculation
necrosis   gangrene

ACUTE RADIATION SYNDROME

nausea   vomiting   diarrhea
anemia   leukopenia

CHRONIC INJURY

anemia   leukemia   cataracts
neoplasia
shortening of life span (?)
genetic mutation (?)

HOW TO HANDLE A RADIATION VICTIM

BEGIN EMERGENCY PROCEDURES IMMEDIATELY

resuscitate and stabilize patient
get detailed history
give symptomatic-treatment of
systemic and skin reactions

DETERMINE INTENSITY OF IRRADIATION AS SOON AS POSSIBLE

map the involved anatomic area

DECONTAMINATE PATIENT

remove clothing and store for analysis
remove penetrating missiles
clean wounds surgically and seal with plastic
wash—do not shower—patient
shampoo and cut—do not shave—hair

PREPARE PATIENT FOR EVACUATION TO RADIATION MEDICAL CENTER

dress him in hospital gown
wrap him in blankets
shield him with plastic sheet

sudden acceleration or deceleration) is greatest if the deceleration or impact force is distributed over the maximum area of his body. For example, the astronauts use a contoured couch for blast-off and reentry so that the force is distributed over the maximum body surface area. The use of wide shoulder straps and lap belts by military pilots and auto racecar drivers illustrates this principle.

Sustained accelerations of several seconds or more cause long-term displacements of organs and internal body fluids. When pulling out of a dive, an airplane pilot may experience a blackout. His blood is displaced toward his feet (one may prefer to say that in a 9-g pullout the weight of the blood is increased ninefold and the heart is incapable of pumping blood this heavy up to the eyes). If the oxygen-rich blood does not reach the eyes, blackout is the result. An anti-g suit has been designed to constrict the large blood vessels of the legs and lower abdomen. The constriction prevents blood from flowing or "pooling" in the legs and helps to diminish blackout.

In *subgravity* environments, including complete weightlessness, different concepts must be utilized than are used for conventional environments. For example, in space a large heavy toolbox floats freely, and it can be moved from place to place with relative ease. This type of environment, then, could result in passageways being designed differently or even requiring unfamiliar dimensions. A wrench for a weightless mechanic has already been devised. The designers were principally involved in compensating for the *equal-and-opposite reaction* that accompanies every *action*. If this principle were not satisfied, the man's effort in actuating the wrench would twist the man instead of twisting the bolt head.

Radiation and Noxious Gases

Man's body is well equipped to monitor and assess the wide range of stimuli in its environment—*provided the environment is similar to the original environment of man.* Light, heat, noise, gravity, forces on the skin and bones, flavor, and noxious fumes are all audited and our watchdog sensors are calibrated to tell us when the various stimuli reach dangerous levels. These warning signals are interpreted as discomfort, displeasure, or pain. When man is forced to deal with some entity that is a newcomer to his natural environment, he may not be equipped to handle it effectively. Such newcomers to the ecologic scene are radiation and noxious gases.

The human body is absolutely incapable of detecting harmful levels of radiation. Radiation alters or destroys living tissue and usually affects the most rapidly growing tissues first (testes, ovaries, and bone marrow). Like other agents, the effects of radiation on biological systems are proportional to intensity and duration of ex-

---

[12] *Emergency Medicine*, March, 1970, p. 61.

posure. Shielding the body with appropriate quantities of lead, concrete, or water provides effective protection.

In addition to shortwave electromagnetic radiation, other segments of the spectrum have biological effects. Ultraviolet light, for instance, is especially effective in destroying the benzene ring, a chemical building block found in living tissue. Hence it can be used effectively in many situations as a sterilizer and germ killer. Glass is a good shield and the atmosphere is an efficient filter for ultraviolet light.

Of the longer wavelengths, the microwaves (radar) exert a selective heating effect on living tissue. The wavelengths best used for cooking are about ten times the size of the article being cooked. Radio waves exert no known biological effect—unless they are converted into sound!

There are gases lethal to man whose presence cannot be detected by human sensors. Carbon monoxide (CO) is one such example. When subjected to heat or radiation some plastics are another source of lethal gases. Neither CO nor the plastic gases were normally present in dangerous concentrations in man's original environment. The engineer must be conscious of this condition and either avoid producing such noxious gases or provide a means to detect and remove them.

social limitations of man

Social influences on the *man–machine system* [9-4] stem from the operational environment. In contrast to biological limitations (which stem from the physical environment), social limitations are more subjective, more variable, and less easily measured. They are subtle.

The designer allocates the various functions between the man and the machine within the system. In many designs, this allocation of functions is the most important task to be accomplished. In the early days of human factors engineering, the designer was confronted with lists that extolled the virtues of men over machines, or machines over men—for specific tasks. A partial listing of such a checksheet is shown in Table 9-1.

The allocation of functional assignments for the components within a man–machine system should never be based solely on lists.

Dr. Alphonse Chapanis, a human factors specialist at Johns Hopkins University, has pointed out that

1. General comparisons are frequently wrong, like many *general* statements.
2. It is not always so important to decide on a component that can do the particular job best. One only needs the component (man or machine) that will do the job *well enough!*

Table 9-1
Man Versus Machine*

Functions That Men Perform Better Than Machines	Functions That Machines Perform Better Than Men
a. *Sensory functions*—Human capacities often surpass those of instruments, especially where the minimum absolute energy for sensory detection is concerned, within the visual and auditory range.	a. *Speed and power*—Machines can be devised to make movements smoother, faster, and with greater power than men.
b. *Perceptual ability*—A man is very good at sizing up complex situations quickly, especially if data are presented with adequate pictorial or familiarly patterned displays.	b. *Routine*—Machines excel men in repetitive routine tasks; they do not become bored and inattentive.
c. *Alertness*—With adequate provisions for activity and interest, the human is alert for changes, or impending changes, and can often prevent impending undesirable consequences.	c. *Computation*—When the rules of operation—the postulates—are built in, machines are more efficient computers than men.
d. *Flexibility*—Where flexibility is required to provide insurance against complete breakdowns in emergencies, human beings can play an important role.	d. *Short-term storage*—Machines can be built which can store quantities of information for short periods of time and erase these memories to make place for a new operation.
e. *Judgment and reasoning*—Where it is impossible to reduce all operations to logical preset procedures, men are needed to make judgments. This is particularly true when it is required to assemble a set of facts from different sources in arriving at problem solutions.	e. *Complexity*—A complex machine is capable of carrying on more different activities simultaneously than man.
	f. *Long-term memory*—Machines (computers) are more efficient than men in tasks that require long-term memory needed in handling unique problems.

*Human Factors Bulletin 55-4H, New York: Flight Safety Foundation.
Knowledge about the division of responsibility between men and machines is not well established. Nonetheless, some general answers can be given based on existing psychological knowledge.

9-28
The astronaut's life-support system must continuously supply his essential needs.

3. General comparisons give us some consideration concerning trade-off possibilities. These *trade-offs* can be visualized as the choice that exists between many different effects—effects such as performance, cost, biological consequences, etc. In the design of a system for exploration of the surface of the moon, for example, would it be preferable to use an astronaut or a totally mechanical system? The astronaut is flexible and can perform many tasks, but his life support system requires a large and heavy supply of food, water, oxygen, and equipment. A totally mechanical exploration system would be less versatile, but its weight would be devoted entirely to the main mission objective. The system-design engineer must consider trade-offs constantly—trade-offs that cannot be readily resolved by the general statements on allocation of man–machine functions.[13]

Many allocation decisions are based on the social, political, and economic influences in the system environment. The design of a man–machine system in the United States would differ from its counterpart in some other countries. We, in America, are accustomed to automation, speed, and accuracy, but in some countries the average citizen prefers employment at the craftsman level. The insertion of vast automation into such a country would upset the social structure. Speed and accuracy might also be accorded entirely different values. Such differences in the culture will affect the assignment of functions between men and machines.

In the assignment of functions to humans there are two general conditions that should be followed: First, the accumulation of tasks should make up a job that is interesting, motivating, and challenging. Second, the tasks should be of suitable difficulty. If the tasks are too easy, man gets bored, becomes careless, or even rebels against the system; if tasks are too hard physically or mentally, he will succumb to stress, or strain, or give up in despair.

There are four broad zones or levels at which men react with other men and with machines: *cultural*, *class*, *group*, and *individual*. In considering social limitations, it is important to give attention to the levels of influence. The engineer must always ask himself the question, "At which level are the 'men' reacting?"

The *cultural* level includes the broad behavior patterns of a large population. The design of a transportation system in China, for example, would involve quite different considerations than designing one in the United States.

The social *class* denotes the various strata or layers that exist within the culture. In some countries (for example India) the difference between social classes is very pronounced. Although there is relatively less difference between classes in the United States, we

[13] Alphonse Chapanis, "On the Allocation of Functions Between Men and Machines," *Occupational Psychology*, January, 1965.

One day, about noon, going towards my boat, I was exceedingly surprised with the print of a man's naked foot on the shore.

DANIEL DEFOE
Robinson Crusoe, 1719

9-29
Automation minimizes indecision.

would design some garden tools differently for a suburbanite than for a farmer.

The *group* consists of smaller units, such as teams, crews, and work groups. These units are goal oriented and they associate by virtue of certain skills, for instance engineers, physicians, golfers, and musicians. Since their goal orientation necessitates that there be a *group consensus,* certain things are mutually understood, and the allocation of functions is of less importance.

The *individual,* as the smallest social unit, is often overlooked because of the priority of prior decisions that have been made at a higher level. In other situations each individual is assumed to be an "average" man, thus neglecting the lefthanded, the partially disabled, the color-blind, and the differences between large and small men.

In the medical world it is recognized that "the physician who treats himself has a fool for a patient." Likewise, the engineer who considers himself to be a typical example of the "average man" and proceeds to design from this position is in danger of making serious errors. A classic example was the design of the original Mercury space capsule. The first drawings allowed space for the "5th percentile man," but it was found that none of the potential astronauts could fit into the allocated space. Eventually the designs were altered to accommodate the "85th percentile man." Such pitfalls can be avoided if human factors design inputs are used from verified data bases or from independently determined data-acquisition experiments.

Sociological Factors

In the era between World War I and World War II considerable work was done in studying group behavior in the machine environment. Many of these investigations were concerned with interactions of workers, with the hope that new methods of increasing worker productivity could be developed. One of these, the famous Hawthorne Studies, began at the Hawthorne Works of the Western Electric Plant in 1927[14], and continued for 12 years.

These studies began as an investigation of the effects of illumination on worker productivity. It was found that when the task illumination was increased, the work output of the study group of female production workers also increased. Other incremental increases in illumination resulted in incremental production increases. However, after a time, it was found that if the illumination was incrementally *decreased,* the production still continued to increase.

The particular group of women had previously been rather isolated, but as the study proceeded they were being involved in production

[14]F. J. Roethlisberger and W. J. Dickson, "Management and the Worker," A Complete Report of the Pioneering Studies at the Hawthorne Plant at the Western Electric Company, Cambridge, Mass.: Harvard University Press, 1946.

9-30

plans; people of importance were taking an interest in them . . .
and every week or so a group of nice young men would come in
and change their light bulbs! It was the improved attention and not
the improved illumination that made the difference in motivation.

Later these studies progressed to cover the effect on production
of such conditions as work hours, rest pauses, and pay incentives.
The summary result of these studies indicated that social factors were
found to be more important in affecting worker productivity than
the environmental conditions themselves. It should not be assumed
that social factors are *always* more important than environmental
conditions—only that they *can* be.

Psychological Factors

Several factors, such as fatigue, boredom, and isolation, have both
social and physical components.

359

9-31
Many a man succumbs to the psychological
pressures of his environment.

The most general survey shows us that the two foes of
human happiness are pain and boredom.
ARTHUR SCHOPENHAUER
Essays. Personality; or, What a Man Is, 1853

Time, with all its celerity, moves slowly to him whose
whole employment is to watch its flight.
SAMUEL JOHNSON
The Idler, No. 21

Isolation is the sum total of wretchedness to man.
THOMAS CARLYLE
Past and Present, 1795-1881

Fatigue is a state of increased discomfort and decreased efficiency
that results from prolonged or excessive exertion. It can affect the
whole body or any of its parts, and it can be treated, prevented,
or diminished by rest. The use of mechanical devices, such as *servos,*
power assists, supportive seating, or the allowance of more time for
the same task, can also minimize fatigue.

Boredom (to be weary with dissatisfaction) is the result of monotony. Women seem emotionally more tolerant of monotony than are
men. The reason apparently lies in their emotional rather than their
physical makeup. Monotony can be alleviated by changing either
the tasks or the co-workers. The more one knows and understands
the total man–machine system, the better equipped he is to deal
with a potentially boring or monotonous subsystem. Ingenuity is the
engineer's best ally in combating these two factors.

When designing physical environments, the engineer should be
certain that people are made aware of others around them. The
effective patterns and seating arrangements of bridge tables, airliners,
restrooms, and restaurants (especially European sidewalk cafes) are
all examples of this philosophy. *Isolation* can produce false inter-
pretations of the sensory inputs, for instance hearing or imagining
strange sights or sounds and inappropriate motor outputs. In general,
women seem less affected by isolation than men—at least for a few
hours.

Other Factors

Social influences also include *social necessities* or responsibilities of designing for human satisfaction. These are ecology, maintenance, and safety (including emergencies). The effect of a particular design on the ecology was discussed in Chapter 1. No lengthy discussion is needed here on the subject of maintenance. The engineer must remember to design for *ease of maintenance*. Those who have been amateur auto mechanics can recall many examples of poor design for maintenance. It has not been many years since the relatively simple task of replacing a throw-out bearing in the clutch assembly in a popular make of automobile necessitated the removal of either the engine or the transmission and rear end.

The desire for safety has been responsible for establishing many of the design criteria used in industry. The transportation industry today is working to make severe impacts survivable and to make painful impacts tolerable. A good motto for the engineer to adopt is "delethalize designs!" Designing for emergency situations is an important part of safety. There are three important criteria to remember in designing emergency-warning equipment:

1. Get the user's attention. A number of ideas have been tried with varying degrees of success. Red lights, blinking lights, horns, bells, or even a soft female voice can be effective at certain times and under certain circumstances.
2. Indicate the course of action that should be taken and the degree of emergency that exists. Also, indicate the time allowed for action.

9-34
Cockpits must be designed to minimize indecision and inaccuracy—a complex engineering assignment.

9-35

9-36

3. Use a separate, independent, and testable power source for emergency systems.

reflections and speculation

It has been predicted that the engineer of the future will be increasingly involved with problems in ecology, society, and health. *Ecology* is the study of the relation of living organisms with their environment. As suggested earlier, the ecology is just as much the responsibility of the engineer as of anyone else. When the engineer designs or modifies a system, he must assume a responsibility for the potential effects that his creation will have upon the balance of nature and upon civilized man. All his designs must reflect this concern.

Society entails the effect of man on man. Since technology will be a big part of all modern social systems, the engineer should be accorded a prominent role in the formation of such systems. This necessitates his understanding the social and emotional needs of man in addition to his physical needs. Because of this role, the engineer must comprehend the language of the sociologists, psychologists, attorneys, and physicians, and be able to work in concert with them to meet the needs of man.

Health is often affected by man-made changes in nature. The *health-care delivery systems* of the future will be designed toward keeping people out of hospitals. This will require a radical change in the design of the system so that total health care is delivered—not just fragmented treatment. The engineer is in a unique position to direct the design of such a system.

Bionics is concerned with the relation of man's biological past to his technological future and is one aspect of human factors engineering. It is the art of applying the knowledge of living systems (for example, the storage capacity of the brain and the mechanical versatility of muscles) to the solving of technical problems. As man learns more about himself and the physical laws of the universe, he seems to receive even more inspiration from nature. The fact that a design has persisted for eons in nature is strong evidence that it is a good (perhaps the best) solution to a specific problem. Through time it has achieved a design satisfactory *for nature's purposes*—and often adaptation and/or evolutionary factors have altered the specifications somewhat. Chapter 3 is concerned with man's recognition of the proprietary rights of nature in the domain of "good design." Bionics should help us to identify more of the problems that nature has already answered.

exercises

9-1. Diagram the envelope of the reach of your arms and delineate cross-over areas (where both arms are involved). Assume that you are seated and that your arms extend over a flat desk-height surface.

9-2. Using someone else's envelope of arm reach, determine the adequacy in terms of location of the knobs, controls, and displays in your automobile.

9-3. Examine your automobile interior to determine the adequacy of instrument placement and legibility safety factors, illumination and glare suppression, and seating comfort. Document changes that you would recommend.

9-4. Design a golf cart using information from this chapter and anthropometric data from Appendix V, as appropriate. Give consideration to the total design (i.e., power plant, materials, color, steering, etc.).

9-5. Visit a local craft shop and observe the work being done. Assuming no increases in personnel, working time, or basic machines, suggest ways to improve production.

9-6. Sketch a conceptual design for an orbiting space clinic to take care of routine medical problems of people voyaging between earth and Jupiter. Include necessary life-support systems.

9-7. List the design criteria for a wheelbarrow to be used by (a) Eskimos, (b) wealthy garden club members of Dallas, and (c) farmers in Alabama.

9-8. Calculate the contrast ratios of five popular logos or trademarks. Recommend improvements that could be made.

9-9. Discuss the contrast ratios found in nature using five specific examples (e.g., snakes, birds, or insects).

9-10. Design an alarm system to warn a deaf pilot of a single-seat propeller airplane that the fuel is dangerously low.

9-11. List the design considerations for an *infant protective device* that is to be utilized in long-distance automobile trips.

9-12. Discuss the differences that one should consider in designing an automobile to be driven in Japan and one to be driven in the United States.

The plight of 5 million Americans whose physical disabilities limit performance of the simplest kitchen chore can be helped immeasurably by the sympathetic and understanding design engineer. The remainder of these questions will deal directly with solutions to problems of a handicapped or hospitalized person.

9-13. Adapt an electric can opener for single-handed use.

9-14. Design a wall-mounted jar opener that works well for homemakers who have use of only one hand or two weak hands.

9-15. Design a knife to be used by a person with a weakened and deformed hand. Assume that the hand is fixed permanently in the semi-closed position.

9-16. Design an electrical hot pot with a capacity of 8 ounces to be used by a homemaker with a weakened grasp. Pay specific attention to allowing the homemaker to use this appliance without being burned.

9-17. In designing electrical appliances to be used by the handicapped, suggest some ways in which the electrical cord and its associated switches can be modified.

9-18. Design an easy-open can, package, and cardboard milk container for use by people who cannot bend their fingers.

9-19. Make some suggestions for the shape and operation of control knobs and devices for electrical appliances, especially ranges and ovens, for use by people with arthritic, weakened, or inoperative hands. Develop several alternative designs for a toaster to be used by an individual with diminished function of the hands and arms.

9-20. Design a functional emergency cart for use in a general hospital ward. The cart must serve the purpose of having all the needed supplies, medications, and equipment for an emergency. The cart should be compact and easily movable, capable of being closed up when not in use, but able to provide complete visibility and accessibility to all medications and supplies, and have a working surface for preparing and recording medications. No drawers will be allowed. (Investigate why this constraint has been specified.) It is strongly suggested that a physician or nurse be consulted to ascertain exactly what medications and supplies are needed, to provide technical expertise, and to develop the communication bridge into another professional domain.

9-21. Redesign a snow shovel for use by the flabby, middle-aged, and out-of-condition male. Pay specific attention to the position of the handle so that it does not impose an unnatural and unnecessary strain on the wrist, the arm, and consequently, the heart.

9-22. Evaluate the advantages and disadvantages, including the ability for "tossing people off," of the three-legged versus the four-legged (conventional) stepladder.

9-23. Comment and evaluate the advantages and disadvantages of the bottom-hinged oven door versus the side-hinged oven door.

9-24. Redesign the telephone dial so that it can be used more readily by people with fat fingers, trembling hands, and poor eyesight.

9-25. Evaluate and give recommendations regarding the position of the "trigger pull" on hand-operated tools. Is there a better way to turn such tools on and off; is the forefinger the best finger to use (or would perhaps the thumb be a better digit); and what about a control to regulate a variable-speed hand instrument.

9-26. Name three designs whose use leads to monotony.

bibliography

BAKER, C. A., and W. F. GRETHER, "Visual Presentation of Information," Air Force, Wright Air Development Center, Technical Report No. 54-160, 1954.

BERGAMINI, DAVID, *Mathematics* (Life Science Library Series), New York: Time, Inc. 1963.

Bioastronautics Data Book, PAUL WEBB (ed.), Prepared under contract for NASA by Webb Associates, Yellow Springs, Ohio, NASA Scientific and Technical Information Division, Washington, D.C., 1964, NASA SP-3006.

BLACKWELL, H. R., "Visual Benefits of Polarized Light," *Journal of the American Institute of Architects*, November, 1963.

CHAPANIS, ALPHONSE, "On the Allocation of Functions Between Men and Machines," *Occupational Psychology*, Vol. 39, No. 1 (January, 1965).

CHAPANIS, ALPHONSE, *Research Techniques in Human Engineering*, Baltimore: Johns Hopkins Press, 1959.

Cornell Aeronautical Laboratory, "Pocket Data for Human Factor Engineering," Cornell University, Buffalo, N.Y., 1958.

DANIELS, G. S., and E. CHURCHILL, "The Average Man," Technical Note WCRD 53-7, Wright Air Development Center, USAF (1952-Dec).

DREYFUSS, HENRY, *The Measure of Man Human Factors in Design*, 2nd ed., New York: Whitney Library of Design, 1967.

FOGEL, L. J., *Biotechnology: Concepts and Applications*, Englewood Cliffs, N.J.: Prentice-Hall, 1963.

FRASER, T. M., "Men Under Stress," *Science and Technology*, January, 1968.

GAGNE, R. M. (ed.), *Psychological Principles in System Development*, New York: Holt, Rinehart and Winston, 1963.

GAGNE, R. M., and E. A. FLEISHMAN, *Psychology and Human Performance*, New York: Holt, Rinehart and Winston, 1959.

HANES, BERNARD, and E. B. FLIPPO, "Anxiety and Work Output," *Journal of Industrial Engineering*, Vol. XIV, No. 5 (September–October, 1963).

HANSEN, ROBERT, D. Y. CORNOG, and H. L. YOH Company with H. T. E. HERTZBERG (ed.), *Annotated Bibliography of Applied Physical Anthropology in Human Engineering*, WADC Technical Report 56-30, USAF, Wright-Patterson AFB, Ohio (1958-May).

HEDGCOCK, R. E., and R. F. CHAILLET, *Human Factors Engineering Design Standard for Vehicle Fighting Compartments*, US Army Human Engineering Laboratories, Aberdeen Proving Ground, Maryland, May, 1964.

HERTZBERG, H. T. E., "Some Contributions of Applied Physical Anthropology To Human Engineering," *Annals of the New York Academy of Sciences*, November 28, 1955, pp. 616–629.

HERTZBERG, H. T. E., "World Diversity in Human Body Size and Its Meaning in American Aid Programs," *Research Review*, December, 1968, Office of Aerospace Research, USAF, Wright Patterson AFB, Ohio, pp. 14–17.

HERTZBERG, H. T. E., G. S. DANIELS, and E. CHURCHILL, "Anthropometry of Flying Personnel," WADC Technical Report 52-321, USAF, Wright-Patterson AFB, Ohio (1954-Sept.).

Illuminating Engineering Society Committee on Residence Lighting, "Functional Visual Activities in the Home," *Illuminating Engineering*, Vol. 46, No. 7 (July, 1951), pp. 375–382.

LAND, E. H., "Experiments in Color Vision," *Scientific American*, May, 1959.

LINDGREN, NILO, "Human Factors in Engineering, Part 1—Man in the Man-Made Environment," *IEEE Spectrum*, March, 1966.

LINDGREN, NILO, "Human Factors in Engineering, Part 2—Advanced Man–Machine Systems and Concepts," *IEEE Spectrum*, April, 1966.

LUXENBERG, H. R., and R. L. KUEHN (eds.), *Display Systems Engineering* (Inter-University Electronics Series, Vol. 5), New York: McGraw-Hill, 1968.

MCCORMICK, E. J., *Human Factors Engineering*, 2nd ed., New York: McGraw-Hill, 1964.

MCFARLAND, R. A., *Human Factors in Air Transportation*, New York: McGraw-Hill, 1953.

NOURSE, A. E., *The Body* (Life Science Library Series), New York: Time, Inc., 1963.

ORDWAY, F. I., J. P. GARDNER, and M. R. SHARPE, *Basic Astronautics: An Introduction to Space Science, Engineering, and Medicine* Prentice-Hall International Series in Space Technology), Englewood Cliffs, N.J.: Prentice-Hall, 1962.

PARENO, JULIUS, *Anatomy for Interior Designers*, 3rd ed., New York: Whitney Library of Design, 1962.

ROBERTSON, P. A., "A Functional Emergency Cart," *American Journal of Nursing*, Vol. 70 (1970), pp. 1684–1686.

ROETHLISBERGER, F. J., and W. J. DICKSON, *Management and the Worker*, Cambridge, Mass: Harvard University Press, 1946.

RUSK, H. A., "Nutrition in The Fourth Phase of Medical Care," *Nutrition Today*, Autumn, 1970.

THOMSON, R. M., et al., "Arrangements of Groups of Men and Machines," Office of Naval Research, ONR Report No. ACR-33, December, 1958.

Time Magazine, "Environment," May 2, 1969, pp. 46, 51.

Time Magazine, "Spring the Trap," Letters to the Editor, May 16, 1969, p. 8.

WILLIAMS, MARIAN, and H. R. LISSNER, *Biomechanics of Human Motion*, Philadelphia: W. B. Saunders, 1962.

WOODSON, W. E., and D. W. CONOVER, *Human Engineering Guide for Equipment Designers*, 2nd ed., Berkeley: University of California Press, 1964.

Copper spheres shown 500× magnification after being sintered for 5 minutes at 900°C in hydrogen.

et us assume that we have completed a feasibility study of a new product. The product appears to function as it should, and at the same time is pleasing to the eye. These aspects of the design have required a consideration of the materials used, functional effectiveness, the environment within which the product will operate, and the effect of the product on people. Now we must consider the effect of people on the product, and in essence this means that we should consider the economic factors.

what is economics?

Economics is that social science that is concerned primarily with the description and analysis of the problems of production, distribution, and use of goods and services. In the United States today, products are not sold because they have been made; they are made because they have been sold. And, they are sold because there is a demand for them. Demand means that at a specific level of product price, a certain number of units can be marketed. The number that can be marketed will determine (in general) the production facilities and processes that are needed.

The Economic Problem

Any economic problem always has two aspects—production and distribution. Every society has had to fashion some kind of system to *produce* the goods and services that its members need or want. Also every society has had to fashion some kind of system to *distribute* the goods and services that are produced. At different times, and in different places, the ways in which a particular society has solved its economic problem have varied sharply.

Solutions to the Economic Problem

Historically, there have been three solutions or methods of controlling the market:

1. Tradition.
2. Command.
3. Market-enterprise (sometimes called *free enterprise*).

Often these solutions do not have sharp boundaries. Each type exists somewhere in the world today, and aspects of each of them can be observed in every society.

Traditional Economies. In traditional economies each family unit provides for most of its own needs. The hunters and gatherers of earliest human history lived from the wild fruits and grains that they could gather and the animals that they could kill. In later more advanced agrarian societies, families learned to plant food and raise

Mere parsimony is not economy. . . . Expense, and great expense, may be an essential part of true economy.
EDMUND BURKE
Letter to a Noble Lord, 1796

There can be no economy where there is no efficiency.
BENJAMIN DISRAELI
1804–1881

Capitalism and communism stand at opposite poles. Their essential difference is this: The communist, seeing the rich man and his fine home, says: "No man should have so much." The capitalist, seeing the same thing, says: "All men should have as much."
PHELPS ADAMS

10-1

domestic animals. In both types of societies there was little trade, and that which did exist was barter. For example, one family with extra corn might trade it to a neighboring family for milk. In this way production was controlled by the needs of each family and the extent to which it was willing to work in order to fill or exceed these needs.

Command Societies. The early command societies were based on the existence of conscripted labor or slavery. Slaves were obtained as a by-product of conquest, by piracy and kidnapping, or, later, by commerce. They were employed as domestics, public servants, artisans, musicians, and teachers, as well as on the farms, in the mines, and in commerce and manufacturing. At the time of the emperor Claudius it was estimated that there were nearly 21 million slaves in all of Italy. The point is that, except for the small allowances paid them, this was all *free* labor.

In modern times in command economies the society (government) itself owns the tools of production and prescribes what is to be produced, how much, and at what price it is to be sold. Russia and China use this method of controlling the market. The important quality to note about both traditional and command societies is that in each case, *wealth follows power*, whereas in market-enterprise societies *power follows wealth*.

Market-enterprise Economies. In market-enterprise societies the quality that regulates what is to be produced, and how much, is *price*. This price is the price at the point of final use. In other words, every time a housewife buys a can of peas and the transaction is recorded

The propensity to truck, barter, and exchange . . . is common to all men, and to be found in no other race of animals.

ADAM SMITH
The Wealth of Nations, 1723–1790

It is a socialist idea that making profits is a vice. I consider the real vice is making losses.

WINSTON CHURCHILL

There are two things needed in these days; first, for rich men to find out how poor men live; and, second, for poor men to know how rich men work.

E. ATKINSON

10-2
In a market enterprise society, customers young and old daily exercise judgments affecting the success or failure of the product.

371

The successful producer of an article sells it for more than it cost him to make, and that's his profit. But the customer buys it only because it is worth *more* to him than he pays for it, and that's his profit. No one can long make a profit *producing* anything unless the customer makes a profit *using* it.

SAMUEL B. PETTENGILL

I don't like to lose, and that isn't so much because it is just a football game, but because defeat means the failure to reach your objective. I don't want a football player who doesn't take defeat to heart, who laughs it off with the thought, "Oh, well, there's another Saturday." The trouble in American life today, in business as well as in sports, is that too many people are afraid of competition. The result is that in some circles people have come to sneer at success if it costs hard work and training and sacrifice.

KNUTE ROCKNE

Where profit is, loss is hidden nearby.

JAPANESE PROVERB

Most men believe that it would benefit them if they could get a little from those who *have* more. How much more would it benefit them if they would learn a little from those who *know* more.

W. J. H. BOETCKER

Money, which represents the prose of life, and which is hardly spoken of in parlors without an apology, is, in its effects and laws, as beautiful as roses.

RALPH WALDO EMERSON
Nominalist and Realist, 1848

10-3

by the supermarket cashier, she is voting on whether another similar can of peas should be produced. The government did not "order" the production of any peas, let alone that specific brand. The producer continues to exist solely because enough housewives vote "yes" in this way. In most cases, they register their favorable votes on the question at hand primarily on the basis of their own family's satisfaction with the product. What is true of the can of peas is equally true of home appliances, lathes, generators, automobiles, and virtually every other product currently available in the American market. Just how all of this affects the engineer and the design process will become clearer as we proceed.

Hallmarks of Market Economies

The United States market represents the most highly developed form of market-enterprise society in the world today. It is a *mass* market of over 200 million people in 50 states between which there are few real restraints on commerce. Consequently, it is relatively easy for anyone with an idea to organize an enterprise to produce and distribute a new product. Although sometimes it seems that this is a country of big business and big unions, it should be noted that currently there are over 300,000 manufacturing enterprises that have fewer than 200 employees each. Over 20,000 new incorporations are recorded each month by the Office of Business Economics, U.S. Department of Commerce. The same agency reports about 35 failures each month for every 10,000 firms that are engaged in business (incorporated and unincorporated). Most fail because not enough attention has been given in the planning phase to the stark realities of market-enterprise economics. We shall discuss below some of the reasons for business successes and failures.

The United States is a society of *contract* rather than a society of *status*. In the time of Thomas Jefferson the laws of *primogeniture* were repealed. Primogeniture was a principle, inherited from the British, in which the eldest son inherited the father's estate. By repeal of this principle we have established the principle that young people should have the right to define their life stations for themselves, rather than having their stations defined for them by means of inheritance. However, in this system the same right that is possessed by one person is also possessed by his competitors. Every American is free to seek gain as he wishes, rather than being "locked in" a particular status by reason of his birth. John Locke[1] argued that "every man has a property in his own person. The labor of his body, and the work of his hands . . . are properly his." Similarly, Adam Smith[2] declared that "the property which every man has in his own

[1] John Locke, "Of Property," Chapter V of *An Essay Concerning the True Original Extent and End of Civil Government,* 1690.
[2] Adam Smith, *Wealth of Nations*, Book I, New York: Modern Library, 1937, p. 121.

labor (as it is the original foundation of all other property) so it is the most sacred and inviolable."

A market-enterprise society cannot exist where there is slavery. If, for example, one fourth of the society kept the other three fourths enslaved, then three fourths of that society would have virtually no income. Under such conditions a market-enterprise economy cannot develop, since the only buyers available to purchase goods are the one fourth of the society that has some expendable revenue.

In a market-enterprise society nearly everyone who works has some income. Therefore, some monetary reward is associated with almost all tasks. The whole society provides a potential market for most of the products that are produced. This condition results in the basic principle of market-society economics: *Quantity of the product demanded is a function of price.* This principle is the implicit regulator that controls the economic constraints in a market-enterprise society.

Where Does Economics Enter the Design Process?

We often hear engineers talk about "R and D," which is a shorthand designation for research and development. Generally, the *research* phase of the design process is considered to be complete upon the development of the *prototype*—the experimental model from which the final design is developed. This early model should be studied carefully to make certain that the design can be manufactured, and this process is what is meant by *development*. It is at this point that certain economic considerations become critical to the future success of the enterprise. The most pertinent economic considerations are those concerned with the realities of the "market," which regulates the production and distribution of goods.

Market-enterprise Parameters for the Designer

While he is engaged in the actual physical activity of creating a design, the designer must keep in mind the following constraints:

1. *The total market.*
2. *That portion of the total market which might "demand" a product like the one that he is designing.*
3. *That portion of the reduced market which might demand his particular design.* This is called "market penetration." As an example, the Kirsch Company of Sturgis, Michigan, not long ago sold 65 per cent of all the venetian blind hardware that was marketed in the United States. In this case its market penetration was 65 per cent.
4. *The price at which competitive products are being sold.* The price at which one's design can be sold is not merely his own cost plus some expected rate of return. Rather, the *price of competitive*

10-4

The quantity demanded of a product is a function of price.

Avarice, the spur of industry.

DAVID HUME
Essays of Civil Liberty, 1741

Which of you, intending to build a tower, sitteth not down first, and counteth the cost, whether he have sufficient to finish it?

LUKE 14:28
The Holy Bible

Money never starts an idea; it is the idea that starts the money.

W. J. CAMERON

Of all human powers operating on the affairs of mankind, none is greater than that of competition.

SENATOR HENRY CLAY
Address before the U.S. Senate, February 2, 1832

373

When looms weave by themselves man's slavery will end.
ARISTOTLE

10-5

Money is the seed of money, and the first guinea is sometimes more difficult to acquire than the second millions.

JEAN JACQUES ROUSSEAU
Discours sur l'Origine et le Fondement de l'Inégalité parmi les Hommes, 1754

90 percent of new products fail, in the sense that they are pulled off the market within four years of launch; in the more specialized areas, such as selling to the Original Equipment Market rather than to the consumer, possibly as many as two-thirds of the new products and processes lose money.

Design News
April 27, 1970

I will build a motor car for the great multitude . . . so low in price that no man . . . will be unable to own one—and enjoy with his family the blessing of pleasure in God's great open spaces.

HENRY FORD

Success is that old ABC—ability, breaks, and courage.
CHARLES LUCKMAN
quoted in the New York Mirror, Sept. 19, 1955

products usually will determine the maximum allowable cost to make and market a new design.

5. *The basic price/sales relation for the product.* For example, more automobiles can be sold for $2,000 each than for $6,000 each.

production and marketing

Thus far we have discussed the economic problem, the different types of economic systems, and especially the market-enterprise solution to the problem.

What Are the Chances for Success of a New Product?

New products are the lifeblood of commerce. What can be said about the chances of success of a new product? Looking at the whole picture, 98 per cent of all new products introduced to the general market fail within 2 years. There is an inexhaustible list of reasons for this. Poor design, poor packaging, poor market research, inexperienced management, insufficient capital, lackadaisical selling effort, and failure to provide maintenance facilities are some of the more prominent reasons.

Among companies that are experienced in the design and introduction of new products to the market, about one new product out of five proves successful. But in many cases one out of five is enough to ensure fame and fortune for the innovators and to provide the capital that market enterprise needs to grow on.

These statistics should encourage the young engineer to consider every aspect of design, packaging, and marketing strategy *before* committing his own capital or that of his company.

What Are the Chances for Success of a New Company?

In recent years more than 400,000 new firms are started each year. However, of the vast total of United States firms more than 350,000 are being discontinued annually, and ownership or control is being transferred in a slightly larger number. The relative frequency of outright failure, however, varies greatly between types of business.

Dun & Bradstreet, which keeps a record of such facts, asked, "What caused 9,154 businesses to fail in 1969?" Here are the answers they found.

	Per cent
Incompetence	45.6
Unbalanced experience	19.5
Lack of managerial experience	13.7
Lack of experience in the line	8.7
Neglect	2.8
Disaster	1.4
Fraud	1.2
Reason unknown	7.1
Total	100.0

Unbalanced experience means that the firm's experience was not well rounded in sales, finance, purchasing, and production on the part of the management unit. Thus nearly 90 per cent of the failures were caused by the management's incompetence. And, of these failures, over half occurred in firms 5 years old or younger.

It should be recognized that the above failures occurred during one of the longest sustained boom periods in our history. For business there has never been a period quite like that of the years 1960–1970. And yet even during this period of expansion and high volume in almost every line of business, something over 40 per cent of all the manufacturing firms in operation showed either no profit or an actual operating loss.

There are as many business objectives as there are human motives, but the primary objective of any operating enterprise must be *profit*. We have said that in a market-enterprise economy the individual must be left free to pursue gain. This is just as true for the firm as it is for the individual. No matter what the other objectives of a company might be, nothing can be accomplished unless that company first makes certain that it earns a profit on its operations. A

The justification of private profit is private risk.
FRANKLIN D. ROOSEVELT

The highest use of capital is not to make more money, but to make money do more for the betterment of life.
HENRY FORD

He who will not reason, is a bigot; he who cannot is a fool; and he who dares not, is a slave.
WILLIAM DRUMMOND

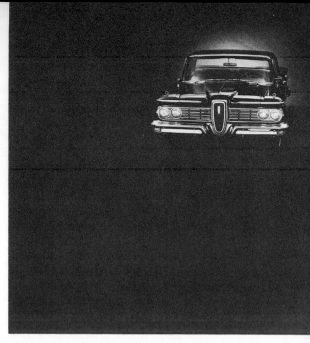

10-6
The Mustang—a marketing success.

10-7
The Edsel—a marketing failure.

"normal" rate of profit must be considered by the designer as an element of the total cost. The economist considers profit to be a residue after expense is subtracted from revenue. And the accountant, who has the responsibility of determining income for tax purposes, is not likely to count profits until they have already occurred. Nevertheless, the designer must plan for profits before the fact, as a part of the design process.

The consumer is a capricious taskmaster. There is no explaining the fickle nature of customer taste, and often the best effort of the designer falls before a subtle change in fashion. There is no known way in which the designer can ensure, beforehand, that the effort he devotes to design will gain that magical response called *consumer acceptance*. However, the root of company success is product success. Even today, with its hundreds of thousands of employees and with its thousands of separate products, the General Motors Corporation views its basic product as the internal combustion engine. Whatever else this company does, it makes very, very sure of the excellence of design and performance of this basic device.

The Xerox Story[3]—One That Made It

The observation that real life is infinitely more complex than fiction is supported by the story of xerography, with its multiple problems, complicated interactions, and worldwide business implications.

[3] E. E. Slowter, "Xerography—An Illustration of BDC's Role," *Resource*, Vol. 1, No. 2 (January, 1970). (Columbus, Ohio: The Battelle Development Corporation of Battelle Memorial Institute.) Reprinted with permission.

It is the story of a poor struggling inventor who concocts a process so novel that knowledgeable scientists question it. When all seems lost, a chance meeting brings technical and financial help that makes the invention practical.

Finally, a small company, under the leadership of its president, risks everything to bring the invention to the marketplace. The device surpasses all expectations, revolutionizes an industry, and brings fabulous fame, wealth, and growth to the major participants.

The basic idea for xerography was the creation of one man—Chester F. Carlson. The idea was so unusual that ten years after the invention, and while it was still being developed, we were told by a usually well informed scientist that the process could not work. When he was shown the results of the process, he remarked, "I do not see how it is possible."

By combining electrostatics with photoconductivity, Carlson had found the right basic concept, and all that remained was to reduce the invention to practice in a laboratory. On October 18, 1937, he applied for a patent for what he called electrophotography to indicate the combination of electrostatics and photography.

Carlson conducted continuing experiments after office hours in the kitchen "laboratory" of his apartment on Long Island. In the fall of 1938, he hired a refugee German physicist, Otto Kornei, to help him, and within a month, on October 22, 1938, in a rented second-floor room over a bar and grill in Astoria, Long Island, they succeeded in producing an image on a photoconductive coating of sulfur deposited on a metal plate.

They first charged the coated plate electrically by rubbing it with a cotton handkerchief. Next, a glass plate with the legend "10-22-38 Astoria"

10-8
The late Chester F. Carlson, inventor of xerography, inspects the hand-built machine on which he sought a patent in 1940.

was placed over the plate, and this sandwich then exposed to a flood lamp for 3 seconds. Dyed lycopodium powder (made from club moss, a creeping evergreen plant) was then dusted across the exposed plate. Lycopodium particles adhered to the portions of the plate which had been protected from exposure to light. When waxed paper was pressed against the sulfur coating, lycopodium particles were transferred to the surface of the wax paper, and a copy thus was produced.

This, then, was the first crude demonstration of the successful marriage of electrostatics and photoconductivity (electrostatic copying) to produce an image which could be transferred to another surface.

Major Industry Not Interested. For the next several years, Carlson tried to develop his invention and obtain help in its perfection and marketing. He contacted 20 or more organizations, including a number of major corporations and the National Inventors Council, but none could be interested.

The invention seemed too far-fetched. For example, when Carlson's first patent, issued on November 19, 1940, was featured in a *New York Times* business column, a young executive of a large corporation recognized the potential and brought it to the attention of several others.

For a year and a half, Carlson corresponded and talked with this group. Finally he staged a demonstration. All agreed that Carlson had a unique invention, but none could see how it could be developed commercially.

In 1944, a Battelle physicist, Dr. Russell W. Dayton, met Carlson, who told Dayton about his invention. Dayton recognized that it might be of interest to The Battelle Development Corporation (BDC), the Battelle subsidiary designed to develop new inventions.

John Crout, then manager of BDC, asked Dayton to invite Carlson to Columbus to give his demonstration. The Battelle demonstration was not highly impressive, but Dayton said, "Whatever else you may think, you have seen for the first time a reproduction made with a dry physical process."

The Battelle Development Corporation was sufficiently interested to sign a contract with Carlson wherein BDC received control of the invention in return for a financial investment and sharing of future income. Carlson was to receive 40 per cent of the proceeds.

How Xerography Works. As mentioned previously, the essence of the invention is that an electrically charged photoconductive plate can be preferentially discharged by the impact of light. In the first step of the process, the plate, coated with a thin film of photoconductive material, is passed under wires that carry about 7,000 volts. This causes an electrical charge to be formed uniformly over the plate—more uniformly than can be done by rubbing with fur or cloth, as was done in Carlson's initial experiments.

The object to be copied then is placed over the charged plate, and exposed to a light source. Where the light is not blocked, the plate is an electrical conductor, and in these areas electrostatic charges leak to the base plate. In the unexposed areas, the charge remains. In commercial xerographic machines, the image is projected onto the plate through a camera lens.

The latent image is developed by bringing electrically charged toner (or ink) particles close to the exposed xerographic plate. Because of a difference in charge, loose particles are attracted to and are bound to the image areas—but not to the uncharged background areas of the plate.

The powder image is transferred from plate to paper by passing the plate and paper through the same sort of electrical device used to charge the plate. As the paper becomes charged, particles are drawn from the plate to the paper. The thermosetting plastic powder is fixed quickly and permanently to the paper by applying a small amount of heat. Powder images can also be fused to cloth, plastics, wood, metal, and glass. The plate can be cleaned by cascading a coarse powder over it, thereby making it ready for use with another image.

During the early years of Battelle's research on xerography, some significant developments occurred. For example, selenium was found to be sensitive enough to permit exposure through a camera lens, thus making direct contact printing unnecessary. The Battelle investigators realized from the outset that the photoconductivity of sulfur was so poor that tremendous exposure times would be required. They also knew that selenium was a much better photoconductor (in fact, they thought it was too conductive to be useful), and so they tried a series of experiments with various combinations of sulfur and selenium, and included pure sulfur and pure selenium.

Complete Darkness Brought an Answer. It eventually turned out that pure selenium was the best photoconductor of all. But experimenters almost missed this fact because they had expected that pure selenium would not hold a charge even in darkness, and that is what the first darkroom tests seemed to show. Fortunately, one of the investigators was thoughtful enough to mistrust the yellow safe light they were using, and, when this light was turned off and the operation was conducted in complete darkness, it was found that pure selenium in the form used retains a charge satisfactorily even though it is a remarkably sensitive conductor when later exposed to light.

About this time (1944), another important development occurred. Joseph C. (Joe) Wilson, 36, became executive vice-president of the Haloid Company, a producer of photographic and photocopy papers and machines in Rochester, New York. Although the company at the time was 40 years old, its earnings were still comparatively small—$101,000 on sales of $6,750,000 in 1946. Haloid had just gone through a management struggle in which Joe's father, the president, had retained control.

The new vice-president recognized that the company had few chances for improving its profit position because of competition in its field. Joe decided that the company's hope lay in finding other products.

A short time before this (1945), Dr. John Dessauer, now executive vice-president of research and development of the Xerox Corporation, had read a description of the new process (by this time called xerography) in *Radio News*. He recognized this as something to investigate, and Dessauer and Wilson came to Columbus to discuss how the Haloid Company could get into this field.

Haloid Joins the Research. After comparatively brief negotiations, Battelle and Haloid agreed that Haloid would sponsor part of Battelle's continuing research in xerography and, in exchange, would receive a license to develop machines that would print up to 20 copies. The Battelle Development Corporation kept rights to everything else. There were arrangements under which Haloid would pay Battelle a royalty on any direct sale of xerographic products and a portion of any gross royalties it might receive from any companies it might license. The whole arrangement was reasonable for the status of the invention in 1946.

In the beginning, Wilson did not believe xerography would require a large investment before it became commercially profitable. However, as the research proceeded, it became obvious that Haloid's resources would be strained greatly. From 1947 to 1952, Haloid earned a total of $2.3 million from its established business, but this entire amount was needed to keep that business going. Haloid actually had to raise $4.3 million for xerographic development and these funds had to be obtained from outside sources because there were no profits from xerography until 1953.

It was obvious from the beginning that xerography had many possible applications, such as xeroprinting and xerophotography. However, Wilson recognized that Haloid could not undertake all of these, and he picked one objective—an office copier. Wilson and Haloid also realized that an office copier using the xerographic principles then known must be a large machine. Wilson decided to gamble on such a copier.

First Machine in 1949. The first commercial product, the Model A Copier, came off the line in 1949. It was a crude machine unsuited for use as an office copier because it required a series of hand operations 3 or 4 minutes in length to produce a single copy. Fortunately, it was found that the machine made good paper lithographic plates. This saved the day temporarily and produced some income. By 1956, xerographic products accounted for almost 40 per cent of Haloid's $23.6 million revenues, even though the first true office copier, the 914, was not yet on the market.

Thus, late in 1955, a new contract was signed which provided that all of Battelle's existing and future rights in xerography would be transferred to Haloid in return for stock in the company. Furthermore, the cash royalty payments were reduced drastically, and Battelle agreed to accept stock for a significant portion of the remaining royalty payments. As provided in the original agreement, Carlson received 40 per cent of the total package.

By 1957, the 914 machine was ready to be manufactured and marketed. Haloid was still short of cash and decided to license the manufacture and sale of the unit and thus collect royalties. Opportunity to produce the 914 was offered to one of the nation's larger corporations, marking the third opportunity that firm had to enter the field. The corporation conducted a survey on the prospects of the 914, decided they were not good, and turned down the proposal. At this point, Wilson had the courage to change his mind and decide that Haloid itself would market and rent the machines.

An Immediate Success. At last, in the spring of 1960, the 914 went on the market, and the 13-year gamble on xerography and the investment of $40 million in the 914 began to pay off. The machine was an almost instantaneous success and revolutionized the office-copying field.

The 914 (so named because it can copy material as large as 9 by 14 inches) produces copies at the rate of one every 8 seconds (after the first copy, which takes 30 seconds). It copies everything from book pages to legal documents, including signatures in any color of ink.

These features, plus the ease of operation, resulted in a massive demand so that by the end of 1960, the company—renamed Haloid Xerox in 1958—had leased about twice as many machines as expected. By 1967, most of the Xerox growth (the name was changed to Xerox Corporation in 1961) in copying and duplicating was coming from an even more advanced machine, the 2400 copier/duplicator. The 2400, introduced in late 1965, makes 2,400 copies per hour—about six times faster than the 914.

Thirty-three Years Later. What has happened in the 33 years since Carlson started his search? The story is not one of overnight success; rather, it is the story of a long, difficult, and continuing struggle interspersed with a few brilliant inventions or decisions.

Carlson became a multimillionaire from his stock and royalty income. Some of his income he shared with his early financial backers; some he shared with Uncle Sam. He died on September 9, 1968, at the age of 62. He left the bulk of his fortune to colleges and social agencies.

The worldwide interests of the Xerox Corporation are well known. Total revenues in 1969 were over $1 billion, with a total employment of more than 32,000—more than a hundredfold increase over the operations of the Haloid Company in 1946. The market value of the company's stock in 1969 was about $8 billion. A $1 investment in Haloid stock in December, 1946, would be worth more than $1,200 today—if you had held your stock!

The Life Cycle of New Products

The life span of a new product depends upon the type of product and may vary from a few years to many decades. In Congressional hearings on the drug industry a few years ago, one of the major pharmaceutical manufacturers testified that 95 per cent of all the products in its current catalog were less than 5 years old. Because of such competitive conditions within the pharmaceutical industry, there is tremendous pressure to develop and market new products at a very high rate. However, this also means a very rapid rate of obsolescence of the products that are currently in production. At the other end of the spectrum we have what are referred to as *producers' goods,* such as water turbines for power generation, or the heavy

Many times an economical design with a predictable life is superior to an expensive design with an indefinite life . . .

GORDON L. GLEGG
The Design of Design, 1969

10-9
Henry Ford's first assembly line of 1915 is acclaimed today as a milestone toward modern manufacturing practice.

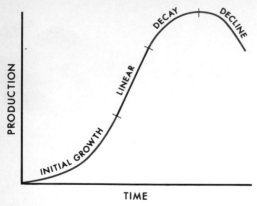

10-10
Typical growth history.

Industry prospers when it offers people articles which they want more than they want anything they now have. The fact is that people never buy what they need. They buy what they want.

CHARLES F. KETTERING

steel rolls for billet mills in the steel industry. Tools such as these are more likely to be objects of continual improvement, rather than of overnight obsolescence.

The life of most successful products follows a trend similar to that shown in [10-10]. This type of *growth curve* is seen often. It describes the typical growth of populations—of people, plants, and animals. Frequently, it also describes new-product life cycles, such as those of the steamboat, the steam locomotive, the automobile, and television. Such a curve has four basic sections. In the early stages it rises at a slow but increasing rate. Then there follows a period during which production is proportional to the passage of time. We usually call this section the *linear* portion of the curve. Then there follows a section late in time, when production is still increasing, but at a decreasing rate. Finally, as with the buggy and then with the steam locomotive, production declines.

What can the designer do to prevent this decay? As time passes and production increases, he must work hard to improve his design. He should test new materials, seek new technical improvements, and perhaps design new packaging and marketing strategies. By such modifications he may extend the product's usefulness to new operating environments or perhaps find totally new uses for it in its present environment. The addition of color has greatly extended the linear portion of the TV life cycle. Combination of TV with computers and with telephones may extend that life even further.

After the designer has completed the prototype of his product, and after he has helped to develop a manufacturable version of it, he is ready to turn to improvement, simplification, and cost reduction. In these ways he can markedly delay the onset of *incipient decline*. And this is one reason that design is such an exciting activity—it is always immersed in action.

Five Ideas That Did Not Succeed

Xerography has proved to be an astonishing success. Its story was told above. Here are presented the stories of five ideas that were *not* successful.[4] Each is a record of a new product that deserved to live, but died unnecessarily. New products sometimes are, in certain respects, like the people who each year appear fleetingly on the public scene, widely heralded, and dynamic. But, when you look again—they are gone!

Libraries and trade journals are full of similar case histories—but always *success* histories—of firms that hit the jackpot when they introduced new products. Unfortunately, there is no place to turn but to the victims themselves to learn of the failures that occur in the ratio of hundreds to one success. Government sources record no such data. Trade associations do not compile it. The fact is that no

[4]*New Product Introduction*, Small Business Management Series No. 17, Washington, D.C.: Small Business Administration, 1961, by permission.

one wants to talk about his failures. Yet, in many cases, only a thorough analysis of failure and its causes can ensure future success.

Shaving Preparation. Traditionally, men are not easy to change from their established habits. A man may be persuaded to switch from one shaving cream to another for a theoretical or a factual advantage, but anyone who undertakes to have him change his entire method of shaving is tackling a very big job. Notwithstanding this, a few years ago one courageous manufacturer introduced a new shaving product which, when applied to the beard, facilitated the work of the razor. It was, in truth, a new principle of shaving.

And it worked. A great many men who tried this new product were delighted with it because they always succeeded in getting a smooth, close shave. For a time it looked as though a radically different shaving idea had come into its own. Distribution was attempted in a few sizable markets. The manufacturer pumped advertising money repeatedly into those markets, but proportionate sales were not realized and, gradually, the product vanished from the dealers' shelves.

Observation: Subsequent investigation disclosed that the product had not been perfected before it had been launched. The item, which was a paste, dried out in the tube and often was caked solid before the tube was half used. Adequate product research and testing would have forestalled this failure.

Automatic Pencil. The subject of this case history is a man who was in the automatic pencil business practically all his business life—almost 30 years. During that period he observed that every new development seemed to result in a wider use of these products and their manufacture at an ever lower cost. His particular dream was to make an automatic pencil that would surpass any previously conceived. This dream was almost 20 years in realization. Being of an ingenious turn of mind, he developed and patented, privately, many little features of an automatic pencil that separately were not very important, but that collectively promised to make his dream come true. He also took careful note of the expiration dates of existing patents on proven features and applied them to his dream pencil.

All the time he was developing this idea he was working diligently, saving his money, and assiduously learning the business of manufacturing, distributing, and selling automatic pencils against the day when he would be able to venture out on his own.

Finally, the day arrived. He bought a sizable tract of land outside a metropolitan area, cleared the ground, erected a plant, designed special machinery, bought other standard equipment, and produced a limited number of pencils before his funds ran out. Under the strain of unaccustomed financial burdens his health gave way, and the project failed.

Observation: Men in the pencil industry who had a great deal of

10-11
When a man says money can do anything, that settles it: he hasn't any.

ED. HOWE

Time is money.

BENJAMIN FRANKLIN

Money is a stupid measurement of achievement but unfortunately it is the only universal measure we have.
CHARLES P. STEINMETZ

personal affection for the manufacturer concerned often ruminate upon this case history. The consensus is that there were two very important things that this man did not learn about launching a business. First, he could have had his specially designed pencil manufactured for him (with complete protection by an established manufacturer with existing plant and facilities) at a fraction of the cost of producing it himself. This would have left him with more than adequate funds for advertising, sale, and promotion of the product. Second, the competitive situation in the pencil industry did not permit a business to exist solely from the manufacture of a single product, unless it had a tremendous volume of sales and production assured from the outset.

Household Aid. A few years ago a man came to an advertising agency with a household appliance that he wanted to sell for $1.49. He was at the time in production, and said that he was arranging for sales agents to distribute the product nationally through hardware stores and the housewares departments of department stores. In discussing the item with him, the agency raised the question of whether there was any real consumer need for the product, since it appeared to possess many of the attributes of a frivolous item, and therefore was not worth the price suggested. He indicated that he had checked with his friends and relatives, all of whom had assured him it had performed satisfactorily and represented a wonderful value at the price. The agency executives decided that they were not in a position to take on this item, and the business man left, never to be heard from again.

Almost a year later a representative of the agency was talking to a sales agent of another agency who had handled the item. Curious about its success, the advertising man asked a number of questions. The product had actually been manufactured in quantity and distributed nationally. However, it had run into noticeable trade and consumer resistance from the very beginning. The sales agent reported that within 30 days after he had begun to advertise the product he learned that a similar item selling for 39 cents had been in distribution a year before through variety stores and had been withdrawn because of lack of consumer interest or need for the product!

Observation: It would be conservative to estimate that the manufacturer lost a minimum of $50,000 in the venture. In this case a few hundred dollars in consumer and trade research would have saved him at least $49,000 by establishing the fact that a comparable product, selling for much less, had failed only a year earlier.

Appliance. Some years ago the end of the common cold was heralded. The newly developed glycol vaporizers were reputed to be the "golden answer." This is the story of one manufacturer of such a product. Being unusually thorough and patient, he commissioned a well-known university to conduct exhaustive tests on the efficacy of treating colds with his type of glycol vaporizer. On the basis of reports that he received, he concluded that the appliance-type product really worked. By carefully designing the product and efficiently planning manufacturing, distribution, and sales, he was able to bring the item, normally a costly unit, down to a $25 retail price. He engaged an advertising agency and they, in turn, designed ads with compelling copy. On an impulse, someone at the agency submitted the proposed advertising copy to the Federal Trade Commission to be certain that the facts and claims contained in the copy were not objectionable. Then the roof fell in!

The Federal Trade Commission took issue with the findings of the university, pointing out that a number of the elements employed in the treatment were potentially dangerous and summing up its complaint by stating that the new product was not in the public interest. By this time the manufacturer is reputed to have invested over $200,000 without any possible prospect of salvage.

Observation: Manufacturers who produce products having a bearing on the public's health, well-being, diet, or physical appearance should recognize that it is always advisable to check the regulations of the Federal Trade Commission, the Food and Drug Administration, the Department of Agriculture, and the American Medical Association at the very earliest stages of the feasibility phase of the design.

Frozen-food Specialty. Many food men have watched with fascination the rapid and seemingly endless growth of the frozen-food industry. While fruits, vegetables, fish, poultry, and other products have become staple items in this field, many firms have introduced such specialties as frozen waffles, potato puffs, and seafood items and have done well with them. One manufacturer, observing this trend, introduced simultaneously in six eastern markets an exotic food for which there was little established acceptance on a broad basis. Because of its nature, it had to be priced high to accommodate the exceptional manufacturing cost and the markups required by distributors and retailers. Despite intensive advertising and promotional support, the product did not achieve satisfactory sales. Since there were many other items with a faster turnover clamoring for the limited space available in a retail deep freeze, this item disappeared within a few months.

Observation: The manufacturer involved was not experienced in the frozen-food field. The marketing peculiarities of frozen foods proved to be quite different from those of dry groceries—the form in which this product was successfully sold before, and is being successfully sold today. The guidance of an experienced, frozen-foods merchandising man, brought into the picture before the new product was introduced, would have accomplished one of the following: (1) It would have caused the manufacturer to withhold his product from distribution through frozen-food channels, or (2) the product would have been subjected to change in unit size, packaging, and so forth. That would have speeded turnover and reduced unit cost to the customer. The mistake here was in failing to recognize the frozen-food business for what it is—an exceedingly tough, competitive field for even the most worthy products.

optimization

The demands of production and of marketing—as well as the correction of the mistakes described—all have two factors in common: they all require substantial allocation of capital, and they all require time. Both of these factors are what the economists call *scarce resources*. Some companies spend most of their capital on engineering and enter bankruptcy after designing the finest product of its kind. Other companies choose to emphasize production to the exclusion of both engineering and marketing. Other firms are extremely sales minded and tend to sacrifice engineering and production on the altar of increased volume. Lack of proper balance in any of these aspects can be disastrous.

In modern business it is not the crook who is to be feared most, it is the honest man who doesn't know what he is doing.

OWEN D. YOUNG

. . . No business, no matter what its size, can be called safe until it has been forced to learn economy and rigidly to measure values of men and materials.

HARVEY S. FIRESTONE

10-12

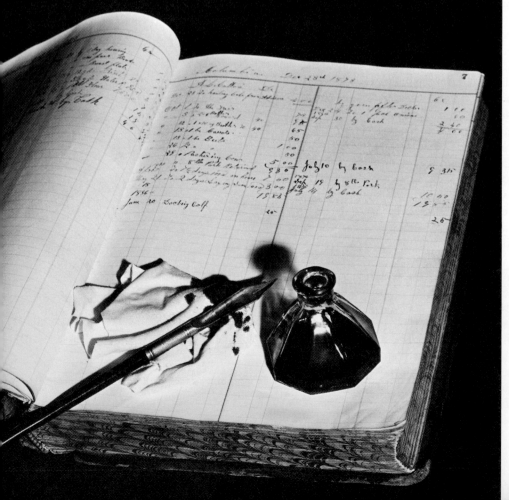

So we see that there are conflicting demands for capital. When we have resolved these conflicts into the best possible overall results under the circumstances, we say that we have *optimized* the performance. This requires what are called trade-offs among the competing demands for a limited supply of capital. If one spends available funds on new machinery, he may not have what he would like to spend on advertising. If we spend our money on inventory to be certain that the factory never runs out of supplies, we may not have enough money to meet the payroll.

How to Tell How You Are Doing

We shall discuss only two of the myriad tools used by the operating businessman to determine whether he is optimizing his overall performance. Many professional and trade associations maintain statistical services for their members, but the two tools we shall mention are absolutely fundamental and therefore are generally available.

Fourteen Important Ratios. Every year in the November issue of *Dun's Review and Modern Industry*, Dun & Bradstreet publishes fourteen important ratios for many lines of manufactures. This company for many, many years has devoted itself to collecting and maintaining files on American businesses. Each year those firms interested in getting and keeping a good credit rating submit their accounting reports, both balance sheets and operating statements, to Dun & Bradstreet. In addition to assigning a credit rating to the respondent firm, Dun & Bradstreet tabulates the data by industry for the benefit of all its subscribers. In recent years the tabulation has been by SIC code number, making it still more useful. SIC is shorthand for Standard Industrial Classification, a publication of the government.

To find out if he is optimizing his overall performance (as compared with his competitors) all a person has to do is to look up the SIC code number for his major product in the SIC manual. Then he turns to the Dun & Bradstreet compilation of the fourteen ratios and finds his particular industry. Under this entry he will find the best, median, and poorest performances for his industry. He will find how his industry performed in ratio of current assets to current debt, sales to inventory, profit to sales, profit to net worth, sales to net worth, and nine other ratios that have come to be regarded as valuable indicators of business performance. Based upon the same ratios from his own accounting reports, the businessman can take corrective action.

Census of Manufactures. In every year ending in a 2 or a 7, the US Department of Commerce conducts a census of manufactures. It is such a huge job that it takes a year or two to tabulate the data and to begin to issue the findings. For this reason these data are not as current as those of Dun & Bradstreet, but they are just as useful, nonetheless. The census lists data for each of 20 industries, for geo-

There is one rule for industrialists and that is: Make the best quality of goods possible at the lowest cost possible, paying the highest wages possible.

HENRY FORD

graphical areas right down to the level of the county in many cases, and for many specific products. Of particular value are the data on value of shipments, value added by manufacture, number of production workers, and man-hours and earnings of production workers. When we divide value added through manufacture by production workers, production worker man-hours, or production worker earnings, we obtain three basic measures of productivity to guide us in our design and development activities. As before, the need for corrective action may be indicated by a comparison of our own firm's data with that for the industry.

By carefully using the data published by Dun & Bradstreet and the Census of Manufactures, the designer can get some idea of how his new product ideas may fare in the market. At the very least, he can identify those new product ideas which are likely to fail.

A Tentative Selling Price

The calculation of a tentative price for a proposed design should be given consideration as a part of the feasibility design study. The primary objective of arriving at a tentative selling price so early in the design process is to make certain that it is possible to achieve the recovery of all costs plus some "specified" return on the company's investment. In general, the costs of production will be a function of the overall investments made in buildings and machinery, the skill classes of labor used, and the processes required in the production of the design. Usually, a number of different manufacturing processes can be employed to achieve the same design result. For instance, a machine part might be manufactured by forging, stamping, casting, or machining. Although a finished part might perform the same function without regard to its method of manufacture, the respective cost to achieve each of the various processes could vary considerably. Also, the initial investment in equipment necessary to accomplish each of the various processes might vary widely, and so might the costs of operation of the equipment. A company's equipment investment will depend upon the complexity of the design and upon the anticipated quantity of the product. Usually, choices will have to be made between securing special or general-purpose machinery, but it may be that the company already has available a sufficient amount of equipment that can be used to produce the design without making any new investment at all.

If new equipment must be purchased, and if a high production rate is anticipated, it might be advantageous to modify the design—for example, so that the part could be stamped from relatively cheap sheet metal instead of being cast or machined. For stamping, the special dies required by a punch press, although expensive initially, may more than pay their way in reducing the labor costs per piece by making possible high production rates. On the other hand, one may wish to utilize presently available special-purpose machines,

One of the cheapest ways to design something is not to design it at all.

GORDON L. GLEGG
The Design of Design, 1969

Labor can do nothing without capital, capital nothing without labor, and neither labor nor capital can do anything without the guiding genius of management; and management, however wise its genius may be, can do nothing without the privileges which the community affords.

W. L. MACKENZIE KING
Canadian Club Speech, 1919

such as automatic lathes, in which case allowance must be made for the increased material and labor costs. Or the company may have a foundry that could take advantage of the relatively cheap labor and material costs and produce the part by casting.

The design engineer should make his decisions only after considering the overall results expected by his management. Such results will be a function of the competitive patterns of the industry in which he works. In determining a final selling price, it is not realistic to simply add up a design's detailed costs, add the desired profit, and announce, "The price shall be thus-and-so." In the final analysis a producer's selling price must take into account his competitor's selling price, if competition does exist. This price must also provide a realistic margin on a product's sales price and one that will yield a specified return on the investment. The specified return on investment is the basic guide for optimization of the overall performance of a firm.

a mechanical jack for automobiles

Let us assume that we have just finished a feasibility design study for a new safety foot for a mechanical jack for automobiles [10-13]. Since the lifting bar and lifting assembly are both patented, both as to process and design, we must buy these parts from the present manufacturer. Our design covers only an improvement to the foot. We should now *price the design* so that our management can decide whether the prospect of producing it makes economic sense. Let us consider how we might proceed to arrive at an answer to this question.

There simply is no universal formula for pricing designs—too much depends upon the particular design. But there are some guidelines, nonetheless, and they are to be found in the general procedures used to calculate prices for manufactured products. Selling price is the sum of manufacturing cost and the required margin. Manufacturing-cost elements are direct material, permanent tools, direct labor, and indirect manufacturing expense.

Direct material is the name applied to raw material that is needed for the production of the design and can still be identified as part of the product when it is finished. Raw material of the same type may be needed for machine repairs or general shop supplies, but such material would be called *indirect material* and would be included in the category of cost called *indirect manufacturing expense.*

Some provision must be made for the amortization of permanent tooling, such as punch and die sets, specifically required by the design. Such tools may be capable of being used for many more units of the design than are presently being planned on, so the charge for permanent tools generally will be that portion of the total cost

Profits decline more during (an economic) crisis than wages. It is because of the fall in profits that unemployment occurs.

JEAN FOURASTIÉ

10-13

of the tooling that will be "used up" in making the planned production.

Direct labor is the product of the labor rate in dollars per hour and the production rate in hours per unit of product. The labor rate must include not only the base day rate of the employees actually making the parts, but must also include allowances for shift premiums, overtime premium, vacation and holiday pay, and other fringe benefits.

Indirect manufacturing expense is also called *overhead* or *burden*, and includes all those expenses of operating the plant that cannot be allocated to the design directly. Examples of such costs might be power and light, water, property taxes, fire insurance, and so forth. Indirect manufacturing expense is frequently applied to the estimate as a percent of direct labor based upon a separate determination of a normal burden rate for the plant as a whole.

The general schedule we shall follow in arriving at a tentative price for the jack foot is the following:

Interpretation

1. Make a preliminary production plan for the year. *How many can we sell?*
2. Prepare route sheets for the piece parts of the design. *How do we make them?*
3. Prepare estimates of the cost of permanent tooling.
4. Prepare schedules for the assembly and packaging of the parts. *What does it cost to make and ship the design?*
5. Calculate a final tentative price of the jack foot. *What can we sell it for?*

After the price is in hand we can

1. Prepare lists of points of superiority of this design over those of competitive designs.
2. Prepare a report for management covering all the foregoing data.

The Preliminary Production Plan

We need now to refer to some of the ideas developed earlier in this chapter. First we need to accomplish steps 1 through 3 in "Market-Enterprise Parameters for the Design" (p. 373). It is essential that we use all available information. Therefore, one of the easiest ways to prepare the initial production plan is to consult the *Census of Manufactures*, which takes into account the market nationally. The key to the *Census* is the *Standard Industrial Classification Manual*, a publication of the Bureau of the Budget. Most libraries will contain both documents. Consulting the *Manual's* alphabetic index we find *Jacks:* lifting, screw, and ratchet (hand tools) listed as number 3423. This number is the SIC code of the industry that will report all information available on jacks. We shall use this number to enter the *Census*, where we can find detailed information under products list code 34231-51 Auto Jacks, Mechanical.

Specifically, we find that the establishments that reported to the *Census* shipped 10,420,000 jacks having a value of $17,886,000. This can be taken as our preliminary estimate of the *total market* for jacks. Of the total shipment, we estimate that one jack was shipped with each of the 7,567,368 new cars sold that year. This would leave a total of 2,852,632 for accessory jack sales. So, the 2,852,632 is the portion of the total market that might want to buy our improved design.

We now try to think of all the ways our entry into this business will affect this reduced portion of the total market. And we try to think of all the variations of our marketing plans for entering the market. We shall consult everyone who can help us. In this case we might finally select 3 per cent as the figure that might reasonably be expected to represent our market penetration.

The 3 per cent estimate represents an initial production plan of almost 100,000 jacks. To allow for a scale or range of production, we shall also prepare our estimates based on 50,000 and 200,000. We can now proceed to obtain material cost estimates from mills or warehouses. First, we estimate the weight required for each quantity. Then we obtain the total price as a sum of base price, size extras, and quantity extras. When the weight required is multiplied by the total price, we have the cost of the direct material for each of the quantities planned.

Next we shall gather data on permanent tooling. If we must secure die sets, for instance, we shall obtain estimates of the tool costs from local tool and die makers.

While these estimates are being prepared, we can proceed with the production estimates. Each piece part of the design should be considered separately. For each of them we should decide the best method of production under the circumstances and try to estimate the production rate in hours per 1,000 pieces. These production estimates will be used to estimate the costs involved by multiplying them by the labor rate and the burden rate.

The Route Sheets

We now prepare a sheet for each piece part of the jack on which we shall record

1. The specification for the material (e.g., $\frac{1}{2}$-inch round AISI 1020 cold-drawn steel).
2. The unit weight of the material required per piece, or per thousand pieces.

Table 10-1

Quantity (thousands)	50 M	100 M	200 M
Material: #12 ga. cold-rolled strip			
Weight required, part 1 (lb)	79,500	159,000	318,000
Weight required, part 2 (lb)	15,500	31,000	62,000
Total weight (lb)	95,000	190,000	380,000
Material unit price ($/cwt)	8.00	6.40	5.10
Cost of purchased material	$ 7,600	$ 12,160	$ 19,380
Unit price of purchased jack parts	$ 1.50	$ 1.28	$ 1.10
Cost of purchased parts	$75,000	$128,000	$220,000
Total Direct Material Cost	$82,600	$140,160	$239,380
Cost of permanent tools	$ 750	$ 1,500	$ 3,000
Direct labor, part 1			
1.0 hr/M @ 3.00 $/hr = 3.00 $/M	$ 150	$ 300	$ 600
Direct labor, part 2			
0.5 hr/M @ 3.00 $/hr = 1.50 $/M	$ 75	$ 150	$ 300
Total Labor	$ 225	$ 450	$ 900
Burden @ 200% of direct labor	$ 450	$ 900	$ 1,800
Total of Material, Tools, Labor and Burden	$84,025	$143,010	$245,080
Add 10% selling and administrative	8,403	14,301	24,508
Gross Cost	$92,428	$157,311	$269,588
Selling Price (Gross Cost/0.95)	$97,293	$165,591	$283,777
Unit Price for the Jack*	$ 1.95	$ 1.66	$ 1.42

*(It should be reemphasized that these unit prices reflect the *minimum* amounts that could be charged to the wholesalers. Adding costs of wholesalers and distributers could easily place a $5.95 price tag on the jack at the local auto-supply house. Also, these estimated unit prices reflect only the *lowest* price that could be charged for the jacks. The market might allow this figure, for example, to vary between $2.75 and $3.00 each.)

3. The subassembly or assembly number on which the piece is to be used.
4. The number of pieces required per finished jack.
5. A list of the production operations needed to make the piece, the machine on which the work will be performed, and the tools needed for the machine.
6. A preliminary estimate of the time required in the shop to make the piece as shown in the route sheet.

The route sheets are later combined into a total *bill of materials*, which will yield the direct cost of the jack. To the direct cost obtained from the route sheets we should add *shop overhead* (this might be estimated as 200 per cent of direct labor) to obtain total manufacturing cost. We should increase the manufacturing cost by a small percentage, to cover administrative expense, selling expense, and packaging costs, to obtain a *gross cost*. When we add the profit required to the gross cost, we shall have our tentative price.

The safety foot for the auto jack for which we want to estimate a price is composed of two parts. Part 1 is a base stamping and part 2 is a cup stamping. The cup and base are spot welded into a single assembly that will hold the lifting bar and jack assembly firmly in place during use. The foot stampings are made of #12 gage (0.105 inch) cold-rolled strip steel. The base measures 6.5 by 8.25 inches and will require about 1.59 pounds per piece in the specified thickness.[5] The cup measures 3 by 3.5 inches and will require 0.31 pounds per piece. The base and cup will be fabricated with progressive dies in a punch press, assembled, spot welded, and painted black on a conveyorized production line in such fashion that we need figure only the labor to punch the two parts. The punch and die sets are estimated to cost $1,500. A set of punches and dies will make approximately 100,000 of the two parts. Table 10-1 summarizes this information on the price sheet.

We must divide the gross cost by the complement of the margin desired on sales to get the final tentative price. The difference be-

[5] Using 0.2833 pound-force/cubic inch as the specific weight of steel.

10-14
"I agree—it works. But at that price no customer will ever buy it! We've got to redesign and cut costs."

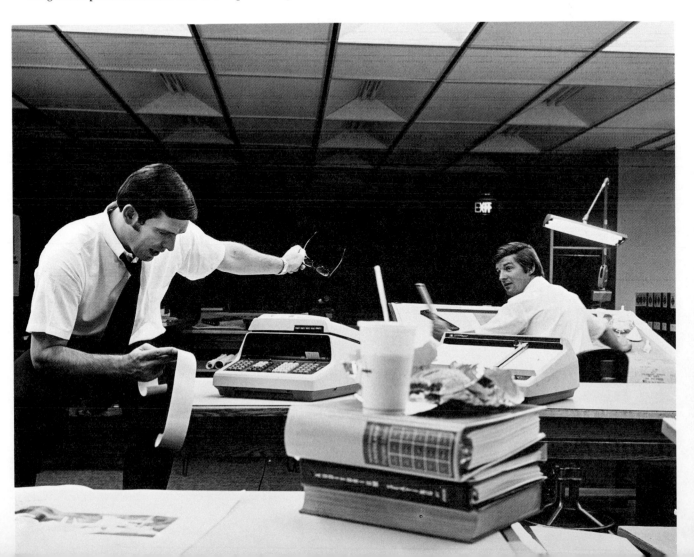

tween selling price and gross cost ($4,865 dollars for the 50,000 quantity) *is* the profit margin. The quotient of the ratio $4,865/$97,293 is seen to be the 5 per cent margin required. It has already been determined as part of the prior planning that the 5 per cent return on sales also will yield the firm's minimum required rate of return on its capital investment.

The unit prices for the three assumed production plans can now be used as the basis for market-research studies. These studies will disclose whether the customer will buy the design at the tentative prices. If it appears that the customer will pay the price of the design as it now exists, we proceed to determine the best marketing strategy for the firm and to prepare the final report for management. If it appears that some redesign will be required to get the price down to a level that the customer will pay, the redesign is done, new prices are computed, and the market study is repeated until it appears reasonable that the production plans can be realized.

problems

10-1. In a market-enterprise society almost every task has some monetary reward or income associated with it. In such a society the quantity of a particular product that can be marketed depends upon this income. Therefore, on what attribute of the *product* does "the quantity demanded by the customer" depend?

10-2. When one speaks of *research and development,* where does research end and development begin?

10-3. Suggest a new product that might be introduced into the do-it-yourself carpentry market. Discuss the likelihood of success of marketing such a product.

10-4. Approximately how many *new* businesses are started each year in the state where you live? Of the firms now in business in the state, approximately how many fail each year?

10-5. Discuss the principal causes of business failure.

10-6. (a) Assume that the permanent tooling required for a given design will cost $75,000. This is a *fixed* cost of the project. If you assume three different production plans of 25,000, 50,000, and 75,000 units, calculate the *unit fixed cost* for each of the three production plans. What is the effect of increasing production on fixed costs per unit?

(b) Variable cost is the difference between fixed and total cost, and it is proportional to output. A proposed project has the following costs associated with it:

Quantity	Total Cost($)	Fixed Cost($)
10,000	75,000	25,000
20,000	125,000	25,000
30,000	175,000	25,000

Calculate the total variable cost and the unit variable cost for each production plan. What is the effect of increased production on unit variable costs?

10-7. Pick five popular product sale items from a newspaper advertisement. Look up the SIC code numbers of the industries that produced them.

10-8. Consult the *Census of Manufactures* for the industry that produces radios. For the product selected, abstract from the *Census*

(a) units shipped

(b) value of shipments

10-9. For an item of sports equipment, abstract from the *Census* the data on production and related employees as follows:

(a) number of employees

(b) man-hours

(c) payroll dollars

Also record the *value added by manufacture* for this product. With these data calculate the following productivity ratios:

(a) value added per production employee

(b) value added per man-hour

(c) value added per payroll dollar

10-10. An engineering design requires a bushing 1.5 inches long to be made from 1.25-inch-round rod stock. The bushing can be made from brass, steel, or aluminum. Price quotations on the metals can be obtained by querying local warehouses. Neglecting relative differences in the cost of machining between brass, steel, and aluminum, calculate the cost of the material required for the job and decide which to specify.

10-11. The machine on which the bushing of the previous problem will be made has a labor rate (direct labor plus overhead) of $5.50 per hour. The geared production rate for the bushing will be 6 seconds/piece if the part is made from brass, 17 seconds/piece from steel, and 7.5 seconds/piece from aluminum. What will be the cost of the 15,000 run for each metal?

10-12. Using the material cost data from Problem 10-10 and the machining cost data from Problem 10-11, what specification for material will yield the minimum job cost?

10-13. Suppose that the industry whose SIC Code Number is 3489 has a productivity ratio equal to 2.75 (value added by manufacture dollars per payroll dollar). Suppose also that your own firm, a member of that same industry, generates 2.27 value added dollars per payroll dollar. Keeping in mind that ratios can be changed by altering either numerator or denominator, suggest some things you could do to become more competitive.

10-14. Discuss the effect on the various productivity ratios mentioned in this chapter of increases and decreases in raw-material costs.

10-15. Assume that a particular parts order requires 8,000 pounds of 1-inch-round brass rod. The pricing practices of the brass mills give an extra half cent per pound discount for orders over 10,000 pounds of one size shipped at one time to one destination. Discuss some of the factors that might warrant such an additional investment, or that might make such an investment unwise.

bibliography

Census of Manufactures, Washington, D.C.: U.S. Department of Commerce, 1963.

CHURCHILL, W. L., *Pricing for Profit*, New York: Macmillan, 1932.

Cost of Doing Business, New York: Dun & Bradstreet, 1969.

Failure Record Through 1963, New York: Dun & Bradstreet, 1970.

FOULKE, R. A., *Practical Financial Statement Analysis,* 6th ed., New York: McGraw-Hill, 1968.

GALLAGHER, P. F., *Project Estimating by Engineering Methods,* New York: Hayden, 1965.

HEILBRONER, R. L., *The Making of Economic Society,* 3rd ed., Englewood Cliffs, N.J.: Prentice-Hall, 1969.

HEMPEL, E. H. (ed.), *Small Plant Management,* New York: McGraw-Hill, 1950.

KNOEPPEL, C. E., and E. G. SEYBOLD, *Managing for Profit,* New York: McGraw-Hill, 1937.

KOTLER, PHILIP, *Marketing Management,* Englewood Cliffs, N.J.: Prentice-Hall, 1967.

McNEILL, T. F., and D. S. CLARK, *Cost Estimating and Contract Pricing,* New York: American Elsevier, 1966.

Small Business Administration Publications:

Small Business Management Series

Improving Materials Handling in Small Plants, SBA 1.12:4.

Cost Accounting for Small Manufacturers, SBA 1.12:9.

A Handbook of Small Business Finance, SBA 1.12:15.

New Product Introduction for Small Business Owners, SBA 1.12:17.

Ratio Analysis for Small Business, SBA 1.12:20.

Guides for Profit Planning, SBA 1.12:25.

Small Business Research Series

Cash Planning in Small Manufacturing Companies, SBA 1.20:1.

The First Two Years, SBA 1.20:2.

Standard Industrial Classification Manual, Washington, D.C.: Bureau of the Budget, 1967.

STANTON, W. J., *Fundamentals of Marketing.* New York: McGraw-Hill, 1967.

This interferogram allows researchers to measure the thickness of a chromium deposit on a decorative plating system. The vertical line is the boundary obtained when the thin layer of chromium was stripped from one side of the field, exposing the underlying nickel. Although the color fringes are continuous and nearly straight on each side of the boundary, they deviate abruptly at this line. The amount of deviation—measured in units of fringe separation—is a measure of the step height of the boundary. In this photograph, the step height and thus the chromium thickness is five millionths of an inch. With this technique, researchers can determine the influence of thickness on corrosion protection.

t hroughout this text, attention has been directed to the quest for improved designs, improved methods, or what may be termed the "best" method under the circumstances. The implication is that an *improved* design will be recognized readily to be an improvement over the existing design and will, therefore, be implemented. In other words, it has been assumed that once all the necessary data are available, a correct decision will be made. However, the truth is that relatively few contributions of man are of such a nature that they are recognized immediately as significant improvements. If the worth of a contribution is not obvious, how can the engineer decide whether or not to implement the new design? To answer this question completely, one would need a detailed study of decision theory, which is beyond the scope of this text. However, in this chapter some of the conditions under which decisions are made and some of the basic principles of decision making will be discussed.

Human activity can be organized into two general classifications: those activities associated with *making decisions* and those associated with *implementing decisions*. Much of the work of an engineer is devoted to making decisions. An engineer's career may, in fact, be measured by the number and magnitude of the decisions he must make. This chapter will discuss briefly some decision processes used by the engineer in conjunction with his work. Early in his professional career he will be called upon to study a variety of situations and to recommend a solution that he has attained with the aid of his acquired skills and knowledge. Frequently, he will not make the final decision but will contribute his findings to assist someone else who has this responsibility. The engineer will progress to positions of greater responsibility as he gains experience in the decision process. Thus, he will progress from an advisory capacity to a position in which the most important and final decisions are his own responsibility.

If all decisions could be made on the basis of accurate engineering data and with the use of correct scientific methods, much guesswork and intuitive reasoning could be eliminated. However, such a condition is not possible. In fact, there is some question as to whether many decisions can be made on a completely scientific basis. It does seem sensible, however, to proceed as far as possible using proven scientific methods to aid in making decisions. Fortunately, the development of the high-speed computer has brought about improvements in decision making that were not dreamed of a few years ago.

An important factor in any decision process is the amount of accurate information available or, in other words, the extent to which scientific methods can be utilized. Many important decisions must be made under conditions of insufficient information. The future always remains unknown, and even the most sophisticated prediction techniques will sometimes give the wrong advice. Yet, the engineer always must strive to make the best decisions under any and all

The world is divided into people who do things as they are, and those who do things as they ought to be.

STOWE

11-1

11-2

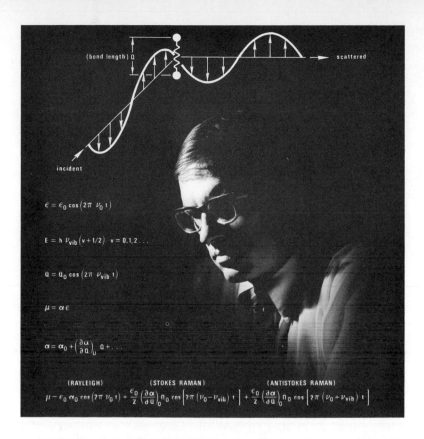

conditions. Let us define a *decision* as the selection of one alternative from a known set of alternatives. There are three types of decisions:

1. Decisions made under certainty.
2. Decisions made under risk.
3. Decisions made under uncertainty.

These types of decisions are shown in [11-3] and they will be explained briefly below.

The selection of an alternative is made according to a *principle of choice*. A principle of choice is a rule that can be applied to any decision process and will lead to the selection of a particular alternative.

the general decision matrix

Before proceeding with an explanation of the types of decisions, some understanding of the general decision matrix would be helpful. A

Multitudes, multitudes in the valley of decision.

JOEL 3:14
The Holy Bible

11-3

Type of Decision	Principle of Choice
Certainty	Maximizing profit
Risk	Maximizing expectation
Risk	Most probable future
Risk	Aspiration level
Uncertainty	Equal probability
Uncertainty	Conservatism
Uncertainty	Regret

DESIGN

Possible Future States (Uncontrollable Factors)

	s_1	s_2	s_3	$\cdots$	s_j	$\cdots$	s_n
a_1	R_{1-1}	R_{1-2}	R_{1-3}	$\cdots$	R_{1-j}	$\cdots$	R_{1-n}
a_2	R_{2-1}	R_{2-2}	R_{2-3}	$\cdots$	R_{2-j}	$\cdots$	R_{2-n}
a_3	R_{3-1}	R_{3-2}	R_{3-3}	$\cdots$	R_{3-j}	$\cdots$	R_{3-n}
$\vdots$	$\vdots$	$\vdots$	$\vdots$		$\vdots$		$\vdots$
a_i	R_{i-1}	R_{i-2}	R_{i-3}	$\cdots$	R_{i-j}	$\cdots$	R_{i-n}
$\vdots$	$\vdots$	$\vdots$	$\vdots$		$\vdots$		$\vdots$
a_m	R_{m-1}	R_{m-2}	R_{m-3}	$\cdots$	R_{m-j}	$\cdots$	R_{m-n}

Available Alternatives (Controllable Factors)

11-4
General decision matrix

general decision matrix is a simple array constructed in such a manner that the rows represent the possible alternatives (controllable factors) available to the engineer in a decision situation. The alternatives are designated by $a_1, a_2, \ldots, a_i, \ldots, a_m$, where a_i represents the general expression in which $i = 1, 2, \ldots, m$. The columns represent possible future states that cannot be controlled by the engineer. The future states are designated $s_1, s_2, \ldots, s_j, \ldots, s_n$, where s_j is the general expression in which $j = 1, 2, \ldots, n$. At the intersection of each column (possible future state) and each row (available alternative) is the result that occurs because alternative a_i was selected and future state s_j did, in fact, occur. The results are designated R_{1-1}, $R_{1-2}, \ldots, R_{i-j}, \ldots, R_{m-n}$, where the first part of the subscript refers to the row (alternative) and the last part represents the column (future state). Thus, in [11-4], R_{2-3} is the result that occurs when alternative a_2 is selected and future state s_3 occurs.

There is another very important consideration—the *probability* associated with the occurrence of a particular possible future state. The assignment of probability is an important and difficult task and

Possible Future States

	P_1	P_2	P_3	$\cdots$	P_j	$\cdots$	P_n
	s_1	s_2	s_3	$\cdots$	s_j	$\cdots$	s_n
a_1	R_{1-1}	R_{1-2}	R_{1-3}	$\cdots$	R_{1-j}	$\cdots$	R_{1-n}
a_2	R_{2-1}	R_{2-2}	R_{2-3}	$\cdots$	R_{2-j}	$\cdots$	R_{2-n}
a_3	R_{3-1}	R_{3-2}	R_{3-3}	$\cdots$	R_{3-j}	$\cdots$	R_{3-n}
$\vdots$	$\vdots$	$\vdots$	$\vdots$		$\vdots$		$\vdots$
a_i	R_{i-1}	R_{i-2}	R_{i-3}	$\cdots$	R_{i-j}	$\cdots$	R_{i-n}
$\vdots$	$\vdots$	$\vdots$	$\vdots$		$\vdots$		$\vdots$
a_m	R_{m-1}	R_{m-2}	R_{m-3}	$\cdots$	R_{m-j}	$\cdots$	R_{m-n}

Alternatives

11-5

will be covered in greater detail later in this chapter. The probability is designated $p_1, p_2, \ldots, p_n$, as shown in [11-5]. It is important to note that for each future state s_j there is a probability of occurrence p_j, where $j = 1, 2, \ldots, n$ as before.

By utilizing these probabilities, the engineer can gain greater insight into his problem, namely, the choice among alternatives. For example, in the manned space program there are many controllable alternatives that are made possible by known scientific principles and current technology. However, in every launch there are many unknown quantities and variables, errors, and other uncontrolled factors that will make themselves known. For each possible malfunction or instrumentation error, however, a probability exists that the event will occur, and a probability can be assigned for each of the possible occurrences.

decisions under certainty

Decisions under certainty are made when it can be assumed that the engineer has complete and accurate knowledge concerning the result that will occur when he chooses any of the available alternatives. This assumption may be made when the amount of risk involved is so small that the decision maker feels safe in neglecting it, or when the difficulty involved in including the risk makes it impractical to do so.

In terms of a decision model (a completed decision matrix for a given situation), if only one future state is possible, that future state will have a probability of occurrence of 1.00. A decision under certainty appears in matrix form as depicted in [11-6]. Note that the idea of a *value* $V(R_{i-j})$ associated with each result has been introduced. This is merely to generalize the matrix. For example, if the results are measurable in dollars, one can readily discuss the value involved. But what if the situation is military, and the results are losses in lives, equipment, and land? The value is then much more difficult to ascertain, and the discussion of the results becomes much more complex. (The student of decision theory will recognize that this leads into the study of *utility*, a study beyond the scope of this material.)

In a decision under certainty there are as many rows in the matrix as there are alternatives, but *only one* possible future state. Therefore, assuming the alternatives are equal in other respects, the engineer should (1) select the alternative that maximizes profit, or (2) select the alternative that minimizes cost. Situations in real life rarely involve considerations of profit and loss alone. Other values—such as the value of human life—may have to be considered.

Sometimes it is a good choice not to choose at all.
MICHEL EYQUEM DE MONTAIGNE
Essays (1533–1592)

Nothing is certain but death and taxes.
BENJAMIN FRANKLIN
Letter to M. Leroy, 1789

11-6
Decision matrix for a decision under certainty where the symbols are as previously defined.

Future State

The calm confidence of a Christian with four aces.
                                    MARK TWAIN

Be wary of the man who urges an action in which he himself incurs no risk.
                        JOAQUIN DE SETANTI
                        Centallas (17th century)

decisions under risk

A decision to be made under risk differs from one to be made under certainty in that the engineer is concerned with the probabilities of occurrence of possible future states. Less information is available to the engineer than in a decision under certainty, but it is possible to assign probabilities to the various possible future states.

An automobile manufacturer is concerned about the quality of a brake lining that is used on his cars. Specifically, he wishes to make the most economical choice of replacing the defective lining in his products. The manufacturer concludes that he may follow one of three alternatives:

a_1: Do not inspect the linings. Those which fail in service will be replaced by the local dealer.

a_2: Inspect every lining utilizing a method that always detects the defectives.

a_3: Adopt an inspection policy that detects the defectives 75 per cent of the time.

Suppose that the following costs have been determined:
The cost of replacing a defective lining in service is $25.00. The cost of inspecting using the method of a_2 is $2.00 per lining and the cost of inspecting using the method of a_3 is $1.00 per lining. Records indicate that 10 per cent of all linings have the defect in question.

Let future state s_1 be that we have a perfect brake lining. Under a_1 there is no expense. Under a_2 there is an expense of $2.00 for the inspection and under a_3 the cost is $1.00 for the inspection. Consider a defective lining to be future state s_2. Policy a_1 results in a cost of $25.00 to replace the defect. Policy a_2 costs $2.00 for the inspection, and it always detects the defectives. Under a_3 there is a cost of $1.00 for the inspection, but 25 per cent of the defective items are not discovered, which later fail in service at a cost of $25.00 each. Therefore, the average cost under a_3 is

$$(0.25)(\$26) + (0.75)(\$1) = \$7.25$$

The previous matrix notation gives us the matrix shown here.

To obtain all this information may be an expensive and inconvenient procedure. Also, the manufacturer still does not know which alternative to select. The most commonly used principle of choice is *Expectation*, which calls for selecting the alternative that has the lowest expected cost. Expected costs are computed as the weighted sum of the costs associated with an alternative, where the weight associated with each cost is the probability of that cost being in-

11-7

	$P_1 = 0.90$	$P_2 = 0.10$
	s_1 = perfect	s_2 = defective
a_1	0	$25.00
a_2	$2.00	$ 2.00
a_3	$1.00	$ 7.25

curred. Thus the expected costs for the three alternatives listed are as follows:

a_1 (0.90)(0) + (0.10)($25) = $2.50
a_2 (0.90)($2) + (0.10)($2)   = $2.00
a_3 (0.90)($1) + (0.10)($7.25) = $1.63

Based on these values, alternative a_3 should be selected on the basis of having the lowest expected cost.

Another principle of choice used in risky situations is called *most probable future*, in which case the decision maker considers only the future state that is most probable and behaves as though it were certain. Specifically, he finds the future state (s_j) for which the probability of occurrence (p_j) is the greatest, and for this state selects the alternative that has the lowest cost. In the example problem, 90 per cent of the brake linings are perfect; therefore, only column 1 is considered in making the decision using the most-probable-future principle. In column 1, the lowest cost is zero dollars and alternative a_1, do not inspect, is selected.

Many decisions are made based upon this principle. For example, most people will agree that there is a nonzero probability of World War III in any year, but the same people make *all* their decisions as though eternal peace were certain.

Another important principle of choice is the *aspiration-level*, a procedure widely used in management decision making. For a decision under risk, this principle is: for a given aspiration level, L, (i.e., the level we hope to achieve) choose the alternative that has the highest probability that the cost will be less than or equal to L.

What type of situation might favor the use of an aspiration level? If the alternatives are expensive or difficult to discover, the *search* for alternatives should be continued *only* until one is found that gives a reasonable probability of achieving the aspiration level. This procedure may be more economical than searching for the alternative that minimizes the expected value.

In the example problem, if the manufacturer aspired *only* to keep his costs below $3.00, he would choose alternative a_2, because it will cost $2.00 with a probability of 1.00. Each of the other alternatives has a probability of 0.10 of exceeding $3.00.

decisions under uncertainty

Of the three classifications of decisions, perhaps the most realistic type is the decision made under uncertainty. This type of decision exists when the possible future states are known but the probabilities of occurrence of each are not available to the engineer. This type of decision making is particularly applicable in industry when a new

Blessed is he who expects nothing, for he shall never be disappointed.

ALEXANDER POPE
Letter to Gay, 1688–1744

No two men can be half an hour together but one will acquire an evident superiority over the other.
SAMUEL JOHNSON
in Boswell's Life, 1776

type of work is being pioneered and no prior data exist, such as is the case for most research and development activities. In terms of the general decision matrix, a decision made under uncertainty appears to be much the same as a decision made under risk—except that the probabilities are missing.

Preliminary Selection Based upon Dominance

In any situation in which a decision is to be made, all alternatives must be checked to see whether any one *dominates* any of the others. If one alternative is always preferred to any other, regardless of which future state may occur, it is said to *dominate* the other. When this condition exists, all dominated alternatives must be eliminated from consideration, because they should never be selected.

For example, consider the problem faced by an engineer concerning his future career. He believes that his possible alternatives are as follows:

1. Go into business for himself.
2. Form a partnership.
3. Go to work for a small engineering firm.
4. Go to work for a large firm.

Assume that the future states with which he is concerned are three possible future economic conditions in the United States. For simplicity, we may classify them as follows:

1. Enter a recession.
2. Continue under present economic conditions.
3. Enter a booming economy.

The cell entries in the matrix represent the profits associated with each situation as designated (by the engineer) on a scale from 0 to 100.

The decision matrix is as follows:

11-8

		s_1 Recession	s_2 Continue	s_3 Boom
a_1	Alone	0	45	100
a_2	Partner	10	30	60
a_3	Small firm	20	40	70
a_4	Large firm	10	70	70

From the matrix it can be seen that no matter what the future holds, the engineer is better off going to work for a small firm than he is joining a partnership (in this example). Therefore, the alternative a_2, "form a partnership," should be eliminated from further consideration because alternative a_3 dominates it.

Decisions Based upon Equal Probability

If the engineer has no reason to suspect that the probability associated with any of the possible future states is different from that of any other future state, he may want to assume that the probabilities are all equal. Therefore, in the preceding example, we would assume that

$$p_1 = p_2 = p_3.$$

Since

$$p_1 + p_2 + p_3 = 1.00$$

we have

$$p_1 = p_2 = p_3 = \tfrac{1}{3}.$$

If the engineer uses the principle of assigning equal probabilities to the possible future states, then the decision may be treated as one to be made under risk. If he now *maximizes* his expected gain, the results would be as follows:

$$E(a_1) = \tfrac{1}{3}(0) + \tfrac{1}{3}(45) + \tfrac{1}{3}(100) = \tfrac{145}{3} = 48\tfrac{1}{3}$$
$$E(a_3) = \tfrac{1}{3}(20) + \tfrac{1}{3}(40) + \tfrac{1}{3}(70) = \tfrac{130}{3} = 43\tfrac{1}{3}$$
$$E(a_4) = \tfrac{1}{3}(10) + \tfrac{1}{3}(70) + \tfrac{1}{3}(70) = \tfrac{150}{3} = 50$$

Then, the engineer would choose alternative a_4 and accept employment with a large firm.

The use of this principle is predicated on the inability of an individual to estimate the likelihood of occurrence of each of the possible future economic states of the nation. In some cases, the indicators generally used to predict such occurrences will contradict each other. For such a situation the probabilities can be assumed to be equal. In most instances, however, the engineer will have *some* opinion of the probable occurrence of the future states, even if it is only a subjective judgment. Methods for using these subjective judgments are currently being explored.

Decisions Based upon Conservatism

Another principle of choice is that of *conservatism*. This principle calls for the engineer to examine the "smallest possible gain" associated with each alternative, then select that alternative which gives him the largest "minimum gain." In other words, the conservative approach says that the least desirable situation will occur and that the engineer should choose the best of the worst. If the

The laws of probability, so true in general, so fallacious in particular.

EDWARD GIBBON
Autobiography, 1790

engineer decides that he should be concerned with costs instead of profits, he will examine the alternatives to determine the *largest* possible cost for each alternative, and then select the *smallest* cost of those maxima. In the example problem on page 404, the application of the conservative approach would result in the selection of alternative a_3, which is to go to work for a small firm.

$$\text{Minimum profit for } a_1 = 0$$
$$\text{Minimum profit for } a_3 = 20$$
$$\text{Minimum profit for } a_4 = 10$$

The maximum of these minima is 20; therefore, alternative a_3 should be selected if one uses the principle of conservatism.

There are many decisions in which the application of this principle would lead to such conservatism that the conclusion would be counter to intuition. Consider the example [7-9], in which the values in the matrix again represent profits. The conservatism principle would lead to the selection of a_2 because it has the greatest *minimum* gain ($\$2$). When, then, might the conservatism principle be applied? Perhaps the most common example is in the insurance industry, where one pays a (relatively) small cost to avoid a large loss.

11-9

	s_1	s_2
a_1	0	$10,000
a_2	$2	$5

The most conservative persons I ever met are college undergraduates.

WOODROW WILSON
in a Speech, New York, 1905

11-10

Profit Matrix

	s_1	s_2	s_3
a_1	0	45	100
a_3	20	40	70
a_4	10	70	70
Column Maximum Values	20	70	100

11-11

Regret Matrix

	s_1	s_2	s_3
a_1	20	25	0
a_3	0	30	30
a_4	10	0	30

Decisions Based upon Regret

One other principle of choice for making decisions under uncertainty is the Savage principle, named for L. J. Savage.[1] This principle suggests that the engineer construct a new matrix called the *regret matrix*, where regret is defined as the difference between the profit that will result and the maximum profit that could be obtained under that future state. That quantity is called the *regret*. After the regret matrix is computed, select the alternative that minimizes the maximum regret. Consider the matrix on page 404. The regret matrix would be computed by subtracting each element in the matrix from the value indicated in the row labeled "Column Maximum Value," as shown in [11-11].

Now, the maximum regrets associated with each of the alternatives are as follows:

$$\text{Maximum regret for } a_1 = 25$$
$$\text{Maximum regret for } a_3 = 30$$
$$\text{Maximum regret for } a_4 = 30$$

[1] W. T. Morris, *Engineering Economy*, Richard D. Irwin, Homewood, Ill.: 1960, p. 315.

Since alternative a_1 has the minimum of the maximum regrets, the decision to go into business alone would be selected.

The preceding discussion gives a cursory look at some of the more common principles of choice. It has been shown that the application of each principle of choice to the same situation may lead to the selection of different alternatives. There is no one principle that is always best, because the final selection of a principle *must* remain a matter of individual preference. Perhaps the merit of utilizing a principle of choice, instead of applying judgment directly to the problem, lies in the fact that the use of a definite principle promotes consistency over a period of time and aids in the understanding of the decision making process.

probability

Perhaps one wonders why there is so much emphasis on the difficulty and importance of assigning probabilities. It is an interesting fact that every man on the street thinks he knows what is meant by the term probability, although mathematicians who have devoted their lives to a study of the subject cannot agree on a mathematical definition of the term. Needless to say, the controversy that has surrounded the subject of probability for centuries will not be resolved in these pages; however, a brief elementary discussion might be helpful.

There are two major types of probabilities: objective and subjective. An objective probability may be thought of as the mathematicians' definition of probability. For example, the probability of rolling a two on one roll of an "honest" die is $\frac{1}{6}$ and the probability of pulling an ace out of a complete deck of 52 playing cards is $\frac{4}{52}$, or $\frac{1}{13}$. Now, let's put the decision maker into the middle of the picture. A student has taken three tests in a particular subject during a semester. In each test he has received a grade of C. Near the end of the course the professor offers the student the option of taking the C he has earned to date for his final grade or taking a comprehensive final examination over the course material. The student feels that the C average he has earned to date is not a true indication of his knowledge; he therefore elects to take the final examination because he *believes* that there is a good probability of raising his grade to a B or an A. This is an example of subjective probability.

Although it may bother some people to use subjective probabilities, in the world of reality the successful engineer *must* use them. Is not the estimate of a qualified judge better than complete ignorance? The importance of the decision under consideration certainly influences the decision maker as to which type of probability he will accept or insist upon.

How often things occur by mere chance which we dared not even hope for.

TERENCE
Phormio, 185–159 B.C.

The difficulty in life is the choice.

GEORGE MOORE
The Bending of the Bough

Young men, we are together for the last time. We have had a very pleasant time. You have been a good class and I have enjoyed working with you.

I have given you the best information available—the best case histories I could find. The textbooks we have used are the most widely accepted and reliable. But before we part company, I want to caution you that the science of medicine is developing so rapidly that in a few years from now perhaps half of the things I have taught you won't be so. Unfortunately, I don't know what half that will be.

AN UNKNOWN PROFESSOR OF MEDICINE
Quoted by CHARLES F. KETTERING
Annual Meeting ASME, 1943

optimization

To optimize means to minimize or maximize some function (a performance variable) by proper selection of design or controllable variables. Optimization often implies a mathematical relationship between the performance variable and the design variable. Such a relationship usually does not exist. Thus, optimum is an overused and often misused term. The same criticism could be leveled at the terms maximum and minimum. For example, one often sees reference to a specification for a product design that achieves maximum reliability at minimum cost. These conditions can never be satisfied, since maximum reliability implies infinite cost, and minimum cost, (zero) implies zero reliability.

The more appropriate specification would be, for example, a reliability greater than 0.95 at a cost/unit not to exceed $1,000. Alternatives would then be evaluated, using the concepts presented in this chapter, to meet these specifications.

Far too much money and efforts are expended by too many engineers and scientists today trying to devise an improvement that, even if developed, would be relatively insignificant. The implication, then, is that it is generally wiser to use a level-of-aspiration principle than to attempt to optimize. When the cost of the improvement exceeds the value of the modification, it is time to discard that project and proceed to others that hold more promise. Most human decision making is concerned with the discovery and selection of satisfactory alternatives; only in exceptional cases is it concerned with the discovery and selection of optimal alternatives.

11-12
It's your move!

problems

11-1. An electronics company is faced with a choice of purchasing one of two machines, either of which will accomplish the desired task satisfactorily. Some pertinent facts concerning the use of the two pieces of equipment are given below:

	Initial Cost	Annual Operating Cost	Service Life	Salvage Value at End of 15 yr
Machine 1	$40,000	$5,000	15 yr	$4,000
Machine 2	$60,000	$4,000	15 yr	$6,000

Which machine would you advise the company to purchase? Why?

11-2. What important assumptions have you made in your analysis in Problem 11-1?

11-3. Mr. Jones wants to buy a certain automobile that Mr. Smith owns. Mr. Smith has asked $1,000 for the vehicle. Mr. Jones has countered with an offer of $1,100 if Smith will wait a year for the money. Smith considers that he can invest his money at the rate of 6 per cent simple interest per year. What action would you advise Smith to take with regard to Jones's offer?

11-4. With regard to the situation described in Problem 11-3, what would you advise Smith to do if Jones offers $1,050 to be paid at the end of one year?

11-5. The Niten-Day taxicab firm must purchase some new vehicles and they are considering two different types. One type uses conventional gasoline and the other type uses diesel fuel. Also, the following information has been obtained:

	Initial Cost	Service Life	Operating Cost per Mile	Expected Miles/yr	Salvage Value
Taxi A—Gasoline	$3,000	5 yr	$0.08	30,000	$300
Taxi B—Diesel Fuel	$4,000	5 yr	$0.06	30,000	$400

Which type of vehicle would you recommend that they purchase? Why?

11-6. If the general conditions described in Problem 11-5 prevail, at what annual mileage would the choice be one of indifference?

11-7. Red and blue have declared war on each other. Each has three strategies, designated r_1, r_2, and r_3, and b_1, b_2, and b_3. A decision matrix may be drawn up as follows (entries represent values to blue):

	r_1	r_2	r_3
b_1	win	lose	draw
b_2	lose	draw	win
b_3	draw	win	lose

(a) Blue's intelligence agents have brought back information that red is planning to employ strategy r_2. Which strategy should blue employ, assuming that total victory is the objective?

(b) If blue's agents were wrong and red employs strategy r_3 instead of r_2, what will happen if blue employs strategy b_3?

11-8. In an engineering design project you have tabulated some values (costs) in the following matrix:

	$p_1 = 0.60$	$p_2 = 0.30$	$p_3 = 0.10$
	s_1	s_2	s_3
a_1	$100	$50	$1,000
a_2	$200	$200	$ 200
a_3	$150	$500	$ 100

Apply the expectation principle to the matrix, and give your recommendation as to the preferred alternative.

11-9. Which alternative would you select in Problem 11-8 if the most-probable-future principle were used?

11-10. If in Problem 11-8 you had established a level of aspiration of "keeping the cost below $400," which alternative would you choose?

11-11. Assume that the values shown in the decision matrix in Problem 11-8 are profits. Apply the expectation principle to the matrix and give your recommendation as to the preferred alternative.

11-12. If the values in the decision matrix in Problem 11-8 were profits, which alternative would you recommend if you use the most-probable-future principle?

11-13. If the values in the decision matrix in Problem 11-8 were profits, which alternative would you choose if your level of aspiration is to make a profit of at least $400?

11-14. Some outcomes are so difficult to evaluate that they can only be classified as satisfactory (s) or unsatisfactory (u). Consider the following matrix:

	$P_1 = 0.50$	$P_2 = 0.30$	$P_3 = 0.20$
	s_1	s_2	s_3
a_1	s	u	u
a_2	s	u	s
a_3	u	s	s

If you aspired to have an acceptable outcome, which alternative would you choose?

11-15. If you apply the expectation principle to the decision matrix in Problem 11-14, which alternative should be selected?

11-16. Discuss briefly the assumptions involved when an engineer applies the expectation principle to a decision matrix such as that in Problem 11-14.

11-17. Consider the following alternatives and future states concerning the purchase of fire insurance:

$$a_1 = \text{Buy fire insurance.}$$
$$a_2 = \text{Do not buy fire insurance.}$$
$$s_1 = \text{A fire occurs.}$$
$$s_2 = \text{A fire does not occur.}$$

The cell entries of your decision matrix will represent the costs to the prospective insurance purchaser. ($500 is the cost of the insurance; $45,000 is the cost of the fire.)

	$p_1 = 0.01$ s_1	$p_2 = 0.99$ s_2
a_1	$500	$500
a_2	$45,000	0

Apply the expectation principle to the above matrix and give your recommendation with regard to purchasing insurance.

11-18. Discuss why the expectation principle may not be an appropriate principle to apply when considering the purchase of insurance.

11-19. Apply the most-probable-future principle to the decision matrix in Problem 11-17. Which alternative do you recommend?

11-20. In Problem 11-17, assume that you aspire to keep the cost below $1000. Apply the level-of-aspiration principle, and make your recommendations concerning the best alternative.

11-21. As plant engineer you have determined that without standby equipment a shutdown will cost an average of $250 a day. Over the past several years the plant has averaged three days per year lost to shutdowns. A standby machine can be purchased for $5,000, which has a service life of 10 years and a salvage value of $500 at that time. Its annual operating cost, including the three days of operation, would be $200. The president of the company has asked your opinion concerning the purchase of standby equipment. What would you advise him?

11-22. With regard to Problem 11-21, discuss the possible application of the level-of-aspiration principle.

11-23. A standard roulette wheel has 38 possible outcomes, 18 red, 18 black, and 2 green (0 and 00). For simplicity, consider wagering on the colors if the following decision matrix applies:

	$p_1 = \frac{18}{38}$ $s_1 = \text{red}$	$p_2 = \frac{18}{38}$ $s_2 = \text{black}$	$p_3 = \frac{2}{38}$ $s_3 = \text{green}$
a_1 bet red	+1	−1	−1
a_2 bet black	−1	+1	−1
a_3 bet green	−1	−1	+17

Using the expectation principle, compute the "best" bet, if one exists.

11-24. Consider the following cost matrix:

	p_1	p_2	p_3
	s_1	s_2	s_3
a_1	$100	$140	$200
a_2	$ 90	$132	$181
a_3	$ 92	$135	$185

Which alternative would you select? Why?

11-25. Consider the matrix in Problem 11-24 to be a profit matrix. Which alternative would you select? Why?

11-26. Consider the following profit matrix:

	s_1	s_2	s_3	s_4
a_1	$15	$25	$ 8	$12
a_2	0	$25	$12	$12
a_3	$20	$20	$10	$15
a_4	$15	$15	$15	$15

(a) Does any strategy (alternative) dominate any other?

(b) Apply the principle of equal probability. Which alternative should be selected?

11-27. Apply the principle of conservatism to the profit matrix in Problem 11-26. Which alternative should be selected?

11-28. Which alternative would be selected in Problem 11-26 if the Savage principle were applied?

11-29. Consider the following cost matrix:

	s_1	s_2	s_3
a_1	$120	$140	$ 90
a_2	$150	$130	$100
a_3	$110	$125	$ 80
a_4	$115	$135	$ 95

Which alternative should be selected?

11-30. Your company is considering purchasing a safety device to protect the drivers for all company cars. Each device costs $100. You have evaluated the cost matrix for the company as follows:

a_1 = Buy the device.
a_2 = Do not buy the device.
s_1 = An accident occurs.
s_2 = No accident occurs.

	s_1	s_2
a_1	$100	$100
a_2	0	$V_{(injury)}$

If the principle of equal probability were applied, when would a_2 be selected?

11-31. Using the decision matrix of Problem 11-30, when would the conservatism principle lead to the selection of a_1?

11-32. With regard to the decision matrix in Problem 11-30, when would the Savage principle lead to the selection of a_1?

11-33. With regard to the problem statement in Problem 11-30, which principle of choice would you apply in this instance? Why?

bibliography

BERNE, E., *Games People Play*. New York: Grove Press, 1964.

CHERNOFF, H., and L. E. MOSES, *Elementary Decision Theory*, New York: Wiley, 1959.

CHURCHMAN, C. W., and R. L. ACKOFF, "An Approximate Measure of Value," *Operations Research*, Vol. 2 (1954), pp. 172–187.

CHURCHMAN, C. W., "Decision and Value Theory," Chap. 2 in Ackoff, R. L. (ed.), *Progress in Operations Research*, Vol. I, New York: Wiley, 1961.

CHURCHMAN, C. W., *Prediction and Optimal Decision*, Englewood Cliffs, N.J.: Prentice-Hall, 1961.

EDWARDS, W., "The Theory of Decision Making," *Psychological Bulletin*, Vol. 51, No. 4 (1954), pp. 380–417.

HALL, A. D., *A Methodology for Systems Engineering*, New York: Reinhold, Van Nostrand 1962, p. 60.

HILLIER, F. S., and G. J. LIEBERMAN, *Introduction to Operations Research*, San Francisco: Holden-Day, 1967.

LUCE, R. D., *Individual Choice Behavior*, New York: Wiley, 1959.

LUCE, R. D., and H. RAIFFA, *Games and Decisions*, New York: Wiley, 1957.

MORRIS, W. T., *Engineering Economy*, Homewood, Ill.: Irwin, 1960, p. 315.

MORRIS, W. T., *The Analysis of Management Decisions*, Homewood, Ill.: Richard D. Irwin, 1964.

SAVAGE, L. J., *The Foundations of Statistics*, New York: Wiley, 1954.

WILLIAMS, J. D., *The Compleat Strategyst*, New York: McGraw-Hill, 1954.

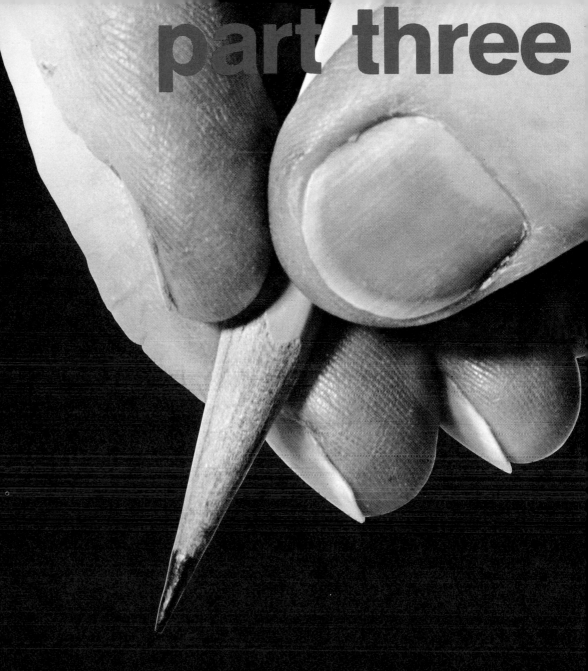

part three

design graphics

Hybrid circuitry for a transistor.

as long as a design is only in the mind of the designer, it is of little use to anyone. It must be communicated to others by word or picture. Notes or descriptions combined with sketches, drawings, and diagrams are most useful for this purpose.

Effective visual communication requires special skills so that the concepts presented are visually accurate and understandable. *Engineering graphics* is the name given to these skills. This chapter and the following five chapters will describe the techniques and tools used in engineering graphics.

There are three general types of activity in engineering graphics which require special tools. The first of these activities is *marking*, that is, making a visible trace or impression on a surface. The tools used for marking are pencils, pens, erasers, and drawing papers.

The second general type of activity is *guiding* a marking tool so that it will consistently and accurately produce the desired visible trace. At one time the only guiding tools were the straight edge and the compass. Now with the growing level of standardization and the requirement

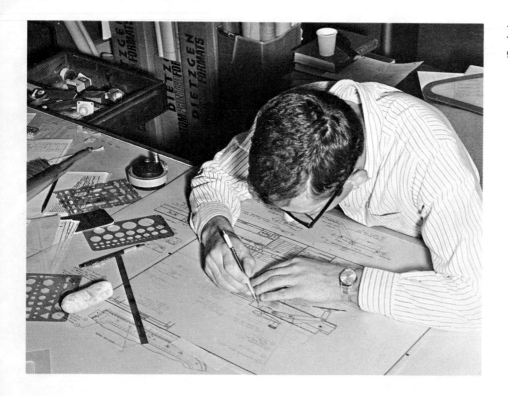

12-1
The designer makes use of many graphic tools.

12-2
Drawing pencils.

12-3
Pencil lead weights.

to reduce production time, the number and types of available guides are quite large. There are circle and ellipse guides, French or irregular curves, and templates for all types of special symbols.

The third general type of activity is *measuring*. Examples of tools for measuring are scales, dividers, and protractors.

marking tools

Of the various types of marking tools used in engineering graphics, the wood-encased graphite lead *pencil* or the mechanical *lead holder* are the most common. These marking devices are used primarily for original sketches and drawings in which frequent corrections will have to be made. The "lead" is made of different mixtures of graphite and clay and ranges from very soft 7B to very hard 9H. The soft leads, 7B to about a B, contain a high percentage of graphite, produce a dark line, and are used primarily for art work. The medium grades of lead, starting at HB and ending at about 3H, have a lower percentage of graphite and are used in technical sketching, lettering, and most mechanical drawing. Finally, the hard leads, starting at 4H and continuing through 9H, have the lowest percentage of graphite and are used in very precise technical work where very fine lines are needed, such as graphical computations and charts, descriptive geometry, and some engineering drawings. The grade is written on the pencil or lead and care should be taken not to sharpen the end that is so marked. In recent years, pencil leads formed from various plastic compounds have become very popular for use on plastic drawing films.

Always conscientiously maintain a properly sharpened point on your pencil or lead. If there is any one thing that will destroy the effectiveness of a drawing, it is a dull point. Expose about $\frac{3}{8}$ to $\frac{1}{2}$ inch of the lead and

12-4
Sandpaper pad and pencil.

12-5
Pencil pointer.

12-6
Pencil point shape.

12-7
Pencil grip.

sharpen this exposed lead by rotating it as it is stroked across a pencil pointing pad [12-4], or by rotating it within a pencil lead pointer [12-5]. The point is shaped into a cone and slightly rounded at the tip [12-6]. Do not leave an extremely sharp point as this is easily broken. Also be sure to wipe off loose graphite particles created by the sharpening process.

The pencil should be held naturally and firmly but not cramped. The thumb and fingers should grasp the pencil about $1\frac{1}{2}$ inches from its point in a manner that allows the pencil to be rotated between the fingers when a line is drawn [12-7]. This produces a line of consistent weight, because the pencil point wears evenly.

Inking tools are used to make drawings of record and tracings of original pencil work. There are two types of marking pens on the market. One type is called a ruling pen and consists of two steel "nibs" that can be adjusted to produce lines of various widths [12-8]. The second type of pen uses hollow tubes of varying diameters to emit ink at fixed line widths [12-9]. Pens of this type usually feature a large ink reservoir to reduce the need to continually fill the pen. Because of the many hours of practice required for good inking skills and the limited use of inked drawings in the design phases of engineering practice, a discussion of the procedures involved has been omitted.

Another marking device useful in engineering is the *felt-tip pen* [12-10]. This is usually an inexpensive plastic pen with a small point made of Nylon or similar material.

12-8
Ruling pen.

12-9
The hollow tube pen.

12-10
The felt-tip pen.

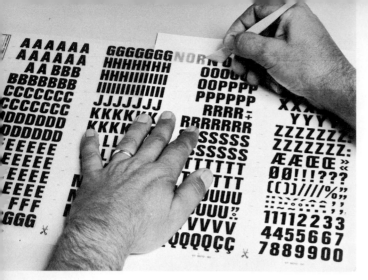

12-11
Press letters and symbols.

12-12
The eraser.

12-13
The erasing shield.

These pens come in a large variety of colors and are very useful to the designer for sketching, emphasizing parts of drawings, and differentiating curves and data points on charts. A word of caution: felt-pen lines are difficult to erase!

One of the most effective new graphic aids is the *transfer symbol*. Letters and symbols of all styles and types are printed on low-adherence paper sheets. By properly locating the desired symbol on the drawing paper and rubbing it in accordance with instructions, one is able to transfer the symbol to the paper [12-11]. The effects that can be achieved with these materials in graphic presentations are limited only by the imagination of the designer.

Erasers

If it is necessary to remove a mark from a sketch or drawing because of a mistake or a change in the concept, the fastest method is to erase the mark. However, erasing should be held to a minimum because it usually detracts from the final appearance of the graphic materials. Often, if large areas of a sketch or drawing need to be erased, it is better to trace the usable portion and continue from there rather than to do an extensive amount of erasing.

Erasers have different hardness and abrasiveness. For most engineering graphics one needs a fairly soft eraser that will remove a mark without causing damage to the paper surface. Erasers that fray the paper should be avoided. Soft white or pink erasers are quite satisfactory for most requirements. In addition to these standard erasers, several newer plastic-based varieties have become available that are especially useful on plastic drawing film. Every means possible should be employed during the creation of a drawing to maintain overall cleanliness. Any attempt to "clean up" an entire drawing when finished (using art gum or erasing compounds) will reduce the sharpness and reproducibility of the lines.

A very useful aid in erasing is an erasing shield [12-13]. It is used to protect the acceptable parts of a graphic presentation while erasing the errors. When used properly, this device can save many sketches and drawings that might otherwise have to be drawn again.

Drawing Surfaces

The surfaces used in engineering graphics range from thin paper to polyester film. The choice depends primarily on how the final graphic material is to be reproduced.

Many reproducing processes, such as diazo printing, require that the surface on which the drawing is produced be translucent. Tracing papers, tracing cloths, and plastic drawing films satisfy this requirement. Graphs, idea sketches, and preliminary layout drawings that are intended to be used without quantity reproduction can be made on opaque drawing paper.

Whether transparent or opaque, it is important that the surface have a grain that will accept readily whatever marking tool is used. It is a good practice to test the marking tool on a small piece of the surface before starting. Look to see if the surface takes a sharp, clean mark without smudges, runs, or indentations. In the case of pencils, check the point wear to see that an excessive amount of lead is not being taken away with each stroke. Test your eraser to see that the marks are removed completely without damaging the working surface.

guiding tools

One of the oldest, simplest, and still most commonly used of all the guiding tools is the *straightedge*. The straightedge can be any smooth-edged object, but the plastic triangle and the T square are the most used. As its name implies, the straightedge aids in drawing straight lines. Properly used, it helps create a precise, sharply defined line. Place the point of your pencil precisely on one of the end points of the line to be drawn. Move the straightedge into contact with the pencil point. Then align the other end of the straightedge with the other end point of the line and draw the straight line.

When using a straightedge, or any other guide, hold the pencil so that the tapered side of the point is parallel to the vertical edge of the guide. This reduces the amount of lead scraped off by the sharp corner of the guide [12-14]. Avoid using a straightedge with small indentations or printed marks along its side, such as a scale. Also avoid using any rulers with a thin metal edge. These indented and sharp-edged tools scrape off small amounts of the pencil lead with each stroke and soon produce smudges on your drawing.

The *T square* is the basic straightedge in most graphics work [12-15]. It establishes and maintains the horizontal orientation of the work and acts as a foundation for other drawing tools. T squares come with various blade lengths.

12-14

12-15
The T square.

12-16
The use of triangles.

12-17
The compass.

12-18
The beam compass.

The fixed head and hardwood blade with transparent plastic edges is the most popular.

The next most useful straightedge-type guiding tools are the *triangles*, generally made from transparent acrylic plastic [12-16]. The two most popular triangles are the 30°–60° triangle and the 45° triangle. They are right triangles with the remaining angles 30° and 60° in the first instance and 45° in the second.

The *compass* is a combination marking and guiding tool used to draw circular arcs. It holds its own lead or pen and can adjust to different radii as required. A common form of compass consists of two legs pinned at one end. They can be spread either manually or through a center wheel [12-17]. Different compasses are made to accommodate arcs of different radii. Most common engineering graphics procedures can be accomplished with a 6-inch bow-type compass. Large circles, with radii of 6 inches and more, are made with a beam compass [12-18]. Note

12-19
The metal point . . . and . . . the lead chisel point.

12-20
Mechanical guides.

the special metal point used on a compass and the lead point sharpened to a chisel shape [12-19].

Mechanical guides are used as an aid in drawing circles, ellipses, various irregular curves [12-20], and special symbols [12-21]. Their value comes not only in making draw-

12-21
Special symbol guides.

12-22

12-23

ing easier, but also in the time savings and the professional appearance added to a sketch or drawing.

With circle and ellipse guides, one needs only to indicate the center point and orientation of the figure and then trace the appropriate size [12-22].

When using mechanical guides for irregular shapes, lightly sketch the desired line or shape without using the guide. Then select the portion of the guide that fits the sketched curve closely, and formally draw in the desired line [12-23].

measuring tools

The third major class of tools consists of the measuring tools: those that measure a length or distance, and those that measure an angle.

Linear Measurement

Tools for linear measurement are called *scales*. There are several types of scales available for use in engineering graphics, of which the architect's, engineer's, and mechanical engineer's scales are the most common.

427

12-24
The architect's scale.

12-25
Scale graduations—architect's scale.

12-26
The engineer's scale.

12-27
Scale graduations—engineer's scale.

12-28
The mechanical engineering scale.

12-29
Scale graduations—mechanical
engineering scale.

The *architect's scale* is a collection of scales usually inscribed on a triangular-shaped tool [12-24]. The architect's scale is designed to show the dimensions of large objects, such as buildings. As a result, all the scales are marked in increments of 1 foot. The large numbers, usually fractions, printed at the ends of each scale indicate what part of an inch is equivalent to 1 foot. As an example, $\frac{1}{4}$ at the end of a scale means that a $\frac{1}{4}$-inch increment on this scale represents 1 foot of actual structure. The very short group of marks near the 0 point represent the subdivision of 1 foot into inches. For example, the 12 small divisions represent 1-inch intervals. The other fractional numbers and the whole numbers on the architect's scale are read in a similar manner. On an engineering drawing the architectural scale used to lay out a design is expressed as $\frac{1}{4}'' = 1'\text{-}0''$, $\frac{1}{2}'' = 1'\text{-}0''$, $1'' = 1'\text{-}0''$, etc.

The *engineer's scale* is used primarily for laying out on a drawing long distances measured in feet or miles, such as might be encountered in roads or pieces of land. Like the architect's scale, it is usually constructed with several scales inscribed on a triangular-shaped tool [12-26]. The scales on the engineer's scale are divided into units of 10, 20, 30, 40, 50, and 60 graduations per inch. By appropriate location of the decimal point, 1 inch on one of these scales can be used to represent 50, 500, or 5,000 feet, etc. On an engineering drawing, the engineer's scale used is expressed as $1'' = 300'$, $1'' = 50$ miles, etc. The scale graduations of tenths make simple work of the decimal system often used in engineering drawings and of plotting computed values on graphs.

Mechanical engineer's scales are usually flat, are marked as half-size, quarter-size, etc., and are used to lay out machinery designs [12-28]. These scales are stated on engineering drawings as $\frac{1}{2}'' = 1''$ or half-size, $\frac{1}{4}'' = 1''$ or quarter-size, $2'' = 1''$ or twice size. With the growth of microfilm records and other copying machines that change the size of drawings, it is useful to draw a scale with its typical graduations on the engineering drawing. The scale commonly found on maps is a good example of this procedure. When the drawing is reduced or enlarged, the scale remains true and is more representative than any written notation that might be found in a title block. Although most mechanical engineer's scales are subdivided into fractions of an inch, decimally divided scales are preferred in many industries.

The growing interest in the metric system, especially

in scientific and some military applications, has led to scales based on the meter. The ease of conversion and the decimal base associated with the metric system are quite attractive, and serious effort is under way to accept the metric standard. If this comes about, the metric scales will become the basis for all engineering graphics [12-30].

When several measurements are to be taken along a given direction, it is best to place the scale carefully and firmly in place and measure all distances at once. Avoid moving the scale for each new measurement since an accumulation of measurement errors is likely to result. For maximum accuracy in layout or measurement of distances, dividers should be used to transfer the distances from the scale to the paper.

The *divider* is similar to a conventional compass, but it does not have a lead holder on either leg. Instead, both legs have very sharp points [12-32]. Dividers are most often used to transfer a known distance from one place to another or to mark off several measurements of the same length.

Angular Measurement

The simplest device for measuring angles is a *protractor*. A protractor is a circular or semicircular plastic or metal disc whose circumference is inscribed with marks representing the degrees of a circle. The protractor is used by placing its base line, indicated by the 0 and 180° marks, on one of the legs or sides of an angle with its center at the vertex of the angle and reading or marking the appropriate degrees from the graduations [12-33].

12-30
The metric scale.

12-31
Scale graduations—metric scale.

12-32
The dividers.

12-33
The protractor.

429

12-34
The adjustable triangle.

12-35
The drafting machine.

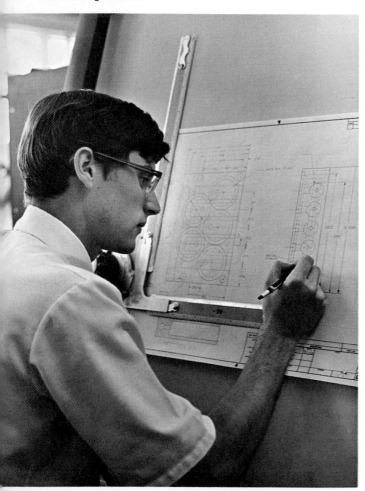

Angles of 30°, 45°, and 60° (or other angles that are multiples of 15°) can be laid out with standard triangles.

The *adjustable triangle* has a protractor incorporated into it, thus allowing the two angles that are not 90° to be varied [12-34].

Finally, there is the *drafting machine*. It is a combination guiding and measuring tool that incorporates a T square, triangles, and protractors. It consists of two arms at right angle to each other that can be moved all over the drafting board without change in orientation. Scales can be attached to the arms [12-35]. The orientation can be adjusted or changed, and a protractor is provided to tell the amount of angular adjustment. These machines are very effective in reducing the time required to produce good engineering drawings.

the work place

The *ideal* environment includes an adjustable desk or table of adequate size. Sketching materials, reference materials, and tools should be conveniently placed. A white, neutral light of high intensity is preferred. Fluorescent lights are best because they minimize shadows. A

12-36
The work place.

good quality flexible-arm drawing lamp is often used to supplement overhead lighting. Unfortunately, such an ideal environment is not always available when the need to make a sketch arises.

types of lines

We have discussed some of the tools useful in engineering graphics. Now we shall discuss techniques for using these tools, beginning with the types of lines used by engineers and draftsmen and how to draw them. Standard definitions for the types of lines may be thought of as a visual alphabet. You need to understand and recognize letters before you can understand words; similarly, you must understand the meaning of lines in order to understand the object being represented.

One important characteristic of lines is the weight or width of the line. Lines are classified as thin, medium, or thick. These are relative terms. It is recommended that the ratios of these widths be 1:2:4; in other words, the medium-width line is twice as wide as the thin line [12-37]. The proper width for a group of lines is governed by the style and purpose of the drawing to be produced. *There must be a distinct contrast between the different widths of lines on a drawing and these contrasts and widths must be consistent and uniform throughout the drawing.* All the lines constructed on a drawing must be clean, dense, and opaque black for legible reproduction.

When constructing lines on a drawing, orient the pencil in the direction of the stroke at an angle of approximately 60° with the paper [12-38]. Draw the line with an even, consistent pressure and, when using a conical point, rotate the pencil slowly between the thumb and forefinger as the line is being drawn. This will maintain a symmetrical point and produce a uniform line weight. If it is necessary, draw over a line several times to get the proper width and contrast.

Lines used in engineering graphics are of two general classes: lines that represent features of actual physical objects, and lines that present information but are not part of the object. Lines used to represent the physical characteristics of an object are called visible and hidden lines. They indicate the intersection of two surfaces, the edge view of a surface, or the contour of a curved surface. The visible line is usually called the *object line* and shows

12-37

LINE WIDTH RATIOS

12-38

12-39
Types of lines.

TYPE	WEIGHT	
OBJECT	THICK	
HIDDEN	MEDIUM	
CENTER	THIN	
PHANTOM	THIN	
EXTENSION & DIMENSION	THIN	
LEADER	THIN	
SECTION	THIN	
CUTTING PLANE	THICK	
SHORT BREAK	THICK	
LONG BREAK	THIN	

12-40

12-41

12-42

12-43

12-44

all the edges, contours, and surfaces of an object seen by an observer. Object lines are drawn as solid, thick lines, and are the most predominant lines of an object. *Hidden lines* represent edges, contours, and surfaces that could be seen only if the object were transparent. Hidden lines are constructed of equally spaced, medium-width dashes. The dashes are about $\frac{1}{8}$ inch long with $\frac{1}{32}$-inch spaces.

Certain conventional practices should be observed when sketching or drawing visible and hidden lines.

1. When a hidden line forms a continuation of a visible line, there must be a clear separation of their intersection [12-40].
2. Intersecting hidden lines should form perpendicular corners, as in the letters "L" and "T" [12-41].
3. The dash of a hidden line should not intersect a visible line [12-42].
4. Parallel hidden lines should be drawn so that the spaces in one line are next to the dashes in the adjacent line [12-43].
5. When hidden lines join at a point, the dashes should touch, as in the case at the bottom of a drilled hole [12-44].

The second class of lines includes center lines, extension lines, leaders, dimension lines, section lines, cutting-plane lines, viewing-plane lines, short-break lines, long-break lines, and phantom lines.

The *center line* is composed of thin alternate long and short dashes. As the name implies, center lines define a central axis of a hole, or indicate the origin of a radius. The center line is also used to indicate an axis of symmetry of an object.

The *extension line* is constructed as a thin solid line. It is used to extend the significant features of an object to a point where dimensions can be applied without cluttering the visual image of the object. When constructing extension lines, leave a gap of about $\frac{1}{32}$ inch between the extension line and the object line being extended. *Leaders* are closely related to extension lines. They are thin solid lines constructed from a descriptive note to a point on the object. *Dimension lines* are also drawn as thin solid lines. More detail about dimension lines, leaders, etc., will be found in Chapter 16.

Section lines are thin solid lines commonly referred to as *cross-hatching*. They represent a surface of solid material that has been cut through by a cutting plane in the drawing. In professional quality work, section lines should be evenly spaced and of uniform width. The *cutting-plane line* is a thick line composed of a series of medium-length dashes. The cutting-plane line is used to show the location where an object has been sliced with an imaginary knife to expose hidden details or internal parts. The *viewing-plane line* is drawn similar to the cutting-plane line and is used to indicate special directions for viewing an object.

The two types of *break lines,* the thick *short-break* and the thin *long-break,* are used to eliminate from the drawing parts of an object that are not needed in the particular view. They represent an intentional disruption of a view of the object and removal of some segments. Break lines are used as a convenience to eliminate unnecessary work and to clarify the drawing. The *phantom line* is used to draw the object in an alternative position, to show length of travel, or to show direction of motion. It is a thin line of two short dashes alternating with one long dash.

Construction lines are not included in the two groups mentioned above. They are composed of very thin, lightweight lines barely visible at arm's length. They are used to lay out the drawing, and are the first lines used when constructing a technical drawing. They are extremely light and need not be erased. *Guiaeunes* tor lettering also fall in this category.

Often two or more lines coincide on a drawing. In such cases, show those lines that present the greatest information to the observer. Visible lines, hidden lines, and center lines require a system of priorities to effectively convey meaning. Visible lines always predominate. In any given drawing, if the visible line is constructed in the same position as a hidden line or center line, the visible line will have precedence. Next in importance are the hidden lines, and finally the center line.

When constructing views of an object, select the view in which the major details of the object are visible and the fewest number of hidden lines are required. It is desirable to keep the number of lines to describe an object to a minimum, and to use consistent methods of depicting visible, hidden, and center-line relationships. This aids in eliminating error on the part of the designer and assists the reader in his understanding of the drawing.

When you have learned to identify these lines and to understand their meaning, you will have an easy time comprehending the shape of the object presented in an engineering drawing.

constructions

A few important techniques are used frequently in basic drawing. The simplest and most effective way to transfer a line parallel to an original line is by using two triangles. Place one of the triangles on the work and carefully align one of its sides with the line to be transferred. When the alignment is true, hold the triangle firmly and place the second triangle in contact with one of the remaining sides [12-45]. (Be sure that no eraser crumbs or other material are caught between the two triangles.) While holding the second triangle firmly in position, slide the first triangle to a new location where a parallel line is desired [12-46]. Any line drawn along the side that was aligned with the original line will be parallel with that line. This technique is helpful in constructing lines parallel with planes, the sides of rectilinear figures, or guidelines for lettering.

To construct one line perpendicular to another, orient the first triangle so that a side other than the hypotenuse is aligned with the line to which a perpendicular line

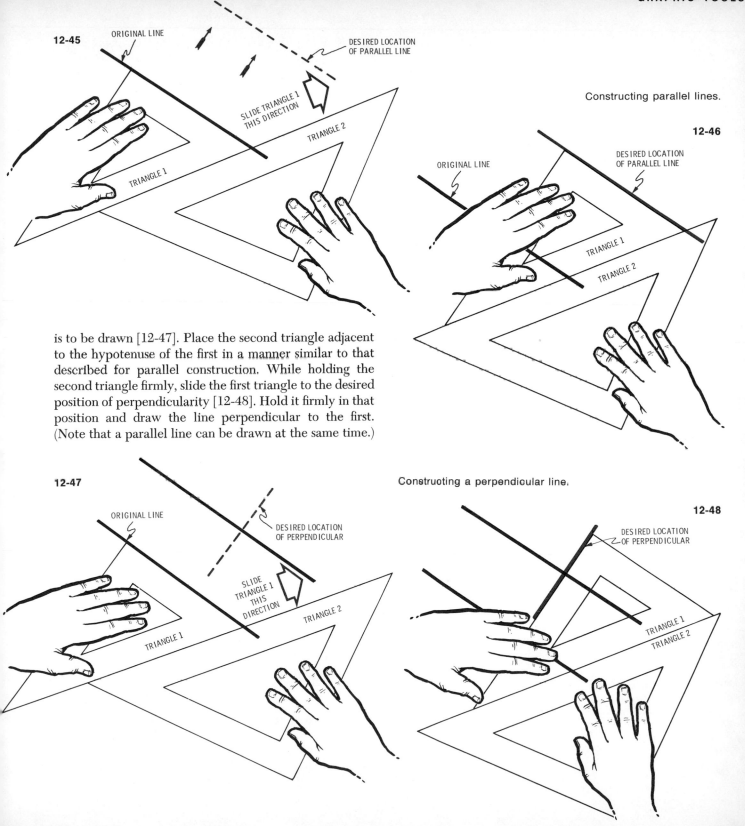

12-45

ORIGINAL LINE

DESIRED LOCATION
OF PARALLEL LINE

SLIDE TRIANGLE 1
THIS DIRECTION

TRIANGLE 2

TRIANGLE 1

Constructing parallel lines.

12-46

ORIGINAL LINE

DESIRED LOCATION
OF PARALLEL LINE

TRIANGLE 1

TRIANGLE 2

is to be drawn [12-47]. Place the second triangle adjacent to the hypotenuse of the first in a manner similar to that described for parallel construction. While holding the second triangle firmly, slide the first triangle to the desired position of perpendicularity [12-48]. Hold it firmly in that position and draw the line perpendicular to the first. (Note that a parallel line can be drawn at the same time.)

12-47

ORIGINAL LINE

DESIRED LOCATION
OF PERPENDICULAR

SLIDE
TRIANGLE 1
THIS
DIRECTION

TRIANGLE 2

TRIANGLE 1

Constructing a perpendicular line.

12-48

DESIRED LOCATION
OF PERPENDICULAR

TRIANGLE 1
TRIANGLE 2

435

This is an effective and accurate method for constructing right-angle corners of rectilinear objects, perpendicular planes, and vertical guidelines for lettering.

lettering

A new design can be described by drawings of its components, but many details of the design are best communicated through words and symbols. The lettering used in engineering graphics is more uniform and more easily read than script. Lettering can be considered as an application of freehand drawing. Great care must be exercised in lettering, because poorly made letters and numbers can be misread and may cause expensive errors in production or fabrication. The preferred style of lettering used in engineering graphics is called single-stroke Gothic. It was

12-49

Basic Vertical
Strokes

Basic Inclined
Strokes

12-50
Vertical lettering.

A B C D E F G H I J K L M N
O P Q R S T U V W X Y Z
0 1 2 3 4 5 6 7 8 9

Upper-Case Vertical Gothic Lettering

a b c d e f g h i j k l m n
o p q r s t u v w x y z

Lower-Case Vertical Gothic Lettering

436

ABCDEFGHIJKLMN
OPQRSTUVWXYZ
0123456789

Upper-Case Inclined Gothic Lettering

abcdefghijklmn
opqrstuvwxyz

Lower-Case Inclined Gothic Lettering

designed and standardized for maximum legibility and easy, rapid execution.

To letter well in the Gothic style, the engineer should be thoroughly familiar with the characteristics of every letter and numeral in the Gothic alphabet [12-50 and 12-51]. He should learn

1. The shape and general proportions of each letter.
2. The recommended order of strokes to draw each letter.
3. The way in which letters are spaced to make words.

Some simple guidelines will assist in the development of lettering skill. Beginners tend to make letters too narrow. As a rule, it is the width of the letters that make them legible. All capital or uppercase letters are almost as wide as they are high, except the letters "I" and "W." The bodies of the small or lowercase letters are approximately two thirds the height of the capitals. Fractional

12-52

12-53

If lettering is not Uniform

It is unprofessional

numbers are about twice the height of uppercase letters, with the numerator and denominator each about three fourths the whole number size. Normally, engineering lettering is $\frac{1}{8}$ inch high. If a reduction of size is anticipated, such as in microfilming, it is desirable to make the lettering somewhat larger, say $\frac{5}{32}$ inch or more. The space between lines of lettering should be at least one half the letter height—more if space is available.

Lettering is composed of two basic graphical elements: the straight line and the curve. Vertical strokes should be made downward with finger movement, and horizontal strokes from left to right with a wrist movement. The forearm should be at approximately a right angle to the line of lettering and resting on the writing surface. Uniformity is important and is best achieved by constructing and using horizontal and vertical lettering guidelines. All guidelines should be drawn *very lightly* with a sharp, hard 4H or 6H pencil. There are four horizontal guidelines: the capline, waistline, baseline, and dropline. The first three of these guidelines are commonly used in lettering practice. The dropline is used only with lowercase letters, and there are but five lowercase letters that require it. Consequently, it is often omitted. The drawing of accurately spaced guidelines is greatly facilitated by the use of an Ames or Braddock lettering guide [12-55].

Vertical guidelines are either truly vertical or inclined about 68° depending on the choice of vertical Gothic or inclined Gothic lettering. Vertical guidelines are spaced randomly throughout a line of lettering and are constructed parallel to each other. The spacing of these guidelines has nothing to do with the spacing of the letters—they are simply a convenience to the letterer.

12-54

It usually makes little difference whether vertical or inclined lettering is used, but once established on a drawing, the lettering must be consistent, uniform, and parallel. Generally, it is easier to produce acceptable vertical lettering, because one's eye is not often used to judge accurately adherence to a specific angle of inclination.

Uniformity in lettering is further emphasized by consistent line thickness or weight. When using a pencil, this is accomplished by evenly applied pressure and frequent sharpening. Use a relatively soft pencil (H or softer) to produce a good black line. A conical point, slightly rounded, is best, and the pencil should be rotated a little before each letter is started. This practice will promote even wearing of the point and maintain its symmetry. The strokes of each letter should be one continuous motion.

Spacing of letters and words on a drawing is a visual and subjective art that is developed only through continued practice. Letter spacing is a function of the blank areas between adjacent letters. Good spacing cannot be accomplished by measuring. It is the visual areas between letters that must appear to be equal, and this changes with each combination of letters. The space between words obviously must be greater than between letters. A good rule is to space words at least the height of a capital letter or just slightly more; in other words, leave at least enough room for a capital "O" between words. Remember that good lettering involves the artistic designing of the black lines and white areas to create a balanced and pleasing appearance.

problems

12-1. Using words only, describe the shape or form of one of the following mechanisms:
(a) desk-top stapler
(b) wall-mounted pencil sharpener
(c) fractional horsepower electric motor
(d) door latch
(e) hand-operated can opener

12-2. Make a freehand sketch of the object's shape that was verbally described in Problem 12-1. Sketch only the most descriptive view of the object. Use unruled $8\frac{1}{2}$ by 11 inch white paper.

12-3. There is an activity of engineering graphics called *marking* that uses a marking tool, an eraser, and a surface on which to mark. A common example is a 2H pencil, an art gum

12-55
The lettering guide.

12-56

A slightly rounded, conical point is best.

Good spacing is related to visual area... not measured distances.

ALLOW EQUAL AREAS BETWEEN LETTERS IN WORDS.

439

eraser, and tracing paper. List five other reasonable combinations of marking tools that might be used by the engineer.

12-4. On an 8½-by 11-inch sheet of unruled paper, randomly place six points at least 3 inches apart. Using a straightedge guiding tool and a 2H pencil, draw lines such that each point is connected to the other five. Be particularly mindful of the proper procedure for using the marking tool with the guiding tool and the method of positioning the guiding tool.

12-5. Using a curved guiding tool, such as a French curve, follow the instructions of Problem 12-4.

12-6. Using the compass as a marking and guiding tool, construct seven concentric circles, starting with a 1-inch radius and increasing each successive radius by $\frac{1}{2}$ inch.

12-7. Using all capital letters $\frac{1}{8}$ inch high, print a list of all the engineering graphics tools that you have collected for use in this class. Indicate on your list the primary use for each tool (marking, measuring, or guiding).

12-8. Using all capital letters, print a list of all the engineering graphics tools that you own that are multiple-activity tools. Include in this list any tools that are not used for marking, measuring, or guiding.

12-9. Using all capital letters, print the names of 6 of the types of *marking* tools that are available for sale in the engineering graphics section of the school supply store.

12-10. List by name 6 of the *guiding tools* as instructed in Problem 12-9.

12-11. List by name 6 of the *measuring tools* as instructed in Problem 12-9.

12-12. Using an architect's scale, accurately lay off a full-size 4½-inch line. In a column under this line, list all the scales available on the architect's scale, and beside each listed scale place the *measured* equivalent of the 4½-inch line.

12-13. Using an engineer's scale and a full-size 3¾-inch line, measure and list the measurements as instructed in Problem 12-12.

12-14. Using a protractor or an adjustable triangle, divide a 6-inch-diameter circle into five equal segments.

12-15. Using a T square, a 30°–60° triangle, and a 45° triangle (singularly and in combination), construct 15° segments of a 6-inch-diameter circle from 0° to 360°. Do not use any other measuring tools.

12-16. Draw three series of 12 parallel lines at any angle other than horizontal or vertical. Make one of the series *thin* weight lines, another *medium* weight, and the third *thick* weight. Draw each line in the series 4 inches long and parallel with $\frac{1}{8}$-inch space between the lines. (Use the parallel-line construction technique involving two triangles. See page 435.)

12-17. Using three or more figures from [12-57] as assigned, place a dot about $\frac{1}{16}$ inch in diameter on every object line shown.

12-57

(1)

(2)

(3)

(4)

(5)

(6)

(7)

(8)

(9)

(10)

(11)

12-18. Identify all the hidden lines as instructed in Problem 12-17.

12-19. Identify all the center lines as instructed in Problem 12-17.

12-20. Using vertical Gothic lettering, uppercase and lowercase, letter the first paragraph under the subtitle "Lettering," which begins with "A new design . . ." Use guidelines and make the letters $\frac{1}{8}$ inch high. (See page 436.)

12-21. Using slant lettering, uppercase and lowercase, letter the same paragraph as instructed in Problem 12-20.

sketching and conceptualization 13

Polarized light microscopy provides a colorful view of polymer chains aligning themselves in the direction of an applied stress. When a partially crystallized polymer is subjected to external stress, its crystallinity increases. Because increased crystallinity generally improves mechanical properties, many polymeric materials, such as nylon, are frequently cold drawn or stretched. At GM Research, additional data about films under stress is gleaned through X-ray diffraction. Studying the effects of stress aids in the development of more durable polymers.

he ability to make clear, concise sketches is important to the engineer, but this does not imply that engineers must have artistic talents. Rather, proficiency in sketching is acquired through practice. Engineering sketches conform to uniform standards and conventions so that people of all disciplines and languages can understand the meaning intended by the designer. This chapter considers both the conventions and techniques of sketching.

Sketching helps to stimulate one's imagination as well as to convey information. For this reason it is ideally suited for the engineer's communication with others *and with himself*. A sketch frequently serves to clarify an original idea and at the same time suggest additional versions, adaptations, and improvements. One often finds that he is able to organize his thoughts more effectively

13-1
The ability to sketch is an essential skill for those in design work.

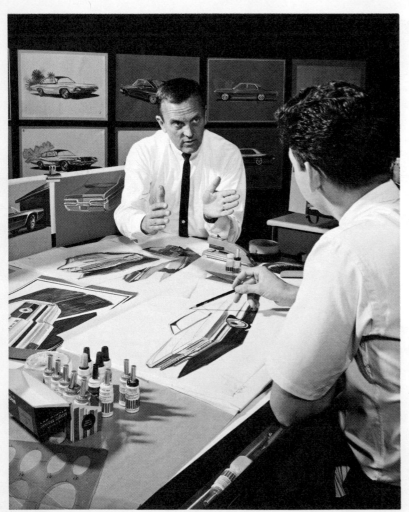

if he can present his mental impressions in graphic form, whether it be a flow chart summarizing the main points of a presentation or a detailed sketch explaining a complicated mechanism.

In general, technical sketching is a mechanical process that conforms to specified guidelines. However, one's physiological makeup does play an important role—particularly the interplay between brain, eye, hand, and arm. A simple experiment will illustrate the remarkable precision of the eye when used as a proportioning instrument. On the line below place a mark at the point you estimate to be the midpoint. Do not use a scale or any other measuring device except your eye.

Now measure the line and locate the midpoint exactly. How closely did you estimate the midpoint? This is just one of many functions of your eye–brain–hand system, *and it becomes more proficient with practice*.

Emphasis in this chapter will be directed toward the freehand sketch which is ideal for conceptualization and ideation and which also can be used effectively in design development and presentation.

One cannot learn to sketch and express himself graphically solely by reading about it, any more than one can learn to swim while standing by the pool. Several examples are shown here [13-2 to 13-12] to illustrate how sketches of all types are used to communicate ideas.

13-2

13-3

13-4

13-5

13-6

℄ PECAN ST.

N. 1° 30' W.

20.0'
10.0
237.8'
98.0'
98.1
238.1
8.0
10.0 R
16.0'
CURB LINE
℄ HARRIS ST.
N 89° 0' E.

SKETCH OF LOT 1
BLOCK 12
RIDGECREST
ADDITION
BEDFORD, OHIO
2-25-72 W. Wilke P.E.

13-7

4.63 DIA.
0.50
0.13
0.06 R
FINE KNURL
THIS SURFACE
THD. RELIEF
1.63
0.75
0.38
DRILL ¼
TYP. 4 PLACES
EQUALLY
SPACED.
4.15 DIA.
0.06 R
E.O. #732
W.O. #430B
T. HODGE, P.E.
7-18-72
THD. 4⅛-16-2
SHAFT CAP
PART OF NO. 13 ASSEMBLY

NOTES : MAKE 1 PC.
MATERIAL
4130 STEEL
NORMALIZED
CADMIUM PLATE
OUTSIDE SURFACE

13-8

W = WHITE
G = GREEN

150K Ω
W
G
G
W
3"
SPKR
2N1304
Q1
2N1304
Q2
0.4f
9V.
4.7 µf
INPUT
JACKS
10
KΩ
47 Ω
15
µf
47 Ω

AUDIO AMPLIFIER FOR TAPE SYSTEM
MOUNT IN ALUMINUM BOX APPROX. 6X6X3 IN.
PAINT OUTSIDE OF BOX FLAT BLACK
3-11-72   D. JERNIGAN P.E.

13-9

SIGNAL LIGHT   13-10

JAMISON VEHICLE

MR. JANIS

ADAMS ST.

NORTH   WEST

JANIS VEHICLE

RIGHT PULMONARY ARTERY   RETURN   HEAD & ARMS

RIGHT PULMONARY VEIN   LEFT PULMONARY ARTERY

LEFT PULMONARY VEIN

RETURN

TRUNK & LEGS   13-12

MAIN LONGITUDINAL TRACHEAL BRANCH

SPIRACULAR BRANCH   GENERALIZED INSECT (KOLBE TRACHEAL SYSTEM)

VISCERAL TRACHEAL BRANCH   SPIRACLE   NERVE CORD

13-11

tools

Sketching requires only a marking tool and a surface upon which to mark. Almost any combination will suffice—from a ball-point pen on a tablecloth to a piece of chalk on a structural I beam.

The ideal tools are a *pencil* and good quality *paper*. The pencil point must be sharpened and shaped according to the thickness of line desired. A conical shape, slightly rounded at the tip, is best. A sharp point will produce a thin line, a dull point a thick line. If the lead is too sharp or pointed, it tends to break when used. Sharpen and shape the pencil point as often as is necessary, and remove its sharp edges on a pad of rough paper or sandpaper.

13-13

YES!   NO!   NO!

The most desirable sketch paper is a good-quality medium-weight transparent vellum. This eliminates the need for most erasing because alterations can be quickly retraced on an overlay. Thin paper is difficult to use for sketching because it tears easily. Smooth or slick paper will not be abrasive enough to give the pencil a "bite" and enable it to form a solid dark line. When vellum is unavailable, a good-quality bond paper is acceptable, as long as its surface has a slightly rougher texture than the paper used in this book. For rough field sketching, many engineers prefer pads of paper having a light cross-hatched background.

Ideally, one should *not* use an *eraser* while sketching. An important objective is confidence—the confidence to act surely and boldly when putting ideas in graphic form. If one knows that he can erase and has an eraser handy, there is a temptation to sketch without conviction. In addition, erasing destroys the paper's surface so that the corrected line on the sketch is poorly defined and has an imprecise appearance. Such techniques produce weak sketches that are unconvincing and devoid of character. An eraser should be used only after the sketch has been completed to remove smudges and extraneous construction lines that may detract from the appearance or clarity of the drawing. For this purpose art gum or other soft erasers are quite effective.

The guiding tools described in Chapter 12 may be especially useful for "finished" sketches, but a good free-hand sketch is most often preferred.

basic sketching techniques

Initial sketches are most often discarded, and no effort should be wasted in finalizing the drawing. Rather, the first sketch should be drawn as a trial sketch to present only the essence of the idea. This practice can actually save time, as well as build confidence and proficiency. When one is learning to sketch, he must be willing to use a lot of paper and to discard unsuccessful efforts without remorse.

Lines in sketching are not intended to be comparable with instrument-drawn work, and their smoothness and uniformity are not as necessary as in instrument drawings. Rather the quality of a line drawn freehand is judged by its accuracy of direction and its density or weight. It is good practice to look where you are going when sketch-

13-14

ing. Place the pencil point at the start of the intended line, then look to the point where the line will be finished. Without shifting your eyes, draw directly to the finish point in a *single* smooth, even stroke. This technique will eliminate one of the most obvious characteristics of an amateur—short, scratchy lines. When drawing lines, always move boldly to the objective. If an error appears, stop and return to the beginning. Do not erase and do not try to repair the wayward line. Final adjustment can be made after the overall sketch has been drawn.

The arm can serve as a large compass with the point of the elbow (the "funny bone") as the pivot [13-14]. With a smooth motion, small portions of a large arc can be sketched as short straight lines. The arm is rather heavy and provides the necessary stability for control. For this reason arm motions should be used when sketching, just as "follow-through" is used in tennis or golf—where smoothness of motion is essential to good performance.

Variations in width and density of lines produce sketches with vitality and interest. Variations lead the eye from one area to another and emphasize important points. Rough construction lines should be very thin, light lines. Dimension lines, center lines, and extension lines should also be lightweight [13-15]. The other lines, how-

13-15
Types of lines.

TYPE	WEIGHT	
OBJECT	THICK	
HIDDEN	MEDIUM	
CENTER	THIN	
PHANTOM	THIN	
EXTENSION & DIMENSION	THIN	
LEADER	THIN	
SECTION	THIN	
CUTTING PLANE	THICK	
SHORT BREAK	THICK	
LONG BREAK	THIN	

ever, should be sharp, distinct, and of a heavier weight. The ends of all lines, including dashes, are slightly accented. The object lines on the sketch should have the heaviest weight. Contrast among the different line weights should be maintained.

Layout

Plan the sketch *before* you begin to draw, and arrange the subject of the sketch in a pleasing and logical composition on the paper. One of the most useful procedures for planning a sketch is to first make a series of *thumbnail sketches*. These are small sketches drawn in a minimum amount of time with little attention to detail. The thumbnail sketch that best satisfies the overall requirements intended by the engineer will become the basis for the more detailed sketches to follow. Remember, vellum or paper is less expensive than time, so use as many sheets as necessary to achieve the most effective layout. Avoid crowding notes and details, and allow ample paper to surround or frame the sketch. This emphasizes the importance of the work and adds to its appearance.

13-16
A crowded condition . . .

13-17
. . . creates confusion and frustration.

Proportioning

Technical sketches are not drawn to an exact scale, but must maintain the *proportions* of the object being sketched. The overall size of the sketch is optional and depends upon its intended use, its complexity, and the size of the paper available. Usually, small objects are sketched oversize, whereas large objects are sketched to some reduced scale.

There are several ways to develop a properly proportioned sketch. One is called *scaffolding*. Scaffolding establishes the foundation for a sketch.

Scaffolding. Using lightweight lines, construct a rectangle that will enclose the overall width and height of the object [13-18]. This rectangle serves in much the same way as the scaffolding used for constructing a building. It can be eliminated when the sketch is finished, just as construction scaffolding is removed from the site once the job is completed.

Subdivide the scaffold into smaller sections representing the major proportions of the object [13-19 and 13-20]. When objects are symmetrically formed about some axis or plane, use center lines [13-21].

13-18

13-19

13-21

13-20

13-22

13-23

Sketch in the remaining details to define the final form of the object. After the rough sketch is completed [13-22], it is traced onto another vellum sheet. This procedure eliminates the need for time-consuming and messy erasing [13-23].

In summary, when sketching an idea, the overall width and height should first be estimated and "blocked," as in [13-24]. Then establish the major proportions of the object and the shapes of the curved parts. Finally, develop and darken the object lines of the completed sketch, and trace the sketch onto another piece of vellum.

Although we have related scaffolding specifically to two-dimensional multiview sketches, the technique can be used also in the more complicated pictorial systems. The main difference is the need for three-dimensional scaffolding boxes in place of the two-dimensional rectangles used for multiview sketches.

Curvilinear Elements. In most instances all curvilinear forms can be simplified to a circle (or portions of circles). Small circles or arcs can be sketched in progressive steps. A scaffold square, whose sides equal the diameter of the circle, is sketched first with very lightweight lines. The center lines are sketched through the midpoints of the sides, and diagonal lines are drawn across the square. The circle or arc is then drawn tangent to the sides of the square [13-25].

Another acceptable technique uses a series of radial lines from the center of the circle. The radius of the circle

13-24

13-25

13-26

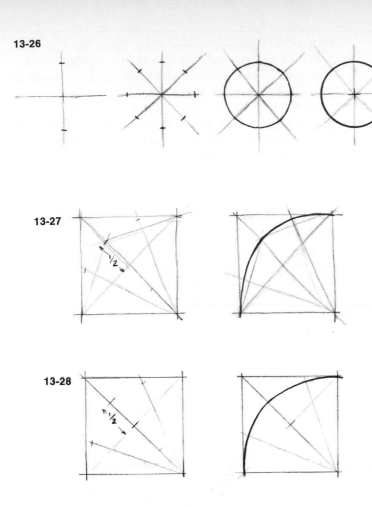

13-27

13-28

is then estimated or measured along each radial line and lightly marked. The circle is drawn through each of the radius points [13-26]. As many radial lines as desired may be drawn, but eight lines are generally enough.

Segments of circles can be drawn freehand using the same techniques [13-27 and 13-28]. Scaffolding lines or radial lines may be used, but it is important that the points of tangency be carefully observed in either case.

In several types of pictorial systems, circles are viewed at an angle. When this happens the circles *appear as ellipses* to the observer. There are several techniques for constructing accurate ellipses, but the following approximate method will suffice for sketching. This technique, known as the four-center ellipse, will work for a large range of varying elliptical axes. Proceed as shown in [13-29 to 13-33].

13-29

Step 1 Sketch a rhombus whose sides are equal to the diameter of the true circle that is to be represented; sketch the diagonal between the two apexes farthest apart [13-29].

13-30

Step 2 Estimate the midpoints of each side of the rhombus, and connect the midpoints of the sides with the rhombus apexes on the opposite side [13-30].

13-31

Step 3 The two intersections of the bisectors will serve as centers from which circular arcs can be sketched at the two apexes farthest apart [13-31].

13-32

Step 4 Complete the ellipse by sketching the two remaining circular arcs, whose radii extend from the nearer apexes [13-32].

13-33

Step 5 Erase the construction lines and darken the outline of the ellipse or retrace the ellipse on clean paper [13-33].

453

13-34

Sources of Visual Material

Frequently, you will want to sketch an object at reduced or enlarged scale from a photograph or drawing. In such instances, construct a grid across the original picture [13-34]. Then make another grid, larger or smaller than the original, as needed. Draw the final sketch into the new grid, using the grid squares to proportion lengths of lines and radii of arcs.

Pictures may be selected from magazines or journals whenever they illustrate a point or an idea that one wants to show. Pictures of people, cars, trees, trucks, and equipment may be used—anything which illustrates or amplifies the idea that one wishes to sketch. There is no reason to make a sketch if a picture is readily available. Photocopy the picture and use it if it is what you have in mind. Such techniques save time and add realism to the sketch. When translucent vellum is used, they may be traced directly. When it is only a close approximation, such as the handle on an appliance [13-35], trace the parts that are relevant to your design and then complete the remainder of the sketch from your own imagination [13-36]. This fundamental technique can be mastered if one learns to *think* graphically. *Think in terms of pictures rather than words.*

13-36

13-35

13-37

Basic Shapes in Sketching

Most objects can be reduced to four basic geometric shapes: cylinders, rectangular prisms, cones, and spheres [13-37]. You should learn to recognize these shapes as components of objects and be able to sketch them realistically. The four basic shapes are found not only in man-made designs [13-39 and 13-40], but also in the structure of living things. If you can draw these four shapes as viewed from various angles and depict their lines of intersection, you can draw almost any object.

13-38
Many designs are composites of the four basic shapes.

13-39

13-40

graphic portrayal systems

Several techniques can be used to sketch a three-dimensional object on two-dimensional paper: orthographic (multiview), oblique, axonometric, and perspective. Each has certain features that make it suitable to specific needs and each has its limitations.

Orthographic (Multiview) System

The *orthographic* or *multiview* is the most frequently used portrayal system in engineering graphics. In this system, two, three, or more views of an object are shown. The views are sketched as if they were projected perpendicularly on the faces of an imaginary transparent glass box that surrounds the object [13-41]. If this glass box is unfolded and laid flat, six views of the object will be seen [13-42]. In this way one can "see" simultaneously

LINES OF SIGHT

13-41

13-42

TOP

REAR   LEFT   RIGHT

BOTTOM

the object from several directions. For a more complete discussion of orthographic projection, refer to Chapter 14.

An orthographic sketch is relatively easy to make, has accurate dimensions, and is particularly useful as a basis for model or prototype construction. Its major limitation is the difficulty of visualization. Since the viewer can concentrate on only one view at a time, he must mentally reassemble the object from the various views in order to understand it. This can be particularly difficult for very complex objects, such as an automobile carburetor. To overcome this limitation, a pictorial sketch, such as the oblique sketch, can be used (see page 462).

Multiview sketches are most frequently used

1. When true shape views are required.
2. When dimensions must be specified.
3. When a model or finished part is to be fabricated from the sketch.
4. When angular or oblique surfaces must be described accurately.
5. To precede the preparation of accurate sectional views.
6. When an accurate description of a detail assembly is required.

Let us consider the block in [13-43]. Ordinarily, the three views used to describe this object would be the front, top, and right or left side views [13-44]. They are

13-43

13-44

TOP VIEW

FRONT VIEW

RIGHT SIDE VIEW

called *principal views*. After the front view is drawn, the top view is obtained by rotating the object 90° up and forward toward the observer. The right side view is obtained by rotating the right side toward the observer [13-45].

Selection of Views. Select appropriate views and minimize their number. Sketch only those views that are necessary for a clear description. The most important view is the one that shows the prominent or characteristic contour of the object. Usually, this view is designated as the front view.

The object shown here [13-46] has three distinctive features that should be described completely by the sketch:

1. The square silhouette top and the rectangular slot in the vertical surface—both of which can be seen from the front view.
2. The hole in the horizontal surface and the beveled front corner—which are described by the top view.
3. The right angle at the rear—which can be seen from the side.

Upon examination we can see that the left side, back, and bottom views are unnecessary because they repeat what is contained in the front, top, and right side views.

In many instances only two principal views are re-

13-45

13-46

SKETCH - SPRING CATCH
MAKE ONE - NOTIFY ENGINEERING
FOR TEST   H. H. Coné 5/8/72

quired [13-47]. Cylindrical, conical, and pyramidal shapes and, in general, any shape that is symmetrical about an axis usually can be described adequately with only two views.

Occasionally, some objects can be described adequately with a single view. When only one view is used, supplementary descriptive notes must be added. In [13-48] the view would be incomplete without the note specifying the thickness. In [13-49] notes are needed to identify the cylindrical shapes of the various portions of the roller and their concentricity.

There are cases when three views will not be adequate and sectional or auxiliary views must be used as supplements. The use of these special types of views will be discussed in Chapters 14, 15, and 16.

Orthographic Sketching. In orthographic sketching the overall dimensions of each view should be blocked in first using the scaffolding technique mentioned earlier. Figure [13-50] shows the successive steps in preparing the multiview sketch of the support bracket. Note the vertical lines drawn between the top and front views to establish the width of the bracket. The horizontal lines drawn between the front and right side views establish the height of the bracket. Diagonals are drawn lightly to serve as locators for the center of the holes.

Grid paper aids the designer in multiview sketching. It will do much to assure proper alignment of the views and realistic proportions [13-51].

13-50

13-51

461

SOLID LINE
(NOT HIDDEN LINE)

13-52

HIDDEN LINE
(NOT CENTER LINE)

13-53

13-54
Fundamental relationships
of an oblique projection.

OBJECT

PICTURE
PLANE

OBSERVER

φ

FRONT
SURFACE
TRUE SHAPE

13-55
All the features of the
front view of an oblique
sketch are drawn as a
true shape.

Precedence and Representation of Lines. Priority of linework is similar to that described in Chapter 12. Visible lines are necessary to establish the physical features of the object and take precedence over all other lines. A solid line can cover a hidden line, but not vice versa. The following order of preference is recommended:

1. Object (visible) lines.
2. Hidden lines.
3. Center lines.
4. Cutting-plane lines.
5. Dimension and extension lines.
6. Cross-hatch lines.

The procedures for dimensioning an orthographic sketch are the same as those discussed in Chapter 16.

Oblique System

Oblique, axonometric, and perspective systems usually are known as *pictorial* because, in contrast with the orthographic system, they provide the viewer with an illusion of depth while he looks at only one view. The *oblique* system is the simplest transition from the orthographic system because the orthographic front view can be used directly as a major portion of the oblique view.

Orthographic views are *perpendicular* projections onto the sides of an imaginary glass box enclosing the object. In oblique projection the object is viewed through a single picture plane, but the observer's line of sight is now at an angle (oblique) to the picture plane [13-54]. This enables him to see depth dimensions as well as an undistorted view of the face of the object parallel to the picture plane [13-55].

An oblique view of an object is sketched in much the same way as an orthographic view, except that the scaffold used is a three-dimensional box following the oblique axes selected [13-56]. The face of the object that best displays the most distinctive or characteristic contours of the object should be oriented parallel to the picture plane to take advantage of the ease of sketching the undistorted image that will appear [13-57]. The angle at which the depth dimension recedes from the horizontal is usually chosen as 45°, but other angles varying from 15° to 60° often provide a better view of secondary surfaces [13-58]. If the shape of an object is such that the conventional or *cavalier* oblique sketch [13-59] appears to distort the

13-56

GIVEN ORTHOGRAPHIC VIEWS

1   2   3

13-57

CORRECT

INCORRECT

CORRECT

INCORRECT

13-58

(A)   (B)

$\Theta = 15^0$ TO 60^0

13-59
Oblique sketch: cavalier.

13-60
Oblique sketch: cabinet.

object too much, a modification known as *cabinet* oblique may be used. In this technique all depth dimensions are reduced by one half [13-60].

Axonometric System

In the *axonometric* portrayal system the object is oriented at an angle with a single picture plane, and the

13-61
Fundamental relationships of an axonometric projection.

OBJECT

PICTURE PLANE

90°

OBSERVER

observer's line of sight is perpendicular to that picture plane [13-61]. As in the oblique system, the image projected on the picture plane gives the observer an illusion of depth in a single view and provides a more realistic and understandable picture than an orthographic sketch. The viewer is able to see the height, width, and depth of an object in one view and does not need to mentally assemble a composite view, as in the case of orthographic projection. The necessity of having to draw several views of an object is also eliminated [13-62].

13-62

13-63
In an isometric sketch, all the angles are 120°.

φ = 120°

The three types of axonometric projection—*isometric, dimetric,* and *trimetric*—differ only in the angular orientation of the object with the picture plane. For example, a cube in the isometric system would be tilted so that all three of its principal edges would form equal angles with the picture plane. This orientation greatly simplifies the construction of isometric sketches, because the angles between the principal edges will appear at 120° with each other [13-63]. Since isometric is the most commonly used form of axonometric projection, it is the only one that will be discussed here.

The steps for making an isometric sketch are

13-64

Step 1 Establish the isometric axes x, y, and z at angles of 120° to each other with the y axis being vertical [13-64].

13-65

Step 2 Construct a scaffolding box large enough to enclose the object with the y isometric axis being the front, vertical edge of the box [13-65].

13-66

Step 3 Place the object to be drawn in the scaffolding. Surfaces and edges parallel to the xy and yz planes should be sketched in their respective places within the scaffold [13-66].

Step 4 Angular surfaces or edges should be sketched by first locating their end points on the scaffolding and then connecting them [13-67].

13-67

13-68

Step 5 Sketch in the holes and arcs as ellipses or partial ellipses; noncircular arcs by the plotting of points [13-68].

13-69

Step 6 Darken the object lines of the finished sketch [13-69] or trace on another piece of vellum. Hidden lines are normally omitted.

13-70
Circles viewed obliquely appear as ellipses.

13-71

13-72
The ellipse guide can speed up your sketching.

Paper with isometric background lines is available and is an effective aid when used either directly or as a reference background under the sketching paper.

Circles viewed obliquely appear as ellipses [13-70]. To sketch such a circle, construct a rhombus with sides equal to the diameter of the circle. The ellipse is formed by sketching arcs that are tangent to the midpoints of the sides of the rhombus. The major axis of the ellipse will be in line with the longer diagonal of the enclosing rhombus—the minor axis aligns with the shorter diagonal [13-71]. An isometric ellipse guide is very useful for quick construction of isometric circles [13-72]. If one is not available, the four-center-ellipse method [13-29 to 13-33] produces a good approximation. Examples of circles in isometric orientation can be seen in [13-73] to [13-75].

13-73

13-74

13-75

13-76

Isometric

Perspective

13-77

The most annoying limitation of isometric sketching is the visual distortion that exists because all receding lines are parallel. This distortion is especially pronounced in objects of considerable depth [13-76]. The distortion of relatively long objects can be alleviated by using perspective sketching techniques [13-77].

Perspective System

Perspective sketching is the most difficult to learn, but is preferred to all other methods when visual realism is important. Three types of perspective sketching are known as one-point, two-point, and three-point, depending upon the number of vanishing points used. For the most part, one- and two-point perspective sketches will suffice.

Perspective sketching differs from isometric sketching in that the observer is a finite distance from the object—rather than infinite; that is, the viewing lines from the corners of the object are not parallel, as in the techniques discussed before, but converge on the eye of the beholder. The view is a close approximation to that obtained by a camera [13-78]. In perspective, objects appear smaller

COMPRESSION/TENSION TESTING DEVICE

13-78

THE PERSPECTIVE STAGE

VISION ℄

VP TO RIGHT VANISHING POINT

HORIZON LINE

VP
TO LEFT VANISHING POINT

IMAGE "FIXED" ONTO PICTURE PLANE

OBJECT IN POSITION

GROUND LEVEL ℄

13-79
The perspective stage.

PICTURE PLANE

LVP

RVP

IMAGE

CONE OF VISION

TOP VIEW OF PERSPECTIVE STAGE

13-80
Perspective charts.

when their distance from the eye increases, parallel lines appear to converge as they recede, and horizontal lines and planes appear to vanish on the horizon. These effects are achieved by selective positioning of the object relative to the picture plane, by proper location of the horizon, and by designation of an appropriate vanishing point or points on the horizon [13-79].

One major advantage of a perspective sketch, when compared with an isometric sketch, is that the engineer can select the most appropriate view of the object. In the isometric sketch, the object must always be placed at the same angle with respect to the picture plane, but in a perspective drawing the object can be placed at *any* angle, thus providing a means to illustrate particular details. Several types of commercially prepared perspective charts are available to the engineer [13-80]. These charts minimize the overall construction requirements of

13-81
One point perspective.

SHADOW ALSO
GOES TO SAME
VANISHING POINT

a perspective drawing, but their use will not assure a realistic view if the engineer fails to adhere to the fundamentals of perspective drawing.

A *one-point perspective* sketch uses but one vanishing point. This means that all receding parallel lines in the sketch terminate at a single point on the horizon of the sketch [13-81]. The one-point perspective is most effective for sketches showing the inside of a space or the internal structure of a mechanism.

Since all the principles used in making a one-point perspective are similar to those used in making a *two-point perspective*, we shall explain the perspective technique by analyzing the more commonly used two-point perspective sketch.

IMPORTANT DETAIL
INSIDE NOT VISIBLE

GUIDE ROD BLENDS TOO
MUCH WITH VERTICAL SUPPORT

GUIDE ROD NOT
VISIBLE -
HANDLE PARTLY
HIDDEN

DECISION WAS MADE TO
SHOW FRONT INSTEAD
OF REAR

13-82

469

13-83

LEFT VANISHING POINT

RIGHT VANISHING POINT

HORIZON

EXTENSIONS OF THE SCAFFOLDING BOX EDGES INTERSECT THE HORIZON AT THE VANISHING PTS.

CORRECTED SKETCH ORIENTED TO BEST VIEW.

CENTER OF VISION LINE

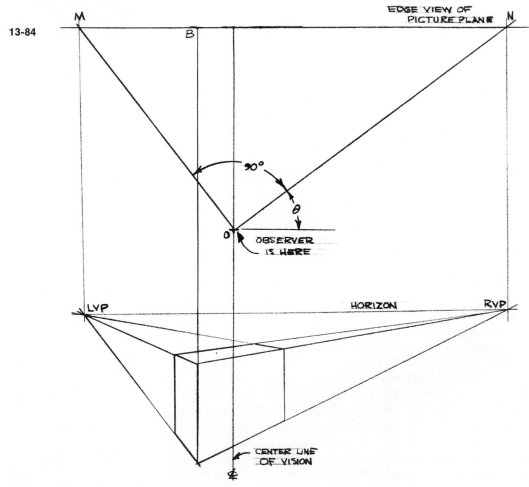

13-84

M

B

EDGE VIEW OF PICTURE PLANE

N

90°

θ

O

OBSERVER IS HERE

LVP

HORIZON

RVP

CENTER LINE OF VISION

First orient the object so that all of its important features are clearly visible. Several preliminary sketches of the scaffolding box in varying orientations should be tried to achieve the most descriptive visual presentation [13–82]. After the best orientation has been selected, left and right vanishing points are obtained by projecting lines along the edges of the box until they intersect the horizon line [13-83]. The vanishing point is that point on the horizon where parallel lines appear to converge—to vanish. The next step is to locate the *center-of-vision* line. The location is purely arbitrary, but in general it should be near the visual center of the object being sketched.

Once the center-of-vision line has been selected, it is extended vertically until it intersects the edge view of the picture plane, which has been drawn immediately above and parallel to the horizon [13-84]. Similar vertical projections are made to the edge of the picture plane from the left and right vanishing points, resulting in intersections M and N. The leading edge of the scaffolding box is projected vertically resulting in the location of point B.

Point O, the position of the observer with respect to the picture plane, is determined by the observer's sight lines to the vanishing points M and N. Since the observer's lines of sight subtend an internal angle of 90°, the location of the sight lines and point O can be found by sliding the apex of a 90° triangle down the center-of-vision line until the two sides of the 90° angle intersect the edge view of the picture plane at points M and N.

Now construct an orthographic top view of the object with the front corner touching the picture plane at point B and with sides BA and BD parallel to observer sight lines OM and ON, respectively [13-85]. Another orthographic view is drawn so that it is aligned horizontally with the leading edge of the perspective view. Intermediate points on the object within the scaffolding box now can be located by extending appropriate projections from the two orthographic views.

The horizon line *always* passes through the eye level of the observer. Therefore, if one were to sketch a view of a refrigerator that is approximately 5 feet high, the horizon line of the sketch should be drawn such that it passes through the refrigerator top [13-86]. The observer's sight line to the horizon should pass approximately through the center of a large object, such as a bus. Objects that are normally viewed from above, such as typewriters, should be located below the horizon. In the case of small

ORTHOGRAPHIC TOP VIEW

PARALLEL

PARALLEL

PICTURE PLANE

M

A

B

N

O

SCAFFOLD BOX

LVP   HORIZON   RVP

GROUND LINE

13-85

ORTHOGRAPHIC SIDE VIEW

13-86

13-87

objects that rest on the ground (like a sidewalk skate-board), the horizon should be located approximately 5 feet above the object. Dramatic effects can be obtained by adjusting the eye level of the observer up or down to emphasize or enhance certain details of a design [13-87]. Additional realism and proportion in sketching can be achieved by adding some familiar object, such as the silhouette of a person [13-88].

13-88

POINT SOURCE AT FINITE DISTANCE

REFLECTED LIGHT

CAST SHADOW

13-89

POINT SOURCE FROM AN INFINITE DISTANCE

CONVENTIONAL LIGHT SOURCE

45°

13-90

LIGHT SOURCE

(A)

(B)

13-91

shading

Shading refers to the light and dark areas of an object created by the light pattern (or lack of it) falling directly on that object or by reflection. Shading adds clarity and realism.

Light originates either from a point source at a finite distance (such as a lamp) or from a point source at a theoretically infinite distance (such as the sun) [13-89]. In either case, light rays travel in straight lines until they are intercepted by an object. When the source of light is undetermined, we should assume that it comes from a single remote source. As a general rule the light is assumed to shine over the left shoulder of the observer at an angle of approximately 45° to the ground [13-90].

Any spot or surface on an object that intercepts the light perpendicularly will give maximum reflection, and this area will appear white, or nearly so, on the sketch. Other surfaces will be shaded in varying degrees, depending upon the amount of light that falls upon them. The gradation of shading on the surfaces will give additional emphasis to the depth of the object.

The form of an object determines the way in which it intercepts light rays [13-91]. The top surface is most directly exposed to the light source and will be the lightest, especially at its near edge. The surface becomes darker as it recedes into the distance. Face *B* (which is hidden from the light source) should receive the darkest shading. The shading becomes darker on this face as it recedes in depth, unless some light is arbitrarily assumed to be reflected from an imaginary surface behind the cube. Face *A* is shaded similarly to Face *B*, but is somewhat lighter, because it is reflecting more light to the observer.

The shading of the curved surface of a cylinder or a sphere will be darkest where the rays of light fall tangent to the surface [13-92 and 13-93]. The lightest area occurs where the light rays strike perpendicularly. If a flat surface is placed on the side of the object opposite the light source, not only will there be a dark shadow cast upon it by the object, but also the surface will return some reflected light to dilute the shading on the back side of the object.

Pencil shading can be applied in two ways. For best results use a pencil with a flattened point and lightly cover the entire area that is to receive shading. The darker shades for particular areas are built up to the desired darkness by repeated strokes. Make sure that each shade blends smoothly into the next. For shading, begin and end lines with a feather edge—a gentle landing and takeoff of the pencil point on the paper surface [13-94]. An eraser may be used to remove small "areas of light" within the dark shaded areas of a sketch.

A second method of shading involves the use of lines of varied weight and spacing [13-95]. No lines are needed

13-92

13-93

13-94

13-95

for the very light areas. This simple and effective technique is particularly useful when speed is a factor or when the sketch is drawn from the imagination.

problems

13-1. Sketch eight straight freehand lines on a sheet of unruled paper. Make the lines of various lengths and angles to each other, but do not allow them to intersect. Segment two of the lines into two equal parts, two of the other lines into three equal parts, two others into four equal parts, and the last two into five equal parts. Accomplish the segmentation by eye; then verify the accuracy of the segments with a scale.

13-2. Using only a pencil and an unruled sheet of paper, sketch 25 *medium* weight lines about 5 inches long. Sketch the lines so that they are all parallel with the top edge of the paper and about $\frac{1}{4}$ inch apart. Sketch each line as a *single stroke* and do not erase.

13-3. Using only a pencil and an unruled sheet of paper, sketch 25 *thin* weight lines about 6 inches long. Sketch the lines parallel with the left-hand edge of the paper and about $\frac{1}{8}$ inch apart. Sketch each line as a *single stroke* and do not erase.

13-4. Sketch 25 *thick* lines about 4 inches long and at a 45° angle using the applicable instructions of Problem 13-2.

13-5. Using a pencil and unruled paper, make four different one-point perspective layout (thumbnail) sketches of one of the figures in Figure [13-96]. After completing the sketches, draw a circle around the layout sketch that best illustrates the main features of the object in a one-point perspective.

13-6. Quickly sketch one of the following objects from memory. Show the proportionate elements of the figure by using scaffolding techniques (1) in the front view of the orthographic system, (2) in the isometric pictorial system, and (3) in the one point perspective system:
(a) coffee cup showing the handle
(b) three legged stool
(c) wall mounted pencil sharpener
(d) side view of a door knob
(e) front view of a TV set
(f) bicycle

13-7. Sketch six circles, starting with a $\frac{1}{2}$-inch diameter. Increase each successive circle diameter by $\frac{1}{2}$ inch. Use the scaffold-square technique for each circle and do not use any measuring tools. Verify the diameters after all six circles have been sketched.

13-8. Sketch six ellipses all having a 2-inch major axis. Make the first ellipse with a minor axis of $\frac{3}{4}$ inch. Increase the minor axis of each successive ellipse by $\frac{1}{4}$ inch. Use the four-center-ellipse technique to construct each ellipse.

13-96

A   B   C

D   E

F   G

13-9. Trace Figure [13-34] on a piece of tracing paper. Do not trace the grid. Construct a $\frac{1}{4}$-inch grid over the tracing. On a second piece of paper construct a $\frac{1}{2}$-inch grid; then sketch the telephone on the $\frac{1}{2}$-inch grid.

13-10. Find a picture in a popular magazine that is basically a single orthographic view, such as front or side view. Construct a grid on the picture; then make a new sketch of the picture that is three times as large as the original, using the grid technique.

13-11. Find pictures of three different products in a magazine. Using a felt tip or a ball point pen, analyze the three products and sketch the relationships of the four basic shapes from which each product is formed. (Sketch the location of each of the basic shapes directly on the picture.)

13-12. In [13-97] the circles indicate the location of missing views. For each problem select a correct view from the 30 choices shown at the bottom of the page and place its number in the appropriate circle.

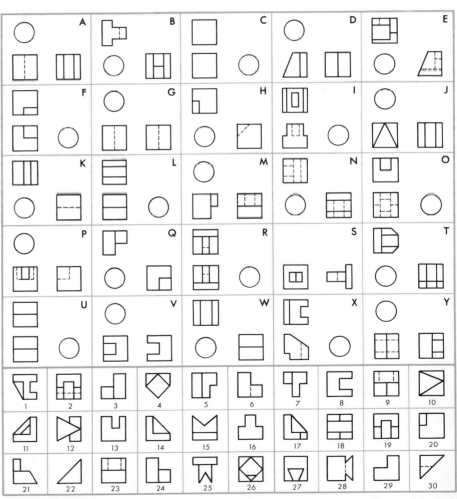

13-97

13-13. In [13-98] the circles indicate the location of missing principal views. For each problem select a correct view from the 30 choices shown at the bottom of the page and place its number in the appropriate circle.

13-98

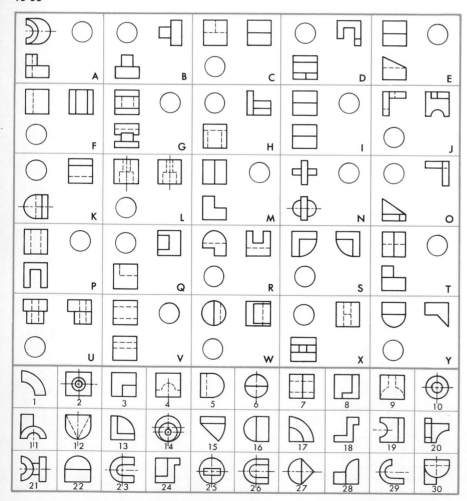

13-14. In [13-99] for each object select one of the 20 views that correctly shows an appropriate principal view having one or more hidden lines. Place its number in the circle provided.

13-99

13-15. Sketch the three principal orthographic views of the objects shown in [13-100]. The arrows represent the line of sight of the viewer.

13-100

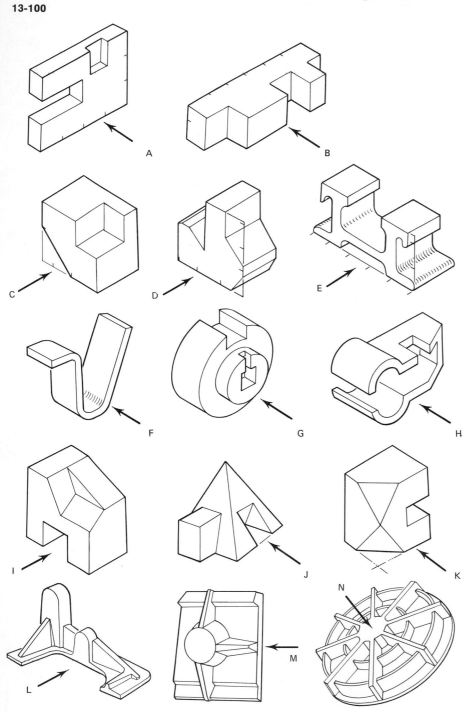

13-16. Sketch three principal orthographic views of the objects shown in [13-101].

13-17. Make a *cavalier oblique* sketch of two of the objects shown in [13-102]. Using the same two objects make a *cabinet* sketch of each. Label each sketch according to the type of oblique used.

13-18. Make an isometric sketch of each object shown in [13-103].

13-102

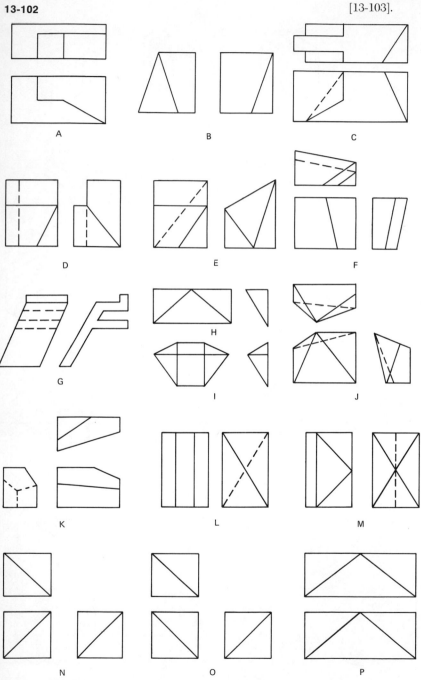

13-19. Using the conventional 45° light source, apply shading to isometric sketches of the objects shown in [13-104]. Use the technique of lines of varied weight and spacing to achieve shading.

13-20. Make a two-point perspective sketch of one of the objects in Figure [13-96].

13-103

13-104

bibliography

FRENCH, T. E., and C. J. VIERCK, *Engineering Drawing and Graphic Technology*, 11th ed., New York: McGraw-Hill, 1972.

FRENCH, T. E., and C. J. VIERCK, *Graphic Science*, 3rd ed., New York: McGraw-Hill, 1970.

GIESECKE, F. E., ALVA MITCHELL, H. C. SPENCER, I. L. HILL, and R. O. LOVING, *Engineering Graphics*, New York: Macmillan, 1969.

GIESECKE, F. E., ALVA MITCHELL, H. C. SPENCER, and I. L. HILL, *Technical Drawing*, 5th ed., New York: Macmillan, 1967.

HAMMOND, R. H., C. P. BUCK, W. B. ROGERS, G. W. WALSH, JR., and H. P. ACKERT, *Engineering Graphics*, 2nd ed., New York: Ronald Press, 1971.

HOELSCHER, R. P., C. H. SPRINGER, and J. S. DOBROVOLNY, *Graphics for Engineers*, New York: Wiley, 1971.

KATZ, H. H., *Technical Sketching and Visualization for Engineers*, New York: Macmillan, 1949.

LEVENS, A. S., *Graphics*, 2nd ed., New York: Wiley, 1968.

LUZADDER, W. J., *Basic Graphics*, 2nd ed., Englewood Cliffs, N.J.: Prentice-Hall, 1968.

LUZADDER, W. J., *Fundamentals of Engineering Drawing*, 6th ed., Englewood Cliffs, N.J.: Prentice-Hall, 1971.

McKIM, R. H., *Experiences in Visual Thinking*, Belmont, Calif.: Brooks/Cole, 1972.

MOCHEL, M. G., *Fundamentals of Engineering Graphics*, Englewood Cliffs, N.J.: Prentice-Hall, 1960.

RULE, J. T., and S. A. COONS, *Graphics*, New York: McGraw-Hill, 1961.

SCHNEERER, W. F., *Programmed Graphics*, New York: McGraw-Hill, 1967.

SVENSEN, C. L., and W. E. STREET, *Engineering Graphics*, New York: Van Nostrand Reinhold, 1962.

WELLMAN, B. L., *Introduction to Graphical Analysis and Design*, New York: McGraw-Hill, 1966.

Oxide growth formed during corrosion of metal surface—magnification 3200×.

14-1
Components of engineering graphics.

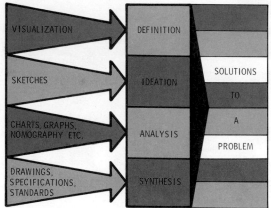

14-2
Graphical inputs to an engineering problem.

Πάντες ἄνθρωποι τοῦ εἰδέναι ὀρέγονται φύσει.

ARISTOTLE

14-3

engineering graphics, a relatively new term, combines areas of specialized knowledge and visual skill, such as *engineering drawing, graphical calculus, nomography, computer aided design* and *technical sketching* [14-1]. Most engineering problems demand the application of some, if not all, of these skills: to define the problem, to clarify ideas for solutions, to present analytical and test results, and to draw the details of the final design [14-2].

Engineering graphics uses certain accepted symbols and conventions just as our written communication system. In writing, the symbols are letters and punctuation marks that can be combined to make words, sentences, paragraphs, and books. The Declaration of Independence, for example, can be understood by all who know the meaning of the symbols. The symbols used in engineering graphics are the point, the line, and their numerous combinations. One must learn and understand these symbols to comprehend the ideas they express, just as one would have to learn to read the Greek written language to appreciate fully the ideas of Aristotle.

engineering drawing

Engineering drawing as used in this text includes the fundamentals of the traditional areas of *mechanical drawing* and *descriptive geometry*. The techniques and skills of mechanical drawing are necessary to draw accurate, understandable pictures of physical objects. Descriptive geometry shows how two or more objects are related to one another in space; it is discussed in Chapter 15. These two areas complement each other in engineering drawing.

Reference Planes

Engineering drawing is a visual communication system based entirely on the existence of the three *dimensional axes—height, width,* and *depth.* Since every physical object occupies space and consequently has volume, it is quite logical that the basis for describing physical objects should be related to volume and the dimensions associated with volume [14-4]. All the axes are mutually perpendicular. This means that they are located at right angles to each other; they are *orthogonal* [14-5]. It is this simple orthogonal relationship of the three major axes of volume that constitutes the basis for most technical drawing systems.

14-4
All physical objects have volume.

14-5
The three axes of volume are
mutually perpendicular (orthogonal).

14-6
Generating an infinite planar surface.

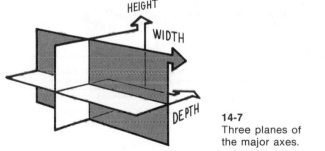

Planar surfaces can be generated by moving each axis sideways, without tilting [14-6]. If this is done for all three axes, an orthogonal set of three planes results. For practical purposes it is convenient to limit the extent of these infinite planes by establishing linear boundaries around them and by making them rectangular in shape [14-7].

At this point the planar surfaces can still move relative to one another. They are not yet fixed in space. To fix them we specify a fixed point in space and then move the planes until they intersect at this point [14-8]. Under these conditions the planes have a definite position and are called *reference planes*. In some phases of engineering graphics we may also refer to them as projection or picture planes.

14-7
Three planes of
the major axes.

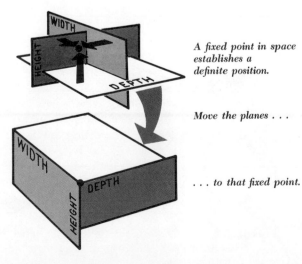

*A fixed point in space
establishes a
definite position.*

Move the planes . . .

. . . to that fixed point.

14-8
Establishing a fixed planar
relationship.

14-9
Names and locations of
reference planes.

14-10
Basic box for
orthographic projection.

14-11
Comparative directions in point location systems.

The plane parallel to the surface of the earth is called the *horizontal* reference plane; the plane that is perpendicular to that surface and faces forward is the *frontal* reference plane; the remaining vertical reference plane is perpendicular to both the frontal and horizontal reference planes and is known as the *profile* reference plane [14-9].

The three reference planes occupy the same positions as do the sides of a cube or a rectilinear box. Such a box would have as its top the horizontal reference plane, as its front the frontal reference plane, and as its right side the profile reference plane [14-10].

Locations in Space

A strong similarity exists between the use of reference planes and the Cartesian coordinate system found in mathematics. The fixed point that was used to establish the reference plane positions is analogous to the point of origin, or zero, in Cartesian coordinates. The intersections of the orthogonal planes correspond to the axes of the Cartesian system. Width corresponds to the x axis, height to the y axis, and depth corresponds to the z axis [14-11A].

In engineering drawing, directions are described somewhat differently than in mathematics. Instead of describing a point as being plus or minus a certain number of units along a given axis, the point is described as being so many units up or down, right or left, and forward or back of the appropriate reference planes [14-11B]. For example, it may be necessary to locate a point A in space. By the Cartesian coordinate system, its location might

14-12
Locating a point.

14-13

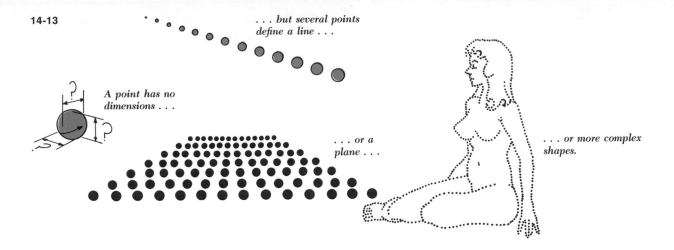

A point has no dimensions . . .

. . . but several points define a line . . .

. . . or a plane . . .

. . . or more complex shapes.

be described as −3 units on the x axis, −5 units on the y axis, and +2 units on the z axis. In engineering drawing this same point would be described as 5 units *below* the horizontal reference plane, 3 units *left* of the profile reference plane, and 2 units *in back of* the frontal reference plane [14-12].

The path of a moving point can generate very complex lines, surfaces, and volumes [14-13]. Learning to draw an object—to communicate visually—might be considered as learning to locate or follow the points that describe the object.

orthographic projection

Orthographic projection is based on the premise that the image of an object should always be viewed at right angles (perpendicularly) to the major planes of that object. As an example, an orthographic view of a tabletop would assume that the observer is looking down from directly above the table [14-14]. In another example, the observer stands directly in front of a painting so that his line of sight is perpendicular to the front plane of the painting. The term *major planes* is used here to suggest that more than one orthographic view of an object is possible. In fact, the orthographic projection system has six *principal views,* which relate directly to the horizontal, frontal, and profile principal reference planes [14-15].

A second and equally important premise of the ortho-graphic-projection system is that the observer must be

14-14
In orthographic projection the line of sight is perpendicular to a plane.

14-15
The perpendicular relationship of the lines of sight with the six views of the orthographic box.

14-16
In orthographic projection the lines of sight are parallel.

PARALLEL LINES OF
SIGHT FROM THE SUN

Moving books closer or farther apart does not change size of shadow

14-17
Orthographic box concept.

located an infinite distance from the object. This premise forms the basis for projecting objects in their true size and shape to an intervening plane, because the lines of sight, when emanating from an infinite point in space, are virtually parallel. A good example of this principle can be demonstrated on a bright, sunny day by holding a small book so that it is perpendicular to the sun's rays. Now hold a larger book at some distance behind and parallel with the smaller book. Notice the size of the shadow that is cast on the larger book. While maintaining the perpendicular relationship with the sun's rays and the parallel relationship between the books, move the books farther apart or closer together. The size and the shape of the shadow does not change, because the light rays (lines of sight) from the sun are essentially parallel [14-16]. These two principles, the perpendicular orientation of the line of sight to a plane and the parallel lines of sight, are basic to the theory of orthographic projection.

The Orthographic-box Concept

Recall the six-sided box that was developed from the three major orthogonal axes. Imagine this box as being transparent, as if it were made of clear plastic or glass, and that some object, for example a stool, is located within the box [14-17].

The orientation of the object should relate to its natural or most useful position. If the object has an obvious base, as most objects do, it should be facing toward the bottom plane of the orthographic box. The object should be oriented within the box so that its longest horizontal dimension is parallel with the frontal plane. Frequently, this will make the dominant or most characteristic contour of the object visible through the frontal plane. The importance of this orientation will be amplified later in the chapter.

This requirement may, in some cases, present the engineer with a puzzling contradiction. For example, it is obvious that an automobile has a front end. However, because the side of the automobile has a longer horizontal length and more important contours, we would normally orient the side view parallel with the frontal plane [14-18].

So it is with other objects, such as a telephone. Since the longer horizontal dimension is found on the "side" of the telephone, it may be best to orient the side parallel to the frontal plane. This results in another dominant

"Side" of an automobile

"Front" of an automobile

"X" is greater than "Y" therefore . . .

. . . the "side" should be oriented parallel to the frontal plane

14-18
Preferred orientation of an automobile within an orthographic box.

"Side" of a telephone   "Front" of a telephone

"X" is greater than "Y" therefore the "side" is oriented parallel to the frontal plane.

contour of the telephone (the conventional "front") being oriented parallel with the profile plane [14-19].

In orthographic projection the observer must be located so that his line of sight is *perpendicular* to one of the six principal planes of the box [14-20]. He may be in front or back, above or below, or to the right or left of the box. The second principle states that the lines of sight to the object are *parallel* to one another when they intercept the principal planes [14-21].

14-19
Orientation of a telephone within an orthographic box.

14-20
Observer positions for lines of sight perpendicular to the orthographic box.

14-21
All lines of sight are parallel to one another and perpendicular to a principal plane.

14-22
A point is projected to a principal plane along the line of sight.

14-23
Projecting points on an object to the principal plane.

Project the painted dots to the frontal plane . . .

. . . and continue the process with all the points on the object.

Projecting the Image

Let us see how a three-dimensional object can be transformed into a two-dimensional picture. Imagine that a very small dot has been painted on a corner of the telephone. The observer, who is located at the ideal *observation position* (where his lines of sight are perpendicular to the frontal plane) will see the designated point on the telephone through the frontal plane. The line of sight passes through the frontal plane of the orthographic box. If we isolate the segment of the line of sight beginning at the point where it pierces the frontal plane and ending at the dot on the telephone, we will have a *projector* that extends from the object to the frontal plane. Imagine sliding the painted dot along this projector back toward the observer until it contacts and adheres to the frontal plane [14-22]. This process is known as *projecting a point to a plane.*

Continuing the process, place a second dot at a different position on the telephone, generate a line of sight to the second point, and project the point back to the frontal plane. Now place another dot, and another, and yet another until all the lines that define the telephone as seen through the frontal plane have been covered with dots, and these dots have been projected to the frontal plane of the orthographic box—thus creating a two-dimensional image—an *orthographic view* [14-23]. Of course, it should be understood that in actual practice one need not laboriously transfer the infinite number of points necessary to generate a complete image of the object. Instead, one makes use of the principle that *two points define a straight line* to simplify and accelerate the projection process. For example, one needs only to project the end points of the line that defines the bottom edge of the telephone to the frontal plane and then draw a line on the frontal plane to connect these two end points.

principal views

Remember that the points could be projected to any of the six principal planes of the orthographic box. The picture obtained by projecting all the points of the object to the frontal plane of the orthographic box is called the *front view* [14-24]. The same process used with other principal planes of the box produces other *principal views* of the object.

14-24
A projected view of
an object on the
frontal plane.

FRONT VIEW
OF THE TELEPHONE

Where is depth?

FRONT

HEIGHT

WIDTH

14-25
A single orthographic view shows
only two dimensions of space.

Unfortunately, two-dimensional orthographic views, such as the front view just described, have one inherent weakness: a two-dimensional view can show only two dimensions of a three-dimensional object [14-25]. With this view alone, it is impossible for the observer to ascertain the third major dimension of the object. To obtain that, he needs another view at right angles to the front view. Any of four possible positions in the orthographic projection system—top, bottom, left, or right side—will provide the necessary information about the third dimension.

Recall the earlier discussion in this chapter concerning the location of a point in space. The point's location within the orthographic box was described relative to the reference planes of the box. In the example used, a point was located two units behind the frontal plane. It is important to remember that if this same point is properly projected to *any* plane perpendicular to the frontal plane, it *still* will be two units behind the frontal plane [14-26].

Most dimensions of objects can be depicted on the principal views, but more than one principal view is needed [14-27]. Since it isn't practical to build a transparent box when we want to make a drawing, a way must be found to show all principal views on one sheet of paper. This is not only practical, but it allows an observer to view all the principal planes of the orthographic box from a single position.

Imagine that all the edges of the transparent orthographic box are hinged [14-28]. Some of the hinges may be removed from certain edges. By this means it would

14-26

A point always projects the same distance from a reference plane . . .

. . . on all the planes that are perpendicular to that reference plane.

14-27
Multiple observation
positions for the six
principal views.

14-28
Rotating principal planes
to a single observation
position.

14-29
Single observation
position for the six
principal planes.

be possible to unfold the box. In this way the images that
had been projected onto the principal planes of the box
would lie flat on a two-dimensional surface [14-29].

Standard Arrangement of Views

There are many possible ways that the box might be
unfolded, but convention has established a preferred arrangement. This arrangement, known as the *six principal
views,* starts with the *front view* of the object. Located
immediately above the front view is the *top view* and
below it is the *bottom view.* To the immediate right of
the front view is the *right side view.* To the immediate
left of it is the *left side view.* The *rear view* normally
is positioned to the left of the left side view [14-30]. To
avoid error in interpretation always follow this convention faithfully, and align the views correctly.

Choice of Views

Although six principal views are possible, it is rarely
necessary to draw all six to describe an object adequately.
Usually, all essential information can be shown in three
of the views. The views most commonly used are the top,
front, and right or left side views [14-31]. This particular
choice is easily understood when one realizes that the
remaining three views are basically reversed images of
the first views, and do not usually provide new informa-

14-30
Six principal views (unfolded orthographic box)
in the preferred arrangement.

tion about the object (especially when all hidden lines
are shown). Sometimes it is possible to completely describe an object with only two views, and in special cases
with only one view and appropriate notes (see p. 460).

Reference Lines

In the example describing the unfolding of the orthographic box [14-28], attention was directed to the hinged
edges of the box. The box was flattened by turning its
sides about these hinges. A closer examination of the
flattened box reveals that the hinged edges have become
the lines that separate the views from one another. However, it is not that the lines separate the views which is
important, but rather that the lines *represent the edge
views* of the reference planes. For this reason they are
called *reference lines* [14-32]. These reference lines
(sometimes called *fold lines* or *hinge lines*), are important
for locating a point in a particular view, because they
perform the same function on a two-dimensional sheet

14-31
The three principal
views most commonly
used.

14-32
Reference lines
between the standard
arrangement of views.

of paper as the reference planes did in three-dimensional
space.

Adjacent and Related Views

Any two views that share a common reference line and
are therefore perpendicular to each other are called *adjacent views*. Using the standard arrangement of views as
an example, let us consider some of the possible adjacent
views. If our attention is centered upon the front view,
then the left side, top, right side, and bottom views are
all adjacent views to that view [14-33]. If, on the other
hand, our attention is centered upon the right side view,
only the front view is adjacent to it.

14-33
Adjacent views.

14-34
Four related views with the front view as
the central view.

Views that are adjacent and perpendicular to the same
central plane are called *related views*. Thus the top, bottom, left, and right side views are related views to one
another, since they are all adjacent views to the front
view.

Projecting Points Between Views

Imagine again the example of the telephone with a dot
painted on its side [14-22]. We know that the point can
be projected to any or all of the viewing planes of the
orthographic box. If we look at the point in each of the
planes adjacent to the front view, we find that its distance
from the reference line is the same in all these views
[14-35]. This is true because the frontal plane is an equal
perpendicular distance, d, from the point in every view
adjacent to the frontal plane. Notice, however, that the
distance d is not found in the frontal view. This demonstrates again that at least two adjacent views are needed
to fully describe an object.

Because points are equidistant from the reference line
in related views, any point in one view can be transferred
directly to any other related view. The transferral process
usually is best accomplished with the aid of dividers
[14-36].

Technique for Projecting Principal Views

Assume you have two adjacent views of an object (or
sufficient descriptive data from which such views can be
constructed), how can you find a third principal view?

14-35
A given point is equidistant from the same
reference plane.

14-36

We shall illustrate the technique using a simplified sketch of the front and top views of the telephone to construct a right side view.

Construct a vertical reference line between the front view and the right side view.

Draw light projection lines connecting the same points in the given (top and front) views.

REFERENCE LINES

ARBITRARILY SELECTED DISTANCES

TOP

A

FRONT

A

RIGHT SIDE (TO BE PROJECTED)

14-37

Draw light horizontal projection lines from the front view across the reference line and into the area in which the right side view will be located.

TOP

FRONT

RIGHT SIDE (TO BE PROJECTED)

14-38

In the top view use dividers to measure how far each point is located away from the reference line separating the top and front views.

Using the reference line separating the front and right side views, transfer to the right side view each of the measurements previously obtained.

TOP

FRONT

A

X

RIGHT SIDE

X

A

A

14-39

Connect the transferred points with lines to complete the image of the telephone in the right side view.

TOP

FRONT

A

RIGHT SIDE

A

A

14-40

498

auxiliary views

With six principal views one would expect to have enough two-dimensional images for all the essential information about a physical object. In most simple, rectilinear objects this is true, but look again at the telephone example. Close inspection of the right side view, for example, shows some ambiguities that are not resolved by the other principal views. The dial face is seen as an ellipse in this view and in all the other views excepting the front and rear where it shows as an edge [14-41]. However, dials on telephones are not elliptical. In fact, all the circular shapes on the telephone appear as ellipses in the principal views. Also, notice the dialing stop. What is its true shape? Obviously, there are many things about the physical characteristics of the telephone that are not explained in the principal views. This lack of visual information exists because the plane of the telephone that contains the dial is not parallel to a principal plane. Since the lines of sight to the dial plane are not perpendicular to any existing plane, an accurate image of the dial cannot appear [14-42].

Location of Auxiliary Planes

To project the true physical characteristics of the telephone dial, we must construct a new plane within the transparent box that permits the line of sight to be perpendicular to the telephone dial. We simply use a viewing plane parallel to the dial of the telephone [14-43]. Such a parallel plane within the orthographic projection box is called an *auxiliary plane*. Lines of sight pierce the

All circles appear to be elliptical.

What is the true shape of the dialing stop?

14-41

Line-of-sight perpendicular to the horizontal plane . . .

. . . and a line-of-sight perpendicular to the profile plane . . .

. . . but there is no plane parallel to the dial face for a perpendicular line-of-sight.

14-42

The lines-of-sight are perpendicular to the auxiliary plane.

Auxiliary plane is parallel to the dial face plane.

14-43
Location of an auxiliary view.

14-44

The points of the object may be projected to an auxiliary plane.

14-45
Many auxiliary planes are possible.

auxiliary plane perpendicularly and terminate on the object in the same manner as they would with a principal plane. The points on the object are then projected back to the auxiliary plane, and the resulting image transferred to it is called an *auxiliary view* [14-44].

In this example an auxiliary plane was constructed to show the view of the dial on the telephone in its true shape. To show the details of the sloping back of the telephone in its true shape, another auxiliary view would have to be constructed using another auxiliary plane parallel to the desired surface. In other words, unlike the six principal views, there is an unlimited number of possible auxiliary views of an object [14-45]. One need construct only those views that will aid in clarifying those parts of an object that need further explanation.

Construction of Auxiliary Views

To construct a typical auxiliary view find the edge view of the plane for which an auxiliary view is needed and then draw an edge view of the auxiliary plane parallel to it.

The *edge view* of a plane, just as the name implies, shows the entire plane as an edge—a straight line. To an observer of the frontal plane, the horizontal and the

14-46

From the ideal observation position the horizontal plane, profile plane, and the dial plane are seen as edge views and are represented by straight lines.

The edge view of the telephone dial is found . . .

14-47

EDGE VIEW OF THE DIAL

EDGE VIEW OF THE DIAL

TOP

REAR   LEFT SIDE   FRONT   RIGHT SIDE

BOTTOM

. . . in the rear view . . .

. . . and the front view, which is normally used.

profile planes are seen as edge views; and when the telephone is viewed from this same position, the dial face appears as a straight line—an edge view [14-46]. A line is drawn parallel to this straight line to form the edge view of the auxiliary plane.

With the telephone, the edge views of the dialing plane appear in the front and rear principal views [14-47]. Since both views provide an edge view of the dial, either can be used to establish the auxiliary plane. Normally, the front view would be used to construct the auxiliary view.

The straight-line edge view of the auxiliary plane is the *folding hinge* by which the auxiliary view may be unfolded. In the flattened configuration, the newly constructed parallel line which was the edge view of the auxiliary plane, is now the *reference line* between the front view and the auxiliary view of the telephone [14-48].

We have constructed here a *primary auxiliary view*—primary because the auxiliary plane is perpendicular to one of the principal planes of the orthographic box. In the example of the telephone, the primary auxiliary plane is perpendicular to the frontal plane and parallel to the dial plane.

Technique for Projecting a Primary Auxiliary View

As with the principal views, a primary auxiliary view can be projected if two adjacent views are given (or if sufficient data to describe the object are available.) The procedure is as follows:

14-48
Unfolding an orthographic box having an auxiliary plane.

TOP

FRONT

AUXILIARY

REFERENCE LINE

Edge view of frontal plane when looking at auxiliary view.

FRONTAL   HORIZONTAL   PROFILE

"FOLDING HINGE"

Draw light projection lines between the points in the front and top views.

Locate the edge view of the dial in the front view and construct a reference line parallel to it at some convenient distance from the dial.

TOP
FRONT

REFERENCE LINE

PARALLEL

EDGE VIEW OF DIAL

14-49

14-50

TOP
FRONT

B

PRIMARY AUXILIARY

FRONT

B

Transfer points from the front view to the primary auxiliary view along the appropriate projection lines. Use a divider to measure the distance of each point in the top view from the reference line between the top and front views. Transfer these distances to the primary auxiliary view where they will appear as the distances from the reference line between the auxiliary and the front view.

14-51

TOP
FRONT

PRIMARY AUXILIARY
FRONT

Draw light projection lines extending from points in the front view and perpendicular to the reference plane just constructed.

14-52

TRUE SHAPE

TOP
FRONT

PRIMARY AUXILIARY
FRONT

Connect the transferred points with lines to complete the image of the telephone in the primary auxiliary view.

14-53
Reduce the size of the orthographic box to concentrate on the details of the dialing stop.

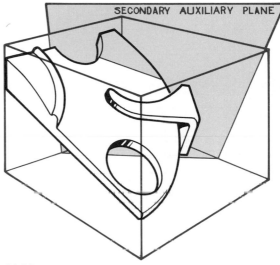

14-54
An enlarged view of the dialing stop showing placement of a secondary auxiliary plane perpendicular to the two planes of the dial stop.

Successive Auxiliary Views

Although it is seldom necessary to use more than principal views and primary auxiliary views, occasionally there is a need for successive auxiliary views to analyze the geometric relationships between specific features of an object. The *secondary auxiliary view* is the image that is projected to the *secondary auxiliary plane* from a primary auxiliary view. The secondary auxiliary plane is adjacent and perpendicular to a primary auxiliary plane; that is, it has the same relation to a primary auxiliary view that the primary had to the principal view.

Like primary auxiliary views, there is an infinitely large number of possible secondary auxiliary views. Furthermore, there are additional auxiliary views that may be constructed in sequence from the secondary auxiliary views. The principles and techniques for the development of these additional auxiliary views are similar to those for construction of the secondary auxiliary views.

As an example of the successive-view concept, let us again refer to the telephone; however, this time let us examine only one of the smaller parts—the dialing stop [14-53]. To see this part effectively, it will be necessary to enlarge our view of the part by considering a smaller orthographic box surrounding the immediate area of the dialing stop [14-54]. Now unfold the box and observe the three principal views of the dialing stop [14-55]. None of the principal views shows any of the meaningful dimensions of the part because the dialing stop is oriented at an angle to all the principal planes. Auxiliary views must therefore be constructed to obtain accurate information.

14-55
Three principal views of the telephone dialing stop.

14-56
Construct a primary auxiliary from the front view to establish true shape of the dialing stop.

14-57
Constructing the secondary auxiliary view of the dialing stop from the primary auxiliary view.

To establish the true shape of the finger recess in the dialing stop, a primary auxiliary view must be constructed parallel to the edge view of the dialing stop that is seen in the front view [14-56]. This primary view shows the true shape of the finger recess, but it does not show the true angle between the planes of the dialing stop. This information is obtained from a secondary auxiliary view perpendicular to and projected from the primary auxiliary view just constructed. This secondary auxiliary must be perpendicular to the line of intersection of the two planes of the stop. Our line of sight in the secondary auxiliary will then produce an image showing the edge views of the two planes and the true angle between them [14-57]. Note that in transferring the points from the primary auxiliary view to the secondary, the required distances are transferred from the front view, because the secondary auxiliary view and the front view are related views with respect to the primary auxiliary view to which they both are adjacent. The principles of projecting true angles are discussed more fully in Chapter 15.

problems

14-1. Using the objects found on page 481, sketch the outline front view of five of the objects as assigned. Select the front view in accordance with the principles of orientation of an object within an orthographic box. Estimate the units of each dimension of the view.

14-2. Using a scale of $\frac{1}{8}$ inch = 1 inch, draw the six principle views in the standard arrangement of two of the following objects. Take the measurements necessary to produce the drawing directly from the object, and use the necessary tools to produce an accurate drawing. *Draw only the object lines in each view.*
(a) door knob (one side of the door)
(b) wall-mounted pencil sharpener

(c) giant bow compass

(d) *Introduction to Engineering Design and Graphics* textbook

(e) an object whose maximum dimension does not exceed 9 inches

14-3. A series of points can describe the form of an object. Select the front view of three of the objects listed below. Describe them by placing a point at all the important intersections and other important features that are *visible*. Connect the points together using the appropriate guiding and marking tools to complete the form.

(a) straight-back chair

(b) eyeglasses

(c) portable television set

(d) pocket knife

(e) shoe for right foot

(f) ink bottle

14-4. Find a window that is easily accessible and has a view of a house, water tower, car, or other stationary object. Recalling the principles of orthographic projection, draw the object lines of the selected object on the window glass with a marking tool such as a grease pencil, whose mark is easily removable.

14-5. List five objects that you think have no obvious base, such as a door knob. Briefly explain the rationale that would be used to orient each object within an orthographic box. Quickly make a proportional drawing of the front view. It is not necessary to draw to exact scale.

14-6. From the following list of objects, name the view that best illustrates the dimension of the object that is in parentheses. Draw that view only in the scale indicated. *Show only the object lines.*

(a) scissors (length; full scale)

(b) paper clip (height; 3 times full scale)

(c) desk chair (width; $\frac{1}{10}$ scale)

(d) wall-mounted doorstop (length; full scale)

(e) ball-point pen (height; full scale)

14-7. Using the six principal views of the objects in Problem 14-2, identify the views that are adjacent to the right side view of the first object by placing a small "a" in the lower left hand corner of the appropriate views. In the same way identify the related views by using a small "r" in the lower right corner. Using the same procedure with the second object, identify the adjacent and related views to the *top* view.

14-8. Visualize a transparent cubical orthographic box, 2 inches on a side. Unfold the box into the 6 principal views in the standard arrangement. Locate and mark in all 6 principal views the 3 points whose positions within the box are described below. Use the symbol indicated in the parentheses.

(a) $1\frac{1}{2}$ inches to the right of the left side view, $\frac{3}{4}$ inch forward of the rear view, and $\frac{7}{8}$ inch below the top view ($\odot$).

(b) $\frac{1}{4}$ inch to the left of the right side view, $\frac{5}{8}$ inch above the bottom view, and $1\frac{3}{8}$ inches behind the front view (*).

(c) 1 inch to the left of the right side view, $\frac{3}{8}$ inch behind the front view, and $1\frac{1}{4}$ inches below the top view ($\boxdot$).

Using the techniques for projecting principal views, complete the appropriate third principal view in the following problems. Measure the various dimensions from the objects in [14-58 to 14-61] and transfer them to your paper at double size.

14-9. Object in [14-58].
14-10. Object in [14-59].
14-11. Object in [14-60].
14-12. Object in [14-61].

14-58

14-59

14-60

14-61

14-13. In [14-62] the circles indicate the location of missing views. For each problem select a correct view from the 30 choices shown at the bottom of the page and place its number in the appropriate circle.

14-62

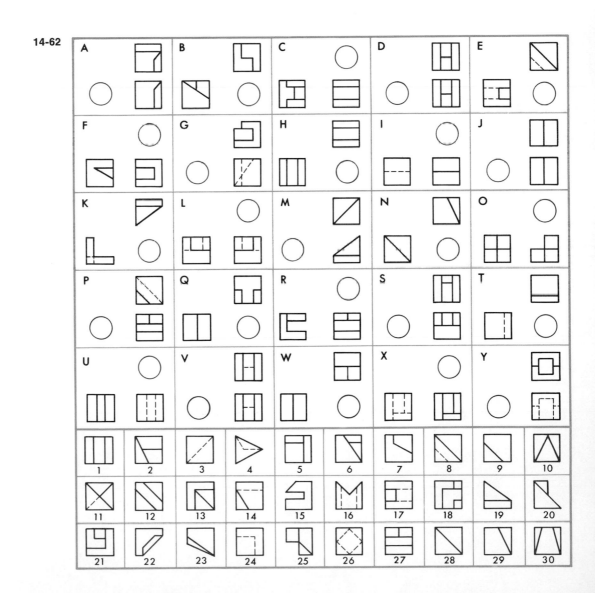

14-14. In [14-63] the circles indicate the location of missing views. For each problem select a correct view from the 30 choices shown at the bottom of the page and place its number in the appropriate circle.

14-63

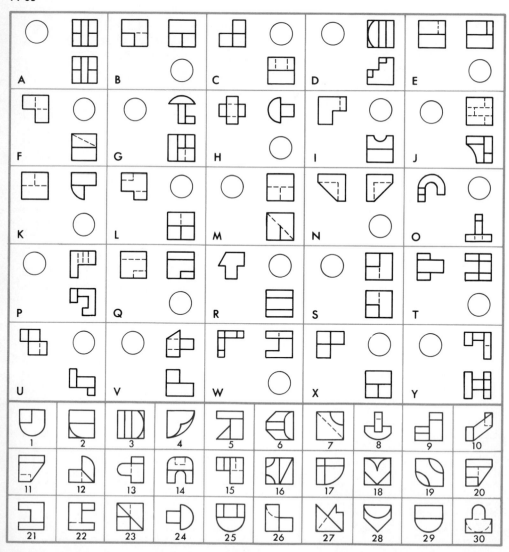

In the following problems, referring to [14-64 to 14-67] and using the designated isometric view, draw the three principal views. Measure the dimensions directly from the isometric view and construct the principal views in true scale.

14-15. Object in [14-64].
14-16. Object in [14-65].
14-17. Object in [14-66].
14-18. Object in [14-67].

14-64

14-65

14-66

14-67

14-19. List five familiar objects that require an auxiliary view to show the true shape of the planes of the object. Make an orthographic drawing showing the necessary auxiliary view for one of the objects on this list.

In the following problems, using the designated isometric view, draw the three major orthographic views, and include any auxiliary views, to show the true shape of the surfaces labeled "A" in [14-68 to 14-71]. Project only the partial auxiliary view of the plane.

14-20. Object in [14-68].
14-21. Object in [14–69].
14-22. Object in [14-70].
14-23. Object in [14-71].

Construct the auxiliary view showing the details of the "A" surfaces.

14-68

14-69

14-70

14-71

Rolling friction on copper crystals.

ngineering drawings often are thought of simply as pictures to be used in the cost estimating, production planning, and fabricating of an object. Although these are important uses, drawings are also used for engineering analysis.

The engineer often must determine if the distances between parts, the angles between planes, or the shapes of surfaces are really the way he wants them. It is frequently impossible, or at least economically undesirable, to build a scale model. Graphic means may be his only practical alternative. Imagine the difficulties an engineer would have determining the locations for the rivets of a bridge truss if he could not graphically show the true angles of the truss [15-1]. The problems of specifying the lengths of pipes and the location of their intersections in a chemical processing plant would be considerable if the engineer could not quickly and easily find the distances, lengths, and intersections by using graphical techniques [15-2].

To assist the engineer in the analysis of physical forms, there are methods in engineering drawing that will provide information about complex forms. These methods are known as *descriptive geometry*. Often they are the only way to solve very complex physical relationships in a direct and efficient manner.

the four fundamental concepts (views)

Four concepts are essential to the graphic analysis of physical objects. These are known as the *true length* of a line, the *point view* of a line, the *edge view* of a plane, and the *true size* of a plane.

Let us examine the two views associated with a line—the *true length* of a line and the *point view* of a line. By definition a line is the shortest distance between two points in space. This definition describes the length of a given line, but it tells the observer nothing about how the line looks to him. The visual image received is directly related to the angle between the observer's line of sight and the position of the line in space [15-3].

A *true-length* view is the most important view of a line. To see true length of a line, the observer must be located so that his line of sight intercepts the line at right angles—perpendicularly. As a practical example, hold your pencil at arm's length in front of you [15-4]. Orient the pencil so that your line of sight is perpendicular to

15-1
A bridge truss requires a graphical analysis to determine the true angles.

512

15-3

A line is the shortest distance between two points . . .

. . . but what is the viewing angle?

15-4
A true-length view of a line.

15-2
A chemical processing plant.

it [15-5]. The view that is presented to your eye is a true-length view of the pencil and tells you how long the pencil is. There are many true-length views possible. With a pencil, some true-length view shows the brand name and its grade. Other true-length views will not. This is so because there are alternative perpendicular positions about a line (or pencil).

Recall that a reference plane is perpendicular with the line of sight just as is the true-length view of the line. Therefore the two must be parallel [15-6].

15-6
The true-length view is parallel to the reference plane because both the plane and the view are perpendicular to the line of sight.

15-5
Hold a pencil so that your line of sight is perpendicular to the long axis.

15-8

Hold a pencil so that you see a . . .

. . . point view.

15-9
The reference plane is perpendicular to the line of sight.

To obtain the *point view* of a line, the observer should be positioned so that his line of sight is parallel to the line [15-7]. The line will then appear to be only a point. To illustrate the point view of a line in a practical way, hold your pencil at arm's length from your eye. Close one of your eyes and, using the other to sight, orient the pencil so that all that is visible to your eye is the graphite point surrounded by the wood case [15-8].

Since the reference plane is always perpendicular to the line of sight, a line viewed as a point is always perpendicular to the reference plane [15-9].

The remaining two relationships deal with views of a plane—the *edge view* of a plane and the *true-size* view of a plane. The edge view of a plane is seen when the line of sight is parallel to the surface of the plane. Using a drawing triangle as an example, hold it so that the line of sight from your eye is parallel with the surface of the triangle. All that will be visible is a line as wide as the thickness of the triangle [15-10]. This is the edge view of the plane of the triangle.

Projected onto the conventional reference plane, the edge view of the triangle would appear as a line [15-11]. Since the line of sight and the plane surface of the triangle are parallel, the plane (of the triangle) is also perpendicular to the reference plane.

The edge view of a plane is similar to the point view of a line in that the edge view can be considered as an infinite number of point views [15-12].

The final concept is the *true-size* view of a plane. As with the true-length view of a line, the true-size view of a plane is oriented parallel with the reference plane [15-13]. The observer's line of sight is perpendicular to the plane being viewed and is perpendicular, by defini-

15-10
Hold a triangle so that the line of sight is parallel to the triangle. This will produce an edge view of a plane.

15-11
A plane seen as an edge view is perpendicular to the reference plane.

515

15-12

The edge view of a plane and the point view of a line in the plane are both parallel with the line of sight; therefore, both are perpendicular to the reference plane.

15-13

The true size view of a plane is oriented parallel with the reference plane; both are perpendicular to the line of sight.

tion, to its reference plane. The similarity between a true-size view of a plane and a true-length line is further emphasized by the fact that all the lines that compose the plane are seen in true length in the true-size view of the plane.

The four fundamental views just discussed form the basis for the analytical capabilities of engineering graphics.

notation systems

The four fundamental views are all related in either a parallel or perpendicular manner with a reference plane. The reference plane used may be one of the three principal reference planes—horizontal, frontal, or profile—that were described in Chapter 14. Or, more often, the plane may be a primary or secondary auxiliary plane, such as those that were developed in the latter part of the same chapter.

Graphic Notation of Reference Planes

A system of planar notation has been developed to tell the user quickly which position or plane he is observing. This system uses letters and numerals related to the reference line common to the adjacent reference planes. The three basic reference planes are denoted by the first letter of their name—capital *H* for the horizontal reference plane, *F* for the frontal, and *P* for the profile [15-14]. Reference planes associated with successive auxiliary views are numbered in the order in which they are constructed. For example, the first auxiliary plane constructed is number 1, the second auxiliary plane is 2, and so on [15-15].

Graphic Notation of Elements

It is also desirable to label the lines and planes of the object being viewed. For the purposes of this text, single points in space, end points of a line, and boundary points of planes will be identified with different capital letters [15-16].

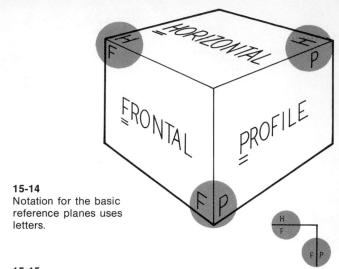

15-14
Notation for the basic reference planes uses letters.

15-15
Notation for the auxiliary planes uses numbers.

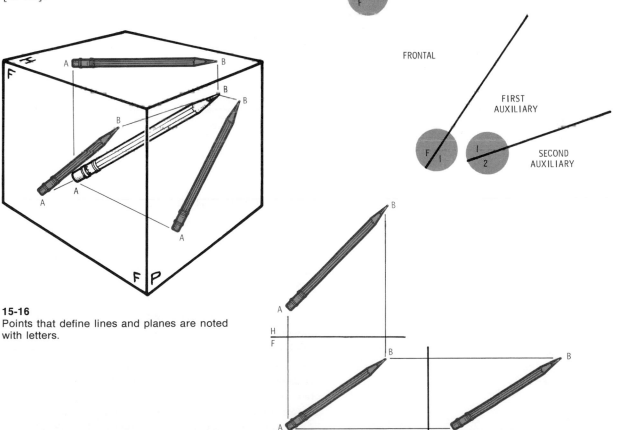

15-16
Points that define lines and planes are noted with letters.

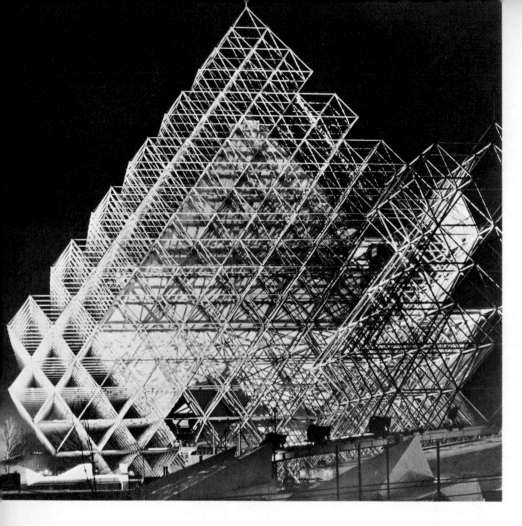

techniques for constructing fundamental views

True-Length View of a Line

A line appears as true length (TL) in a view that is parallel to the line.

In the first case, if a line is seen in a principal view as being parallel to a principal reference plane, then the adjacent view will show the true length of the line [15-18 and 15-19].

In the second, more general case, the line is seen as an oblique or foreshortened line in all the principal reference planes. In other words, the line is not parallel to any of the principal reference planes [15-20]. Consequently, an auxiliary view must be constructed to show

When a line is parallel to the reference line, it is seen in true length in its adjacent view.

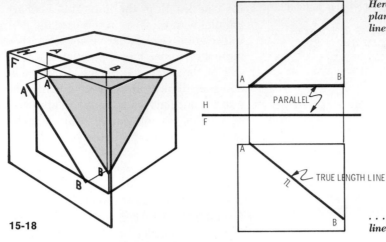

15-18

Here line AB is seen through the horizontal plane as being parallel to the H/F reference line

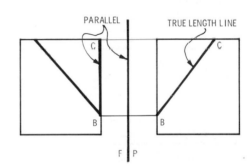

. . . therefore, AB appears as a true length line when viewed through the frontal plane.

Here line BC is seen through the frontal plane as being parallel to the F/P reference line; so . . .

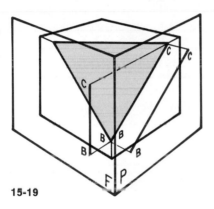

15-19

. . . it will be seen on the adjacent profile plane as a true length line.

An oblique line is not parallel to any of the principal planes.

15-20

15-21

To obtain a true length view of a line, it is necessary to construct a reference line that is parallel to one view of the line.

Reference line F/1 is constructed parallel to line AB.

the true length of the line. This auxiliary view must be parallel with the line (in this case the pencil). To achieve this relation, the auxiliary plane is constructed so that the mutual reference line is parallel to a view of the line on one of the reference planes [15-21]. The end points *A* and *B* of the line are projected across the reference line into the auxiliary view. In the related view, the distances d_A and d_B are measured from the reference line and transferred to the auxiliary view along the appropriate projection lines [15-22]. After the points have been transferred, they are connected and a true-length view of the line is drawn [15-23].

Even though this example used the horizontal and frontal planes to construct the true-length view, it is possible to use this technique with any pair of adjacent views that are available. Except in the case, in which one view of the line is already parallel to a reference plane, two adjacent views and one auxiliary view are necessary to show the true length of a line.

The true-length-line concept is basic to further developments in the analytical uses of engineering graphics. It is used in determining such relationships as the angles between lines, the slope of a line, and the construction of a point view of a line.

15-22

Points A and B are projected into newly constructed auxiliary view 1, and . . .

. . . the distances to points A and B are measured in the related view H.

These distances are transferred along their respective projection lines in auxiliary view 1.

15-23

After all the appropriate distances have been transferred to the auxiliary view, . . .

. . . they are connected by a line that is the true length (TL).

15-24

To develop the point view of the line AB, it is necessary to construct an auxiliary view perpendicular to a true-length view of the line.

The true length of line AB is developed. A reference line 1/2 is constructed perpendicular to the axis of the true length line.

A projection line is drawn from auxiliary view 1 into auxiliary view 2.

15-25

The distance from the reference line F/1 to parallel line AB is measured, and . . .

. . . is transferred into auxiliary view 2 on the projection line. The newly located point is the point view of line AB.

15-26

Point View of a Line

A line appears as a point in a view that is perpendicular to a true-length view of the line. Constructing a point view of a line is begun by constructing a true-length view of the line. Using the example of the pencil oriented obliquely with the principal reference planes [15-24], let us now construct a point view from the true-length line in auxiliary view 1 [15-23]. Since the point view is perpendicular to the true-length view, a reference line should be constructed perpendicular to the axis of the true-length line. A projection line is then constructed across this reference line into the newly constructed auxiliary view 2 [15-25]. The point view of the line will be located on this projected line. Its location is determined by measuring the distance *d* to the line (pencil) from the reference line in the related view—in this case the front view. Notice that this related view is the one which had the *F/1* reference line constructed parallel to it thus making the end points of the line *AB* equidistant from the reference line. The distance is transferred to auxiliary view 2 and the desired point view plotted on the projection line [15-26].

521

15-27
An edge view of a plane.

Edge View of a Plane

A plane appears as an edge view (EV) in a view that contains a point view of a line within that plane.

If it is desired to obtain an edge view of a plane *ABC* [15-28], which is obliquely oriented with respect to the three principal reference planes, it is first necessary to select an appropriate line in the plane. Since a true-length line is necessary to find the point view of the line, the line selected in the plane should be one that will appear true length in a principal view. In plane *ABC* establish a true-length line by drawing a line parallel with the reference line *H/F* in one of the views. In this example, construct such a line *CD* in the horizontal view [15-29].

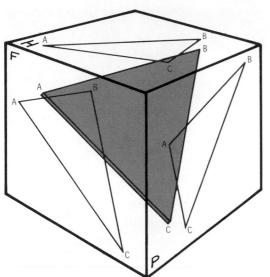

15-28
Construct the edge view of the plane *ABC*.

15-29

Select two views of the plane ABC to construct the edge view . . .

. . . then construct a line in the plane parallel with the reference line H/F. Project this line to the frontal view to obtain a true length line.

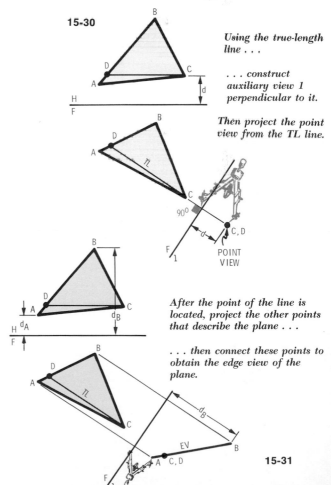

15-30

Using the true-length line . . .

. . . construct auxiliary view 1 perpendicular to it.

Then project the point view from the TL line.

After the point of the line is located, project the other points that describe the plane . . .

. . . then connect these points to obtain the edge view of the plane.

15-31

After the parallel line *CD* is constructed in the horizontal view, project point *D* to locate the true-length frontal view of the line. Because this line connects two points of the plane *ABC*, it is within the plane.

Now to get a point view of line *CD*, construct a reference line *F*/1 perpendicular to the true length line and project the points *C* and *D* across the reference line into auxiliary view 1, just as in [15-26]. Return to the horizontal view and measure the related distance *d* between the reference line and the parallel line. Transfer this distance along the projection line in auxiliary view 1 and establish the location of the point view of the line *CD* [15-30].

After the point view of the line *CD* within the plane has been located, project the remaining points *A* and *B* that define the plane into the auxiliary view. Measure the distances d_A and d_B to these points from the reference line of the related view and transfer them to the auxiliary view. Connect these transferred points in the auxiliary view to get the edge view (EV) of the plane *ABC* [15-31]. The points *ABCD* in the auxiliary view must fall in a straight line or else there is an error in the construction. Using the method just described, one auxiliary view is sufficient to obtain an edge view of a plane.

The edge view of a plane is required for the construction of the fourth fundamental view—the true size of a plane.

15-32

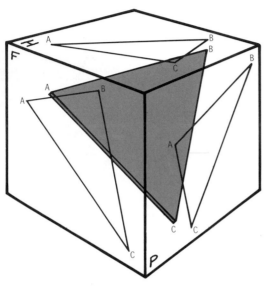

15-33
Construct a true-size view of the plane.

15-34

H
F

*Construct an edge view
(EV) of plane ABC . . .*

True Size of a Plane

A plane appears as true size (TS) in a view that is parallel to the edge view of that plane. In our earlier discussion of the true size of a plane, it was stated that the line of sight must be perpendicular to the plane being viewed. Therefore, if an auxiliary view is constructed parallel with an edge view of a plane and the plane is projected into this auxiliary view, the plane must appear as true size.

Since the true size of the plane is usually developed from an edge view that has been found in a first auxiliary view, a second auxiliary view must be established. If it is desired to obtain a true size of plane ABC [15-33], an edge view must be constructed as before [15-34]. A new reference line 1/2 for a second auxiliary view is drawn parallel to the edge view of the plane [15-35]. The projection lines for the points A, B, and C are drawn across the reference line 1/2 and some distance into the second auxiliary view.

The distances d_A, d_B, and d_C in the frontal view from reference line $F/1$ to the points A, B, and C of the plane are then measured. These distances are plotted from the reference line 1/2 along their respective projection lines in the second auxiliary view. When lines are drawn connecting the transferred points, the resulting figure is the true size of the plane ABC [15-36].

The dependence of each view on the preceding one

15-35

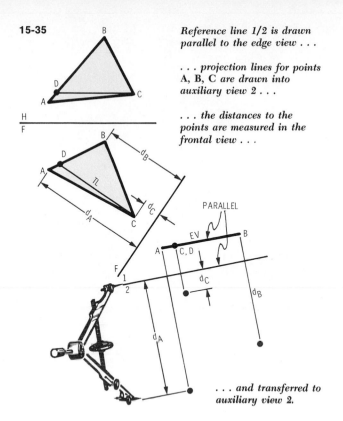

Reference line 1/2 is drawn parallel to the edge view . . .

. . . projection lines for points A, B, C are drawn into auxiliary view 2 . . .

. . . the distances to the points are measured in the frontal view . . .

. . . and transferred to auxiliary view 2.

15-36

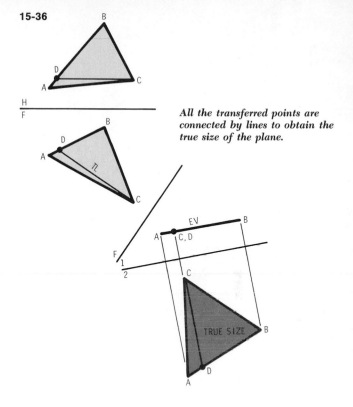

All the transferred points are connected by lines to obtain the true size of the plane.

is apparent. The true length of a line is basic and is used to develop the point view of the line. The point view of a line in a plane leads to an edge view of that plane. And finally, the edge view is used to construct the true size of a plane. The development of these four fundamentals is like the parts of a Chinese puzzle: one will not work alone. All the concepts depend on each other. They are also required to develop some of the concepts of graphical analysis that follow.

relationship of geometric elements

The four fundamental views previously discussed often may be applied directly to the solution of engineering problems. For example, the techniques for finding the true length of a line may be useful in determining the length of the control cables, tubing, and wiring in an airplane. The techniques for finding the true size of a plane may be useful in designing the various body and wing panels of the airplane.

15-37
The many intersections of this hanger construction may be analyzed using engineering graphics.

The fundamental views become especially valuable when used as tools to solve problems involving the relationships between geometric elements. The remainder of this chapter uses our knowledge of the four fundamental views to develop, first, the techniques required to analyze the angular relationships between elements, such as the structural members seen in the hanger roof [15-37], and, second, the distance relationships between the elements of objects, such as those of the airplane and the surrounding hangar structure.

Most analytical problems associated with engineering graphics can be simplified into relationships that exist between lines and lines, lines and planes, or planes and planes. Perhaps the most basic relationship between these geometric elements is that they are intersecting or non-intersecting.

Line-to-line Relationships

Intersecting lines meet at a point. That point is mutually shared by each line [15-38]. If lines intersect, it is usually important that we be able to determine their angle of intersection. The special case in which the two lines are perpendicular to each other [15-39] is used to determine the distance between a point and a line, or between two lines. Unless stated otherwise, the *distance* between elements of objects is always considered to be the *shortest* distance—the perpendicular distance.

Although two lines may appear to intersect in one orthographic view, it is important to check an adjacent view to determine if the point of apparent intersection in one view is really the mutual point of intersection shared by both lines. If projection to an adjacent view shows the apparent intersection point to be really two points, then the lines are *nonintersecting* [15-40]. A spe-

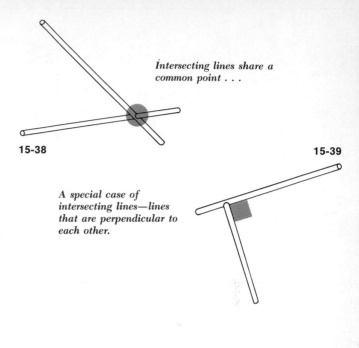

15-38

Intersecting lines share a common point . . .

15-39

A special case of intersecting lines—lines that are perpendicular to each other.

15-40

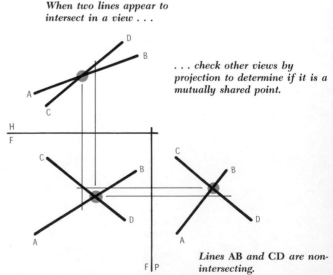

When two lines appear to intersect in a view . . .

. . . check other views by projection to determine if it is a mutually shared point.

Lines AB and CD are nonintersecting.

Parallel lines are nonintersecting lines. Parallel lines will be parallel in every view.

15-41

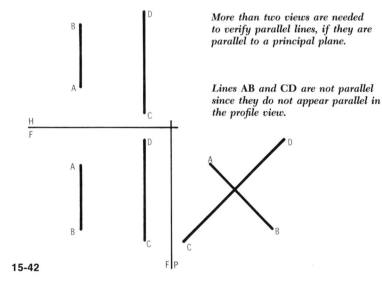

More than two views are needed to verify parallel lines, if they are parallel to a principal plane.

Lines AB and CD are not parallel since they do not appear parallel in the profile view.

15-42

Skew lines are nonparallel, nonintersecting lines.

15-43

cial case of nonintersecting lines occurs when lines are parallel to one another [15-41]. *Parallel lines will appear to be parallel regardless of the viewing position of the observer.* Generally, only two orthographic views are required to verify parallelism. However, if the lines are parallel to a principal reference plane, a third view is usually required to verify parallelism [15-42]. *Skew* lines are lines that do not intersect and are not parallel to one another [15-43].

Line-to-plane Relationships

Just as a line may intersect a line, a line may also intersect a plane. The angle between a line and a plane is often of interest to the engineer. The special case in which the line is perpendicular to the plane is useful for establishing and measuring the true distances between a point and a plane, between a line and a plane, or between two planes.

One way to verify if a line does intersect a plane is to obtain a view showing both the edge view of the plane and the line [15-44]. This view will show whether the line intersects the plane or is parallel to it. The techniques for locating such an intersection will be described in Chapter 16.

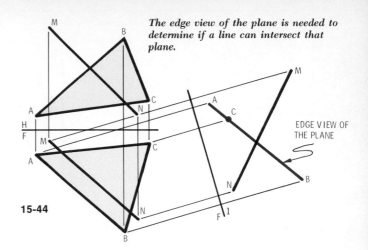

The edge view of the plane is needed to determine if a line can intersect that plane.

EDGE VIEW OF THE PLANE

15-44

Plane-to-plane Relationships

The final analytical relationship of interest is that of one plane to another plane. Just as lines may intersect each other, so may planes. However, instead of having a point of intersection, intersecting planes have a line of intersection [15-45]. The most common angle of intersection formed is 90°, but other angles are of equal importance to the engineer. Planes may also be parallel to each other. Often these conditions of intersection or parallelism may be verified by finding the edge views of the planes.

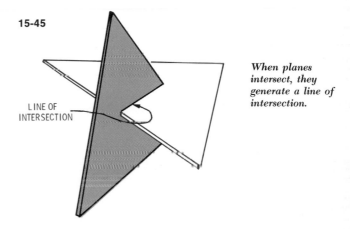

15-45

LINE OF INTERSECTION

When planes intersect, they generate a line of intersection.

true angles

One general area of geometric analysis of great interest to the engineer is the determination of *true angles* at the intersection of one geometric element (such as a line or a plane) with another [15-46].

True Angle Between a Line and a Line

The true angle between two lines appears when both lines are true length in the same view. This applies to the true angles between both intersecting and noninter-secting lines.

In the case of intersecting lines, both can be seen as true length in the view that shows the true size of the plane formed by these lines. Therefore, the method necessary to establish the true angle between two intersecting lines is simply that of finding the true size of a plane.

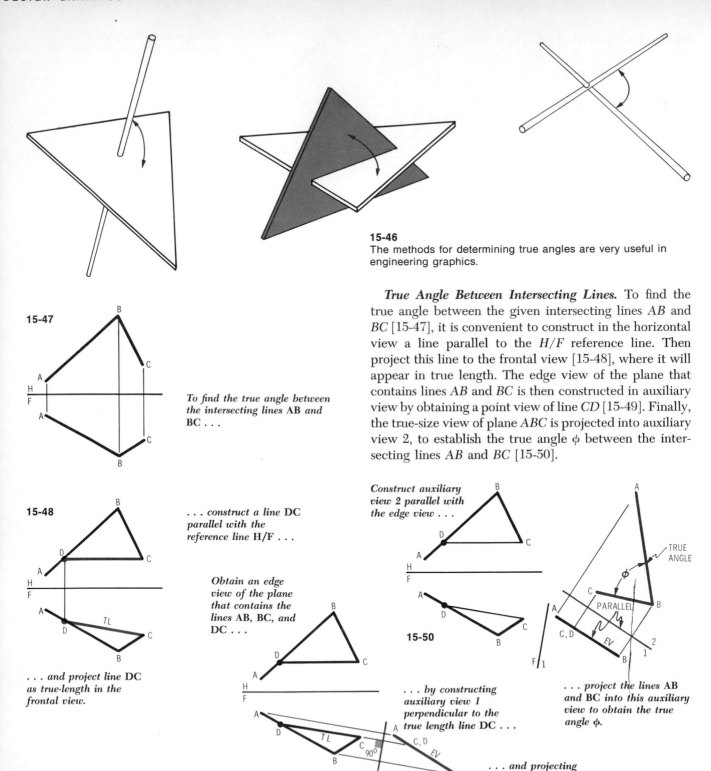

15-46
The methods for determining true angles are very useful in engineering graphics.

15-47

To find the true angle between the intersecting lines AB and BC . . .

True Angle Between Intersecting Lines. To find the true angle between the given intersecting lines *AB* and *BC* [15-47], it is convenient to construct in the horizontal view a line parallel to the *H/F* reference line. Then project this line to the frontal view [15-48], where it will appear in true length. The edge view of the plane that contains lines *AB* and *BC* is then constructed in auxiliary view by obtaining a point view of line *CD* [15-49]. Finally, the true-size view of plane *ABC* is projected into auxiliary view 2, to establish the true angle ϕ between the intersecting lines *AB* and *BC* [15-50].

15-48

. . . construct a line DC parallel with the reference line H/F . . .

. . . and project line DC as true-length in the frontal view.

Obtain an edge view of the plane that contains the lines AB, BC, and DC . . .

15-49

. . . by constructing auxiliary view 1 perpendicular to the true length line DC . . .

Construct auxiliary view 2 parallel with the edge view . . .

15-50

. . . project the lines AB and BC into this auxiliary view to obtain the true angle ϕ.

. . . and projecting all points into it.

530

15-51

To find the true angle between the skew lines AB and CD, it is necessary to see both lines as true length in the same view.

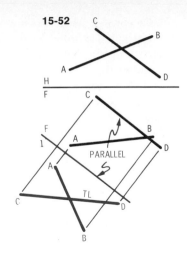

15-52

Establish the true length of line CD by constructing auxiliary view 1 parallel to line CD . . .

. . . project the line CD into the view as true-length . . .

. . . project line AB into auxiliary view 1.

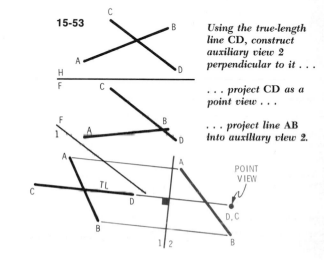

15-53

Using the true-length line CD, construct auxiliary view 2 perpendicular to it . . .

. . . project CD as a point view . . .

. . . project line AB into auxiliary view 2.

To obtain the true lengths of both AB and CD, construct auxiliary view 3 parallel with line AB . . .

. . . project lines AB and CD into auxiliary view 3 as true-length . . .

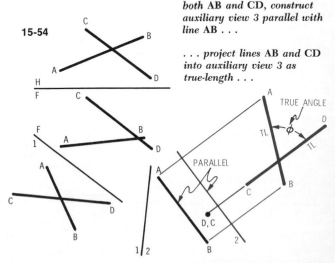

15-54

. . . measure the true angle φ between lines AB and CD.

True Angle Between Nonintersecting (Skew) Lines.

The procedure to establish the true angle between skew lines is a bit more complex than determining the true angle between intersecting lines, even though the same principle is used—that of finding the true length of both lines in the same view. The method used requires that we first establish the point view of one of the lines. Since any view adjacent to a point view will be true length, a view created parallel to the second line will then show the true length of both lines in the same view.

To find the true angle between the skew lines AB and CD [15-51], first project CD in true length into auxiliary view 1. Then project AB into the same auxiliary view [15-52]. Now find the point view of line CD by constructing auxiliary view 2 and projecting CD into it. Line AB is also projected into the third view [15-53]. Now that the point view of line CD is established, we must develop a true-length view of line AB. This is accomplished by the use of a third auxiliary view constructed parallel with line AB. This line is then projected into auxiliary view 3 in its true length. Because line CD is in a point view in auxiliary view 2, it will be projected into the third auxiliary view as a true-length line. Now both lines show in true length in the same view so we can measure the true angle φ that exists between them [15-54].

True Angle Between a Line and a Plane

The true angle between a line and a plane appears when the line is true length and the plane is an edge view in the same view. The method used to accomplish this involves finding the true size of the plane. Since any view

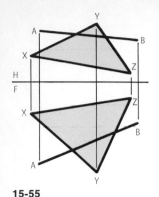

To find the true angle between the line AB and the plane XYZ . . .

. . . the line must be true length and the plane must be an edge view in the same view.

15-55

The edge view of plane XYZ is obtained by constructing line XO parallel with the reference line H/F . . .

. . . and projecting line XO as a true length line in the plane XYZ.

The first auxiliary view is constructed perpendicular to the true length line XO . . .

. . . and the plane XYZ is projected into view 1 as an edge view.

The line AB is projected into auxiliary view 1.

15-56

adjacent to a true-size view will be an edge view, a view constructed parallel to the line will then show the true length of the line and the edge view of the plane in the same view.

To find the true angle between the line *AB* and the plane *XYZ* [15-55], it is first necessary to develop the true size of the plane. This is accomplished by line *XO* in the horizontal view parallel with the reference line *H/F*. This line in plane *XYZ* then appears as true length in the frontal view. A first auxiliary view is constructed perpendicular to the true length to develop the edge view of the plane. Although an edge view has been established, the line *AB* in this view is not true length [15-56]. Therefore, additional auxiliary views are necessary. Auxiliary view 2 is constructed parallel with the edge view of the plane *XYZ*. The plane is transferred as true size into this view along with the line [15-57]. Auxiliary view 3 is constructed parallel with line *AB* in auxiliary view 2. This construction leads to a true-length view of the line *AB* in auxiliary view 3. Since the plane *XYZ* is true size in auxiliary view 2, it will appear as an edge view again in auxiliary view 3 [15-58]. This condition satisfies the requirements of the true angle between the line and the plane, so the angle φ may now be measured accurately.

Rotation of a Line

Another technique convenient for establishing the true angle between a line and a plane is the *rotation* method. This method utilizes the principle that if a line is rotated about an axis, its length is not altered [15-59]. If the new

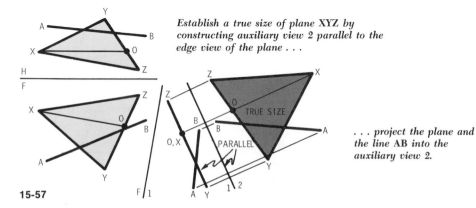

Establish a true size of plane XYZ by constructing auxiliary view 2 parallel to the edge view of the plane . . .

. . . project the plane and the line AB into the auxiliary view 2.

15-57

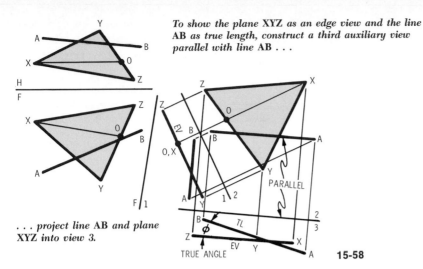

*To show the plane XYZ as an edge view and the line
AB as true length, construct a third auxiliary view
parallel with line AB . . .*

*. . . project line AB and plane
XYZ into view 3.*

15-58

Then the true angle φ can be measured.

position of the line happens to be parallel with a reference plane, the line will appear as true length in this
adjacent view. Also, this method of rotation about a central axis generates a cone whose base angle is the angle
between the line and the plane upon whose surface one
end of the line has rotated [15-60].

If it is desired to find a true-length view of the line
AB in the frontal plane, an axis perpendicular to the
horizontal plane is constructed through point A. This is

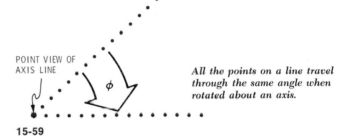

POINT VIEW OF
AXIS LINE

*All the points on a line travel
through the same angle when
rotated about an axis.*

15-59

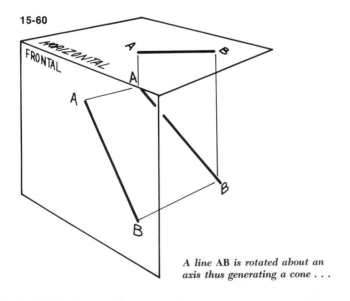

15-60

*A line AB is rotated about an
axis thus generating a cone . . .*

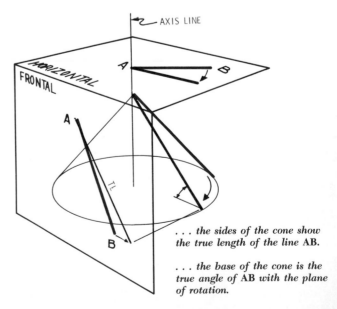

AXIS LINE

*. . . the sides of the cone show
the true length of the line AB.*

*. . . the base of the cone is the
true angle of AB with the plane
of rotation.*

533

15-61

To develop a true length line in the frontal view . . .

. . . a perpendicular axis of rotation is constructed between the points A in the two views.

15-62

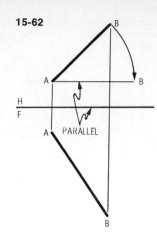

The line AB is rotated about the axis at point A until it is parallel with the reference line H/F.

15-63

The point B is then projected into the frontal view.

The point B is extended parallel with the reference line H/F to intersect the projection line.

By connecting points A and B, a true length view of line AB is obtained.

15-64

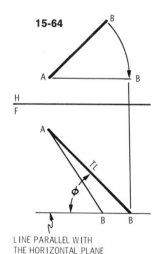

The rotated true length line AB defines the true angle ϕ with the horizontal plane.

the *axis of rotation* [15-61]. The line *AB* in the horizontal view is then rotated about point *A* until it is parallel with the reference line *H/F*, and the rotated point *B* is projected into the frontal view [15-62]. Point *B* in the frontal view is extended along a path parallel with the reference line *H/F* until it intersects the projection line. This new position of point *B* is then connected to point *A* to produce a true-length line *AB* in the frontal view [15-63].

At the same time that the true length of the line *AB* is established, the true angle between the line *AB* and the horizontal plane is available, since that is the plane upon which point *B* has been rotated. The true angle can be measured between the true-length line *AB* and the line through point *B* parallel to the horizontal plane [15-64].

15-65

To show the true angle between line MN and plane ABC, an edge view of the plane is needed.

. . . construct line CD parallel with reference line H/F . . .

. . . and project line CD into the frontal view as true length.

15-66

Construct auxiliary view 1 perpendicular to the true length line CD . . .

. . . and project plane ABC into auxiliary view 1 as an edge view . . .

. . . project line MN into the view.

True Angle Between a Line and a Plane (Rotation Method)

The general situation for finding the true angle between a line and plane using the rotation method is somewhat simpler than the auxiliary-view method because a smaller number of auxiliary views is necessary.

In order to obtain the angle that a line makes with a plane, it is necessary for the axis to be perpendicular to that plane. To find the true angle between line *AB* and plane *XYZ* by the rotation method, it is necessary to establish an edge view of the plane and then rotate the line into true length in the same view. In the horizontal view, construct a line *CD* in the plane *ABC* parallel with the reference plane *H/F*. Project this line *CD* into the frontal view as a true-length line [15-65].

Construct auxiliary view 1 perpendicular to line *CD* and project the plane *ABC* as an edge view. Line *MN* is also projected into this auxiliary view [15-66].

Now with an edge view of the plane established in the auxiliary view 1, it is necessary to get the line *MN* into true length in the same view using the rotation method. A second auxiliary view is constructed parallel with the edge view of the plane *ABC*. Only the line *MN* is then projected into this view. Point *N* is designated as the axis of rotation and the line *MN* is revolved until it is parallel with the reference line 1/2 [15-67].

The point *M* is then projected back to auxiliary view 1 until it intersects the parallel extension of point *M* parallel to reference line 1/2. This intersection point is then connected to point *N* to generate the true-length line *MN* and the true angle φ between line *MN* and the plane *ABC* [15-68].

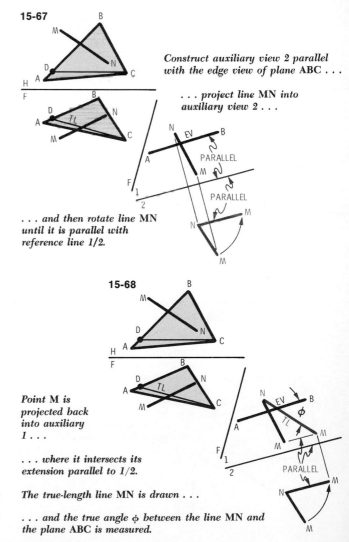

15-67

Construct auxiliary view 2 parallel with the edge view of plane ABC . . .

. . . project line MN into auxiliary view 2 . . .

. . . and then rotate line MN until it is parallel with reference line 1/2.

15-68

Point M is projected back into auxiliary 1 . . .

. . . where it intersects its extension parallel to 1/2.

The true-length line MN is drawn . . .

. . . and the true angle φ between the line MN and the plane ABC is measured.

535

15-69

To find the true angle between planes ABC and BCD . . .

. . . it is necessary to have an edge view of both planes in the same view.

15-70

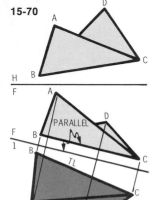

The edge view of both planes is achieved by establishing a point view of the mutually shared line of intersection BC.

Construct auxiliary view 1 parallel with the frontal view of line BC . . .

. . . and project BC as true length into view 1.

Project all the remaining lines into auxiliary view 1.

15-71

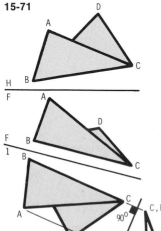

The point view of line BC is found by constructing the second auxiliary view perpendicular to the line.

Project the boundary lines of planes ABC and BCD into view 3 as edge views . . .

. . . and measure the true angle φ between them.

It is important to note that auxiliary view 2 was created to establish a path of rotation for point *M* in auxiliary view 1 that is parallel to the edge view of plane *ABC*, thus producing a true angle with *ABC*.

True Angle Between a Plane and a Plane

The true angle between two planes appears when both planes are edge views in the same view. The true angle between planes is often referred to as the *dihedral angle*. Two possible conditions confront the engineer: (1) the line of intersection is known; and (2) the line of intersection is *not* known. Of these, the first is the more common.

To find the true angle between planes *ABC* and *BCD* [15-69], all that is necessary is to obtain a point view of the line of intersection *BC*. Since this line is common to both planes, a point view of it will produce edge views of both planes in the same view. The point view of line *BC* is obtained by constructing auxiliary plane 1 parallel to this line of intersection. Project line *BC* in its true length into this newly constructed view. The other boundary lines of the planes are projected into auxiliary view 1 as well [15-70]. From there it is a simple matter to obtain the point view of the common line of intersection and the associated edge views of the planes by constructing auxiliary view 2 perpendicular to the true-length view of line *BC*. With the edge views of the planes complete, one can now measure the true angle φ between the planes—the dihedral angle [15-71].

If no common line of intersection is available, the basic principle of acquiring edge views of the planes in the

15-72

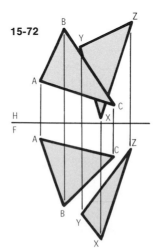

To find the true angle between planes ABC and XYZ when there is no intersecting line given . . .

. . . it is necessary to show both planes as edge views in the same view.

15-73

The dihedral angle between planes ABC and XYZ is found . . .

. . . by establishing an edge view of one plane, ABC, in the first auxiliary view.

The plane XYZ is projected into view 1.

Plane XYZ must become an edge view also.

15-74

Construct auxiliary view 2 parallel with edge view ABC . . .

. . . and construct a line OY parallel with the reference line 1/2.

Project the plane ABC as true size in auxiliary view 2 . . .

. . . and project plane XYZ with the true length line OY.

same view still applies, but the procedure used is somewhat different.

To find the dihedral angle between the given planes *ABC* and *XYZ* [15-72], it is necessary first to establish the edge view of one of the planes. In this example, the edge view of plane *ABC* is projected into auxiliary view 1 using a true-length line *AD* [15-73]. The plane *XYZ* is also projected into this view. Auxiliary view 2 is constructed parallel with the edge view of plane *ABC*, and at the same time a line *OY* parallel to reference line 1/2 is constructed within the plane *XYZ*. The two planes are projected into auxiliary view 2 with plane *ABC* being in true size and the line *OY* in *XYZ* being in true length [15-74].

One additional auxiliary view is now constructed that is perpendicular to the true-length line in plane *XYZ*. The two planes are projected into auxiliary view 3 as edge views. Since we now have edge views of two planes in the same view, we can measure the true angle φ between them [15-75].

specifications of a line

The relationship between lines and principal reference planes has such common usage in engineering practice

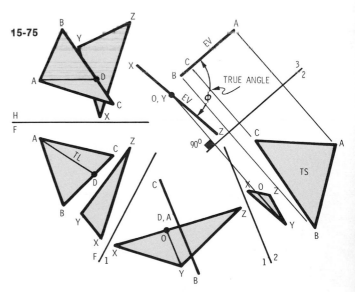

15-75

Construct auxiliary view 3 perpendicular to line OY . . .

. . . and project planes ABC and XYZ into the view as edge views.

Measure the true angle φ between the two planes.

The bearing of a line is designated by the angle between the line and the north–south axis of the earth.

BEARING ANGLE
N Ø⁰ W

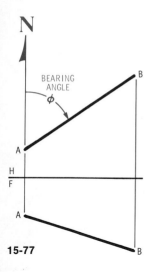

BEARING ANGLE
φ

The bearing of a line is measured in the horizontal view.

15-77

that names for specific relationships have evolved. The most familiar names are *bearing* and *slope*.

The *bearing* of a line is used to specify the line's direction with respect to the earth's axis. Specifically, the bearing designates the angle between the line in question and the north–south axis of the earth [15-76]. Although the earth is basically a sphere, its surface is so great that a small segment of the surface can be regarded as a planar surface—the horizontal plane. The horizontal view that shows this is used to measure the bearing of a line. By convention, the top of the horizontal view in an engineering drawing is assumed to be north unless some other direction in the horizontal view is specified [15-77]. Since direction is the only consideration in a bearing, the angle can be measured directly from the horizontal view without having to establish the true length of the line. The bearing of a line is always less than 90° and is read as a deviation from north or south in the direction that the line is pointing, utilizing the quadrants of the compass [15-78].

The other important specification of a line's orientation in space is the *slope*. Slope is defined as the true angle between a line and the horizontal plane. Slope can therefore be measured in an auxiliary view oriented so that both the true length of the line and the edge view of the horizontal plane are seen [15-79]. Slope can also be found by the rotation method, as shown in [15-64].

15-78
Various bearing angles with the compass quadrants.

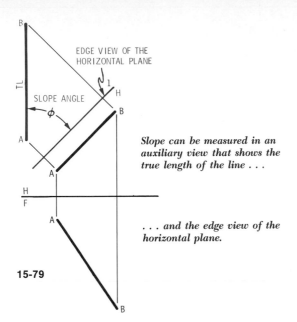

Slope can be measured in an auxiliary view that shows the true length of the line . . .

. . . and the edge view of the horizontal plane.

15-79

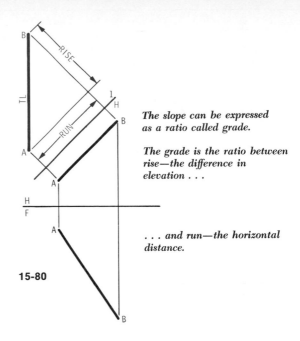

The slope can be expressed as a ratio called grade.

The grade is the ratio between rise—the difference in elevation . . .

. . . and run—the horizontal distance.

15-80

Instead of stating an angle in degrees, slope may also be stated as a ratio called *grade*. Grade is the ratio of the vertical difference in elevation of the end points of the line (*rise*) to the horizontal distance between the end points (*run*) [15-80]. This numerical ratio is multiplied by 100 to express the answer as a percentage. Grade can also be obtained by finding the tangent of the slope angle in a table of trigonometric functions and converting this to a percentage. The true values of rise and run can be measured readily on the same auxiliary view (or rotated view) of a line that shows the true slope angle. Grade is the term civil engineers use to designate the inclination of highways. A 6 per cent grade, for example, refers to a rise of 6 feet in every 100 feet of horizontal distance [15-81].

specifications of a plane

There is often a need to specify the location of a plane in space. Common terms used in such a specification are *strike* and *dip*. These terms come from the mining industry and describe the orientation of a vein of ore. The usefulness of the concepts has made them adaptable to other engineering applications.

The *strike* of a plane is the bearing of a horizontal line in the plane. It is found by constructing a horizontal line in the front view of the plane and projecting it into the

15-81
The grade of a highway is the rise for 100 feet of horizontal distance.

15-82

The strike of a plane is the direction that a horizontal line in the plane assumes when it is projected into the horizontal view.

The strike of plane ABC is N φ° W.

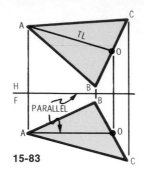

15-83

The dip of plane ABC is found by constructing a horizontal line AO in the frontal view . . .

. . . and projecting as true length into the horizontal view.

15-84

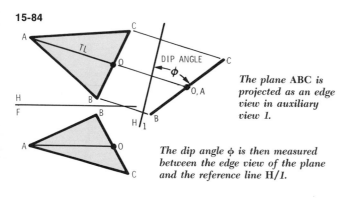

The plane ABC is projected as an edge view in auxiliary view 1.

The dip angle φ is then measured between the edge view of the plane and the reference line H/1.

15-85

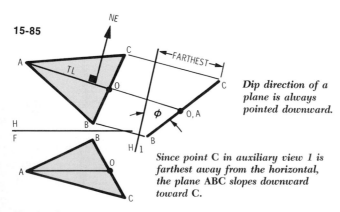

Dip direction of a plane is always pointed downward.

Since point C in auxiliary view 1 is farthest away from the horizontal, the plane ABC slopes downward toward C.

The dip direction is shown in the horizontal view as an arrow perpendicular to the strike line and pointing downward to the point C side of the plane.

horizontal view. The angle between this projected line and a north–south line—the bearing—is the strike of the plane [15-82].

Dip is the true angle between a given plane and the horizontal plane. It is always an acute angle, and the compass direction of downward slope must also be stated. The dip of a plane, therefore, is specified by two characteristics—the angle of the downward slope and its direction.

The dip of a plane is found by constructing a line *AO* parallel with the horizontal plane in the front view [15-83]. By projecting this line and plane *ABC* as an edge view into an auxiliary view adjacent to the horizontal plane, the angle may be measured. This dip angle is the true angle between the plane and the horizontal plane [15-84].

The dip direction is the general compass direction that the plane slopes downhill. This direction is indicated in the horizontal view by constructing an arrow perpendicular to the true-length horizontal line and pointed towards the low side of the plane (North-East) [15-85]. There is no angular connotation to dip direction, since it is used merely to differentiate between two planes having the same strike and dip angle.

true distances

Another important concept in engineering graphics is that of *true distances* between geometric elements. The shortest distance (often called *clearance*) between the various elements is most commonly used, but distances having a specific angle of inclination are not unusual.

Two lines are perpendicular if the angle between them is 90° in any view where either line appears as true-length.

15-86

The shortest distance or clearance between geometric elements is the true length of a perpendicular line constructed between these elements—whether they are points, lines, or planes. *Two lines are perpendicular if the angle between them is 90° in any view where either line appears as true length* [15-86]. The importance of this rule will become evident in the following discussions of true distances.

Shortest Distance Between a Point and a Line

The shortest (perpendicular) distance between a point and a line appears as true length when the line is seen as a point view. To find the shortest distance between point *X* and line *AB*, it is first necessary to establish

The shortest distance between a point and a line is the true perpendicular distance.

15-87

541

15-88

To find the shortest distance between point X and line AB . . .

. . . it is necessary to show the point and a point view of line AB in the same view.

15-89

Construct auxiliary view 1 parallel with line AB in the front view . . .

. . . and project line AB in true length into the auxiliary view 1.

Project point X into the auxiliary view.

the true length of line *AB* [15-88]. This is done by constructing an auxiliary view parallel with the front view of line *AB* and projecting the line and the point into this auxiliary view 1 [15-89]. Once the true-length line has been established, it must be projected as a point view into a second auxiliary view. This view is constructed perpendicular to the line *AB* [15-90]. The point *X* and the point view of line *AB* are then projected into auxiliary view 2. A line drawn connecting these points represents a perpendicular line between point *X* and line *AB*. As such, it is the true length of the shortest distance—the clearance—between the point and the line.

If it is necessary to find the point of intersection of the clearance line with line *AB*, we must return to auxil-

15-90

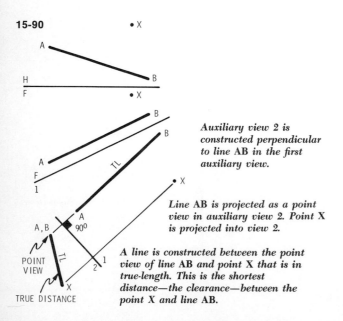

Auxiliary view 2 is constructed perpendicular to line AB in the first auxiliary view.

Line AB is projected as a point view in auxiliary view 2. Point X is projected into view 2.

A line is constructed between the point view of line AB and point X that is in true-length. This is the shortest distance—the clearance—between point X and line AB.

15-91

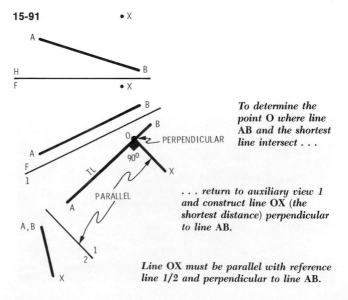

To determine the point O where line AB and the shortest line intersect . . .

. . . return to auxiliary view 1 and construct line OX (the shortest distance) perpendicular to line AB.

Line OX must be parallel with reference line 1/2 and perpendicular to line AB.

542

iary view 1. Recalling that two lines are perpendicular when the angle between them is 90° in any view where either is true length, construct a line from point X that is perpendicular to line AB [15-91]. Note that this line is also parallel with the reference line 1/2, thus verifying the statement that the same line in auxiliary view 2 is in true length. This perpendicular construction locates the point of intersection O on line AB, which can be projected to the preceding views of line AB and point X [15-92].

Shortest Distance Between Two Lines

The shortest (perpendicular) distance between two lines appears as true length when either line is seen as a point view. The true distance in this definition is the common perpendicular between two skew lines.

To find the shortest distance between the given skew lines AB and XY [15-93], we must establish the true length of one of the lines in auxiliary view 1 [15-94]. Although we now have established a true-length view of one of the lines, our definition indicates the need to develop a point view of a line to determine the common perpendicular. A second auxiliary view is constructed to obtain a point view of line XY along with a view of AB. Now construct a line PO from the point view XY perpendicular to line AB [15-95]. This line is the common perpendicular between AB and XY and is true length, as in the case of the shortest distance between a point and a line. As such it represents the shortest distance (clearance) between the skew lines.

Often it is desirable to find the points on each line where the shortest distance line intersects. This is accom-

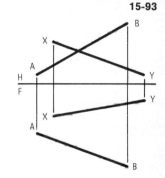

Project point O to the preceding views . . .

. . . construct lines that connect O and X to show the location of the shortest distance in each view.

15-92

15-93

To find the shortest distance between the skew lines AB and XY . . .

. . . it is necessary to find a point view of one of the lines.

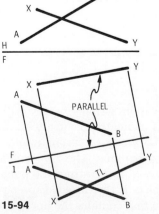

Construct auxiliary view 1 parallel to line XY in the front view.

Project line XY in true length into auxiliary view 1.

Project line AB into view 1.

15-94

Construct auxiliary view 2 perpendicular to the true-length line XY.

Project line XY as a point view . . .

. . . and line AB into auxiliary view 2.

Draw the true-distance line from XY perpendicular to line AB at point O.

15-95

543

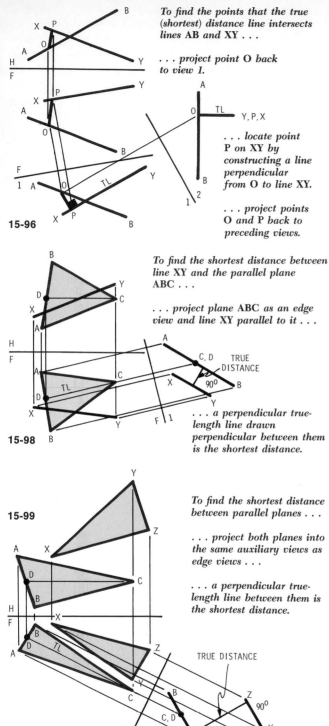

To find the points that the true (shortest) distance line intersects lines AB and XY . . .

. . . project point O back to view 1.

. . . locate point P on XY by constructing a line perpendicular from O to line XY.

. . . project points O and P back to preceding views.

15-96

To find the shortest distance between line XY and the parallel plane ABC . . .

. . . project plane ABC as an edge view and line XY parallel to it . . .

. . . a perpendicular true-length line drawn perpendicular between them is the shortest distance.

15-98

15-99

To find the shortest distance between parallel planes . . .

. . . project both planes into the same auxiliary views as edge views . . .

. . . a perpendicular true-length line between them is the shortest distance.

15-97

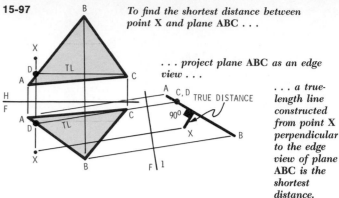

To find the shortest distance between point X and plane ABC . . .

. . . project plane ABC as an edge view . . .

. . . a true-length line constructed from point X perpendicular to the edge view of plane ABC is the shortest distance.

plished by projecting the true-distance line *PO* back into the preceding views of the line, just as in the example of the shortest distance between a point and a line [15-96]. (Note that line *PO* must be drawn perpendicular to line *XY* in the first auxiliary view, since *XY* appears as true length in this view.) In the first auxiliary view, the true-distance line is drawn from point *O* on line *AB* perpendicular to line *XY* at point *B*.

The true distances between other geometric elements are simply extensions of the analytical methods just discussed. As an example, to find the shortest distance between a point and plane, we must first obtain the edge view of the plane. Since the edge view is in effect a line, the method of finding the shortest distance between a point and a line applies [15-97]. Similarly, if an analysis requires the shortest distance between a line and a parallel plane, the edge view of the plane is once again needed. After this is accomplished, a perpendicular true (shortest) length line can be drawn between them [15-98]. The distance between parallel planes is found through the technique of viewing both planes as edge views in the same view [15-99].

summary

Analysis of visual communication systems begins with the four fundamental views of geometric elements—lines and planes. These fundamental views are strongly inter-related and dependent on each other. The *true-length* view of a line is basic and is used to construct the point view of the line. The *point view* is then needed to construct an edge view of a plane that contains the line. This

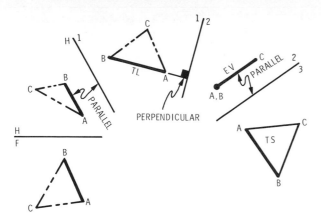

edge view of a plane in turn leads to the development of the *true size* of the plane.

These fundamental views are then the means by which the two general classes of geometric relationships—*true angles* and *true distances*—are analyzed. True angles between lines require that lines be seen as true length in the same view. True angles between lines and planes require that the lines be true length and that the planes be edge views in the same view. True angles between planes require that the planes be edge views.

Certain special true-angle relationships, important to the engineer, are the *bearing* and *slope* of lines and the *strike* and *dip* of planes. Bearing describes the direction of the line relative to the north–south axis of the earth. The slope of a line is the true angle between the line and the horizontal plane. The strike of a plane is the bearing of a horizontal line in that plane. Dip defines the true angular relationship of the plane with the horizontal plane.

The true distances between various geometric elements are found by using the fundamental views to obtain true lengths and point views of a line and edge views of planes. Perpendicular lines are constructed between these elements to define the most important true distance . . . the shortest or clearance distance.

problems

15-1. Complete the missing third view in the three figures [15-101, 15-102, and 15-103] and identify every true-length line with the letters TL in each of the principal views. If a true-length line does not exist in a figure, print NO TL in the upper-right-hand corner of the view.

15-101

15-102

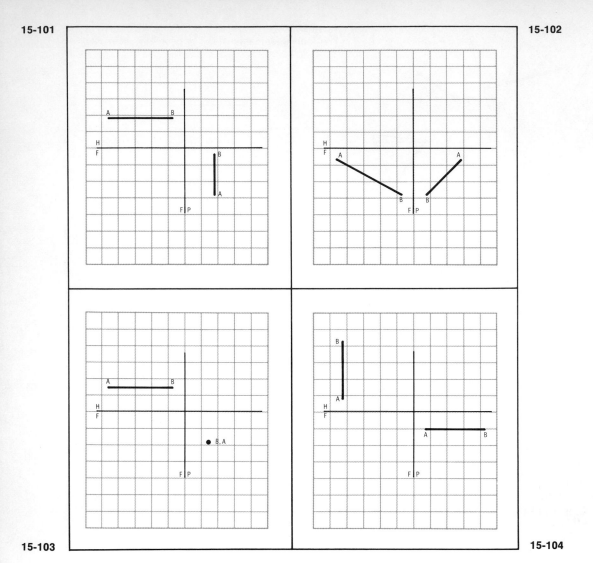

15-103

15-104

15-2. Complete the missing third view in the three figures [15-104, 15-105, and 15-106] and identify every point view of a line with the letters PV. If a point view of a line does not exist in a figure, print NO PV in the upper-right-hand corner of the view.

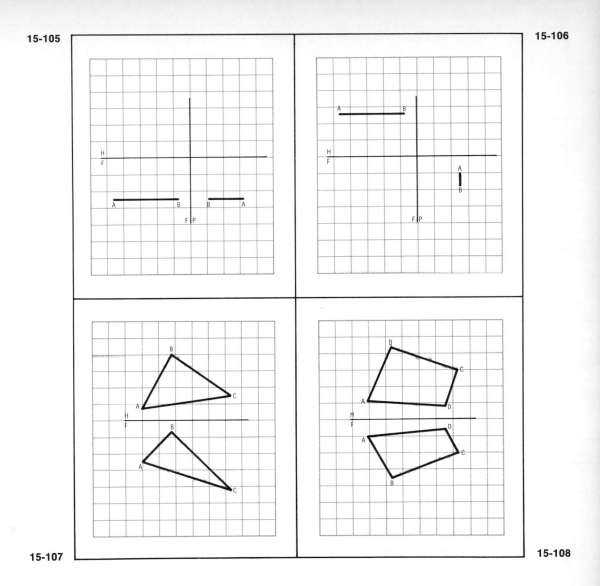

15-105

15-106

15-107

15-108

15-3. Construct the edge view of the planes shown in [15-107 and 15-108]. Using measuring and marking tools, transfer each figure to an 8½- by 11-inch sheet of paper and increase the scale to double size before constructing the edge view. Plan the layout so that the views are neatly arranged on the paper while it is vertically oriented.

15-4. Construct the true-size view of the planes shown in [15-109 and 15-110]. Using measuring and marking tools, transfer each figure in double size to an 8½- by 11-inch sheet of paper before completing the true-size view. Plan the layout so that the views are neatly arranged on the paper.

547

15-5. Determine if the lines given in [15-111 to 15-116] are intersecting. Measure and transfer each figure at double size to an $8\frac{1}{2}$- by 11-inch sheet of paper and complete the necessary views to determine the intersection. If the lines intersect, letter INT in the upper-right-hand corner; if not, letter SKEW.

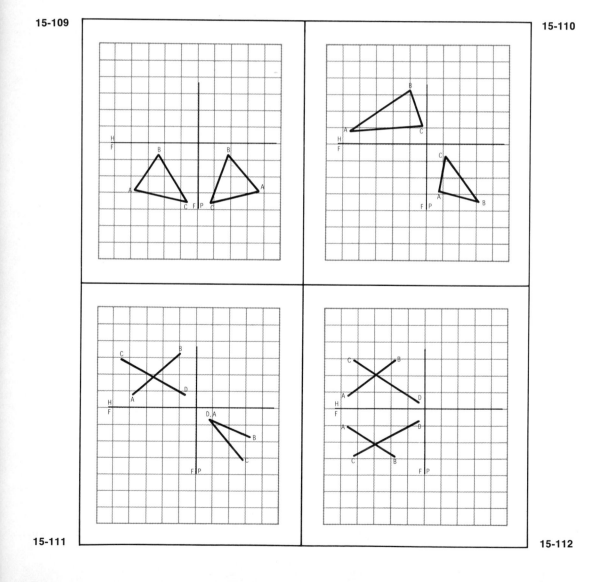

15-109

15-110

15-111

15-112

15-6. Determine if the lines given in [15-117 to 15-122] are parallel. Measure and transfer each figure at double size to an 8½- by 11-inch sheet of unruled paper and complete the necessary views to determine parallelism. If the lines are parallel, letter PAR in the upper-right-hand corner; if not, letter NON.

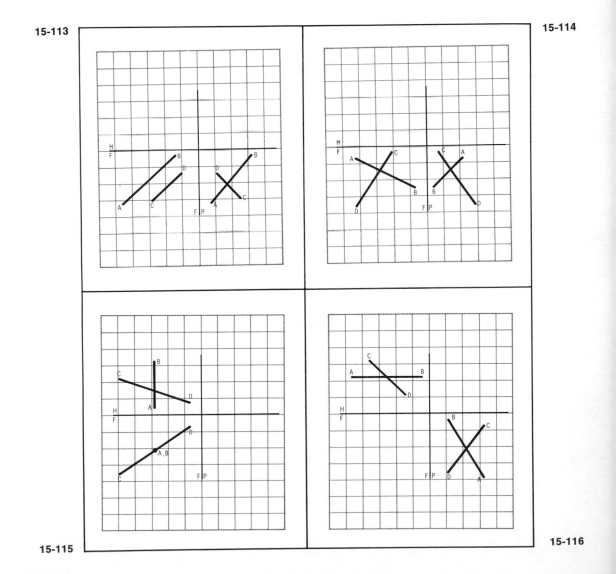

15-113

15-114

15-115

15-116

549

15-7. Determine the true angles between the pairs of lines given in [15-123 to 15-128]. Measure and transfer each figure at double size to an 8½- by 11-inch sheet of paper and complete the necessary views to determine the true angle. Letter the angular value between the lines in the true-angle view.

15-117

15-118

15-119

15-120

15-8. Using the auxiliary-view method, determine the true angle between the line and the plane in [15-129, 15-130, and 15-131]. Measure and transfer each figure at full size to an $8\frac{1}{2}$- by 11-inch sheet of paper and complete any necessary views to determine the true angle. Letter the angular value on the true-angle view.

15-9. Using the rotation method, determine the true angle between the line and the plane in [15-132, 15-133, and 15-134]. Measure and transfer each figure at full size to an $8\frac{1}{2}$- by 11-inch sheet of paper and complete any necessary views to determine the true angles. Letter the angular value on the true-angle view.

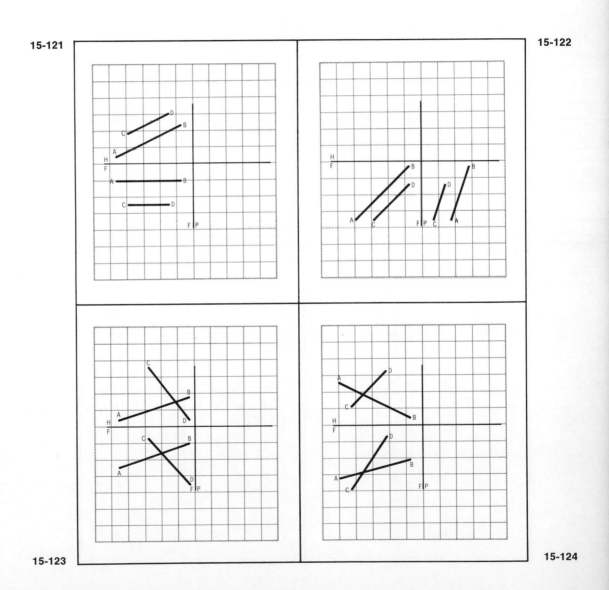

15-121

15-122

15-123

15-124

15-10. Specify the bearing of the lines *AB* in [15-129, 15-130, and 15-131]. Measure and transfer each figure at double size to an $8\frac{1}{2}$- by 11-inch sheet of paper and complete any necessary views to determine the bearing of the line. Letter the angular value on the proper view. Read the bearing along the line from point *A* to point *B*.

15-11. Specify the slope of lines *AB* in [15-132, 15-133, and 15-134]. Measure and transfer each figure at double size to an $8\frac{1}{2}$- by 11-inch sheet of paper and complete any necessary views to determine the slope of the line. Letter the angular value on the proper view.

15-12. For Problem 15-11 specify the grade of the lines *AB* instead of the slope.

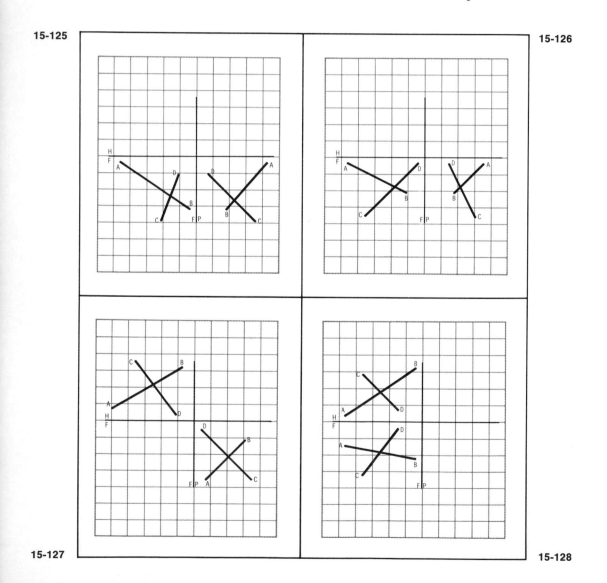

15-13. Determine the true angles between the intersecting planes in [15-135, 15-136, and 15-137]. Measure and transfer each figure at full size to an 8½- by 11-inch sheet of paper and complete the necessary views to determine the true angles. Letter the angular value on the true-angle view.

15-14. Determine the true angles between the nonintersecting planes in [15-138, 15-139, and 15-140] as instructed in Problem 15-13.

15-15. Specify the strike of the planes *ABC* in [15-135, 15-136, and 15-137]. Measure and transfer *only* the plane *ABC* for each figure at double size to an 8½- by 11-inch sheet of paper and complete the necessary views to specify the strike. Letter the value of the strike angle in the appropriate view.

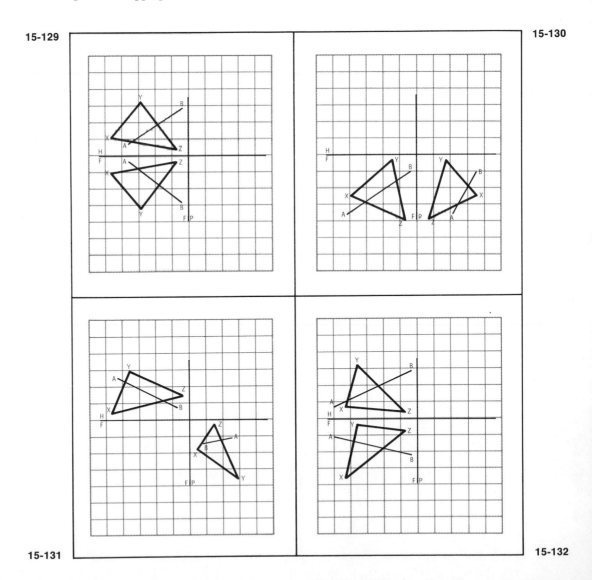

15-129

15-130

15-131

15-132

15-16. Specify the dip of the plane *XYZ* in [15-129, 15-130, and 15-131]. Measure and transfer *only* the plane *XYZ* for each figure at double size to an 8½- by 11-inch sheet of paper and complete the necessary views to specify the dip. Letter the value of the dip angle in the appropriate view. Also, show the dip direction in the appropriate view.

15-17. Determine the shortest distance between the point *X* and the line *AB* in [15-141, 15-142, and 15-143]. Measure and transfer each figure at full size to an 8½- by 11-inch sheet of paper and complete the necessary views to determine the true distance. Measure and letter the true distance on the appropriate view.

15-18. Determine the shortest distance between the two lines *AB* and *XY* in [15-144, 15-145, and 15-146] as instructed in Problem 15-17.

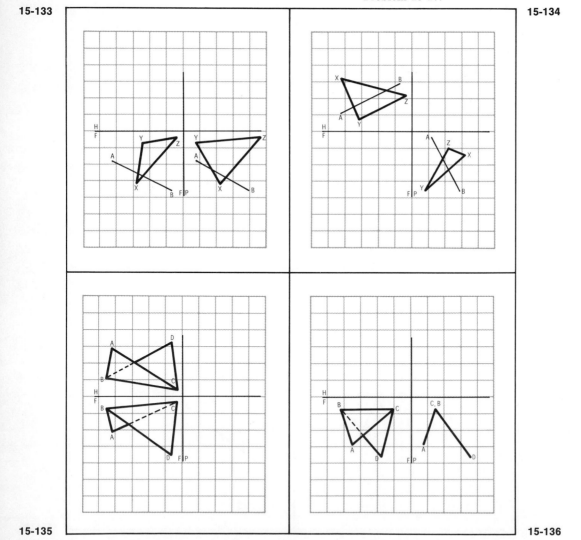

15-133

15-134

15-135

15-136

15-19. A policeman and a dangerous criminal are involved in a gun battle on Main Street (which is an east-west street). The policeman is shooting from a street position on the south side of the street at the corner of the Commercial Building. The criminal is across the street and is crouched on the third-story landing of a fire escape 30 feet above street level, firing back. The fire escape is on the south wall of the Enterprise Building, 90 feet from the corner that is opposite the policeman. Main Street, which is 65 feet wide including the sidewalks, separates the Commercial and Enterprise Buildings. Using graphical techniques, determine the distance the policeman is shooting and the angle from the street level.

15-137

15-138

15-139

15-140

This ornament's
decorative shape arose
from the rectilinear
limitation of spheroids.

16-1

A
B
C

Shape alone does not provide all *the information . . .*

. . . dimensions are necessary.

X

Y

most of us have an awareness of the value of technical sketches and engineering drawings. However, many of us may not have realized that competent sketches and drawings must provide much more information than the general shape of the object. Many symbols and standardized procedures are needed to convey precise information. Dimensioning, tolerancing, sectioning, threaded fasteners, etc., all require specialized but uniform treatment. Also, in designing it is frequently necessary to expand the principles discussed in Chapters 14 and 15 to include the precise location of intersecting prisms or planes and the development of surface areas. This chapter is devoted to an explanation of the general principles involved for these specialized conventions and applications.

dimensioning

Although the graphic image of a design is very important, it alone is not sufficient. If we wish to manufacture the design, dimensions are needed to specify sizes, locations, and other pertinent information so that it can be constructed accurately and repeatedly.

Dimensioning refers to the numbers and notes on a drawing that define the size of the object, the methods of manufacture, or the relation of the object to other objects. To produce correctly dimensioned sketches and drawings, the engineer must be able to visualize the final form of the product, the function it is intended to per-

1 QUART

... and the location relative to other objects.

SAN FRANCISCO

410 MILES

LOS ANGELES

A dimension defines the size . . .

16-2

16-3
The engineer MUST understand the final form of his design.

Do not provide confusing dimensions.

16-4

DRILL HOLE
2" FROM END

form, how it will be manufactured, and how it will be checked for conformity with the specifications.

Dimensions enable craftsmen to build the design. Remember, it is the craftsman's responsibility to build the part, product, or device—not to design it. If he must stop the manufacturing process and calculate or scale a missing dimension, or reset his machine tools to accommodate an inaccessible reference point, the dimensions provided him have been poorly conceived and inadequately presented.

Practically all man-made objects can be reduced to various combinations of four geometric shapes: rectangular prisms, cylinders, cones, and spheres. The primary function of dimensioning is to specify the *size* of the geometric elements and their relative *location* one to another.

RECTANGULAR PRISM

SPHERE

CYLINDER

CONE

16-5
Four basic solids of man-made objects.

Dimensioning Conventions

Dimensioning is a language, a way of communicating information from the engineer to the craftsman. Often the design engineer and the craftsmen never meet, so the drawing must convey all the information needed. Therefore, dimensions used must transmit consistent and mean-

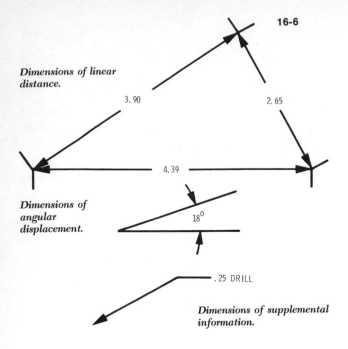

16-6

Dimensions of linear distance.

3.90   2.65

4.39

Dimensions of angular displacement.

18°

.25 DRILL

Dimensions of supplemental information.

FULL SIZE	or	1.00 = 1.00	or	1 = 1	or	1/1
HALF SIZE	or	.50 = 1.00	or	$\frac{1}{2}$ = 1	or	1/2
QUARTER SIZE	or	.25 = 1.00	or	$\frac{1}{4}$ = 1	or	1/4
EIGHTH SIZE	or	.125 = 1.00	or	$\frac{1}{8}$ = 1	or	1/8
TWICE SIZE	or	2.00 = 1.00	or	2 = 1	or	2/1
TEN TIMES SIZE	or	10.00 = 1.00	or	10 = 1	or	10/1

16-7
Specification of scales.

X.XX

16-8
Dimension line.

ingful information. To accomplish this, certain conventions and standard procedures have been developed.

Scale

Unlike sketches, drawings must be drawn to *scale*, that is, all dimensions on the drawing made in the same proportion (or scale) to their counterpart on the real object. Selection of an appropriate scale is usually determined by the size of the object and the size of the paper on which it is to be drawn. Large objects, such as buildings, ships, and bridges, must be drawn at a scale less than full size. On the other hand, very small objects (such as the parts of a watch) usually are drawn larger than actual size so that the detail and dimensional notation may be seen and understood. Whatever scale is selected must be clearly indicated on the drawing [16-7]. In some cases it is advantageous to include on the drawing a measured scale length with appropriate divisions (similar to a map scale). Then, if the drawing is photographically reduced, the scale length will be consistent with the new size.

Dimensioning Symbology

Dimensioning uses many symbols, of which lines are an important part. Four lines are used extensively: *dimension lines, extension lines, center lines,* and *leaders*. Each of these lines has a specific meaning and rules that govern its use.

Dimension Lines. Dimension lines are thin solid lines with arrows at each end [16-8]. In most applications there is a space at or near the midpoint of dimension lines to accommodate the dimension numerals. Dimension lines are drawn parallel to the feature being dimensioned, and they are placed a minimum of $\frac{3}{8}$ inch away from the object [16-9]. Succeeding dimension lines should be placed at constant intervals of at least $\frac{1}{4}$ inch with shorter

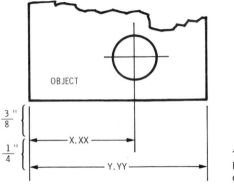

16-9
Placement of dimension lines.

dimensions placed inside longer ones. Dimension lines must *never* be crossed by *any* type of line. Remember that dimensions, although important, must never interfere with a clear view of the object.

Extension Lines. Extension lines are thin solid lines that extend the edge of the object or the location of an important feature to a place that permits convenient and clear dimensioning [16-10]. The extension line should leave a small visible gap (about $\frac{1}{32}$ inch) at the object and terminate approximately $\frac{1}{8}$ inch past the last dimension line. Extension lines may cross object lines and other extension lines.

Center Lines. Center lines are thin, alternately long and short dashed lines and are used to indicate the center of a cylindrical form or the axis of symmetry of an object. When center lines cross, as at the center of a circle, there must be a definite crossing of either two short or two long dashes. Center lines are used also as extension lines when locating cylindrical forms.

Leaders. Leaders are thin solid lines that have an arrow or a small dot at one end. They are used to show where a dimension or a note applies [16-12]. When an arrow is used, the leader must aim at the center of the feature with its point just touching the feature. When a dot is used, the note usually relates to a general area on the object, and the dot is placed inside the area. Leaders are never drawn horizontally or vertically and should terminate with a short horizontal line meeting the center of the first line of the note.

Arrowheads. Well-executed arrowheads on leaders and dimension lines do much to improve the clarity and attractiveness of a drawing. Arrowheads should be about $\frac{1}{8}$ inch long in a ratio of three units long to one unit wide [16-13]. If the space between the extension lines is very small, the arrows should be placed outside the extension lines, pointing inward [16-14].

16-10
Extension lines.

16-11
Center lines.

16-12
Leaders.

16-13
Arrowheads.

16-14

16-15
Lettering.

16-16
Typical uses of notes.

.75 DIA THRU

$\frac{3}{8}$ -16 UNC – 2A

.68 DRILL – .50 DEEP

Dimensional Lettering

Except for the case of notes, the majority of dimensional lettering consists of numbers and associated symbols, such as degree, inch, and foot marks. The style of lettering used should be either vertical or inclined single-stroke Gothic, as discussed in Chapter 12. Recall that most letters and numbers are about $\frac{1}{8}$ inch high with fractions being $\frac{1}{4}$ inch [16-15]. Use guidelines to assist in producing clear and attractive lettering.

Units. Always identify the units that apply to a dimensional figure unless all or nearly all are identical. In the United States, where dimensions on mechanical engineering drawings normally are stated in inches, it is conventional practice to omit the inch marks. However, to avoid the possibility of confusion, it is wise to use a general note, such as ALL DIMENSIONS IN INCHES UNLESS OTHERWISE SPECIFIED. A good rule of thumb for showing units might be: if their use eliminates confusion—use them. For example, the notation, 1 VALVE, is decidedly different from 1″ VALVE.

Dimensional Number Systems. Historically, dimensions on drawings in the United States have appeared as combinations of whole and fractional numbers such as $10\frac{7}{16}$, $3\frac{1}{4}$, $7\frac{13}{32}$, and so on. As a result of this practice, many standard parts are known by their fractional dimensions, such as a $\frac{5}{8}$ inch bolt, $\frac{3}{4}$ inch board, $1\frac{1}{4}$ inch pipe, and $\frac{1}{4}$ inch plate. Although cumbersome, it is quite likely that these names and the procedures for specifying them will remain unchanged for some time. However, with the increasing requirements of mass production, the need for greater accuracy, and convenience of base-ten mathematical systems, more and more industries are adopting decimal measurement. Preferably, most decimal measurements are written with two significant figures to the right of the decimal point; however, three significant figures are quite common because of increased accuracy requirements. For numbers less than 1, the zero before the decimal point is omitted on drawings.

Dimensional Notes. When there is a need to specify or describe a feature on a drawing other than a length or an angle, a *note* is often used. Notes usually specify such things as the dimensions of a hole, the size and type of screw thread, or a machine process, such as drilling, countersinking, or reaming [16-16]. Notes should always be oriented horizontally with the drawing and usually are connected to the feature that they describe by leaders.

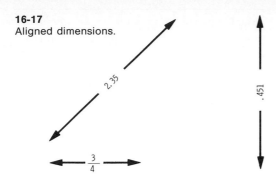

16-17
Aligned dimensions.

2.35

.451

3/4

16-18
Unidirectional dimensions.

2.35

.451

3/4

Orientation of Numbers. Dimension numbers either may be *aligned* with the corresponding dimension line, or they may be *unidirectional.* If they are aligned, the numbers are oriented so that they are either read from left to right or from bottom to top (that is, from the bottom or right side of the drawing) [16-17]. Unidirectional dimensions are becoming the more popular. They are always horizontal and are read from the bottom of the drawing [16-18].

Placement of Dimensions

Dimensions must define precisely the shape of the object and be placed so as not to detract from the views of the object. Each feature of the object should be defined by one and only one dimension. For example, if the depth of an object is given in a right side view, it should not be repeated in the top or in any other view [16-19]. Dimensions are normally placed outside the outline of the object and positioned so as to maintain at least a $\frac{3}{8}$-inch open space around the object [16-20].

Overall dimensions are normally desirable, because they are needed for raw material requisitions and other facets of the manufacturing process [16-21]. If the indi-

16-19

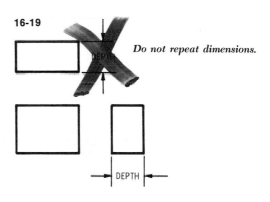

Do not repeat dimensions.

DEPTH

16-20

Leave $\frac{3}{8}''$ minimum open space around object . . .

16-21

Normally show overall dimensions . . .

. . . but omit overall dimension or mark "REF" if component parts must be specified.

REF

16-22

.38R   .38R

1.25

on rounded end objects . . .
omit overall dimensions.

16-23

Dimension view where
contour is clearly visible . . .

16-24
Rectangular prisms.

DEPTH

WIDTH

HEIGHT

16-25
Solid cylinders.

DIAMETER

HEIGHT

.06 X 45° CHAM

.12

30°

16-26
Chamfers.

vidual dimensions making up an overall dimension are more important, the overall dimension is accompanied by the note REF. This indicates that the dimension is to be used for reference only and not for manufacturing. One situation in which overall dimensions are seldom used (unless REF is added) is in the case of rounded-end objects, where both the distance between radius centers and the size of the radii must be specified [16-22].

Dimensions can be understood best when directly related to that view which pictures the shape or contour most clearly [16-23]. Avoid dimensioning to hidden lines. Extension lines are directed to only one view and must extend fully to the feature being dimensioned.

Size Dimensions

Preferred methods for specifying the size and location of the four basic geometric shapes commonly found in manufactured objects have been developed through the years. The rectangular prism is the most common of these.

Rectangular Prisms. When dimensioning a prism, the height and the width are usually specified in the front view [16-24]. The depth is shown in either the top or side views. If a dimension (such as width) applies to more than one view, it is good practice to place it between the two views. If possible, related dimensions are grouped together for clarity.

Cylinders. Next to the prism, the cylinder is the most commonly used geometric shape. The cylinder can be a bolt, a drive shaft, a wheel, or a round hole. The size (diameter and height) of a solid cylinder is preferably indicated in the view that shows the cylinder as a rectangle [16-25]. Full circles are dimensioned by their diameters, but partial circles (arcs) are dimensioned by their radii [16-28].

It is much more graphic and understandable to provide two views of a cylindrical form, although not entirely necessary. When two views are given, place the diameter dimension between the rectangular and circular views. If only one view (the rectangular view) is given, it is necessary to follow the diameter dimension with the note DIA. Chamfers are dimensioned by their angle and width [16-26].

Cylindrical holes are normally dimensioned in the circular view with a leader and a note specifying the diameter and the depth of the hole [16-27]. Manufacturing-process information required to make the hole is

16-27
Holes (hollow cylinders).

.25 DIA−.75 DEEP

.25 DRILL−THRU

16-28
Arcs.

.06R

.06R

.50R

.75R

often included in the note. The depth is not specified if the hole goes through the object. If this is not readily apparent from the drawing, the note THRU follows the diameter specification. When more than one hole has exactly the same size, only a single leader pointing to one of the holes is used with the number of holes added to the note [16-39].

Arcs and Irregular Curves. Arcs are dimensioned in the circular view using a leader [16-28]. The size is specified as a radius and is always followed by the symbol R. If the object has many fillets and rounds of the same radius, a general note such as, ALL FILLETS AND ROUNDS .06 R UNLESS OTHERWISE SPECIFIED, is used. An alternative method is to use a leader with a note .06R TYP (typical) pointing to one radius of the group. Irregular curves are best dimensioned using a coordinate system bounded by two datum lines that have been established at right angles [16-29].

Sphere and Cones. Spheres are dimensioned by giving their diameter. Partial spheres are dimensioned by their radius [16-30]. For cones or portions of conical shapes, it is common practice to dimension the height and the diameter in the triangular or trapezoidal view [16-31]. Occasionally, it may be useful to dimension a cone using an angular measurement with the angle being specified in the triangular view.

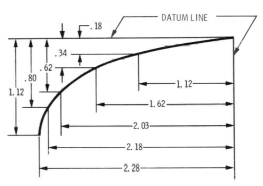

DATUM LINE

.18

.34

.62

.80

1.12

1.12

1.62

2.03

2.18

2.28

16-29
Noncircular curves.

16-30
Spheres.

1.75 DIA SPHER

1.12 R SPHER

16-31
Cones.

565

FIRST DATUM PLANE

SECOND DATUM PLANE

90°

THIRD DATUM PLANE

90°

90°

16-32
The use of datum planes in dimensioning.

Location Dimensions

In dimensioning, the location as well as the size of each geometric shape must be specified. The first step in establishing location dimensions is to select a single appropriate set of planes of the object to serve as reference planes or datums from which to initiate all location dimensions [16-32]. Often the choice of these datums is obvious from the shape of the object, its intended use, or its relationship to adjacent parts. In general, the largest or most prominent flat surface in each of the three basic directions (height, width, and depth) is selected. In the case of a symmetrical object, the center line (or lines) is normally taken as a datum [16-33].

Prisms must be located as well as sized in the view that clearly shows the contour [16-23]. Round features—

16-33

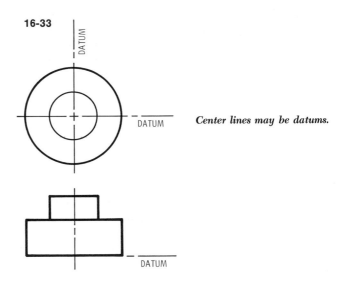

Center lines may be datums.

16-34

Locate solid cylinders and holes in the circular view . . .

16-35
Angular dimensioning.

16-36
Coordinate dimensioning.

both solid cylinders and holes—must be located by their center lines in the circular view [16-34]. Holes arranged in a circular pattern called a *bolt circle* may be located by their angular separation and the diameter of the circle [16-35]. For more accurate location, coordinate dimensions are usually used [16-36].

Threaded Fasteners

Fasteners are perhaps the most common features found in manufactured objects. Special methods have been established for drawing and dimensioning threaded fasteners and the holes associated with them. Threads may be drawn as they actually appear, but since this is very time consuming, either *schematic* or *simplified* thread symbols are usually used [16-37]. Schematic symbols use short thick lines to represent the roots of the thread with thin longer lines representing the crests. Simplified symbols use hidden lines to represent the root circle of the thread.

Threads are usually dimensioned with a note specifying in sequence the diameter, pitch (number of threads per inch), thread series, class of fit, and the letter A for external thread or B for internal thread (if a Unified thread series) [16-38]. If the thread is not a standard right-hand thread, the letters LH must be added to indicate left-hand thread.

The leader for an external thread note is usually directed to the rectangular view [16-38]. The leader for an internal thread note points to the circular view, but the thread size in the note must be preceded by a specification for the size of the hole that must be made prior to cutting the threads [16-39]. The diameter of this hole, called the *tap drill size*, is slightly larger than the root

16-37
Thread symbols.

16-38
Dimensioning external threads.

16-39
Dimensioning internal
threads.

16-40
Threaded fasteners.

BOLT   SCREW

diameter of the thread and may be found in standard thread tables.

The method for representing bolts and screws on drawings is shown in [16-40]. In addition to thread size, fastener specifications usually include such things as length, finish, material, type of drive, head shape, and type of fastener. See Appendix IV for detailed information on types of threads and fasteners.

Special Holes

The most common type of hole associated with fasteners is a drilled hole [16-41]. Note that the specified depth does not include the cone point left by the drill. (The point angle of the drill is standard and need not be specified. It is usually drawn at 30°.)

Other common types of holes and the tools that produce them are shown in [16-41]. Typical dimension notes are also shown. Reamers are used to bring an existing hole (usually drilled) to exact size. Counterbores create an enlarged hole to permit recessing the head of a fastener. The spotfacing tool is used only to produce a smooth surface for the fastener to bear upon and requires no

16-41

DRILL

REAM

COUNTERBORE

SPOTFACE

COUNTERSINK

depth specification. A countersink creates a conically shaped depression to permit recessing the head of a flat or oval head screw. Note that the size of a countersink is the included angle of the point rather than the diameter, and that the diameter required at the surface is specified instead of depth.

tolerancing

Modern technology and the increased production capability of industry allow a product to be designed in one place, the component parts to be manufactured in another (or even in numerous plants throughout the world), and the final assembly to take place in yet another location. How can we assure that all parts, components, and subassemblies fit together?

The engineer may have accurately specified the size, location, and form of all parts of a design. But what do we mean by "accurate"? May an actual dimension of the final part differ from the one specified by $\frac{1}{4}$ inch? by $\frac{1}{16}$ inch? by 0.001 inch? Variations in the raw materials, in the adjustment of machine tools, and in the errors of the gages used to measure the parts all contribute to inaccuracies. These can be reduced but not eliminated. *Tolerances* are the maximum inaccuracies that can be permitted if the finished object is to be assembled and operate as originally designed.

The function of a design determines the level of tolerance needed. For example, the function of a skate board allows greater component tolerance than does the function of a lunar-excursion module. As a general rule, the smaller the tolerance the higher will be the production cost of the design. Thus, if skate boards were built to the same tolerances as lunar-excursion modules, their cost would be such that few people would consider buying them.

Terms of Tolerancing

Tolerance is the total allowable variation of a dimension. The dimensions involved may relate to size, position, and form of an object.

The *nominal* size is an approximate size that has been assigned for easy identification. Examples are $\frac{1}{2}$-inch pipe, $\frac{3}{4}$-inch board, and $\frac{1}{2}$- by 1-inch bar stock. The nominal size may vary considerably from the actual size. For example, while the outside diameter of $\frac{1}{2}$-inch pipe re-

16-42
A dispersed production system needs a method to make things fit together . . . tolerancing.

DESIGN

MANUFACTURE

ASSEMBLY

Generally a close tolerance . . .

. . . costs more than a wide tolerance.

16-43

Tolerances specify
permissible variations
in size . . .

. . . in position . . .

. . . and in form.

16-44

16-45
Nominal size.

NOMINAL SIZE:
$\frac{1}{4}$" BOLT

BASIC SIZE:
1.500 DIA
SHAFT

16-46
Tolerances are
applied to the basic
size.

1.500

TOLERANCE:
$\pm$.005

1.495

1.505

LIMITS

mains constant at 0.840", the inside diameter may vary
from 0.622" (standard) to 0.252" (XX-strong), depending
upon wall thickness.

The *basic* size is that size from which the total tolerance is established.

Limits are the maximum and minimum values of the
basic size plus or minus the tolerance.

Allowance is the intentional difference in size between
two mating parts [16-47]. If the internal part is always
smaller than the external part (positive allowance), a
clearance fit is said to exist. If the internal part is always

16-47
Allowances.

CLEARANCE ALLOWANCE
(POSITIVE)

INTERFERENCE ALLOWANCE
(NEGATIVE)

16-48
Tolerance.

1.500 $^{+.005}_{-.000}$

UNILATERAL TOLERANCE

1.500 $^{+.005}_{-.005}$

BILATERAL TOLERANCE

larger than the external part (negative allowance), an *interference* fit is said to exist. If the maximum and minimum limits on both parts are established such that either clearance or interference could exist, the result is a *transition* fit.

A tolerance established such that variation is permitted in only one direction from the basic size is called a *unilateral* tolerance (for example, $1.500 \, ^{+.005}_{-.000}$) [16-48]. When variation is permitted in both directions, this is a *bilateral* tolerance (for example, $1.500 \, ^{+.005}_{-.005}$). The tolerance on a dimension may be specified on a drawing by stating the basic size followed by the plus and minus tolerance ($1.500 \pm .005$, $1.500 \, ^{+.005}_{-.005}$) or by stating the limits directly ($\frac{1.505}{1.495}$). To save having to state a tolerance on each dimension, a general note is very often used on the drawing to cover the majority of dimensions. A typical note might be ALL LINEAR DIMENSIONS $\pm .015$; ALL ANGULAR DIMENSIONS $\pm .5°$; UNLESS OTHERWISE SPECIFIED.

Tolerances of Position

Tolerances of position are the basis for locating precisely one part in relation to another. For example, if gears mounted on parallel shafts are to run together smoothly, the distance between the shafts must be precisely controlled by the tolerances on the hole locations in the shaft mounting plates [16-49]. Positional tolerances are established on the basic dimensions that locate a feature from specific *datum* (reference) points, lines, or planes. These datums must be used for all related features on an object and on all mating parts [16-50].

Tolerancing Systems

There are two systems for specifying location tolerances—*coordinate* and *true position*. The coordinate system is the older of the two and is based on the use of coordinate axes. Since most manufacturing machinery is also constructed to operate on the coordinate system (to move either the work piece or the working tool in coordinate directions), this system of tolerancing is very commonly used.

The coordinate system of tolerancing first specifies a particular dimension and then specifies the allowable tolerance for that dimension. Because of the rectangular nature of the coordinate system, the tolerance zone (variance from the exact location) is also rectangular [16-52]. The diagonal of this rectangle permits consid-

16-49

16-50
Mating parts use the same datum lines.

DATUM B

DATUM A

DATUM B

DATUM A

16-51
Coordinate tolerances are based on the coordinate system.

16-52
The tolerance zone is rectangular in the coordinate system.

TOLERANCE ZONE

TOLERANCE ZONE

EXACT POSITION

16-53
The range of variance in the coordinate system.

The basic position is exactly located . . .

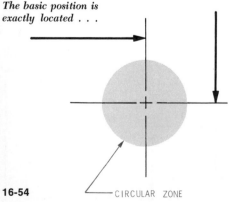

16-54

CIRCULAR ZONE

. . . and the tolerance is within a circular zone in the true position system.

erably larger variation than either of the coordinate dimensions [16-53].

The true-position system of tolerancing overcomes this limitation by first specifying an exact location and then applying a tolerance relative to that location in the form of a note or a symbol. This system develops a circular tolerance zone, where the allowable variance from the exact dimension is the same in all directions [16-54]. The manner of specifying this on a drawing is shown in [16-55].

In using a particular system, the engineer must be aware of the capabilities of a machine shop so that he can specify tolerances that are economically attainable and still allow the design to function. Often an incorrectly specified tolerance will lead to misinterpretation by a craftsman or inspector. When such misinterpretation occurs, the designer is at fault for not specifying the tolerances clearly.

Tolerances of Form

Tolerances of form specify the permissible variation in the geometric shape or contour of an object. Examples

16-55
True-position tolerancing.

.XXX-.XXX DIA
LOC. AT TRUE POS
WITHIN .014 DIA.

1.000
BSC

1.000
BSC

.XXX-.XXX DIA
.014 DIA

1.000

1.000

DRAWING CALLOUT

INTERPRETATION

16-56
Specifying flatness.

.010

BY SYMBOL

.010 WIDE TOLERANCE ZONE

The surface must be within the specified tolerance of size and must lie between two parallel planes (.010 apart).

FLAT WITHIN
.010 TOTAL

BY NOTE

"A" "B"
1.750 ± .005
.312 ± .002
6 STEPS EACH .250
6 STEPS EACH .250
.005
.340 ± .005
.688
.688
.844
.906 .781
.859
.938 .906
2.312 ± .005
.250 ± .005
.010
BETWEEN A AND B

BY SYMBOL

"A" "B" .340 ± .005
1.750 ± .005
.250 ± .005
.312 ± .002
.005
.005
.340 ± .005
.688
.688
.688
.844
.906 .781
.859
.938 .906
2.312 ± .005
TOLERANCE AT ALL POINTS OF PROFILE OF SURFACE BETWEEN A AND B
BY NOTE

16-57
Specifying the profile of a surface.

16-58
The cutting plane.

An imaginary cutting plane is passed through and . . .

. . . a section view results.

CUTTING PLANE

of geometric tolerances are flatness, straightness, roundness, parallelism, and perpendicularity. Such characteristics can be toleranced using symbols or notes on the drawing [16-56]. Contour tolerances specify the variation that is acceptable in profile elements, particularly curvilinear forms—regular and irregular [16-57].

section views

Many objects have complex internal features. When orthographic (multiview) drawings or sketches are made of such objects, the resulting multiplicity of hidden lines (necessary to depict the internal shape of the object) frequently is confusing. *Section views* can be used to reduce the confusion and clarify the design.

16-59
The cutting-plane line.

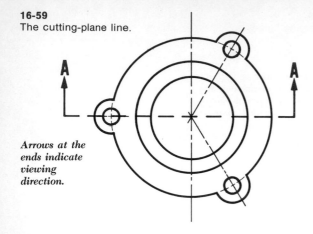

A

A

Arrows at the ends indicate viewing direction.

16-60
Sectioning of adjacent parts.

45°

60°

45°

SCREW

KEY

SHAFT

RIB

16-61
Section lines.

Cutting Plane

A section view is created by drawing the object as if part of it had been removed—cut away. An imaginary plane or combination of planes (known as *cutting planes*) is passed through selected parts of the object. The image that would be projected onto the cutting plane is the section view. It is drawn in accordance with the rules of orthographic projection.

Cutting-plane Line

The edge view of the cutting plane is represented by a *cutting-plane line*. This line is composed of a series of thick dashed lines. An arrow is placed at each end of the cutting-plane line to indicate the direction that the viewer is looking at the cut surface of the object. When more than one section view is cut through a drawing, each pair of arrows of the individual cutting-plane lines is lettered successively using capital letters, such as *AA*, *BB*, etc.

Section Lines

To distinguish between material that has been cut by the cutting plane and the remainder of the object, the surface of the cut material is crosshatched with thin, solid, parallel lines called *section lines*. These lines are drawn at some constant angle relative to the object, usually 45° with the horizontal, and are spaced $\frac{1}{16}$ to $\frac{1}{8}$ inch apart. Other angles (especially 30° and 60°) are used to avoid having the section lines parallel with a principal line of the object and for additional contrast between adjacent parts [16-60]. Cut portions of the same part are designated throughout the drawing with section lines that have the *same* slant and spacing. Cut portions of different pieces in the same view are differentiated by section lines at different angles and spacing. If any of the mating parts at the cutting plane are shafts, ribs, or standard parts (such as screws, pins, rivets, or keys) these parts are *not* sectioned [16-61]. Hidden lines behind the cut surface are omitted unless absolutely necessary for clarity. Specific patterns of section lines are sometimes used to represent different types of materials (see Appendix I).

Types of Sections

A cutting plane may cut through an object in a variety of ways, resulting in different portions of the object being removed.

16-62
A half-section.

A half-section is developed by passing the cutting plane through the object to the center line.

16-63
Broken-out sections.

Full Section. A full section is generated by passing a cutting plane through the entire object [16-58]. This is generally done so that it divides the object into halves. By removing the front half, a full view of all the internal features can be seen. If the object is symmetrical and the cutting plane passes through the axis of symmetry, it is not necessary to draw the cutting-plane line.

Half Section. Many times it is desirable to show both external and internal features of an object in the same view. This is especially useful with symmetrical objects. When such a view is needed, a cutting plane can be passed through the object up to the midpoint (normally the center line). The resulting view is a *half-section* showing both external and internal features [16-62]. In this type of view, hidden lines are normally omitted from the entire drawing. However, the center line or a visible line representing the end point of the cutting plane must be shown.

Broken-out Section. A *broken-out section* is formed by passing a cutting plane through only a small selected

575

16-64
Revolved sections.

16-65
Removed sections.

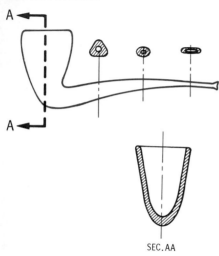

SEC. AA

portion of the object. This is often useful in pictorial drawings as well as in orthographic drawings.

Revolved Section. At times it is desirable to draw a section view of a long object, such as a pipe, beam, or handle. A *revolved section* can be used to show the section contour at desired locations. Here the cutting plane is passed perpendicular to the object's long axis. The resulting section is then revolved 90° in place to reveal the cut section in true size. Break lines may be used if desired to separate the section from the view.

Removed Section. A *removed section* is similar to a revolved section, except that it is drawn at some removed location, preferably in line with the axis of the cut. If the removed section must be placed at some other location on the sheet, it must be carefully labeled to correspond with the appropriate cutting-plane line.

Offset Section. The *offset section* is similar to the full section, except that the path of the cutting plane is not straight. Rather, it conforms (using 90° turns) to the significant features of the object. Note that there are no vertical lines in the section view or changes in the sec-

16-66

When the cutting plane conforms to the significant features . . .

. . . an offset section is developed.

tion-line pattern where the cutting plane has changed direction.

Aligned Section. Some objects do not lend themselves readily to section views. In these cases it may be necessary to rotate a portion of the object to a more suitable position before sectioning. This practice is particularly common in circular objects with odd numbers of radial features, such as a spoked hand wheel. When this situation arises, the element of concern is rotated to a new position that lends itself to conventional section practice. If rotation were not used, a standard section view would make the object appear unsymmetrical and might be misleading.

Some features are rotated to get a conventional view.

intersections

Most manufactured objects are composed of simple geometric shapes. The line at which any two of these shapes meet is called their *intersection*. This intersection may be a straight or a curved line.

The engineer often must find intersection lines on his drawings so that he can specify such things as the location of fasteners, the shape of the intersecting forms, and the quantity of materials required. Since any line is defined by a series of points, the process for defining an intersection involves establishing the necessary intersection points. To illustrate the techniques for establishing an intersection, we shall use the simplest and most general intersection—a line intersecting a plane. Two methods are commonly used to determine this point, the *edge-view* method and the *cutting-plane* method.

16-67
An aligned section.

Intersection of a Line and a Plane

Edge View Method. Standard orthographic views of common objects very often show edge views that give intersection points directly [16-68]. If not, the intersection point of a line oblique to a plane is found by establishing the edge view of the plane in an auxiliary view [16-69]. In the example, line *AB* and plane *XYZ* are given, and the intersection point between the line and the plane is desired. The line *AB* is left incomplete, since the intersection point is not known at this time.

A line *XO* is constructed in the horizontal view parallel to the reference line *H/F* and projected into the frontal

16-68
The intersection point often can be found directly from the edge view.

The intersection point of line AB and plane XYZ is found . . .

. . . by constructing the horizontal line XO . . .

. . . and projecting it as true length.

16-69

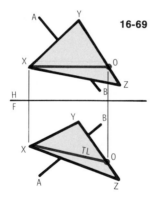

view as a true-length line. The edge view of the plane is found in auxiliary view 1 by projecting a point view of the true-length line *XO*. The line *AB* also is projected into the auxiliary view and the intersection point with the plane is established [16-70].

The original views can be completed to show the intersection point of line *AB* with the plane *XYZ* by projecting the intersection point found in the auxiliary view back into the frontal and then into the horizontal view. These views of line *AB* are then completed by extension to the intersection point as visible or hidden lines [16-71].

The plane XYZ is projected as an edge view in the auxiliary view . . .

. . . along with line AB . . .

. . . and the intersection point established.

16-70

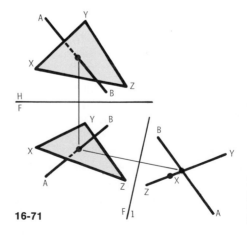

The intersection point is projected back to the preceding views.

16-71

578

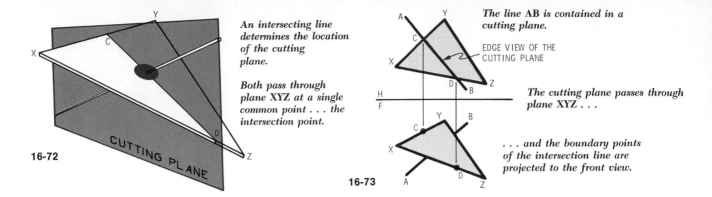

16-72

An intersecting line determines the location of the cutting plane.

Both pass through plane XYZ at a single common point . . . the intersection point.

The line AB is contained in a cutting plane.

EDGE VIEW OF THE CUTTING PLANE

The cutting plane passes through plane XYZ . . .

. . . and the boundary points of the intersection line are projected to the front view.

16-73

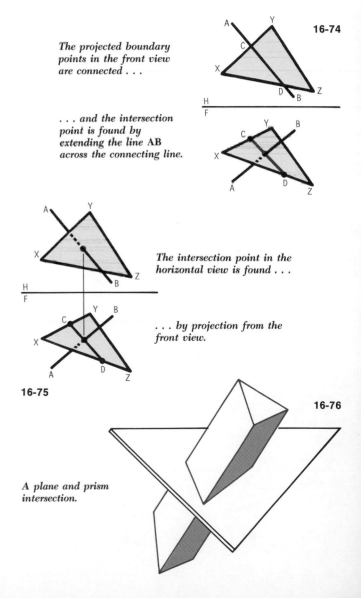

16-74

The projected boundary points in the front view are connected . . .

. . . and the intersection point is found by extending the line AB across the connecting line.

The intersection point in the horizontal view is found . . .

. . . by projection from the front view.

16-75

16-76

A plane and prism intersection.

Cutting-plane Method. Using the same line *AB* and plane *XYZ* as in the previous example, the intersection point also can be found by the cutting-plane method. The intersecting line is considered as lying within a plane that cuts through the subject plane [16-72]. The edge view of a plane is passed through the horizontal view of line *AB* and cutting plane *XYZ*. The points *C* and *D*, where the cutting plane crosses the boundaries of the plane *XYZ*, are projected into the front view [16-73]. These projected points are connected with a straight line, which represents the intersection line of the cutting plane with the plane *XYZ*. The point at which the line *AB* crosses the intersection line in the front view is the intersection point [16-74]. The intersection point in the horizontal view is found by projection from the front view [16-75]. The number of geometric shapes used in design creates a large number of possible intersection conditions. Most intersection problems involve more complex geometric elements than just a line and a plane, but the methods are the same. Because of the complexity, it is a good practice to number the intersection points as they are developed and to pay careful attention to the relative visibility of the major lines.

The basic types of intersections that will be discussed are the intersection of a plane and a prism, of a plane and a cylinder, of two prisms, and of two cylinders.

Intersection of a Plane and a Prism

Since the intersection of a plane and a prism [16-76] is a basic and common type of intersection, we shall discuss the use of both the edge-view method and the cutting-plane method.

16-77

Using the triangular prism *ABCDEF* and the plane *XYZ* . . .

. . . find the intersection lines.

16-78

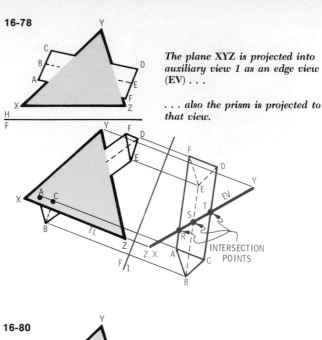

The plane *XYZ* is projected into auxiliary view 1 as an edge view (EV) . . .

. . . also the prism is projected to that view.

16-79

The points of intersection from the edge view . . .

. . . are projected to their corresponding positions in the front view.

The points are connected to define the shape of the intersection.

16-80

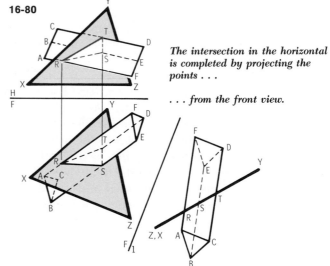

The intersection in the horizontal is completed by projecting the points . . .

. . . from the front view.

Edge-view Method. The first example is the intersection of the triangular prism *ABCDEF* with the plane *XYZ* [16-77]. Note that the views are incomplete at this time, and the plane is not seen as an edge view. We must first construct the auxiliary view 1, which shows the plane *XYZ* as an edge view passing through the triangular prism [16-78]. The intersection points *R*, *S*, and *T* of the edge view of the plane and the vertex lines of the prism are then projected back from the auxiliary view to the front view and to the horizontal view. These points are con-

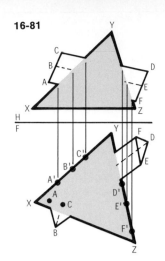

16-81

Finding the intersection by the cutting plane method . . .

. . . cutting planes AF, BE and CD are established.

Their points of intersection with plane XYZ are projected to the front view.

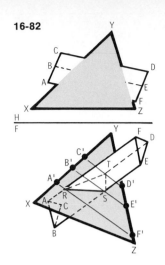

16-82

The cutting plane intersection lines A'F', B'E', and C'D' cross the appropriate vertex lines to develop the intersection points.

nected by straight lines to establish the shape of the intersection in both views [16-79 and 16-80].

Cutting-plane Method. The cutting-plane method is generally preferred to the edge-view method because it requires less construction. Using the same example of the triangular prism and the plane *XYZ*, cutting planes are passed through the vertex lines of the triangular prism in the horizontal view. The points at which these cutting planes pass through the boundaries of the plane *XYZ* are found and projected to their appropriate positions in the front view [16-81]. These points are then connected with lines that represent the intersection of the respective cutting planes with the plane *XYZ*. Where these lines cross vertex lines of the prism, intersection points *R*, *S*, and *T* are defined. These intersection points are then connected with straight lines, and the shape of the intersection in the front view is established [16-82]. By projection, the points are then transferred to the horizontal view and connected with straight lines [16-83].

The intersection points are projected to the horizontal view to establish the shape of the intersection.

16-83

Intersection of a Plane and a Cylinder

The intersection of a plane and a cylinder is another common type of intersection problem [16-84]. To find the intersection between the cylinder and the plane *ABCD* [16-85], we shall use the cutting-plane method. The views are incomplete because the intersection has not yet been defined.

Using light construction lines, complete both views of the intersecting shapes. Since the cylinder does not have

16-84

The plane and cylinder intersection.

581

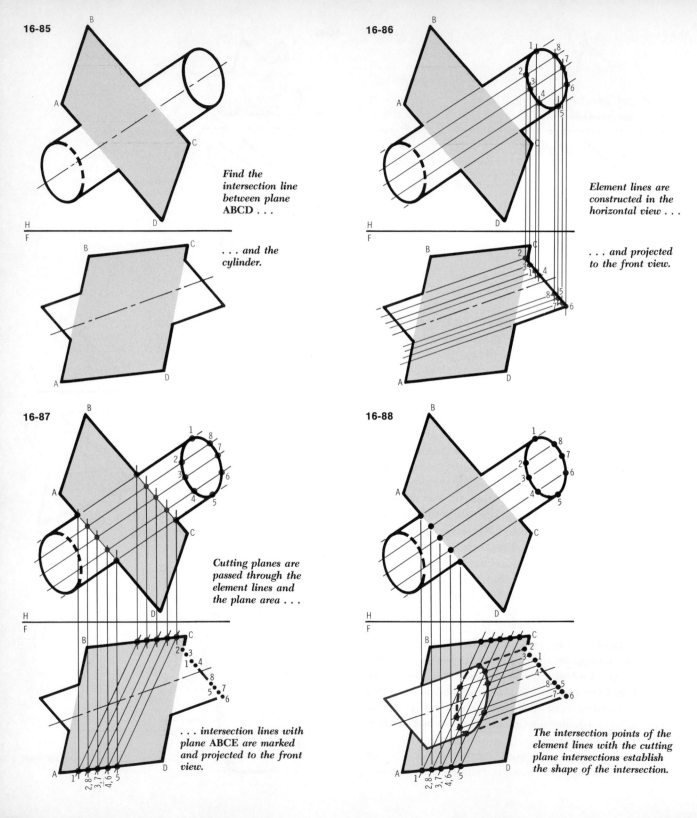

16-85

Find the intersection line between plane ABCD . . .

. . . and the cylinder.

16-86

Element lines are constructed in the horizontal view . . .

. . . and projected to the front view.

16-87

Cutting planes are passed through the element lines and the plane area . . .

. . . intersection lines with plane ABCE are marked and projected to the front view.

16-88

The intersection points of the element lines with the cutting plane intersections establish the shape of the intersection.

582

lines corresponding to the vertex lines of the prism on which intersection points can be located, it is first necessary to construct parallel element lines on the surface of the cylinder at regular intervals in the horizontal view [16-86]. The points where these lines meet the end of the cylinder are numbered and projected to the front view. The element lines are then extended from these points parallel to the axes of the cylinder in the front views.

Cutting planes are now passed through the element lines in the horizontal view [16-87]. The lines of intersection of the cutting planes with plane *ABCD* are marked and projected to the front view. The intersection points of the element lines are now defined in the front view, where these lines cross the cutting-plane intersection lines. These points must be connected to complete the description of the shape of the intersection [16-88]. The shape of the intersection in the horizontal view is found by projecting the points from the front view to the appropriate element lines in the horizontal view and drawing the intersection line [16-89].

Intersection of Two Prisms

The intersection of two prisms is essentially the problem of multiple planes intersecting each other. The lines of intersection of the various planes are determined by the intersection points of the lines of one prism piercing the planes of the other and vice versa. The edge-view and the cutting-plane methods of establishing the intersection points may be used independently or cooperatively. The example shows a rectangular prism and a triangular prism intersecting [16-90]. Inspection of the given views reveals that the planes of the rectangular prism appear as edges in the horizontal view. The intersection points of the vertex lines of the triangular prism with the planes of the rectangular prism are therefore immediately available and may be projected directly to their appropriate locations in the front view [16-91].

This, however, does not complete the shape of the intersection because the points for the intersection of the vertical corner line of the rectangular prism with the planes of the triangular prism are not defined yet. To establish the location of these points, the cutting-plane method is applied. In the horizontal view the cutting plane (CP) is drawn through the corner line and parallel with the vertex lines of the triangular prism [16-92]. The cutting-plane intersection lines are projected to the front

16-89

The intersection in the horizontal view is found by projecting . . .

. . . the points from the front view.

16-90

The intersection of two prisms . . .

. . . is the same as the intersection of multiple planes.

16-91

The intersection points along the edge views . . .

. . . are projected directly to the front view.

16-92

A cutting plane (CP) is passed through the corner of the rectangular prism . . .

. . . intersection lines are projected to the front view . . .

. . . and intersection points located.

16-93

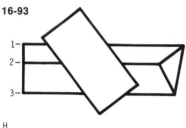

view and extended parallel with the vertex lines of the triangular prism. (Since the corner is the point of interest, there is no need to extend the lines beyond the projection of the corner.) Note that the cutting plane passes through two faces of the triangular prism and that both intersection lines are projected to the front view. The intersection points are now connected with straight lines to define the shape of the intersection [16-93].

16-94
Some designs require an understanding of how two cylinders can be joined together.

The points are connected to define the shape of the intersection.

Often it is difficult to visualize the final shape of the intersection, so careful analysis of the various intersecting planes and lines is necessary. This analysis is performed with both views of the prisms to define their basic relationships. Each line of each object must be studied to determine its possible intersection with each plane . . . if it does and where.

Intersection of Two Cylinders

The intersection of two cylinders is quite similar in principle to the intersection of two prisms. The primary difference is that cylinders are continuous surfaces; they have no vertex lines, as did the prisms. It is therefore necessary to construct parallel element lines on the surface of the small cylinder as in the case of the intersection of a cylinder and a plane. In the example [16-95], eight linear elements are drawn on the surface of the smaller cylinder parallel with its axis. These lines are then projected to the front view. The number and location of the cylinder elements are selected to give the best definition to the curved intersection line that will result from their intersection with the large cylinder. For accuracy more than eight cylinder elements are frequently necessary.

The intersection points of the element lines of the small cylinder with the large cylinder can be seen in the horizontal view, where the large cylinder appears as an edge view. These intersection points can be projected to the front view of the element lines and a smooth curve drawn through them [16-96 and 16-97].

16-95

To find the intersection of two cylinders, element lines are constructed on the small cylinder.

16-96

The intersection points of the element lines with the edge view of the larger cylinder . . .

. . . are projected to the element lines in the front view.

16-97

The points are connected to define the shape of the intersection.

a tomato juice can . . .

. . . cut along the seam . . .

. . . and rolled flat is a development of a cylinder.

16-98

16-99
Many manufactured products are formed from flat sheet stock.

developments

A development is the flattened-out surface of a hollow geometric shape. Developments are used mostly in industries that manufacture sheet metal parts. Air conditioning and heating ducts, metal furniture, and the skin of airplane wings are a few examples.

If we were to take an old tomato juice can, remove the top and bottom, cut it along its seam, and roll it out into a flat sheet, we would have the development of a cylinder [16-98]. Similarly, the orthographic box in Chapter 14 that was unfolded to show the six principal views is a development of a rectangular prism [14-29]. The surface of the orthographic box is composed of a series of flat planes; the tomato juice can is a continuous single-curved surface. Any geometric shape that is composed of several plane or single-curved surfaces can be developed. Complex surfaces such as double-curved and warped surfaces cannot be developed except by special techniques that provide reasonable approximations of a developable form.

The principle that governs most developable surfaces is that the surface must be definable with straight lines. Each of these lines must be a true-length line on the developed surface.

Developments are classified according to the orientation of the linear elements that compose the geometric forms. Our discussion will be limited to the two most common classes—*parallel-line developments* and *radial-line developments*.

16-100
The cylinder and the rectangular
prism are examples of parallel-line
geometric shapes.

Parallel-line developments apply to all geometric shapes whose linear elements are parallel with each other. The cylinder and the rectangular prism are good examples of this group [16-100].

The linear elements of a radial-line development converge to a point. The cone and the pyramid are good examples of this type [16-101].

Since a development represents only the surface of a developable geometric form, this surface can be viewed from either the inside or the outside. In the case of an inside development, the layout lines will appear on the inside of the object after it is formed. In an outside development the layout lines appear on the exterior surface after forming [16-102].

16-101
The cone and the pyramid are examples of radial-line
geometric shapes.

16-102

*The layout marks of
an inside pattern
are on the interior
surface.*

*The layout marks of an
outside pattern are on the
exterior surface.*

BEND LINE

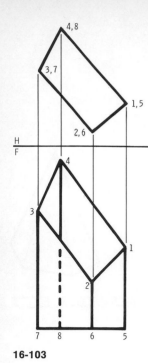

Construct a development for a hollow, rectilinear prism.

16-103

Development of a Prism

All parallel-line geometric shapes are developed on the same basic principles. We shall develop a hollow prism to demonstrate these basic principles [16-103]. Remember that every line on the surface of the form must be seen as *true length* in the development. In the example, every plane that encloses the prism will have to be shown as true size. This could be achieved by constructing four auxiliary views around the horizontal view of the prism [16-104]. With these true-size planes we could construct the rectilinear solid that they define. In this configuration, however, it would be a cumbersome process requiring cutting out each of the planes, positioning them properly relative to each other, and then fastening them together.

This is far too time consuming and unacceptable to industry because of the many seams involved. A better approach is to unfold the prism sequentially, thus retaining the common lines between the true-size planes as

16-104

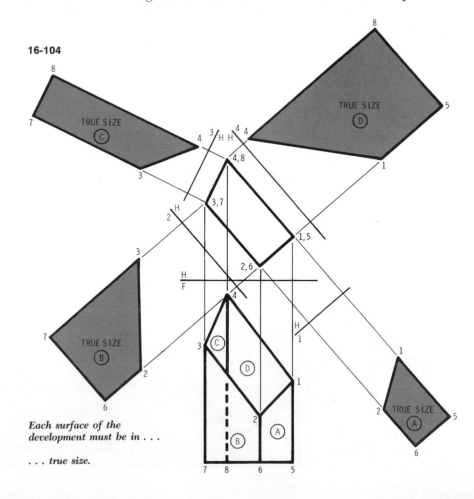

Each surface of the development must be in . . .

. . . true size.

TRUE WIDTH PLANE Ⓒ

TRUE WIDTH PLANE Ⓓ

The true-plane widths in the horizontal view . . .

TRUE WIDTH PLANE Ⓑ

TRUE WIDTH PLANE Ⓐ

. . . are used to lay out the stretch out line.

BEND LINES

STRETCH-OUT LINE

TRUE WIDTH PLANE Ⓐ | TRUE WIDTH PLANE Ⓑ | TRUE WIDTH PLANE Ⓒ | TRUE WIDTH PLANE Ⓓ

16-105

bend lines. This can be done with a *stretch-out line* constructed perpendicular to the axis of the prism and having a length equal to the perimeter of the prism. Examination of [16-105] shows that the true length of the perimeter can be found in the horizontal view, where the edge

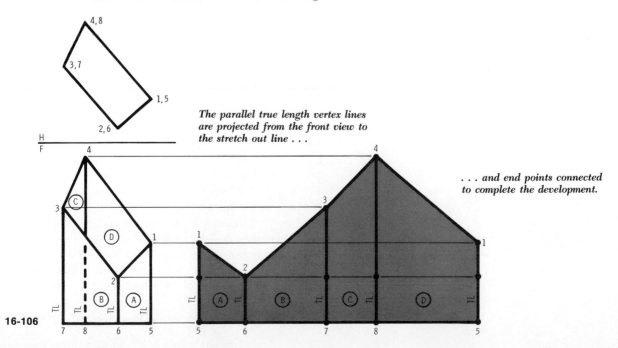

The parallel true length vertex lines are projected from the front view to the stretch out line . . .

. . . and end points connected to complete the development.

16-106

views of the prism's planes can be seen. The width of each plane is transferred to the stretch-out line in sequence Ⓐ Ⓑ Ⓒ Ⓓ, starting with the 1-5 line. Since the vertex lines of the prism are all true length in the front view, they can now be transferred parallel to the appropriate locations on the stretch-out line to indicate where the material must later be bent [16-106].

The projected end points of the vertex lines are connected by straight lines to define the shape of the development. Compare the true-size planes that comprise this development with the true-size planes made earlier [16-104]—they are the same. This method is not only quicker but also joins the planes in their proper relationship for easy fabrication by bending and fastening along only one seam. Note that this example shows the interior surface of the prism, so this is an inside development. To produce an outside development, the same procedure can be used, except that the planes must be laid out in reverse sequence—Ⓓ Ⓒ Ⓑ Ⓐ.

Development of a Cylinder

The methods for constructing the development of a cylinder are basically the same as those for a prism. A stretch-out line is constructed perpendicular to the axis of the cylinder with a length equal to its circumference. Although there are methods for graphically determining this circumference, the simplest method is to calculate it mathematically.

Since a cylinder is a continuous single-curved surface, no edges or corners are available. It is therefore necessary to construct a representative group of parallel linear elements on the surface of the cylinder. The number of lines is arbitrary, but the greater the number, the greater the accuracy, just as in the case of intersections. Eight equal segments were chosen in the example [16-107]. The stretch-out line is similarly segmented into eight equal parts and numbered to correspond with the segments on the circumference of the circle in the horizontal view. The segment points on the edge of the cylinder are projected into the front view, and parallel elements drawn.

Since the element lines are true length in the front view, they may now be projected directly over to appropriate locations on the stretch-out line. The end points of the element lines are connected with a smooth curve to complete the shape of the development for the hollow cylinder [16-108].

In the parallel-line forms developed above, the length

16-107

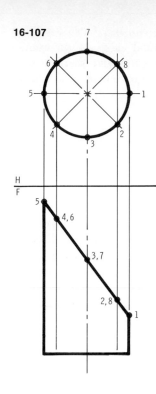

To construct a development of a cylinder, segment the circle. . .

. . . project the points to the front view to obtain parallel elements . . .

. . . and divide the stretch out line into lengths equal to the segments.

EQUAL TO AN
ARC LENGTH

STRETCH-OUT
LINE

16-108

Project the parallel true length element lines from the front view to the stretch out line . . .

Complete the development by connecting the end points with a smooth curve.

STRETCH-OUT
LINE

of the stretch-out line was found by using the true widths from the edge views (the horizontal views on our examples). When the edge view of a geometric shape is not available, one must establish its edge view in an auxiliary view and transfer its dimensions to the stretch-out line.

Development of a Pyramid

The triangular pyramid [16-109] is an excellent example of a geometric form whose linear elements have a radial orientation. Again, all lines that comprise the surface of the development must be in true length, but a different method of layout must be used. Following the example of the prism, the development of the pyramid could be obtained by rotation of the planes or by constructing the necessary auxiliary views to show each plane in true size [16-110]. Note that two auxiliary views would be needed for each plane, since the edge views are not given. The planes then could be cut out, properly aligned, and fastened together again. This procedure is just as unacceptable here as it was before. The better approach is to sequentially unfold the triangular planes using the radial boundaries as bend lines. Unfortunately, radial-line forms cannot be developed with a stretch-out line because the linear elements are not parallel. Instead, the true lengths of the boundary lines of each triangular plane

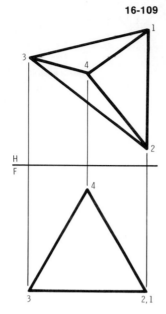

To develop a radial line form, all the lines of the form must be true length.

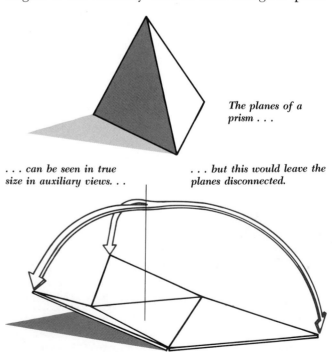

The planes of a prism . . .

. . . can be seen in true size in auxiliary views. . .

. . . but this would leave the planes disconnected.

16-110

16-111

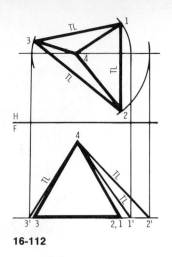

16-112

True-length lines are found . . .

. . . by inspection and by rotation.

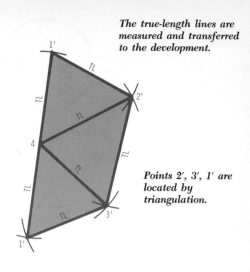

The true-length lines are measured and transferred to the development.

Points 2', 3', 1' are located by triangulation.

must be found and transferred to the development. If the lines do not appear true length in one of the given views, the rotation method is often very convenient for determining the required true lengths [16-111].

The development is started with a convenient line 4-1' adjacent to the given views [16-112]. After that, arcs equal to the true lengths of sides 1-2 and 4-2 are swung from points 1' and 4, respectively, on the development. The intersection of these two arcs will determine the location of point 2'. This procedure, called *triangulation*, is continued until all the points of the development are completed. The points are joined with straight lines to complete the outline of the development. (Note that in this case we have produced an outside development. If we reverse our procedure and locate point 3 first, instead of point 2, an inside development will be produced.)

The triangulation procedure discussed above is basic to all radial-line forms. Since radial lines converge at some point, the surfaces of the object always are based on true-size triangles in the development.

Development of a Cone

The cone is related to the pyramid as the cylinder is related to the prism. As with the cylinder, the surface of the cone is continuous, so no corners or edges exist. It is therefore necessary to create radial linear elements in order to develop the cone. The circular view of the cone is segmented into an arbitrary number of equally spaced sections. These are projected to the front view to establish the linear elements of the cone [16-113]. The true length of each of the linear elements is found by inspection and by rotation [16-114], and transferred to

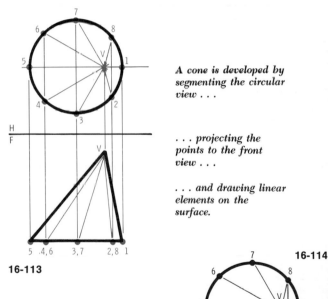

A cone is developed by segmenting the circular view . . .

. . . projecting the points to the front view . . .

. . . and drawing linear elements on the surface.

16-113

16-114

By inspection and rotation methods . . .

. . . the true length of each linear element is established.

593

16-115

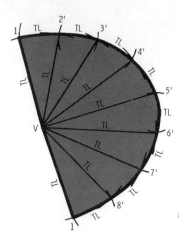

The true-length elements are measured and transferred to the development.

The final shape is developed using the triangulation technique.

the development using the triangulation method [16-115]. After all the points have been established, the shape of the development is completed with a smooth curve.

problems

16-1. Select one of the objects listed below. Measure the object and make a drawing of the three principal views. Dimension the drawing using the scale indicated (unidirectional dimensions). Include all appropriate dimensional symbols.
(a) desk chair (eighth size)
(b) four-drawer file cabinet (eighth size)
(c) chalkboard eraser (full size)
(d) door knob (full size)
(e) waste paper basket (quarter size)

16-2. Using a table of decimal equivalents, convert the following fractional numbers to decimal numbers of three significant figures. Carefully letter the numerals using single-stroke vertical Gothic style.

$10\frac{3}{4}$	$12\frac{1}{16}$	$7\frac{3}{4}$	$2\frac{9}{16}$	$6\frac{19}{24}$
$1\frac{7}{8}$	$\frac{5}{8}$	$41\frac{1}{4}$	$7\frac{27}{32}$	$9\frac{1}{8}$
$3\frac{3}{32}$	$5\frac{13}{16}$	$\frac{25}{64}$	$4\frac{13}{16}$	$\frac{15}{16}$

16-3. Make a list of ten items with which you are familiar that are identified by their *nominal size.*

16-4. Using the list established in Problem 16-3, determine the *basic size* of each of the ten items using decimal notation.

16-5. Give five examples in which dimensions in decimal notation are preferable to fractional notation.

16-6. Dimension [16-116 and 16-117] using aligned dimensions. Add extension, dimension, and center lines necessary to complete the drawings. Scale the drawings to establish the dimensions. Redraw the figures at double size on an $8\frac{1}{2}$- by 11-inch sheet of paper.

16-7. Dimension [16-118 and 16-119] using undirectional dimensions. Prepare the drawing as described in Problem 16-6.

16-8. Using the dimension 0.750 inch as the basic size of a shaft, write the specifications for a hole and a shaft using a tolerance of ± 0.002 to always accomplish an interference fit. Make a drawing in full size, similar to [16-47], and apply those specifications.

16-116

16-117

16-118

16-119

16-9. Using the dimension 1.250 inches as the basic size with a maximum limit of 0.005 inch and minimum limit of 0.002 inch, prepare the following:

(a) Make a drawing in full size of a cylinder that has a height and diameter equal to the basic size.

(b) Show the unilateral tolerances for the height and the bilateral tolerances for the diameter on the drawing.

16-10. In the problems in [16-120], the views indicated by the circles and arrows are to be changed to full sectional views taken along the center line in the direction indicated by the arrows in the remaining view. For each, select the correct answer from the 24 proposed views shown at the right, and place its number in the appropriate circle.

16-120

16-11. In the problems in [16-121], the views indicated by the circles and arrows are to be changed to half sectional views as indicated by the letters A–A taken along the center line in the remaining view. For each, select the correct answer from the 24 proposed views shown at the right, and place its number in the appropriate circle.

16-121

16-12. From the 30 section views shown in [16-122], select one to complete each problem and place its number in the appropriate circle.

16-122

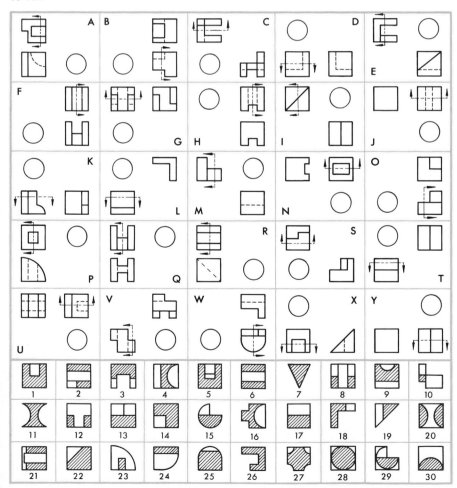

16-13. From the 30 section views shown in [16-123], select one to complete each problem and place its number in the appropriate circle.

16-123

16-124

16-125

16-126

16-127

16-128

16-14. Figure [16-124] is an exploded drawing of a *whidjet*. Make a full-section drawing at double scale of the whidjet using a cutting plane that slices along the vertical center line of the bolt. Draw the full section as if the whidjet were assembled and use appropriate section lines to distinguish the various components of the assembly.

16-15. Make a half-section drawing of a coffee mug. Orient the side view so that a section view of the handle will result. Draw the mug in full size and dimension it appropriately.

16-16. Study several issues of current technical and trade magazines. Using a copying machine, reproduce three examples of different types of section views, such as full sections, half-sections, revolved, and removed sections. On each reproduction, write the type of section shown and explain why you think it was used as an illustration.

16-17. In [16-125 and 16-126], determine if the lines XY intersect the planes ABC. Use the edge-view method to find the intersection point (if any) and complete the views accordingly, showing the line XY where it is visible. Draw the views on $8\frac{1}{2}$- by 11-inch paper, one problem to a page at double size.

16-18. Find the intersection point of lines XY and planes ABC in [16-125 and 16-126], using the cutting-plane method. Prepare the drawings double size, as described in Problem 16-16. Show the line XY where it is visible.

16-19. In [16-127] establish the intersection lines between the plane and the triangular prism using the cutting-plane method. Scale the dimensions in the text and reproduce the drawing double size on $8\frac{1}{2}$- by 11-inch paper. Indicate all visible lines.

16-20. Make an isometric sketch of [16-127]. Orient the sketch such that the intersection between the plane and the prism is clearly visible and the end of the prism with the letters XYZ is on the left. (To work this problem, it may be necessary to complete Problem 16-19 in order to visualize the shape and general location of the intersection.)

16-21. Find the intersection between the plane and the cylinder in [16-128]. Use the cutting-plane method and make the necessary measurements from the text. Produce the drawing at double size on $8\frac{1}{2}$- by 11-inch paper. Show all lines where they are visible.

16-22. Make an isometric sketch of [16-128].

16-23. Draw a development of the portion of the triangular prism that lies to the left of the intersection line in Problem 16-20. Use the lettered (XYZ) end of the prism as the base. Assume plane $ABCD$ passes entirely through the prism.

16-24. Find an unusual example of intersecting prisms that exists on your campus. (Some examples to investigate might be heating and air conditioning ducts, hallways and buildings, and storage bins.) Make the necessary measurements to draw the prisms and then establish the shape of the intersection using the cutting-plane method. Select a scale such that the drawing can be presented on an $8\frac{1}{2}$- by 11-inch sheet of paper.

16-25. Following the general procedure outlined in Problem 16-24, construct a drawing of cylinders intersecting at other than a right angle.

graphic presentation and computation 17

Manganese precipitates.

603

17-1

DOW JONES
30 INDUSTRIALS

920

910

900

Mon. Tues. Wed. Thur. Fri.

1971

1050

1000

950

900

850

800

J F M A M J   J A S O N D

a lthough the engineer may complete a superb design, a valid test, or a study of great importance, the significance of his efforts may be ignored or misunderstood if he is unable to communicate properly the results of his work. For this reason it is very important that he understand the most effective ways to present technical data. This chapter deals with the presentation of numerical data— such as computed performance figures, the results of experiments, and survey data. The use of design drawings and diagrams and the layout of a written or oral report are discussed elsewhere in this book.

The engineer must write for two different audiences: the general public and technically trained people. Certain techniques and types of graphic format lend themselves more readily to general understanding and popular appeal; others are more useful for technical audiences. Simplicity of format and emphasis on gross dynamic changes between variables are more important factors for the general public [17-1]; accuracy and preciseness of 'the presentation of the data are paramount considerations in engineering and science [17-2].

Data may be presented in several different formats or styles as follows:

1. Tables
2. Charts
        Pictorial charts
        Bar charts
        Pie charts
        Segment charts
        Organizational charts
        Flow charts
        Alignment charts
3. Graphs
        Rectilinear graphs
        Semilogarithmic graphs
        Logarithmic graphs
        Polar graphs

The progression of data presentations shown in [17-3] illustrates the use of tables, graphs, and charts to communicate the same information.

tables

Frequently, raw data are presented in tabular format. Tables are useful for detail and exactness, but it is recommended that some other graphic form be used for a final presentation. In a table, data are arrayed in rows (horizontally) and columns (vertically), usually in ascending or descending order. Each row and column should be labeled clearly and completely, and the table should be assigned a title that effectively describes its function or purpose. For examples of tables, see Appendix V.

charts

Charts are most useful in communicating with nontechnical audiences. They are particularly effective when comparing several dependent variables with a single independent variable. For charts, it is usually best to use commercially prepared chart board or paper. If a pre-printed grid does not exist, one should be prepared to accommodate the ranges of each variable.

Pictorial Charts

The average layman has little interest in evaluating technical information. Therefore, the simplest form of

17-2

Saturation Curve of a 300-volt D-C Generator

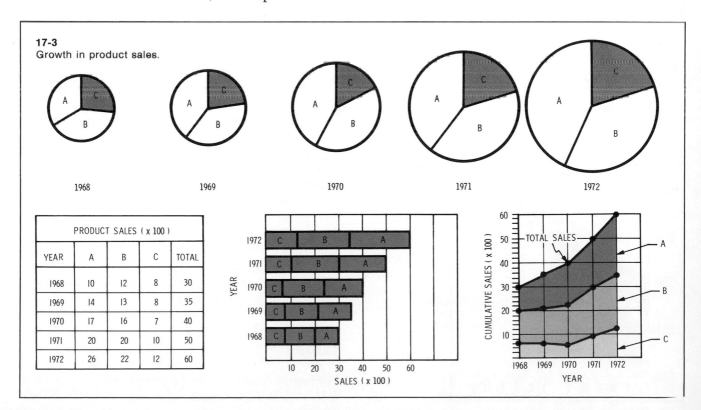

17-3
Growth in product sales.

1968   1969   1970   1971   1972

PRODUCT SALES (x 100)				
YEAR	A	B	C	TOTAL
1968	10	12	8	30
1969	14	13	8	35
1970	17	16	7	40
1971	20	20	10	50
1972	26	22	12	60

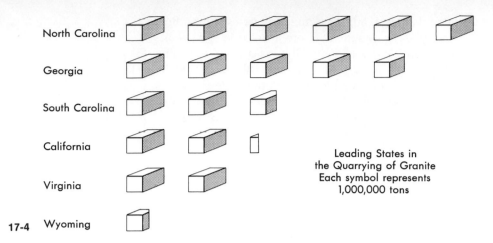

North Carolina

Georgia

South Carolina

California

Leading States in
the Quarrying of Granite
Each symbol represents
1,000,000 tons

Virginia

17-4   Wyoming

chart should be used for presentations to the general public. The pictorial chart or map-type chart is most commonly used for such purposes [17-4 and 1-9].

Bar Charts

Bar charts are commonly used in popular literature, particularly when the results of economic or industrial surveys are reported. The bars may be drawn horizontally or vertically, but they should extend from a common base (axis). Horizontal bars are preferable for most applications because their respective positioning facilitates length comparison [17-5]. Vertical bars are particularly useful when time is the independent variable [17-6]. For emphasis and clarity the exact value represented by each bar may be printed within the body of the bar or adjacent to it.

Custom more than anything else dictates which variable will be plotted on the horizontal axis. (The horizontal X axis is called the *abscissa* and the vertical, or Y axis, is called the *ordinate*.) Generally, we would expect to find the controlled or *independent-variable* scale values plotted horizontally from left to right and the *dependent-variable* scale values plotted vertically from bottom to top.

The choice of scales is perhaps the most important step in bar-chart construction, because the selections have a controlling influence on the viewer's interpretation of the relationships that are presented. It would be a breach of professional ethics, therefore, for the engineer to relatively stretch a horizontal or vertical scale to create an erroneous impression. The same care must be exercised when using volume or area relationships. For example, in [17-7] the relative comparison of A, B, and C is easy,

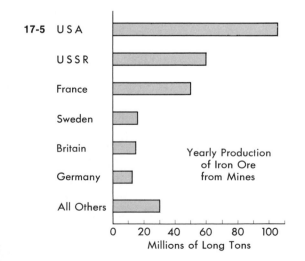

17-5

USA

USSR

France

Sweden

Britain

Germany

All Others

Yearly Production
of Iron Ore
from Mines

0   20   40   60   80   100
Millions of Long Tons

17-6

Distribution of failures of 75-watt lamps operated at rated voltage

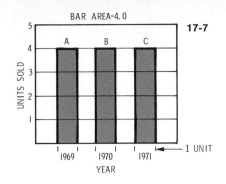

17-7

BAR AREA=4.0

The engineer should not stretch a horizontal or vertical scale which might create an erroneous impression.

but in [17-8] (where areas are also used), the comparison is likely to be misunderstood. If a visual comparison is desired, the zero point should be clearly indicated. The charts [17-9 and 17-10] demonstrate the differences in interpretation that may result.

It is also important that each scale or part of the chart be labeled clearly and neatly. The printed information should be readable from the bottom and right side of the paper. Each chart should have a title that is clear, concise, and complete. Legends or keys are sometimes useful in conveying necessary explanatory information.

17-8

BAR AREA=4.0

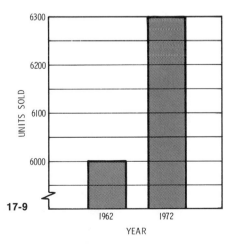

17-9

The zero point should be clearly indicated.

17-10

17-11
Pie chart.

Approximate yield of products
obtained during the refining of
petroleum

Pie Charts

One of the most effective ways to show the percentage or distribution of related parts of a unit is to make a pie chart [17-11]. The total area of the circle represents 100 per cent of the sample and the sectors represent percentages of the total. Each sector should be identified, and the lettering should be completed prior to adding the shading or coloring. For added emphasis one or more sectors can be removed slightly from their normal position [17-12].

Segment Charts

Segment charts are useful to show how some total quantity is divided into individual components—somewhat similar in this respect to the pie chart. The base of the chart (assumed to be 100 per cent) should be wide enough to provide an adequate area for the smallest width limb [17-13].

Organizational Charts

From time to time management studies, computer analyses, and material or energy flows (for example, in the process industries) all require charts that identify and clarify the sequence of the operations involved [14-1].

Alignment Charts

The purpose of alignment charts (frequently called *nomographs*) is to reduce laborious and repetitive calculations of mathematical relationships and to study the interrelationships among the variables. A more complete explanation of this type of chart begins on page 622.

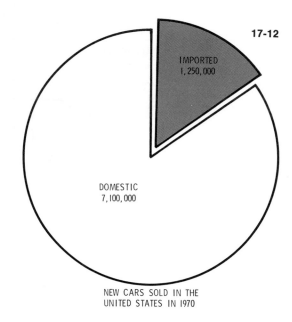

17-12

IMPORTED
1,250,000

DOMESTIC
7,100,000

NEW CARS SOLD IN THE
UNITED STATES IN 1970

graphs

For the technical audience, graphs are the most useful form of graphical presentation and are especially advantageous when technical facts must be grasped readily. They also aid in the analysis of engineering data and facilitate the presentation of statistical and test information. Graphs also offer an opportunity to interpolate or extrapolate values, and to draw conclusions as to the behavior of the variable quantities involved. In general, they are composed of a grid background, calibrated scales, and one or more trend lines. Some basic procedures in the preparation of rectangular coordinate graphs are noted here.

17-13
Segment chart.

1. Graphs are most often drawn on special preprinted paper and, of those available, rectangular-coordinate paper is the most common. Its grid is formed by horizontally and vertically equally spaced lines that form small rectangles. Other types of grid rulings will be discussed below. Popular types are those whose squares are 1 millimeter, $\frac{1}{10}$ inch, or $\frac{1}{20}$ inch on a side. In each case the ruling of every fifth or tenth line is emphasized by being slightly wider or darker, or both.

2. As with charts, the dependent variable is plotted on the vertical axis and the independent variable on the horizontal. The axes are drawn as heavy lines and should intersect near the lower-left corner of the paper[1] about 1 inch inside the grid field to allow for lettering. The sheet may be turned so that the abscissa is along either the short or long side of the paper. If the graph is prepared for a report, the margin for the binding should be either to the left or at the top of the sheet.

3. Scale selection is a function of the engineer's sublety and discernment. An appropriate scale selection will do much to place the viewer in a proper mental attitude to evaluate the significance of the orientation of the trend line (curve). A poor choice might lead to a misunderstanding of the data [17-14]. Also, the scales should be consistent with the precision of the data. A trial computation to select the scale on each axis can be made with the following expression:

$$\text{scale} = \frac{\text{range in the variable}}{\text{scale length available}}$$

4. Scale divisions should start at zero, unless the curve would be compressed unnecessarily, and each unit (small square) on the scale should represent 1, 2, 5, or 10 units of measurement, multiplied by 1, 10, 100, 10^{-3}, 10^{-8}, etc., for very large or very small numbers. Do not use a scale that will require awkward fractions in the smallest calibration on the paper. Normally, only the accented lines of the printed grid are designated by graduations.

[1] When both positive and negative values of a function are to be plotted, the origin should be located so that all desired values can be shown.

EXPANDED VERTICAL

ORIGINAL SCALE

CONTRACTED HORIZONTAL

CONTRACTED VERTICAL

17-14

EXPANDED HORIZONTAL

5. The ordinate and abscissa should be labeled with the names and dimensional units of the variable it represents. For example, WEIGHT IN POUNDS. Considerable care should be taken to ensure that the lettering is neat, uncrowded, and well proportioned. It should be about $\frac{3}{16}$ inch high and may be either vertical or slant lettering. Always place a cipher to the left of

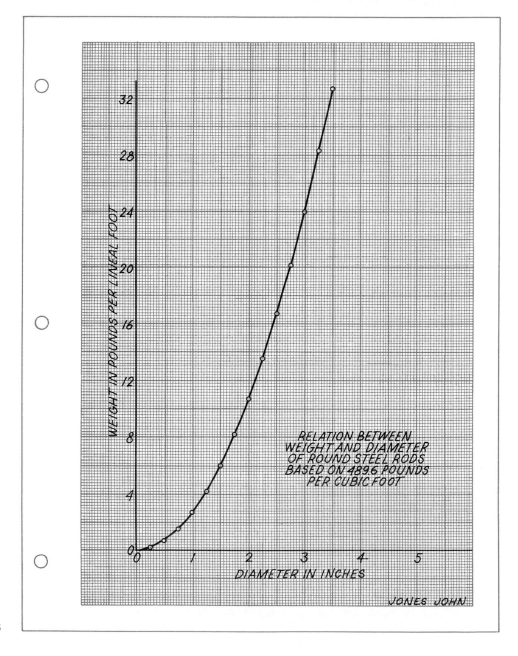

17-15

the decimal point if decimal fractions are used. When space is limited, standard abbreviations such as those in Appendix II should be used, particularly for designating the unit of measurement.

6. If the data represent a set of experimental observations, the plotted points of a single trend line should be marked by small circles having a diameter of $\frac{1}{10}$ inch or less. Where several trend lines are to be indicated on a single graph, partially filled in circles, open squares and triangles, and filled in squares and triangles may be used to locate the plotted points of the various curves. Filled in symbols should be drawn $\frac{1}{16}$ inch or less in diameter. Do not use crosses or X's.

7. Most frequently, the engineer will be concerned with plotting data that are related to physical phenomena for which the relationships are apt to be direct and continuous—resulting in a smooth trend line. When such a line approaches one of the plotted points, it will touch but not pass through the small circle circumscribing the plotted point [17-15]. Where multiple trend lines are shown on the same graph, identification can be enhanced by using different lines, such as solid lines, dashed lines, or long dash–short dash lines. Trend lines that have been determined theoretically will not normally have point designations. Data points in measured relationships not supported by mathematical theory or empirical relationships should be connected by straight lines drawn directly from point to point [17-14].

When plotted, much experimentally determined data will not fall on a smooth trend line. This is due to experimental errors and other factors. When this happens draw a smooth trend line (straight or curved) as the data indicate, which as accurately as possible (by eye) will average the plotted points. A light freehand line will aid in locating the average, but the final line should be drawn with the assistance of mechanical aids (irregular curve, French curve, etc.). The graph [17-17] displays data from an actual test. Note the dispersion of the data points.

8. The title of the graph may include the names of the plotted quantities and other descriptive information, such as sizes, weights, names of equipment, date that the data were obtained, serial numbers of apparatus, name of manufacturer, and any other information that would help describe the graph. Usually, graphs are designated by naming ordinate values first, then

17-16

○ △ □ ☆ ⬡
● ▲ ■ ★ ●

17-17

VIBRATION CHARACTERISTICS
Aircraft Model 16B Serial No. 5
Test Flight No. 11, Jan. 9, 1970
Altitude – 7000 ft.
Gross wt. – 2883 lb
Measurements taken on cockpit floor with a vertical accelerometer

Frequency 10.8 cps

Frequency 5.4 cps

Acceleration in G's

True Airspeed in Knots

abscissa quantities. The title should be placed on the sheet where it will not interfere with the graph. The title section of display graphs is usually placed across the top of the sheet. Simple graphs that comprise parts of reports frequently have the title in either the lower-right or upper-left quadrant. The name of the person preparing the graph may be placed in the lower-right corner of the sheet [17-15].

Plotting on Semilogarithmic Graph Paper

The preceding discussion has concerned the graphing of data on rectangular-coordinate paper. There are cases when the variation of the data is such that it may be desirable to compress a variable. To do this, semilogarithmic graph paper may be used. Semilog paper, as it is usually called, is graph paper that has one coordinate ruled in equal increments and the other coordinate ruled in logarithmic increments. When plotting on this type of paper, it can be turned so that either the horizontal coordinate or the vertical coordinate will have the logarithmic divisions. Semilog paper is available in either one-cycle, two-cycle, three-cycle, four-cycle, or five-cycle ruling.

A semilog grid is especially useful in the derivation of relationships where it is difficult to analyze the rate of change or trend as depicted on rectangular-coordinate paper. Data that will plot as a curve on rectangular-coordinate paper may plot as a straight line on semilog paper. If this happens the rate of change of the variable is constant. Where straight lines do not occur on a semilog grid, the rate of change is varying.

The same rules apply for plotting on semilog paper as were given for rectangular-coordinate paper, except that the numbering of the logarithmic divisions cannot begin with zero. Each cycle on the paper represents a multiple of 10 in value, and the graduations may begin with any power of 10. When reading from a logarithmic graph, interpolations should be made logarithmically rather than arithmetically. An example of data plotted on semilog paper is shown in [17-18].

Plotting on Log–Log Graph Paper

Log–log graph paper, as its name indicates, has both coordinate divisions expressed as logarithmic functions. This serves to compress data. In addition, data that plotted as a curve on rectangular-coordinate paper may plot as a straight line on log–log paper.

17-18

S-N CURVE FOR
81 BK 314 TRUNIONS
Test conducted in Model 2
Fatigue Fixture
Date of Test:
9-22-70 thru 10-14-70
Testing terminates at
10^7 cycles

MB MANUFACTURING COMPANY
A Division of Textron Inc.

TYPICAL FREQUENCY RESPONSE — MB VIBRATION PICKUPS
MODELS 124, 125, 126, 127

$\dfrac{\text{SENSITIVITY}}{\text{BASIC SENSITIVITY}}$ vs. FREQUENCY

BASIC SENSITIVITY at 40 cps Models 124, 126
100 cps Models 125, 127

96.3 mv(rms)/in/sec (rms) with 2 meg load
93.2 mv(rms)/in/sec (rms) with 20k ohm load

Types 125, 127 (Undamped)

Types 124, 126 (Damped)

17-19

FREQUENCY IN CPS

T-307A

As an example, the plot of the algebraic expression

$$X = Y^2$$

on rectangular-coordinate paper is a parabola. However, if its values are plotted on log–log paper, it forms the expression

$$\log X = 2(\log Y)$$

This is a linear equation having a slope of 2. Thus, a relationship of variable quantities that may be expressed as $X = Y^2$ when plotted on log–log paper will be a straight line with a slope of 2.

Log–log paper may be secured with one or more cycles for each coordinate direction. The axis lines are drawn on the sheet in a manner similar to the procedure described for plotting on rectangular-coordinate paper. However, the beginning values for the axes will never be zero but will always be a power of 10.

An example of data plotted on log–log paper is shown in [17-19].

613

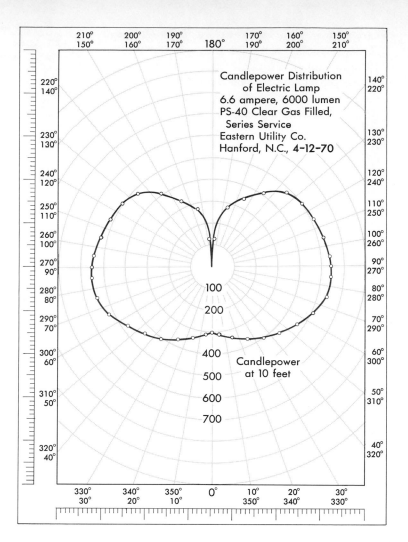

Candlepower Distribution
of Electric Lamp
6.6 ampere, 6000 lumen
PS-40 Clear Gas Filled,
Series Service
Eastern Utility Co.
Hanford, N.C., 4-12-70

Candlepower
at 10 feet

17-20

Plotting on Polar Graph Paper

Polar graphs are sometimes used when a variable quantity is to be examined with respect to various angular positions. The same general principles of plotting apply as were outlined for rectangular plots, except that the outer border is marked off in degrees for the independent variable, and either the horizontal or vertical radial line is marked off for the dependent variable.

Polar graphs frequently are used to display the light output of luminous sources, the response of microphone pickups, and the behavior of rotating objects at various angular positions. An example of a graph plotted on polar-coordinate paper is shown in [17-20].

Determining Empirical Equations from Curves

Experimentally determined data when plotted often will approximate a straight line or a simple curve. By plotting experimentally determined data, it is frequently possible to obtain a mathematical equation that closely expressed the relations of the variables.

Many equations encountered in engineering work have the form

$$y - k = m(x - h)^n$$

where n may have either positive or negative values. If the exponent n is 1, the equation reduces to the familiar straight-line slope-intercept form. If the value of n is other than 1 but positive, the equation is parabolic; if the value of n is negative, the equation is hyperbolic. This expression affords a means of securing empirical equations from experimental data.

If experimental data are to be plotted and an empirical equation is to be determined, it is advisable first to plot the test data on rectangular-coordinate paper in order to gain some idea of the shape of the graph. If the locus approximates a straight line, the general equation $y = mx + b$ may be assumed. The Y intercept b and the slope m may be measured by taking a straight line drawn so as to average the plotted points.

A plot of data taken in the laboratory for a test involving the magnitude of frictional forces is shown in [17-21]. A straight line is drawn to average the plotted points, and the slope of the line is found by taking any two points along the line and determining the X component and the Y component between the two points according to the plotted scales. In this example, the slope is approximately $\frac{65}{500}$, or 0.13. If the line is projected to the Y axis, corresponding to a value of $x = 0$, the Y intercept is seen to correspond approximately to 14 pounds. An approximate equation of these data would be $y = 0.13x + 14$.

If a plot of experimental data on rectangular-coordinate paper should appear to be approximately parabolic or hyperbolic in shape, an empirical equation may be obtained by plotting the data points on log–log paper. The slope of the line determines the exponent of the independent variable, and the Y intercept, when $x = 1$, defines the coefficient of the independent variable. For example, a plot of data taken in the laboratory is shown in [17-22].

A straight line is drawn to average the plotted points.

17-21

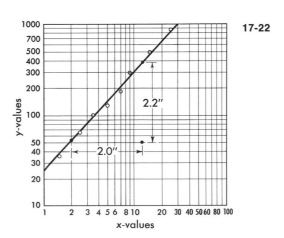

17-22

615

Using a linear scale, measure the X component and Y component values for two points on the plotted line. The slope of the graph in [17-22] is 2.2/2.0, or 1.1, and the Y intercept is 23.3. Substituting these values in the basic equation of a parabola gives $y = 23.3(x^{1.1})$ for the approximate equation.

In case the plotted points on log–log paper curve upward as x increases, the expression may approximate the form $y = ax^n + k$, or $y - k = ax^n$. To straighten the curve, try subtracting a constant from the y values. By trial and error, a value of k may be found that will cause the plot to follow a straight line. If this is done, the approximate equation may be determined.

There are other methods of determining empirical equations, such as the method of least squares, but a complete discussion of such techniques is beyond the scope of this book. Also, data that plot into curves following harmonic laws or exponential laws are not discussed here.

calculation and analysis

Graphical methods of analysis can be used as aids in determining functions, calculating areas, or developing procedures for simple repetitive calculation. Graphical techniques can solve arithmetic, algebraic, and calculus problems. They are particularly advantageous when one type of equation or formula must be solved repeatedly for different conditions or variables. For example, a chemical engineer who designs heat exchangers has to deal repeatedly with tubes of various length, diameter, and wall thickness. He may need to know surface area, volume, or weight for all types of tubes again and again. Although he could calculate these data easily, he is better off with a quick way of looking them up—and graphs or nomographs are useful aids.

In addition, certain types of equations cannot be solved easily by purely mathematical methods but are quickly handled graphically.

We shall illustrate some of these techniques next. One word of caution: graphical solutions are inherently less accurate than numerical ones. How accurate they are depends, of course, on the competence of the draftsman and the size of paper and scale he uses. One per cent accuracies are not too hard to achieve usually, but when

17-23
Heat exchanger tube.

much greater accuracy is needed, the cost of achieving it graphically tends to become prohibitive.

Besides the construction of graphical equations and nomographs, we shall deal briefly with vectors.

Graphical Arithmetic

Graphical-arithmetic charts consist of a plot of three or more variables on a coordinate grid such that the value of any one variable can be found quickly if the others are known. For example, the chemical engineer needs the outside surface area of his heat-exchanger tubes and is tired of calculating it every time from the equation

$$\text{area } A \text{ (in.}^2) = \pi \times \text{diameter } D \text{ (in.)}$$
$$\times \text{length } L \text{ (ft)} \times 12 \text{ (in./ft)}$$

or

$$A = 37.7DL$$

He knows he will have to deal with tubes of all lengths up to 20 feet, but only with four different standard diameter sizes: $\frac{1}{2}$, 1, $1\frac{1}{2}$, and 2 inch. He first selects his scales; he decides to plot length on the abscissa or horizontal axis; it will go from 0 to 20 feet. He also decides to read his answer, the surface area, on the ordinate, or vertical axis. To find his vertical scale, he computes the largest possible area: 1,508 square inches for a 2-inch diameter, 20-foot-long tube. This establishes his scales [17-24].

Now he wants one line for each tube diameter that will permit him to find the surface area for any length of that size tube. For example, he computes that 15 feet of $1\frac{1}{2}$-inch-diameter tube has a surface area of 849 square inches (see point A in [17-25]). He also realizes that 0 length of any size tube has zero surface area; that is, each line goes through the origin. So he draws a straight line between 0 and A,[2] and he labels the line with the pipe diameter [17-25].

For the other pipe diameters he produces similar lines [17-26]. Such lines are often called *parametric* lines, and the variable that fixes them—in this case the pipe diameter—is called the *parameter*. His graphical equation is now completed. Any time he has to find a surface area he goes from the proper length on the abscissa vertically upward to the appropriate diameter line. When he meets

[2] The relation between pipe length and surface area is linear. If it had not been linear, the line would have to be curved.

17-24

17-25

CHART TO CALCULATE
AREA = 37.7 D L

17-26

that line he "turns left" until he meets the ordinate, where he reads the area he wants. (Example: A 12-foot-long, $1\frac{1}{2}$-inch-diameter tube has a surface area of 680 square inches—as shown with the dotted line in [17-26].)

The graphical method can be used for more than one parameter by putting several graphs back to back. If, for example, the engineer is interested in the total amount of heat transferred from the tube, this is determined by the equation

$$Q = A \times \Delta T \times k$$

where Q is the heat transferred (Btu/hour)

A is the surface area, as before (ft²)

ΔT is the temperature difference between the inside and the outside of the tube (°F)

k is the heat transfer coefficient (Btu/hour-ft²-°F)

This equation has two new parameters, ΔT and k. How these are used graphically will become self-evident when you study [17-27].

CHART TO CALCULATE Q = AΔT k

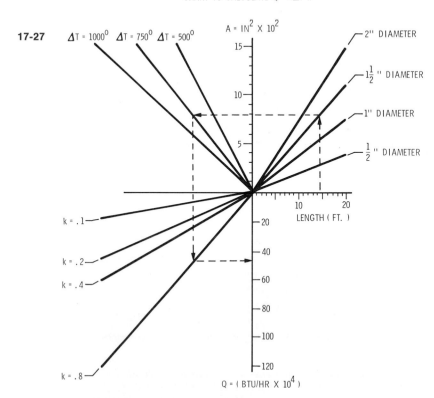

17-27

Graphical Algebra

Graphics can be used to solve equations in one or two variables. This is particularly worthwhile when the equation does not have a simple algebraic solution. For example, the equation

$$\tan X = 1 + \cos X$$

can be solved for X only by trial and error—or graphically, as follows:

1. Make yourself a table that contains the values of the right-hand side (RHS) and left-hand side (LHS) of the equation for various values of X.
2. Plot RHS and LHS versus X separately [17-28].
3. Find the intersection. It gives the desired value of X ($57.2°$).

Another useful place for graphical solutions is in problems where it is easy to plot the relations but difficult to express them in algebraic form. For example:

A car leaves Chicago traveling toward Atlanta at an average speed of 55 miles per hour and increases this speed to 65 miles per hour after 3 hours. A 1-hour lunch stop is made after traveling for 5 hours, and then an average speed of 55 miles per hour is maintained. A bus leaves Atlanta toward Chicago 2 hours after the car leaves Chicago and averages 70 miles per hour. How many hours after the car left Chicago will the bus and car meet, assuming that they both travel the same route, the bus makes no stops, and the distance between cities is 700 miles? How far from Atlanta will they meet?

The solution to this problem would be quite complex algebraically but can be solved graphically by following these steps.

1. Develop a coordinate grid with miles on the horizontal axis (to 700) and hours on the vertical (to 10).
2. Plot the path of the car on the grid [17-29]. The slope of the line is determined by the car's velocity: 55 miles per hour for 3 hours; then 65 miles per hour for 2 hours. The 1-hour rest stop produces no change on the horizontal axis because no distance is traveled. The velocity then returns to 55 miles per hour.
3. Plot the path of the bus on the same grid [17-30]. The plot is started from the 700 value of the horizontal

Solve the equation
tan X = 1 + cos X

X	LHS	RHS
45°	1.000	1.707
50°	1.192	1.645
55°	1.429	1.573
60°	1.731	1.500
65°	2.141	1.423

17-28

17-29
Car travel.

17-30
Bus travel.

17-31
Combined car and bus travel.

GRAPHICAL CALCULUS

TEMPERATURE IN PODUNK
FEBRUARY 19, 1937

17-32

scale, since the bus starts in Atlanta. Its slope is toward the 0 value since it is traveling toward Chicago.

4. The coordinates of the intersection of these lines are 7.0 and 350, indicating the bus will pass the car 7 hours after the car leaves Chicago and 350 miles from Atlanta [17-31].

Graphical Calculus

Graphical techniques are powerful tools to differentiate or integrate a function that cannot be expressed easily in algebraic form, such as the readings of an instrument during most any experiment [17-32].

We shall illustrate one method of graphical integration,[3] and use it to find the average temperature from the graph shown. Mathematically, the average is the integral of the curve with respect to time, divided by the integration period. In other words, it is the area under the curve from midnight to midnight (in degrees Fahrenheit-hours) divided by 24 hours.

To determine the area beneath a curve, select several intervals along the *X* axis (the time axis) and construct lines parallel to the *Y* axis (the temperature axis) through the original curve. Each interval selected is chosen to intersect a relatively straight portion of the original curve. This will necessitate selecting smaller intervals in those areas where curve change is great [17-33].

Rectangles are formed by drawing a horizontal line through each interval so as to strike the curve where the area improperly excluded from the rectangle approximates the area improperly included. The area of this rectangle is a close approximation of the area beneath that section of the curve, and the summation of the areas of all these rectangles approximates the area beneath the whole curve. The approximation is good because small

[3] For other integration methods and for graphical differentiation, see A. S. Levens, *Graphics,* New York: Wiley, 1968, p. 287ff.

GRAPHICAL CALCULUS   TEMPERATURE IN PODUNK
FEBRUARY 19, 1937

17-33

GRAPHICAL CALCULUS   TEMPERATURE IN PODUNK
FEBRUARY 19, 1937

17-34

Time	Δt	Temp.	°F × Hr
0:00	—	—	
4:00	4.0	19°	76.0
6:00	2.0	10.5°	21.0
6:30	.5	6°	3.0
7:00	.5	5°	2.5
7:30	.5	5°	2.5
8:00	.5	6°	3.0
8:30	.5	7°	3.5
9:00	.5	10°	5.0
12:00	3.0	22°	66.0
13:00	1.0	32°	32.0
14:00	1.0	33°	33.0
15:00	1.0	34°	34.0
16:00	1.0	34°	34.0
24:00	8.0	25°	200.0
	24.0		515.5

The average temperature is

$$\frac{515.5°F - Hr}{24.0 \ Hr}$$

errors of line location are rarely cumulative, and most often offset one another [17-34]. A table helps in accumulating the data.

Nomography

The *nomograph* or alignment chart is another method for depicting a mathematical relationship so that it can be solved quickly and easily. It is an elaboration and refinement of the graphical methods described earlier, and it is used for much the same purpose, that is, to simplify solving equations that are used frequently. The nomograph always uses a linear (straight-line) relationship between scales. To take care of nonlinear equations, the scales can be generated nonlinearly and they can be inclined to one another. (In some cases they can even be curved.)

To construct a scale you need to know the values of its end points, that is, the biggest and the smallest value to be marked on the scale. The difference between the two is the scale's *range*. When you have decided how long the scale is to be and divide the length by the range, you obtain the *scale modulus* (M_s).

If the scale is linear, one can lay it out by a convenient graphical technique. This technique consists of placing a calibrated ruler at an arbitrary angle with the new scale making the origins coincide [17-35]. A line is drawn from the other end of the new scale to that number on the ruler which corresponds to the largest value on the scale. A line is drawn along the edge of the ruler and the desired graduations are marked along it [17-36]. Lines are then drawn through each of these graduations parallel to the line between the terminal values. The intersection of these lines on the new scale forms the graduations desired [17-37].

For example, let us construct a temperature conversion scale, to convert degrees Celsius to degrees Fahrenheit. It is to go from $-60°C$ to $+140°C$, a range of $200°C$. Let us assume we wish to make the Celsius scale 9 inches long. Then the scale modulus is $9/200 = 0.045$ inch/°C. The corresponding end points of the Fahrenheit scale are $-76°F$ and $+284°F$, a range of $360°F$. If we want to make the Fahrenheit scale equal in length to the Celsius scale, its modulus will be $9/360$ or 0.025 inch/°F. Both scales are linear, so they are easy to graduate graphically. Since we made them the same length, we can put them back to back for easy reading [17-38]. Such scales are called *adjacent conversion* scales.

Another type of nomograph, which might be described as nonadjacent conversion scales, uses separate scales for each variable and places the scales parallel to each other. The scales are constructed inversely so that the minimum value of one scale is opposite the maximum value of the other. A pivot point is determined by the intersection of lines connecting the minimum and maximum values of each scale. Figure [17-39] shows such a nomograph used to convert inches of liquid in a 55-gallon drum to gallons. One advantage of this type of nomograph is that the length of both scales is arbitrary. A more important ad-

17-35

17-36

17-37

17-38

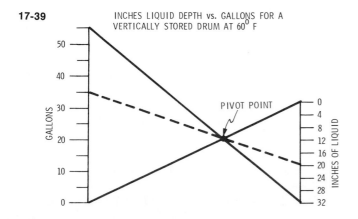

17-39

INCHES LIQUID DEPTH vs. GALLONS FOR A VERTICALLY STORED DRUM AT 60° F

PIVOT POINT

GALLONS

INCHES OF LIQUID

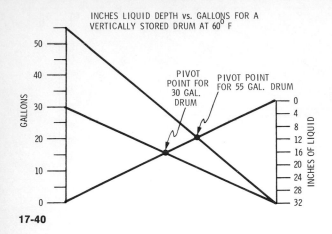

INCHES LIQUID DEPTH vs. GALLONS FOR A
VERTICALLY STORED DRUM AT 60° F

PIVOT
POINT FOR
30 GAL.
DRUM

PIVOT POINT
FOR 55 GAL. DRUM

17-40

INCHES LIQUID DEPTH vs. GALLONS FOR A
VERTICALLY STORED DRUM AT 60° F

SIZE OF DRUM

17-41

$$I = (bd^3) / 12$$

THIS EQUATION DEFINES I, THE MOMENT OF
INERTIA OF A RECTANGLE WHERE b IS THE
WIDTH OF THE RECTANGLE, AND d IS THE
DEPTH OF THE RECTANGLE - BOTH GIVEN IN
INCHES AND I IN (INCHES)^4.

RECTANGLE

17-42

vantage is that it is possible to use the same nomograph for different equations of the same type. If, for example, there were another, smaller diameter drum that contains only 30 gallons when the depth of liquid is 32 inches, its equation can be added easily by finding the appropriate pivot point [17-40].

For a whole series of different-diameter drums, the line on which the pivot points lie could become another scale [17-41]. A nomograph of this type is called an N or Z alignment chart (depending on whether the parallel scales are vertical or horizontal). Two useful N or Z charts follow. The first chart [17-42] is used to find the moment of inertia of a rectangle about a horizontal axis through its midpoint. (The moment of inertia is important when calculating stresses and deflections of a beam with that cross section.) Note that the d scale is not linear, since the dimension d enters the equation as the cube.

The second [17-43], though not strictly an N or Z chart (for none of the lines are parallel), is of a type that represents the equation $1/u + 1/v = 1/f$; u, v, and f may be the actual variables as in the example, in which case the scales are linear; or they may be functions of some other basic variables, in which case the scales may not be linear. In any event, for this type of relation the scales—if extended—will converge at a common point.

Nomographs may be used to solve equations with more than three variables. For example, assume that the chemical engineer designing heat exchangers (p. 617) must often find the combined surface area (inside plus outside) of his tubes. The equation he would have to solve is

$$A = [\pi D + \pi(D - 2t)] \times 12L = 75.4(D - t)L$$

17-43

$$\frac{1}{U} + \frac{1}{V} = \frac{1}{f}$$

THIS FORMULA GIVES THE FOCAL LENGTH f,
WHEN THE OBJECT DISTANCE u, AND THE IMAGE
DISTANCE v ARE GIVEN. BOTH u AND v ARE
GIVEN IN INCHES.

where *t* is the wall thickness in inches, *D* is the outside diameter, and *L* is the length. The three leftmost vertical lines are used to find $D - t$, whose value is then used in the N chart to find A [17-44].

Vectors

Certain physical units, such as velocities and forces, must be defined by direction as well as magnitude. It is not enough to say that two forces of 100 pounds push on a cart, unless we also say in which direction each one pushes. Graphically, a force can be represented by a *vector*, a line with an arrowhead on one end. The length of the line represents the magnitude of the force, and the arrowhead points in the direction in which it acts.

When determining what forces act on a body, it is necessary to mentally (or on a drawing) remove the body from its surroundings and *replace its environment with forces* that are equivalent to the action of the surroundings. When this is completed we have a *free-body diagram*[4] [17-46].

[4]Compare Chapter 6, page 219.

17-44   MULTIPLE VARIABLE NOMOGRAM $A = [\pi D + \pi(D-2t)] \times 12L$

17-45

Often we may not know the magnitude or direction of all the forces and may have to find them. A graphical method, called the *polygon of forces,* is very useful for this. What is it and how is it used? Let us illustrate by some very simple examples:[5]

A ball resting on a horizontal floor [17-47] is easy to turn into a free-body diagram [17-48]. Also, it is obvious that the push from the floor is just equal in size and opposite in direction to the pull of gravity (the weight) of the ball. No graphical construction is needed here.

If the same ball is resting on an incline [17-49], we have a different free-body diagram [17-50]. Now the size of the "pushes" from the floor and the stop are not obvious, although we do know their direction. Their size can be found by drawing the force vectors to scale and in the proper direction. After the weight vector has been drawn, we trace two lines of action in the direction of the two pushing forces, one from each end of the weight vector. The point at which the two lines meet must be the head of one push vector and the tail of the other [17-51]. A closed triangle like the one shown implies that the body is in equilibrium (i.e., all forces that act on the body act with such magnitudes and directions that no net external force results). For three forces the *force polygon* is a triangle. If there are more than three forces, the *polygon* will have more sides.

[5] See also page 223; this discussion is limited to concurrent forces, that is, forces whose lines of action go through the same point.

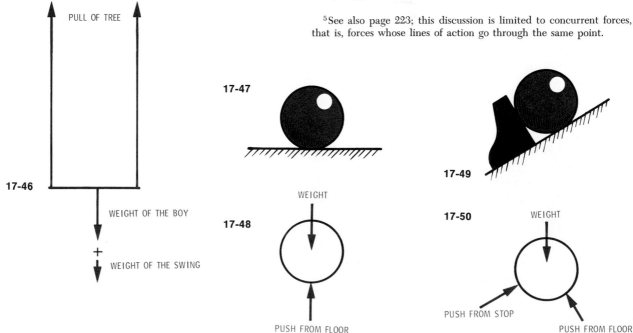

17-46

PULL OF TREE

WEIGHT OF THE BOY

+

WEIGHT OF THE SWING

17-47

17-48

WEIGHT

PUSH FROM FLOOR

17-49

17-50

WEIGHT

PUSH FROM STOP

PUSH FROM FLOOR

One can look at [17-50] in another equally valid way. If the two pushing forces were replaced by a single equivalent force, this force would have to be equal in size and opposite in direction to the weight, just as the push from the horizontal floor in [17-48]. This equivalent force is often called the *resultant*. The resultant is a force equivalent to two or more individual forces[6] [17-52].

So far we have talked only of forces in one plane in which each of the force vectors was drawn full length. The method is still useful when forces are not coplanar. In that case, the *projections* of all forces on every one of the three perpendicular projection planes sum up to the projection of the resultant (which must be zero if the body is in equilibrium). We shall not attempt to prove this statement. Rotation methods for finding true lengths of lines are convenient in some non-coplanar situations [17-53].

[6]The resultant of *all* forces acting on a body in equilibrium is always zero.

17-51

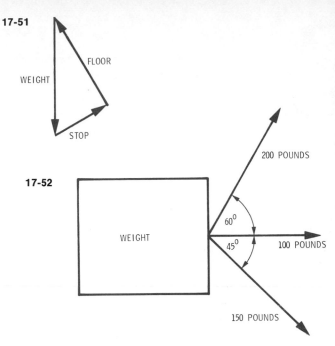

17-52

In the situation shown the three forces are not in equilibrium. However their resultant can be determined graphically by adding the force vectors.

17-53

17-54
The computer can reassemble these symbols and density
values . . .

If forces are not concurrent, that is, if they do not meet
in one point, their resultant must still be zero if the body
is to be in equilibrium; but this condition, though necessary, is not sufficient. Other conditions which assure that
the body does not rotate must also be fulfilled. For more
information on these conditions, see any fundamental text
on static mechanics.[7]

[7]For example, F. P. Beer and E. R. Johnston, Jr., *Statics*, New York:
McGraw-Hill, 1972.

computer-aided graphics

As in so many other areas of engineering, the digital computer has found a place in graphics. Here its major function is to relieve the designer of drudgery and repetitive tasks and to free his time for creative design and experimentation with new ideas. To do this, techniques have been developed to have the computer "read" a drawing, to have it display what it has read on a big TV screen, and to permit the designer to alter the drawing stored in the computer easily and quickly.

Just how the computer reads a drawing is not important here and will vary from one computer installation to another. Basically, a grid is placed over the drawing and the coordinates of every point and line are entered into the computer's memory. Originally, this required manual reading and transferring onto punched cards or paper tape. More recently, optical readers have been

17-55

. . . into a meaningful pattern. (Place the book about 10 feet away and observe how the small details of the micropatterns fuse together, and the overall picture takes on the quality of a continuous-tone photograph.)

17-56
It is sometimes advantageous to direct the computer to "rotate the drawing," as shown here in considering a design for maximum pilot comfort.

17-57
Working with a light pen.

developed that can do this tedious transfer automatically.

Once in the computer memory, the drawing can be displayed visually on the screen of a cathode-ray tube (TV screen). More important, computer programs are now available to magnify portions of the drawing for

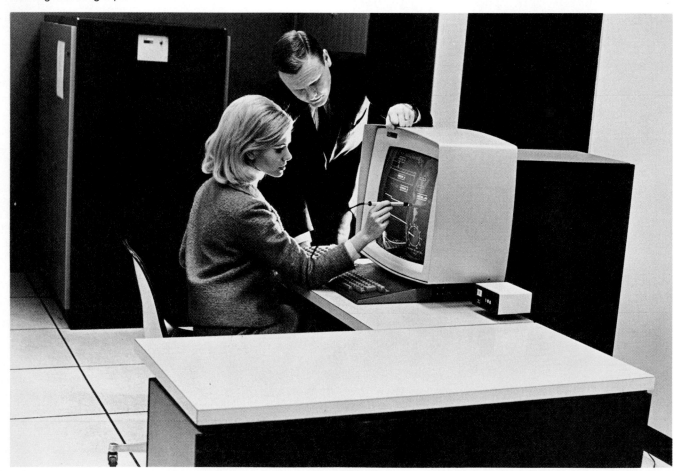

closer analysis, to rotate the drawing and present different views from those originally read in, and to combine the drawing with *stored* drawings of other parts to produce assemblies [17-56]. Most important, however, is the ability to modify stored drawings at the TV screen, to erase lines, and to add others quickly and easily. This is done with a light pen, much like a pocket-size flashlight with a narrow light beam at the tip [17-57]. By playing this light on the TV screen and pressing appropriate switches on the console, one can erase or add at the places where the light shines. The computer automatically smoothes out small wiggles in the new lines.

Many mathematical analyses can be performed by the computer on the part whose drawing is stored in its memory. It can be loaded, heated, vibrated, impacted, and the test results printed out. Of course, every important change in the design can be retested. The extent of the program is limited only by the ingenuity of the designer—and the cost of operating the computer. A point of caution: although the results of such computer tests have all the appearance of authentic experiments, they are still subject to the validity of the assumptions made in the selection of the model. They are not equivalent to and should never be confused with prototype testing.

Once a computer-stored drawing has been approved for production, the computer can be used to compute raw-material requirements and to program the machine tools that are to make the part. Many modern machine tools can be operated directly by programs produced in a computer and stored on punched cards, punched paper tape, or on magnetic tape.

problems

17-1. Investigate several issues of a scientific or technical journal that are available in the library. Select five different methods of graphically portraying technical data and make copying machine reproductions of each type. Write a brief discussion describing the advantages and limitations of each type.

17-2. From the want ads of a daily newspaper, select your favorite brand of American-made automobile. Find five listings of the two-door models for this year and for each of the preceding 4 years. Prepare a table that shows the price of the 25 cars. Use a separate column to indicate each year. Title and label the table.

17-3. Using the raw data developed in Problem 17-2, calculate the average yearly price for the two-door sedans. Construct a vertical bar chart that shows these yearly averages. Construct the chart on an $8\frac{1}{2}$- by 11-inch sheet of paper and complete it with title and proper labeling.

17-4. Using last month as a basis, calculate your total living expenses. Include your rent (with utilities), food, school supplies including prorated book costs, entertainment costs, transportation (such as bus fares or car expenses), and other miscellaneous expenses. Construct a pie chart showing these six costs and label it appropriately.

17-5. Construct an organization chart of the management structure of your university or college. Start at the level of the president, chancellor, or provost, and continue to the student body of your discipline.

17-6. From the admissions office or other appropriate office at your school, determine the number of students that were enrolled as engineering students for each of the past 10 years, including this year. Collect similar data for at least two other major disciplines at your school. Plot a graph of the data collected on rectangular-coordinate graph paper. Use different symbols for each group of data. Title and label the graph.

17-7. Analyze the trend lines developed in Problem 17-6. Write a brief summary of your conclusions about the growth or decline of engineering enrollment relative to the other two disciplines at your school. Assuming a continuation of the indicated trends, what will be the likely enrollments of these disciplines 5 years in the future?

17-8. Plot a graph showing the relation of weight to diameter for round steel rods. Plot values for every quarter-inch to and including $3\frac{1}{2}$ inches in diameter.

Weight of Round Steel Rods in Pounds Per Lineal Foot (Based on 489.6 lb/ft^3)

Size, in	Weight, lb/ft	Size, in	Weight, lb/ft
$\frac{1}{4}$	0.167	2	10.66
$\frac{1}{2}$	0.668	$2\frac{1}{4}$	13.50
$\frac{3}{4}$	1.50	$2\frac{1}{2}$	16.64
1	2.68	$2\frac{3}{4}$	20.20
$1\frac{1}{4}$	4.17	3	24.00
$1\frac{1}{2}$	6.00	$3\frac{1}{4}$	28.30
$1\frac{3}{4}$	8.18	$3\frac{1}{2}$	32.70

17-9. Plot a graph for the following experimental data showing the relation between the period in seconds and the mass of a vibrating spiral spring.

Period, Sec	Mass, G	Period, Sec	Mass, G
0.246	10	0.650	70
0.348	20	0.740	90
0.430	30	0.810	110
0.495	40	0.900	130
0.570	50	0.950	150

17-10. Plot a graph of the variation of the boiling point of water with pressure.

Boiling Point, °C	Pressure, cm Mercury	Boiling Point, °C	Pressure, cm Mercury
33	3.8	98	72.9
44	5.3	102	85.8
63	17.2	105	93.7
79	34.0	107	102.2
87	48.1	110	113.5
94	69.1		

17-11. Plot the variation of pressure with volume, using data as obtained from a Boyle's-law apparatus.

Pressure, cm Mercury	Volume, cm³	Pressure, cm Mercury	Volume, cm³
50.3	23.2	76.8	15.1
52.5	22.4	79.7	14.7
54.5	21.5	82.7	14.1
56.9	20.9	84.2	13.6
59.4	19.6	87.9	13.2
63.0	18.5	90.6	12.8
65.3	17.8	93.5	12.5
67.2	17.3	95.7	12.3
72.6	16.1	101.9	11.4
74.5	15.6		

17-12. The formula for converting temperatures in degrees Fahrenheit to the equivalent reading in degrees Celsius is

$$C° = \tfrac{5}{9}(F° - 32°)$$

Plot a graph so that by taking any given Fahrenheit reading between 0° and 220° and using the graph, the corresponding Celsius reading can be determined.

17-13. The following data were taken in the laboratory for a 60-watt, gas-filled, tungsten-filament light bulb. Plot a resistance–voltage curve.

Voltage, V	Resistance, Ω	Voltage, V	Resistance, Ω
10	47.5	70	160.2
20	77.5	80	170.0
30	100.3	90	178.3
40	119.0	100	189.0
50	132.6	110	200.1
60	144.2		

17-14. Plot the variations of efficiency with load for a $\frac{1}{4}$-horsepower, 110-volt, direct-current electric motor, using the following data taken in the laboratory.

Load Output, hp	Efficiency, %
0	0
0.019	24.0
0.050	42.0
0.084	44.9
0.135	50.7
0.175	56.5
0.195	58.0
0.248	59.1
0.306	58.0
0.326	56.2

17-15. Plot the values given in Problem 17-8 on semilog paper.

17-16. Plot the values given in Problem 17-8 on log–log paper.

17-17. Plot the values given in Problem 17-11 on log–log paper. Determine the slope of the line and give the approximate form of the equation shown by the plot.

17-18. The electrical frequency response of a Type X501 microphone is given below.

Frequency, Hz	Relative Response, dB
20	−40
40	−33
80	−22
100	−18
200	−11
400	−5
600	−2
1,000	+1
2,000	+2
4,000	−1
6,000	−4
10,000	−10

Plot a graph on semilog paper showing the decibel response with frequency.

17-19. Some test specimens of a crank arm, part No. 466-1, were tested for the number of cycles needed to produce fatigue failure at various loadings. The results of the tests are tabulated below.

Specimen Number	Oscillatory Load, lb	Operating Cycles to Produce Failure
1	960	1.1×10^5
2	960	2.2×10^5
3	850	1.5×10^5
4	850	2.4×10^5
5	800	4.2×10^5
6	800	6.0×10^5
7	700	2.4×10^5
8	700	3.1×10^5
9	700	5.1×10^5
10	650	1.8×10^6
11	650	2.6×10^6
12	600	7.7×10^6
13	550	1.0×10^7

Plot a graph of load against operating cycles (S-N curve) on semilog paper for the tests above.

17-20. A test on an acorn-type street lighting unit shows the mean vertical candlepower distribution to be as given in the table below.

Midzone Angle, Deg	Candlepower at 10 ft	Midzone Angle, Deg	Candlepower at 10 ft
180	0	85	156
175	0	75	1110
165	0	65	1050
155	1.5	55	710
145	3.5	45	575
135	5.5	35	500
125	8.5	25	520
115	13.5	15	470
105	22.0	5	370
95	40.0	0	370

Plot the data above. (Although data for only half the plot are given, the other half of the plot can be made from symmetry of the light pattern.)

17-21. From data determined by the student, draw a circle chart (pie chart) to show one of the following.

(a) Consumption of sulfur by various industries in the United States.

(b) Budget allocation of the tax dollar in your state.

(c) Chemical composition of bituminous coal.

(d) Production of aluminum ingots by various countries.

17-22. Using the data collected in Problem 17-6, plot the graph on one-cycle semilog graph paper. Compare the shape of the trend line with that in Problem 17-6.

17-23. Prepare a line chart that will permit converting readings from grams to ounces up to 64 ounces and a line chart that will convert readings from pounds to kilograms up to 10 pounds.

17-24. Using data and divisions described in Problem 17-4, construct a segment chart.

17-25. Prepare a graphical arithmetic chart to calculate the board feet of lumber in various lengths of standard widths of 2-inch-thick planks. The nominal widths are 4, 6, 8 and 10 inches, and the maximum length is 20 feet.

17-26. Graphical arithmetic charts can be combined to provide additional related information about a variable. Using the chart developed in Problem 17-25, combine another arithmetic chart that calculates the cost of four types of lumber based on the board feet. The woods used are oak ($1.10/board foot), pine ($0.85/board foot), maple ($1.35/board foot), and teak ($1.75/board foot).

17-27. Construct a concurrent scale that shows the conversion between English and metric systems of measuring length. Use the inch and the centimeter as the basic units and construct the scale at true size. Make the scale 10 inches long.

17-28. Construct a concurrent scale that shows the conversion between quarts and liters. One side of the scale should have a range of 0 to 100 quarts and be 8 inches long.

17-29. Construct a nomograph that will convert miles traveled by automobile to gallons of gasoline consumed. Use the average gasoline mileage of your car (or a car with which you are familiar) as the pivot point of the nomograph.

17-30. Construct a nomograph that converts gallons of root beer to number of mugs. Use a 12-ounce mug as the pivot point of the nomograph and a standard beer keg to establish the maximum gallons.

17-31. Construct a Z chart that will compute the average gasoline consumption in gallons per mile of your automobile. Use 400 miles and 30 gallons as the maximum values of each parallel scale.

17-32. Construct a Z chart that will calculate the cost of lumber as outlined in Problem 17-26. Design the chart to calculate the board-foot cost through the range of costs that are listed.

17-33. Draw a free-body diagram of this book resting on some inclined surface of your choice. From this free-body diagram, determine graphically the value of the force that prevents the book from sliding off the inclined surface. Use a scale of $\frac{1}{2}$ inch $= 1$ pound.

17-34. Imagine an old tire suspended by two ropes from a large limb of a tree. The limb grows at a 15° angle upward from the horizontal. One rope is 12 feet long and is attached to the tree 2 feet from the trunk (measured along the limb). The second rope, 17 feet long, is attached 10 feet from the trunk. Both ropes attach to the tire at the same point. If a 160-pound person were to sit in the tire and lift his feet from the ground, what would be the forces acting along each rope. Determine your answer by graphical analysis.

A cluster of cadmium-chromium-selenide crystals grown by a novel-liquid-phase transport technique is shown on a background of iron filings organized by a magnetic field. These crystals are unique in that they display hole-election and spin-wave phenomena as well as other exotic effects.

appendixes

SEQUENCE OF STROKES VERTICAL LETTERS

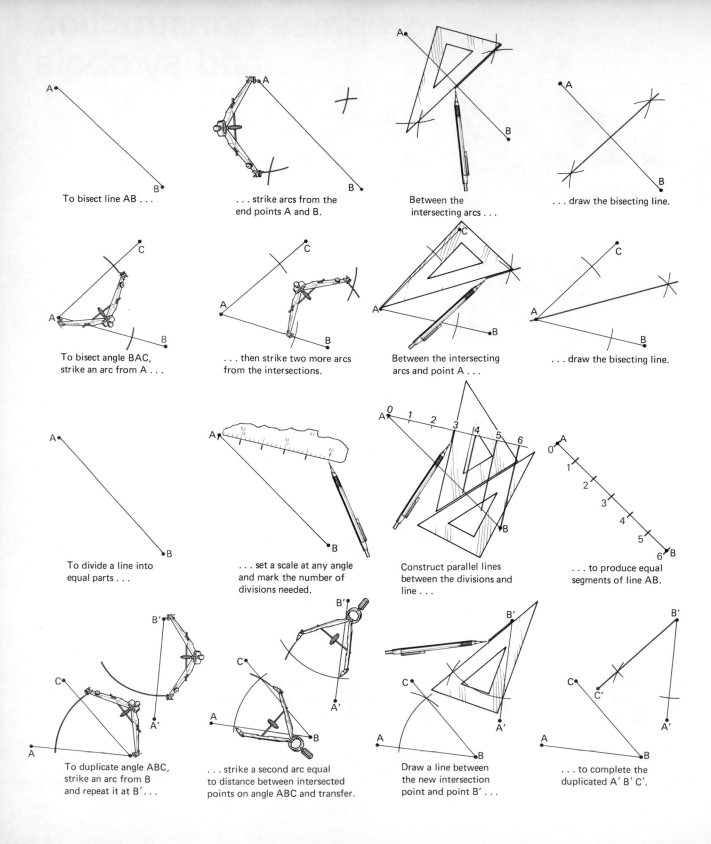

To bisect line AB . . .

. . . strike arcs from the end points A and B.

Between the intersecting arcs . . .

. . . draw the bisecting line.

To bisect angle BAC, strike an arc from A . . .

. . . then strike two more arcs from the intersections.

Between the intersecting arcs and point A . . .

. . . draw the bisecting line.

To divide a line into equal parts . . .

. . . set a scale at any angle and mark the number of divisions needed.

Construct parallel lines between the divisions and line . . .

. . . to produce equal segments of line AB.

To duplicate angle ABC, strike an arc from B and repeat it at B' . . .

. . . strike a second arc equal to distance between intersected points on angle ABC and transfer.

Draw a line between the new intersection point and point B' . . .

. . . to complete the duplicated A' B' C'.

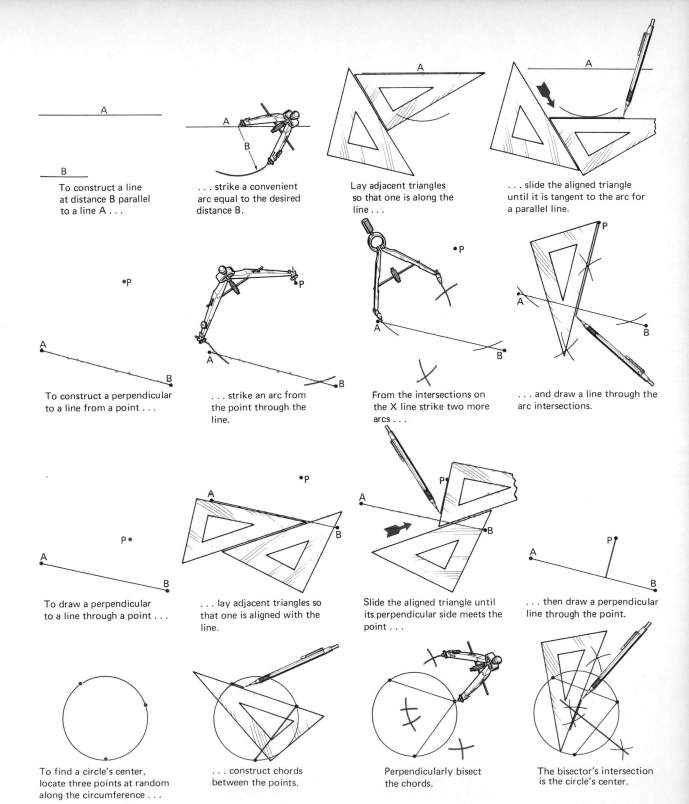

To construct a line at distance B parallel to a line A . . .

. . . strike a convenient arc equal to the desired distance B.

Lay adjacent triangles so that one is along the line . . .

. . . slide the aligned triangle until it is tangent to the arc for a parallel line.

To construct a perpendicular to a line from a point . . .

. . . strike an arc from the point through the line.

From the intersections on the X line strike two more arcs . . . .

. . . and draw a line through the arc intersections.

To draw a perpendicular to a line through a point . . .

. . . lay adjacent triangles so that one is aligned with the line.

Slide the aligned triangle until its perpendicular side meets the point . . .

. . . then draw a perpendicular line through the point.

To find a circle's center, locate three points at random along the circumference . . .

. . . construct chords between the points.

Perpendicularly bisect the chords.

The bisector's intersection is the circle's center.

A

B

C

To construct a triangle
from three given lines . . .

. . . strike an arc equal
in length to one line . . .

. . . then another arc equal
to the second line . . .

. . . and connect the end
points of the lines.

To construct an equilateral
triangle . . .

. . . strike an arc equal to
the given side . . .

. . . strike another arc
equal to the given side . . .

. . . connect the ends of the given
side and the arcs' intersection.

To construct a square, draw
a perpendicular at one end
of the initial side . . .

. . . strike an arc to establish
the length of the perpendicular.

Determine the final corner
by striking arcs from the ends
of the two lines . . .

. . . connect all corners
to complete the square.

To construct a square inside
a given circle . . .

. . . draw lines to connect the
center line and circumference
intersections.

To construct a square
outside a given circle . . .

Parallel

. . . connect center line
extensions with 45° tangents.

644

To construct a pentagon, bisect a radius of a circle . . . that would enclose it . . .

. . . using the bisected radius, strike an arc of radius A.

The resulting radius R is . . .

. . . used to establish the five points of a pentagon.

To construct a hexagon transfer the radius R of a circle that would enclose it . . .

. . . to the circumference . . .

. . . and mark the six points . . .

. . . used to establish a hexagon.

To construct a hexagon around a given circle . . .

. . . draw parallel lines, using a "T" square, that are tangent to opposite sides of the circle.

Using a 30° —60° triangle, construct two pairs of parallel lines that . . .

. . . are tangent to the circle to complete the hexagon.

To draw an arc of radius R tangent to a line and through a point . . .

. . . draw a parallel at distance R.

Intersect the parallel with an arc R from the point.

Using the intersection draw an arc tangent to the line through P.

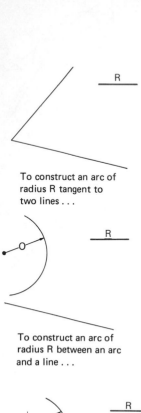

To construct an arc of radius R tangent to two lines . . .

. . . draw a line parallel to one line at distance R . . .

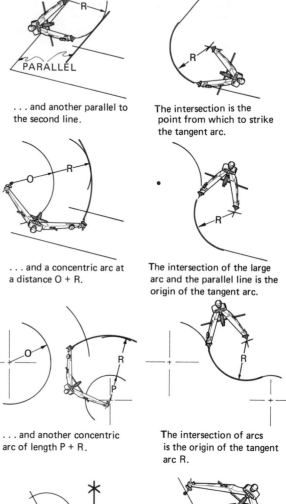

. . . and another parallel to the second line.

The intersection is the point from which to strike the tangent arc.

To construct an arc of radius R between an arc and a line . . .

. . . draw a line parallel to the line at distance R . . .

. . . and a concentric arc at a distance O + R.

The intersection of the large arc and the parallel line is the origin of the tangent arc.

To construct an arc of radius R between two arcs . . .

. . . draw a concentric arc of length O + R . . .

. . . and another concentric arc of length P + R.

The intersection of arcs is the origin of the tangent arc R.

To construct an approximate ellipse, draw a line between the end points (A and B) of the major and minor axes.

Construct OD equal to OB and AC equal to AD.

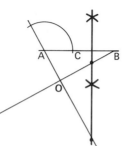

Construct a perpendicular bisector of CB to obtain pivot points on the major and minor axes.

Using these pivot points, draw arcs to form the ellipse.

Abbreviations for Use on Drawings, Specifications, Standards, and in Technical Documents

A

AB	anchor bolt
ABBR	abbreviate
ABN	airborne
ABNL	abnormal
ABRSV	abrasive
ABS	absolute
ABSORB	absorption
ABSTR	abstract
ABT	about
ABV	above
AC	alternating current
AC	asbestos cement
ACB	air circuit breaker
ACB	asbestos-cement board
ACC	accumulator
ACCEL	accelerate
ACCESS	accessory
ACCOM	accommodate
ACCT	account
ACCUM	accumulate
ACCUR	accurate
ACFT	aircraft
ACI	American Concrete Institute
ACLD	aircooled
ACPT	accept
ACR	across
ACS	access
ACS	alternating current synchronous
ACST	acoustic
ACTR	actuator
AD	ampere demand meter
AD	anode
ADD	addendum
ADD	addition
ADH	adhere
ADH	adhesive
ADJ	adjacent
ADJ	adjust
ADP	automatic data processing
ADPTR	adapter
ADV	advance
AERO	aeronautic
AERODYN	aerodynamic
AF	audio frequency
AFB	antifriction bearing
AFC	automatic frequency control
AFT	after

AFT	automatic fine tuning
AGA	American Gas Association
AGC	automatic gain control
AGDS	American Gage Design Standard
AGGR	aggregate
AGMA	American Gear Manufacturers Association
AHM	ampere-hour meter
AIL	aileron
AISC	American Institute of Steel Construction
AISI	American Iron and Steel Institute
AIR COND	air condition
AL	aluminum
AL	amber light
ALIGN	alignment
ALLOW	allowance
ALM	alarm
ALT	altitude
ALTN	alternate
ALY	alloy
AM	amplitude modulation
AMB	amber
AMB	ambient
AMER	American
AMLG	amalgam
AMM	ammeter
AMP	ampere
AMPH	amphibious
AMPL	amplifier
AMPTD	amplitude
AMS	aeronautical material specification
AMT	amount
AMT	armature
AN	alphanumeric
AN	Army-Navy
ANDZ	anodize
ANG	angle
ANHYD	anhydrous
ANL	anneal
ANLG	analog
ANLR	angular
ANLR	annular
ANN	annunciator
ANO	alphanumeric output
ANSI	American National Standards Institute
ANT	antenna

AO	access opening
AOQ	average outgoing quality
AOQL	average outgoing quality limit
AP	access panel
AP	acidproof
APC	automatic phase control
APERT	aperture
API	American Petroleum Institute
APL	airplane
APLQ	applique
APP	appearance
APPAR	apparatus
APPD	approved (altn abbr)
APPROX	approximate
APPV	approve
APPVL	approval
APPX	appendix
APR	April
APRT	airport
APS	auxiliary power supply
APT	apartment
APVD	approved
AQL	acceptable quality level
AQT	acceptable quality test
AR	acid resisting
AR	as required
ARB	arbitrary
ARCW	arc weld
ARL	acceptable reliability level
ARM	armature
ARMD	armored
ARR	arrange, arrangement
ARS	asbestos roof shingles
ARSR	arrestor
ART	article
ARTF	artificial
AS	airspeed
AS	automatic sprinkler
ASA	American Standards Association (now ANSI)
ASAP	as soon as possible
ASB	asbestos
ASGMT	assignment
ASGN	assign
ASME	American Society of Mechanical Engineers
ASPH	asphalt

Extracted from MIL-STD-12C, Supp. 1 (Feb. 1, 1971).

ASR	automatic sprinkler riser	B/L	bill of lading	BIL	blue indicating light
ASRT	assort	B/M	bill of material	BIN	binary
ASSEM	assemble	BA	backlash allowance	BIOL	biological
ASSN	association	BAB	babbit	BIT	binary digit
ASSOC	associate	BACT	bacteriological	BITUM	bituminous
ASST	assistant	BAF	baffle	BK	black (altn abbr)
ASSY	assembly	BAG	baggage	BK	brake
ASTM	American Society for Testing and Materials	BAL	balance	BKLT	booklet
		BAL	ballistic	BL	base line
ASV	angle stop valve	BARO	barometer	BL	bend line
ASW	auxiliary switch	BAT	battery	BL	billet
ASWG	American Steel Wire Gage	BAY	bayonet	BL	blade
		BB	bulletin board	BL	blue (altn abbr)
ASYM	asymmetric	BBB	body bound bolts	BL	building line
ASYMP	asymptote	BBL	barrel	BLDG	building
AT	airtight	BBRG	ball bearing	BLK	black
AT	ampere turn	BC	back-connected	BLK	blank
ATC	acoustic tile ceiling	BC	between centers	BLKG	blanking
ATCH	attach, attachment	BC	binary counter	BLO	blower
ATM	atmosphere	BC	bolt circle	BLR	boiler
ATMG	atomizing	BC	bottom chord	BLST	ballast
ATTD	attitude	BCD	binary coded decimal	BLT	bolt
ATTN	attention	BCI	binary coded information	BLTIN	built-in
AUD	audible			BLU	blue
AUD	audio	BCL	base contour line	BLVD	boulevard
AUG	August	BD	binary decoder	BLW	below
AUTH	authorize	BD	board	BM	beam
AUTO	automatic	BDG	binding	BM	bench mark
AUTO	automobile	BDGH	binding head	BMEP	brake mean effective pressure
AUTOM	automotive	BDL	bundle		
AUX	auxiliary	BDN	bend down	BMTLC	bimetallic
AV	audio-visual	BDR	binder	BND	bonded
AVAIL	available	BDY	boundary	BNDG	bonding
AVC	automatic volume control	BE	Baume	BNDZ	bonderize
		BETW	between	BNG	bending
AVDP	avoirdupois	BEV	bevel	BNR	burner
AVE	avenue	BF	beat frequency	BNSH	burnish
AVG	average	BF	boiler feed	BO	black out
AVN	aviation	BF	both faces	BO	blowoff
AW	all weather	BFG	buffing	BOC	blowout coil
AWG	American Wire Gage	BFO	beat-frequency oscillator	BOLS	bolster
AWS	American War Standard			BOT	bottom
		BFP	boiler feed pump	BP	back pressure
AWS	American Welding Society	BFR	before	BP	base pitch
		BFR	buffer	BP	base plate
AZ	azimuth	BFW	boiler feed water	BP	between perpendiculars
		BG	back gear	BP	blueprint
		BGP	barrier, grease proof	BP	boiling point
	B	BH	Brinell hardness	BPD	barrels per day
		BHD	bulkhead	BPH	barrels per hour
B TO B	back to back	BHN	Brinell hardness number	BPRF	bulletproof
B&S	bell and spigot			BPS	bits per second
B&S	Brown and Sharp Wire Gage	BHP	boiler horsepower	BR	bedroom
		BHP	brake horsepower	BR	bend radius
B&W	black and white	BI	black iron	BR	branch

BR	brown (altn abbr)	CAL	calibration	CDEL	constant delivery
BR STD	British Standard	CAL	calorie	CDP	compressor discharge pressure
BRC	brace	CALC	calculate		
BRCH	broach	CAM	camber	CDR	current directional relay
BRD	braided	CAM	checkout and automatic monitoring		
BRG	bearing			CDRILL	counterdrill
BRK	break	CANC	cancel	CDS	cold-drawn steel
BRK	brick	CAND	candelabra	CDW	chilled drinking water
BRKR	breaker	CANV	canvas	CE	common emitter
BRKT	bracket	CAP	capacitor	CE	commutator end
BRN	brown	CAP	capacity	CEA	circular error average
BRS	brass	CAP	capital	CEI	contract end item
BRZ	braze	CARB	carburize	CEL	celestial
BRZ	bronze	CARR	carrier	CEM	cement
BRZG	brazing	CAS	castle	CEP	circular error probability
BS	both sides	CAT	catalog		
BSC	basic	CAT	category	CER	ceramic
BSHG	bushing	CATH	cathode	CERMET	ceramic metal element
BSKT	basket	CATV	community antenna television	CERT	certify
BSMT	basement			CET	cumulative elapsed time
BSTR	booster	CAV	cavity		
BT	bent	CB	catch basin	CF	carrier frequency
BT	bus tie	CB	center of buoyancy	CF	cathode follower
BTFL	butterfly	CB	circuit breaker	CF	cement floor
BTL	bottle	CB	continuous blowdown	CF	center of flotation
BTN	button	CBAL	counterbalance	CF	centrifugal force
BTRY	battery	CBD	carbide	CF	cold finished
BTU	British thermal unit	CBORE	counterbore	CF	cooling fan
BTWLD	buttweld	CBS	call box station	CFE	contractor-furnished equipment
BU	bureau	CC	close coupled		
BU	bushel	CC	closing coil	CFL	calibrated focal length
BULL	bulletin	CC	color code	CFLG	counterflashing
BUP	bend up	OO	common collector	CFM	cubic feet per minute
BUS	business	CC	cubic centimeter	CFP	contractor-furnished property
BUSH	bushing (altn abbr)	CCB	concrete block		
BUTN	butane	CCG	cargo center of gravity	CFS	cold finished steel
BUZ	buzzer	CCN	contract change notice	CFS	cubic feet per second
BW	bandwidth	CCR	control contactor	CG	center of gravity
BW	both ways	CCT	constant current transformer	CG	chain grate
BWG	Birmingham Wire Gage			CGS	centimeter-gram-second
BWP	barrier, waterproof	CCTV	closed-circuit television	CGU	ceramic glazed units
BWS	beveled wood siding	CCW	counterclockwise	CH	case harden
BYNT	buoyant	CD	cable duct	CH	chain
BYP	bypass	CD	candle	CH	chief
		CD	card	CH	choke
		CD	center distance	CHAM	chamfer
	C	CD	cold-drawn	CHAN	channel
		CD	common digitizer	CHAP	chapter
C	Celsius	CD	cord	CHAR	character
3/C	three conductor	CD	current density	CHAS	chassis
C TO C	center to center	CD PL	cadmium plate	CHC	choke coil
C/W	carrier wave	CDR	critical design review	CHD	chord
CA	cable	CDRL	contract data requirements list	CHEM	chemical
CA	clear aperture			CHG	change (altn abbr)
CAB	cabinet	CD RDR	card reader	CHG	charge
CAL	caliber				

649

CHGOV	change-over	CLR	collar	COEF	coefficient
CHGR	charger	CLR	color	COL	column
CHK	check	CLR	cooler	COLIM	collimator
CHKR	checker	CLR	current-limiting resistor	COLL	collector
CHLD	chilled	CLRG	collector ring	COM	common
CHNG	change	CLTG	collecting	COMB	combination
CHR	character register	CLV	clevis	COMB	combustion
CHR	chromium	CLWG	clear wire glass	COML	commercial
CHRST	characteristic	CMBD	combined	COMM	communication
CHW	chilled water	CMD	command	COMM	commutator
CI	cast iron	CMET	coated metal	COMP	companion
CI	circuit interrupter	CMF	coherent memory filter	COMP	compensator
CID	component identification	CMFLR	cam follower	COMPL	complete
CIL	clear indicating light	CMIL	circular mil	COMPR	composition roof
CIN	carrier input	CML	current-mode logic	COMPR	compressor (altn abbr)
CIN	code identification number	CMP	corrugated metal pipe	COMPSG	compensating
CINE	cinematographic	CMPD	compound	COMPT	compartment
CIP	cast-iron pipe	CMPLM	complement	COMPTR	comparator
CIP	compressor inlet pressure	CMPNT	component	COMSAT	communications satellite
CIR	circle	CMPS	centimeters per second	COMSN	commission
CIRC	circular	CMPSN	composition	CONC	concentrate
CIT	compressor inlet temperature	CMPST	composite	CONC	concentric (altn abbr)
CK	cork	CMPT	compute	CONC	concrete
CKBD	cork board	CMPTG	computing	COND	condenser
CKD	completely knocked down	CMPTR	computer	COND	conductor (altn abbr)
CKPT	cockpit	CMR	common-mode rejection	CONF	confidential
CKT	check template	CMRLR	cam roller	CONN	connection
CKT	circuit	CMS	current-mode switching	CONN	connector
CKT BKR	circuit breaker (altn abbr)	CN	change notice	CONST	constant
CL	carload	CNCL	concealed	CONSTR	construction
CL	center line	CNCR	concurrent	CONT	contact
CL	class	CNCTRC	concentric	CONT	contents
CL	clearance	CNCV	concave	CONT	continued
CL	close	CND	conduit	CONT	control
CL	closing	CNDCT	conductor	CONT	controller
CL	clutch	CNDS	condensate	CONTR	contract
CLASS	classification	CNTBRD	centerboard	CONTR	contractor
CLB	center line bend	CNTD	contained	CONV	convention
CLD	cooled	CENTFGL	centrifugal	COOL	coolant
CLE	closed end	CNTNR	container	COORD	coordinate
CLG	ceiling	CNTOR	contactor	COP	copper
CLG	cooling	CNTR	counter	COR	corner
CLK	clock	CNVC	convenience	CORP	corporation
CLKG	caulking	CNVR	conveyor	CORR	correct
CLN	clean	CO	change order	CORR	corrugate
CLO	closet	CO	cleanout	COT	cotter
CLP	clamp	CO	company	COV	cover
CLPR	caliper	CO	cutoff	COV	cutout valve
CLR	clear	CO	cutout	COWL	cowling
		COAM	coaming	CP	candlepower
		COAX	coaxial	CP	center of pressure
		COE	cab over engine	CP	center punch
		COED	computer-operated electronic display	CP	cesspool
				CP	chemically pure

CP	circular pitch	CRPL	chromium plate	CVNTL	conventional
CP	circular polarization	CRS	coarse	CVRSN	conversion
CP	coefficient of performance	CRS	cold-rolled steel	CVX	convex
		CRSN	corrosion	CW	clockwise
CP	cold-punched	CRSV	corrosive	CW	cold water
CP	command pulse	CRSVR	crossover	CW	continuous wave
CP	cone point	CRT	cathode-ray tube	CWP	circulating water pump
CP	constant pressure	CRTG	cartridge	CWT	hundredweight
CP	control point	CRV	curve	CY	cycle
CPD	contact potential difference	CRYST	crystalline	CYL	cylinder, cylindrical
		CS	carbon steel	CYN	cyanide
CPE	circular probable error	CS	case		
CPFF	cost plus fixed fee	CS	cast steel		D
CPI	cost plus incentive	CS	Commercial Standard		
CPL	cement plaster	CS	control switch	1/2DP	half dog point
CPL	couple	CSD	cold side	D/A	digital-to-analog
CPLD	coupled	CSD	constant-speed drive	DAC	digital-to-analog converter
CPLG	coupling	CSG	casing		
CPLR	coupler	CSHAFT	crankshaft	DACT	direct acting
CPM	critical-path method	CSK	countersink	DAD	double-acting door
CPNTR	carpenter	CSKH	countersunk head	DAT	datum
CPPD	capped	CSL	console	DB	decibel
CPRSN	compression	CSTG	casting	DB	distribution box
CPRSR	compressor	CSTL	castellate	DB	double braid (insul)
CPS	circuit package schematic	CSTR	canister	DB	dry bulb
		CSW	control power switch	DBAO	digital block AND-OR gate
CPSL	capsule	CT	center tap		
CPSN	capstan	CT	ceramic tile	DBB	detector back bias
CPT	control power transformer	CT	current transformer	DBC	diameter bolt circle
		CTC	cam timing contact	DBF	demodulator band filter
CPUNCH	counterpunch	CTD	coated	DBHP	drawbar horsepower
CQ	commercial quality	CTF	ceramic-tile floor	DBL	double
CR	cathode ray	CTG	coating	DBP	drawbar pull
CR	change request	CTG	crating	DBUT	data base update time
CR	cold-rolled	CTG	cutting	DC	direct current
CR	control relay	CTL	central	DC	double contact
CR	control room	CTN	carton	DCD	decode
CR	credit	CTR	center	DCDR	decoder
CR	crystal rectifier	CTR	contour	DCKG	docking
CR	current relay	CTRG	centering	DCL	door closer
CR MOLY	chrome molybdenum	CTRS	contrast	DCN	design change notice
CR VAN	chrome vanadium	CTSK	countersunk	DCN	drawing change notice
CRAM	card random access memory	CTT	card-to-tape tape	DCR	drawing change request
		CTWT	counterweight		
CRCLT	circulate	CU	crystal unit, piezoelectric	DCTP	duct type
CRCMF	circumference			DDA	digital differential analyzer
CRE	corrosion-resistant	CU	cubic		
CRG	carriage	CULV	culvert	DDR	direct drive
CRIT	critical	CUM	cumulative	DE	drive end
CRK	crank	CUP	cupboard	DEC	December
CRM	chrome	CUR	current	DEC	decimal
CRN	crown	CURT	curtain	DECAL	decalcomania
CRO	cathode-ray oscilloscope	CUSH	cushion	DECR	decrease
		CUST	customer	DED	dedendum
CRP	crimp	CV	check valve	DEF	defective

DEF	definition	DN	down	DT	dual tires
DEFT	definite time	DNA	does not apply	DT	dust tight
DEG	degree	DNG	dining	DTD	dated
DEGUSG	degaussing	DO	ditto	DTL	diode transistor logic
DEL	delineation	DOC	document	DTR	definite-time relay
DENS	density	DOM	domestic	DTR	demand-totalizing relay
DEPT	department	DOZ	dozen	DUP	duplicate
DERIV	derivative	DP	depth	DVM	digital voltmeter
DES	designation	DP	dew point	DVTL	dovetail
DET	detail	DP	diametral pitch	DW	distilled water
DET	detector	DP	double-pole	DWG	drawing
DETN	detention	DP	dripproof	DWL	dowel
DEV	development	DP	dual purpose	DWN	drawn
DEVN	deviation	DPDT	double-pole	DWT	deadweight
DF	double feeder		double-throw	DWT	pennyweight
DF	Douglas fir	DPG	damping	DX	duplex
DF	drinking fountain	DPH	diamond-pyramid	DYHR	dehydrator
DF	drive fit		hardness	DYN	dynamic
DF	drop forge	DPLR	doppler	DYNMT	dynamometer
DFT	draft	DPLXR	duplexer		
DFTG	drafting	DPM	data-processing		
DFTR	deflector		machine		E
DFTSMN	draftsman	DPNL	distribution panel		
DGTL	digital	DPO	dripproof open	E	east
DHMY	dehumidify	DPP	dripproof protected	E	emitter (electron
DHW	double-hung windows	DPR	diazoprint		device)
DIA	diameter	DPR	double pulse ranging	E&SP	equipment and spare
DIAG	diagonal	DPS	dripproof semienclosed		parts
DIAG	diagram	DPST	double-pole	EA	each
DIAPH	diaphragm		single-throw	ECC	eccentric
DIEL	dielectric	DPT	dripproof	ECC	error correction code
DIFF	difference		totally-enclosed	ECD	estimated completion
DIFF	differential	DPV	dry pipe valve		date
DIFFR	diffraction	DR	door	ECL	emitter-coupled logic
DIM	dimension	DR	drafting request	ECN	engineering change
DIR	direct	DR	dram		notice
DIR	direction, directional	DR	drill	ECO	electron-coupled
DISC	disconnect	DR	drive		oscillator
DISCH	discharge	DRM	drafting room manual	ECO	electronic checkout
DISM	dismantle	DRS	dressed (lumber)	ECO	engineering change
DISP	dispatcher	DRTL	diode resistor transistor		order
DISP	dispenser		logic	ECP	engineering change
DISPL	displacement	DRVR	driver		proposal
DIST	distance	DS	disconnect switch	ECR	engineering change
DIST	district	DS	domestic service		request
DISTR	distributor	DS&R	data storage and	ED	edition
DIV	division		retrieval	EDGW	edgewise
DJ	drill jig	DSCONT	discontinue	EDP	electronic data
DK	dark	DSGN	design		processing
DK	deck	DSL	diesel	EDR	equivalent direct
DL	dead load	DSPL	display		radiation
DL	delay line	DSPL	disposal	EDT	electrical discharge
DLX	deluxe	DSTL	distill		tube
DLY	delay	DT	decay time	EF	extra fine (threads)
DM	demand meter	DT	double-throw	EFF	effective

EFF	efficiency	EP	explosion-proof	EXP JT	expansion joint
EFL	effective focal length	EP	extreme pressure	EXT	extension
EFL	equivalent focal length	EPT	external pipe thread	EXT	exterior
EG	for example	EPWR	emergency power	EXT	external
EGT	exhaust gas temperature	EQ	equal (altn abbr)	EXT	extinguisher
		EQ	equation	EXTD	extrude
EHF	extremely high frequency	EQ SP	equally spaced (altn abbr)	EXTM	extreme
				EXTR	extrude (altn abbr)
EHP	effective horsepower	EQL	equal		
EL	elastic limit	EQL SP	equally spaced		F
EL	elevation	EQPT	equipment		
ELAS	elastic	EQUIL	equilibrium	F	Fahrenheit
ELB	elbow	EQUIV	equivalent	F	force
ELEC	electric, electrical	ERECT	erection	FA	final assembly
ELEK	electronic	ERN	engineering release notice	FAB	fabricate
ELEM	elementary			FABL	fire alarm bell
ELEV	elevator	ERR	error	FABX	fire alarm box
ELEX	electronics	ERRC	error correction	FACIL	facility
ELIG	eligible	ES	electrostatic	FACT	fully automatic compiler-translator
ELMCH	electromechanical	ESHP	equivalent shaft horsepower		
ELONG	elongation			FAO	finish all over
ELP	elliptical	ESK	engineering sketch	FAX	facsimile
ELPC	electroluminescent-photoconductive	ESP	especially	FB	flat bar
		ESPEC	electrical specifications	FB	fuse block
ELPNEU	electropneumatic	ESR	equivalent series resistance	FBCK	firebrick
ELV	electrically operated valve			FBM	board foot (measure)
		ESS	electronic switching system	FBR	feedback resistance
EM	electromagnetic			FBR	fiber
EM	engineering memorandum	EST	estimate	FBRBD	fiberboard
		ESU	electrostatic units	FBRS	fibrous
EM	expanded metal	ET	elapsed time	FC	file cabinet
EMB	emboss	ETC	and so forth, et cetera	FC	front-connected
EMER	emergency	EVAC	evacuator	FCB	free cutting brass
EMF	electromotive force	EVAP	evaporator	FCG	facing
EMPL	employee	EVM	electronic voltmeter	FCSG	focusing
EMT	electrical metallic tubing	EVOM	electronic volt-ohmmeter	FCST	forecast
				FCT	filament center tap
EMTR	emitter	EWO	engineering work order	FCTN	function
EMU	electromagnetic units	EX	example	FCTY	factory
EMUL	emulsion	EX	extra	FD	feed
EN	engineering notice	EXAM	examination	FD	floor drain
ENAM	enamel	EXC	except	FD	forced draft
ENCL	enclosure	EXC	excitation	FDB	forced-draft blower
ENG	engine	EXCH	exchange	FDBK	feedback
ENG	English	EXCL	exclusive	FDC	fire-department connection
ENGR	engineer	EXCTO	exciter		
ENGRG	engineering	EXEC	executive	FDI	field discharge
ENTR	entrance	EXER	exercise	FDM	frequency division multiplex
ENV	envelope	EXH	exhaust		
ENVIR	environment	EXH	exhibit	FDN	foundation
EO	engineering order	EXP	expansion	FDP	full dog point
EOLM	electro-optical light modulator	EXP	expense	FDPL	fluid pressure line
		EXP	experiment	FDR	feeder
EP	electrical panel	EXP	exposed	FDR	fire door
EP	epitaxial planar	EXP	express	FDRY	foundry

FDW	feed water	FLR	filler	FS	finish specification (number)
FEB	February	FLRD	flared		
FED	Federal	FLRT	flow rate	FS	full size
FEM	female	FLSW	flow switch	FSBL	fusible
FET	field-effect transistor	FLT	flight	FSC	Federal supply class
FEXT	fire extinguisher	FLT	float	FSC	full scale
FF	flip flop	FLTD	fluted	FSN	Federal Stock Number
FF	following	FLTG	floating	FST	forged steel
FFC	flip flop complementary	FLTP	flush type	FSTNR	fastener
FFL	female flared	FLTR	filter	FT	feet
FFL	flip flop latch	FLUOR	fluorescent	FT LB	foot-pound
FFL	front focal length	FLW	flat washer	FTD	fitted
FFP	firm fixed price	FM	fathom	FTF	flared tube fitting
FG	filament ground	FM	field manual	FTG	fitting
FGD	forged	FM	fire main	FTG	footing
FGN	foreign	FM	frequency modulation	FTHRD	female thread
FH	fire hose	FMAN	foreman	FTP	fuel transfer pump
FH	flat head (altn abbr)	FMS	free-machining steel	FU	fuse
FH	full hard	FNI	fan in	FUBX	fuse box
FHC	fire-hose cabinet	FNO	fan out	FUND	fundamental
FHP	fractional horsepower	FNPT	fusion point	FUR	furnace
FHP	friction horsepower	FNSH	finish	FURN	furnish
FHR	fire-hose rack	FOC	focal	FUS	fuselage (altn abbr)
FHT	fully heat-treated	FORG	forging	FUSLG	fuselage
FHY	fire hydrant	FORM	formula	FV	flush valve
FIC	frequency interference control	FOUO	for official use only	FV	front view
		FP	fireplace	FV	full voltage
FIG	figure	FP	flat point	FW	fire wall
FIIN	Federal item identification number	FP	freezing point	FW	fresh water
		FP	fungus proof	FWD	forward
FIL	filament	FPI	fluorescent penetrant inspection	FWP	feed water pump
FIL	fillet			FWP	fresh-water pump
FIL	fillister	FPL	fire plug	FXD	fixed
FILH	fillister head	FPM	feet per minute	FXP	fixed point
FIN	financial	FPRF	fireproof	FXTR	fixture
FIN	finish (altn abbr)	FPS	feet per second	FYIG	for your information and guidance
FL	flashing	FPS	foot-pound-second (system)		
FL	flat			FZ	fuze
FL	floor	FPT	female pipe thread		
FL	flow	FR	failure rate		
FL	fluid	FR	fast release (relay)		G
FL	flush	FR	field reversing		
FL	focal length	FR	frame	G	gram
FL	footlambert	FR	from	G	gravity
FL/W	flash welding	FR	front	G	green (altn abbr)
FLD	field	FRAC	fractional	G	grid
FLDG	folding	FREQ	frequency	GA	gage
FLEX	flexible	FRES	fire resistant	GAL	gallons
FLG	flange	FRICT	friction	GALV	galvanize
FLG	flooring	FRMR	former	GALVI	galvanized iron
FLH	flat head	FRT	freight	GALVS	galvanized steel
FLMB	flammable	FRWK	framework	GAR	garage
FLMPRF	flameproof	FRZR	freezer	GAS	gasoline
FLMT	flushmount	FS	far side	GAS/W	gas weld
FLN	flatten	FS	Federal Specification	GBG	garbage
FLOT	flotation			GD	guard
				GEN	generator

GENL	general	GSIL	German silver	HKP	hookup
GEOL	geological	GSKT	gasket	HLCL	helical
GFE	government-furnished equipment	GSU	glazed structural units	HLDG	holding
		GSV	globe stop valve	HLDR	holder
GFLD	generator field	GSWR	galvanized steel wire rope	HLNG	headlining
GI	gray iron			HLP	helper
GIL	green indicating lamp	GT	gastight	HLXA	helix angle
GL	grade line	GT	grease trap	HNDWL	hand wheel
GL	green light	GT	gross ton	HNG	hanging
GLB	glass block	GTRB	gas turbine	HNG	hinge
GLD	gold	GTV	gate valve	HNTG	hunting
GLOSS	glossary	GUT	gutter	HNYCMB	honeycomb
GLPG	glowplug	GLV	gravel	HOL	hollow
GLT	guide light	GVW	gross vehicle weight	HON	honorary
GLV	globe valve	GWB	gypsum wallboard	HORIZ	horizon (altn abbr)
GLZ	glaze	GWT	glazed wall tile	HORIZ	horizontal
GM	geometric mean	GY	gray (altn abbr)	HOSP	hospital
GMBL	gimbal	GYM	gymnasium	HP	high pressure
GMET	gun metal	GYP	gypsum	HP	horsepower
GMLDG	garnish molding	GYRO	gyroscope	HP HR	horsepower hour
GMT	Greenwich mean time	GZ	ground zero	HQ	headquarters
GMV	guaranteed minimum value			HR	hot rolled
				HR	hour
GND	ground		**H**	HRPO	hot rolled, pickled and oiled
GNLTD	granulated	1/2H	half-hard		
GOV	governor	HAZ	hazardous	HRS	hot-rolled steel
GOVT	government	HB	hose bib	HRZN	horizon
GOX	gaseous oxygen	HC	holding coil	HS	high speed
GP	general purpose	HCL	horizontal center line	HSE	house
GP	group	HCS	high-carbon steel	HSG	housing
GPC	gypsum-plaster ceiling	HD	hard	HSHLD	household
GPH	gallons per hour	HD	head	HSR	high-speed reader
GPH	graphite	HD	heavy duty	HSS	high-speed steel
GPM	gallons per minute	HD CR	hard chromium	HST	hoist
GPW	gypsum-plaster wall	HD DRN	hard-drawn	HSTH	hose thread
GR	gear	HDBK	handbook	HT	heat
GR	grade	HDG	heading	HT	high tension
GR	grain	HDL	handle	HT	hollow tile
GR	gross	HDLG	handling	HT RES	heat resisting
GRA	gray	HDLS	headless	HT TR	heat treat
GRAD	gradient	HDN	harden	HTCI	high-tensile cast iron
GRAN	granite	HDNS	hardness	HTD	heated
GRBX	gearbox	HDR	header	HTG	heating
GRC	gearcase	HDST	headset	HTM	high temperature
GRD	grind	HDW	hardware	HTR	heater
GRDTN	graduation	HDWC	hardware cloth	HV	high velocity
GRG	gearing	HDWD	hardwood	HV	high voltage
GRL	grille	HEX	hexagon	HVR	high-voltage regulator
GRN	green	HEX HD	hexagonal head	HVY	heavy
GROM	grommet	HEX SOCH	hexagonal socket head	HW	half-wave
GRPH	graphic	HF	holding fixture	HW	hot water
GRS	grease	HGBN	herringbone	HWC	hot-water circulating
GRTG	grating	HGR	hanger	HWH	hot-water heater
GRV	groove	HGT	height	HWY	highway
GRVD	grooved	HI FI	high fidelity	HYB	hybrid
GRWT	gross weight	HIPRI	high priority	HYD	hydraulic (altn abbr)

HYDM	hydrometer	IMPLS	impulse	IP	instruction plate
HYDR	hydraulic	IMPROV	improvement	IP	instruction pulse
		IMPRSN	impression	IP	intermediate pressure
	I	IN	inch	IP	iron pipe
		IN LB	inch-pound	IPB	illustrated parts
I/O	input/output	INBD	inboard		breakdown
IAS	indicated air speed	INC	incorporated	IPM	interruptions per
IB	instruction book	INCAND	incandescent		minute
IBID	the same as	INCIN	incinerator	IPS	inches per second
IC	instruction card	INCL	inclusive	IPS	Internal Pipe Standard
IC	integrated circuit	INCLR	intercooler	IPS	interruptions per
IC	internal combustion	INCLS	inclosure		second
ICF	inspection check	INCM	incoming	IPS	iron pipe size
	fixture	INCND	incendiary	IPT	internal pipe thread
ICS	Intercommunication	INCOH	incoherent	IPT	iron pipe thread
	System	INCR	increase	IR	infared
ICT	inspection check	IND	indicating	IR	inside radius
	template	IND	induction	IRREG	irregular
ICT	international critical	IND	industry	IS	island
	tables	IND LP	indicating lamp	ISGN	insignia
ICW	interrupted continuous	INDEP	independent	ISO	International
	wave	INDL	industrial		Organization for
ID	induced draft	INF	infinite		Standardization
ID	inside diameter	INFO	information	ISO	isometric
ID LT	identification light	INIT	initial	ITR	inverse time relay
ID NO	identification number	INJ	injection	IV	initial velocity
IDENT	identification	INOP	inoperative		
IDL	idler	INORG	inorganic		
IDP	integrated data	INP	input		
	processing	INQ	inquiry		J
IDX	index	INRT	inert		
IE	that is	INRTG	inert gas	JAN	January
IF	inside frosted	INRTL	inertial	JAN	Joint Army-Navy
IF	instruction folder	INS	inside	JB	junction box
IF	intermediate frequency	INSOL	insoluble	JC	janitor closet
IFL	inflatable	INSP	inspection	JC	joint compound
IG	inertial guidance	INST	instantaneous	JCT	junction
IGN	ignition	INST	institute	JFET	junction field-effect
IGN	ignitron	INST	instrument (altn abbr)		transistor
IGNTR	ignitor	INSTL	installation	JKT	jacket
IGS	inertial guidance	INSTM	instrumentation	JMPR	jumper
	system	INSTPN	instrument panel	JNL	journal
IGV	inlet guide vane	INSTR	instruction	JO	job order
IHP	indicated horsepower	INSTR	instrument	JOG	joggle
IL	index list	INSUL	insulation	JR	junior
ILLUM	illuminate	INT	interrupter (relay)	JT	joint
ILLUS	illustrate	INTEG	integrating	JUL	July
IMAG	imaginary	INTEN	intensity	JUN	June
IMEP	indicated mean	INTK	intake		
	effective pressure	INTL	internal		
IMIT	imitation	INTL	international		K
IMPD	impedance	INTRO	introduction		
IMPF	imperfect	INV	inverter	K	Kelvin
IMPRG	impregnate	IOM	interoffice	K	kip (1000 lb)
IMPL	implement		memorandum	KD	kiln-dried
IMPLR	impeller	IP	initial point	KD	knock down
				KN	knot
				KN SW	knife switch

KO	knockout	LKR	locker	MAINT	maintenance
KPL	kick plate	LKROT	locked rotor	MAJ	major
KST	keyseat	LKT	lookout	MAL	malleable
KVAH	kilovoltampere hour	LKWR	lockwire	MALF	malfunction
KWY	keyway	LL	live load	MAM	milliammeter
KYBD	keyboard	LL	low level	MAN	manual (altn abbr)
		LLYP	longleaf yellow pine	MANF	manifold
		LMTR	limiter	MAR	March
	L	LNG	lining	MAR	marine
L	left	LNTL	lintel	MARG	margin
L	long	LOA	length overall	MASU	machined surface
LA	lead angle	LONG	longitude	MAT	matrix
LA	lightning arrester	LOS	line of sight	MAX	maximum
LAB	laboratory	LOX	liquid oxygen	MBL	mobile
LAD	ladder	LP	low pressure	MBR	mechanical buffer
LANG	language	LPW	lumen per watt		register
LAQ	lacquer	LR	load ration	MBR	member
LAT	latitude	LR	load resistor (relay)	MBT	main ballast tank
LAU	laundry	LR	long range	MC	manhole cover
LAV	lavatory	LS	left side	MC	medicine cabinet
LB	pound	LS	limestone	MC	momentary contact
LB FT	pound-force foot	LS	loudspeaker	MC	multiple-contact
LB IN	pound-force inch	LT	lead time	MCD	metal-covered door
LBL	label	LTD	limited	MOH	mail chutes
LBR	lumber	LTG	lighting	MCHRY	machinery
LBRY	library	LTHR	leather	MCHST	machinist
LBYR	labyrinth	LTR	letter	MCM	magnetic core memory
LC	inductance-capacitance	LTSW	light switch	MCSW	motor circuit switch
LC	laundry chute	LUB	lubricate	MCW	metal casement
LC	lead-covered	LUBT	lubricant		window
LC	learning curve	LUM	luminous	MDC	motor direct connected
LC	load center	LV	leave	MDGT	midget
LC	lower case	LV	low voltage	MDL	middle
LCL	local	LVD	louvered door	MDL	module
LCTN	location	LVL	level	MDM	medium
LD	leading	LVO	louver opening	MDN	median
LD MK	land mark	LVP	low-voltage protection	MDRL	mandrel
LDG	landing	LVR	lever	MDS	minimum discernible
LDG	loading	LVR	louver		signal
LDR	leader	LWB	long wheelbase	MDSE	merchandise
LE	leading edge	LWC	lightweight concrete	MEAS	measure
LF	low frequency	LWIC	lightweight insulating	MECH	mechanical
LG	long (altn abbr)		concrete	MED	medical
LGC	logic	LWL	low-water line	MED	medium (altn abbr)
LGE	large	LWR	lower	MED	microelectronic device
LH	left hand	LYR	layer	MEM	memory
LIC	license	LYT	layout	MEMO	memorandum
LIC	linear integrated circuit			MEP	mean effective pressure
LIM	limit		**M**	MER	meridian
LIN	lineal			MET	metal
LIN	linear	MACH	machine	MET	metallurgical
LIQ	liquid	MAG	magazine	METF	metal flashing
LK WASH	lock washer	MAG	magnetic	METG	metal grill
LKD	locked	MAGN	magnetron	METP	metal partition
LKGE	linkage	MAGTD	magnitude	METRL	meteorological
LKNT	locknut	MAH	mahogany	MEZZ	mezzanine

MF	main feed	MNPWR	manpower	MVG	moving
MF	microfilm	MNRL	mineral	MVT	movement
MF	motor field	MO	month	MWG	Music Wire Gage
MFD	manufactured	MO	motor operated	MWP	membrane
MFG	manufacturing	MOD	model		waterproofing
MFLRD	male flared	MOD	modification	MWV	maximum working
MFR	manufacture	MOD	modulator		voltage
MG	motor generator	MOL	molecule	MXFL	mixed flow
MG	multigage	MOL WT	molecular weight	MXG	mixing
MGC	manual gain control	MOM	momentary	MXT	mixture
MGN	magneto	MON	monitor		
MGR	manager	MON	monument		N
MGS	metal gravel stop	MORT	morse taper		
MGT	management	MOST	metal-oxide-	N	north
MH	manhole		semiconductor	NA	not applicable
MHD	magnetohydrodynamics		transistor	NA	not available
MHE	materials handling	MOT	motor	NAR	narrow
	equipment	MP	melting point	NAS	National Aircraft
MHT	mean high tide	MPG	miles per gallon		Standards
MI	malleable iron	MPH	miles per hour	NAT	natural
MI	mile	MPI	magnetic particle	NATL	national
MIC	micrometer		inspection	NAUT	nautical
MIC	microphone	MPT	male pipe thread	NAV	naval
MIC	monolithic integrated	MR	marble	NB	narrow band
	circuit	MRD	metal rolling door	NB	no bias (relay)
MICAM	microammeter	MS	manuscript	NBFU	National Board of Fire
MICR	magnetic ink character	MS	military standard		Underwriters
	recognition		(sheet)	NBS	National Bureau of
MID	middle (altn abbr)	MSCR	machine screw		Standards
MIL	military	MSG	message	NC	National coarse
MILSPEC	military specification	MSL	mean sea level		(thread)
MIL-STD	military standard (book)	MSNRY	masonry	NC	no change
MIN	minimum	MST	machine steel	NC	no connection
MIN	minor	MSW	master switch	NC	normally closed
MIN	minute	MT	mean tide	NC	numerical control
MISC	miscellaneous	MT	mean time	NCH	notched
MIX	mixture	MT	metal threshold	NCOMBL	noncombustible
MJ	mastic joint	MT	mount	NDL	needle
MK	mark	MTBF	mean time between	NDRO	nondestructive read-out
MKD	marked		failure	NDT	nondestructive testing
MKGS	markings	MTD	mounted	NEC	National Electrical
MKR	marker	MTG	meeting		Code
MKS	meter-kilogram-second	MTG	mounting	NEC	necessary
ML	material list	MTLC	metallic	NECS	National Electrical
ML	mold line	MTN	motion		Code Standards
ML	monolithic	MTR	meter	NEF	National extra fine
MLD	molded	MTTF	mean time to failure		(thread)
MLDG	molding	MTZ	motorized	NEG	negative
MLT	mean low tide	MU	multiple unit	NEIL	neon indicating light
MMC	maximum material	MUF	muffler	NEMA	National Electrical
	condition	MULT	multiple	NESC	National Electric Safety
MMF	magnetomotive force	MULTH	multilith		Code
MMOD	micromodule	MULTR	multiplier	NEUT	neutral
MN	main	MUW	music wire	NF	National fine (thread)
MNG	managing	MV	muzzle velocity	NF	National formulary
MNL	manual	MVBL	movable	NF	near face

NF	noise frequency	NPTF	National taper pipe thread for dry seal pressure tight joints	ODPP	open dripproof protected
NFL	navy standard flange			OE	open end
NFSD	nonfused	NPTR	National taper pipe thread for railing fixtures	OEM	original equipment manufacturer
NG	narrow gage				
NG	no good			OF	outside face
NGO	National gas outlet (thread)	NR	nonreactive (relay)	OFCE	office
		NR	nuclear reactor	OFCL	official
NI SIL	nickel-silver	NS	National special (thread)	OFR	overfrequency relay
NIP	nipple			OFS	offset
NIS	not in stock	NS	near side	OFT	outfit
NK	neck	NSS	Navy Secondary Standards	OGL	obscure glass
NKL	nickel			OGR	outgoing repeater
NLNR	nonlinear	NST	nonslip tread	OGT	outgoing trunk
NM	noise meter	NTFY	notify	OGT	outlet gas temperature
NM	nonmetallic	NTN	neutron	OH	open hearth
NMAG	nonmagnetic	NTP	normal temperature and pressure	OHM	ohmmeter
NMI	nautical miles			OI	oil immersed
NO	normally open	NTS	not to scale	OI	oil insulated
NO	number	NTWK	network	OIFC	oil-insulated fan-cooled
NOI	not otherwise identified	NTWT	net weight	OIL	orange indicating light
NOM	nominal	NUC	nuclear	OISC	oil-insulated self-cooled
NOMEN	nomenclature	NUM	numeral, numerical	OIWC	oil-immersed water-cooled
NONFLMB	nonflammable	NWG	National Wire Gage		
NONSTD	nonstandard	NWT	nonwatertight	OLVL	oil level
NONSYN	nonsynchronous	NYL	nylon	OML	outside mold line
NOP	number of passes			OMNI	omnidirection
NOR	notice of revision			OP	oil pump
NORM	normal			OP	oilproof
NORM	normalize		**O**	OPA	opaque
NOS	nor otherwise specified			OPLG	oil plug
NOV	November	O	orange (altn abbr)	OPN	operation
NOZ	nozzle	O&R	overhaul and repair	OPNG	opening
NP	nickle plated	O/P	ozalid print	OPP	octal print punch
NPL	nameplate	OA	overall	OPP	opposite
NPN	negative-positive-negative (transistor)	OBJ	object	OPT	optical
		OBJV	objective	OPT	optimum
NPRN	neoprene	OBL	oblique	OPT	optional (altn abbr)
NPS	Navy Primary Standards	OBS	obsolete	OPTL	optional
		OBSV	observation	OR	output register
NPSC	National straight pipe thread in pipe couplings	OC	on center	OR	outside radius
		OC	overcurrent	ORD	order
		OCB	oil circuit breaker	ORD	ordnance
NPSF	National straight pipe thread for dry seal pressure tight joints	OCC	occupation	ORF	orifice
		OCLD	oil cooled	ORG	organic
		OCLNR	oil cleaner	ORG	organization
NPSH	National straight pipe thread for hose couplings and nipples	OCLR	oil cooler	ORIENT	orientation
		OCR	optical character recognition	ORIG	origin
				ORLY	overload relay
NPSL	National straight pipe thread for locknuts and locknut pipe threads	OCR	overcurrent relay	ORN	orange
		OCT	octagon	ORN	ornament
		OCT	octane	OS	oil switch
		OCT	October	OS	otherwise specified
NPSM	National straight pipe thread for mech joints	OD	olive drab	OS&D	over, short and damage
		OD	outside	OSC	oscillator
NPT	National taper pipe thread	OD	ouside diameter	OSCG	oscillating
		ODP	open dripproof		

OSP	operating steam pressure	PACE	performance and cost evaluation	PED	pedestal		
OSR	output shift register	PAM	pulse-amplitude	PEJ	premolded expansion joint		
OT	oiltight		modulation	PELEC	photoelectric		
OT&E	operational test and evaluation	PAN	panoramic	PEN	penetrate		
		PAN	pantry	PEND	pending		
OTR	outer	PANT	pantograph	PENT	pentode		
OUT	outgoing	PAR	parallel (altn abbr)	PEP	planar epitaxial passivated (transistor)		
OUT	outlet	PARA	paragraph				
OUT	output	PARK	parkerized	PER	person		
OUT	outside	PARV	paravane	PERC	percussion		
OUTBD	outboard	PASS	passage	PERF	perforate		
OV	open ventilated	PASS	passenger	PERF	performed		
OV	over	PAT	patent	PERI	perimeter		
OVBD	overboard	PATPEND	patent pending	PERM	permanent		
OVFL	overflow	PATT	pattern	PERMB	permeability		
OVH	oval head	PAX	private automatic exchange	PERP	perpendicular		
OVHD	overhead			PERS	personnel		
OVHG	overhanging	PB	pull box	PERSP	perspective		
OVHL	overhaul	PB	push button	PERT	performance evaluation and review technique		
OVLD	overload	PB STA	push button station				
OVP	oval point	PBD	paperboard	PES	photoelectric scanner		
OVSP	overspeed	PBD	pressboard	PETRO	petroleum		
OVTR	overtravel	PBX	private branch exchange	PEU	polyeurethane		
OVV	overvoltage			PF	power factor		
OWF	optimum working frequency	PC	parts catalog	PF	profile		
		PC	piece	PF	pulse frequency		
OWGL	obscure wire glass	PC	pitch circle	PFD	preferred		
OXD	oxide	PC	printed circuit	PFM	power factor meter		
OXD	oxidized	PC&H	packing, crating and handling	PFM	pulse-frequency modulation		
OXY	oxygen						
OZ	ounce	PC MK	piece mark	PG	pressure gage		
OZ IN	ounce-inch	PCB	power circuit breaker	PGMT	pigment		
		PCB	printed circuit board	pH	hydrogen ion concentration		
		PCF	pounds per cubic foot				
	P	PCH	punch	PH	phase		
3PH	three phase	PCHT	parchment	PH BRZ	phosphor bronze		
P	page	PCM	pulse-code modulation	PHEN	phenolic		
P	pitch	PCP	program change proposal	PHM	phase meter		
P	plate (electron device)			PHOC	photocopy		
P	pole	PCT	percent	PHONO	phonograph		
P&L	power and lighting	PCTM	pulse-count modulation	PHOS	phosphate		
P&O	pickled and oiled	PD	pitch diameter	PHP	propeller horsepower		
P-D	punch-die	PD	potential difference	PHR	phrase		
P-P	peak to peak	PD	pulse doppler	PHR	preheater		
P/I	production illustration	PDIO	photodiode	PHSP	phase-splitter		
P/O	part of	PDISCH	pump discharge	PHT	preheat		
PA	pending availability	PDISPL	pump displacement	PHYS	physical		
PA	power amplifier	PDM	pulse-duration modulation	PI	point of impact		
PA	pressure angle			PI	point of intersection		
PA	profile angle	PDR	power directional relay	PI	programmed instruction		
PA	public address	PDS	purchasing department specification	PIL	purple indicating light		
PA	pulse amplifier			PIM	pulse interval modulation		
PABX	private automatic branch exchange	PE	probable error				
		PE	professional engineer	PIN	pinion		
PAC	primary address code	PEC	photoelectric cell	PIN	position indicator		

PIN	positive-intrinsic-negative (transistor)	PME	precision measuring equipment	PRCH	precharge
		PMFLT	pamphlet	PRCMT	procurement
PIX	picture	PMP	pump	PRCN	precision
PJTN	projection	PMT	payment	PRCS	process
PJTR	projector	PMVR	prime mover	PRCST	precast
PK	pack	PN	part number	PREAMP	preamplifier
PK	peak	PNEU	pneumatic	PRED	prediction
PKG	package	PNH	pan head	PREF	prefocused
PKG	packing	PNL	panel	PREFAB	prefabricated
PKT	pocket	PNP	positive-negative-positive (transistor)	PREFMD	preformed
PKWY	parkway			PRELIM	preliminary
PL	parting line (castings)	PNT	paint	PREP	preparation
PL	parts list	PO	post office	PRESS	pressure
PL	pitch line	PO	power oscillator	PREV	previous
PL	place	PO	production order	PRF	proof
PL	plain	PO	purchase order	PRF	pulse-repetition frequency
PL	plate	POI	program of instruction		
PL	plug	POL	petroleum, oils and lubricants	PRFM	performance
PL	property line			PRFRD	proofread
PL	proportional limit	POL	polar	PRFT	press fit
PLAS	plaster	POL	polish	PRGM	program
PLAT	platinum	POLTHN	polyethylene (insul)	PRGMR	programmer
PLATF	platform	POLEST	polyester	PRI	primary
PLBLK	pillow block	PORC	porcelain	PRI	priority
PLCY	policy	PORM	plus or minus	PRIN	principal
PLD	pay load	PORT	portable	PRL	parallel
PLD	plated	POS	position (altn abbr)	PRM	prime
PLG	piling	POS	positive	PRMLD	premolded
PLGL	plate glass	POSN	position	PRMTR	parameter
PLGR	plunger	POT	potential	PRNTG	printing
PLK	plank	POT	potentiometer	PROB	probability
PLL	pallet	PP	piping	PROB	problem
PLMB	plumbing	PP	power plant	PROC	procedure
PLR	pillar	PP	pressureproof	PROC	proceedings
PLRT	polarity	PP	push-pull	PROC	procurement (altn abbr)
PLS	pulse	PPG	pipe plug		
PLSN	pulsation	PPI	plan position indicator	PROCU	processing unit
PLSTC	plastic	PPLN	pipeline	PROD	product
PLT	pilot	PPM	parts per million	PROD	production
PLT	procurement lead time	PPM	pulse-position modulation	PROF	professional
PLTG	plating			PROG	progress
PLTR	plotter	PPR	paper	PROJ	project
PLVRZD	pulverized	PPS	pulses per second	PROP	propeller
PLYPH	polyphase	PPT	poppet	PROP	property
PLYWD	plywood	PPT	precipitate	PROT	protective
PLZ	polarize	PPT	product positioning time	PROTR	protractor
PLZD	polarized			PROV	provision
PLZN	polarization	PR	pair	PRP	purple
PM	permanent magnet (speaker)	PR	pipe rail	PRPHL	peripheral
		PR	pressure ratio	PRPLN	propulsion
PM	phase modulation	PR	purchase request	PRPNE	propane
PM	pilot motor	PRAC	practice	PRPSD	proposed
PM	preventive maintenance	PRBNT	prebent	PRPSL	proposal
PMD	program monitoring and diagnosis	PRC	pierce	PRR	pulse-repetition rate
		PRC	point of reverse curve	PRS	press
				PRSD	pressed

PRSRZ	pressurize	PVT	pressure-volume-	RALW	radioactive liquid waste
PRSTC	prosthetic		temperature	RB	relay block
PRT	pulse-repetition time	PW	pulse width	RB	rubber base
PRV	pressure reducing valve	PWB	printed wiring board	RBE	relative biological effectiveness
PS	polystyrene	PWC	process water cooler	RBN	radio beacon
PS	process specification (number)	PWD	powder	RBN	ribbon
		PWM	pulse width modulation	RBR	rubber
PSF	pound-force per square foot	PWR	power	RC	reinforced concrete
		PWRH	powerhouse	RC	remote control
PSI	pound-force per square inch	PYR	pyramid	RC	resistance-capacitance
				RCC	reader common contact
PSIA	pound-force per square inch absolute		**Q**	RCC	rubber-covered cable
		Q&A	question and answer	RCD	record
PSIG	pound-force per square inch gage	QA	quality assurance	RCD	reverse current device
		QA	quick-acting	RCDG	recording
PSIV	passive	QB	quick break	RCDR	recorder
PSL	pipe sleeve	QC	quality control	RCHT	ratchet
PSL	pressure seal	QDISC	quick disconnect	RCL	recall
PSM	prism	QDRNT	quadrant	RCN	recreation
PSNR	positioner	QIK	quick	RCNDT	recondition
PST	point of spiral tangent	QOD	quick-opening device	RCO	reactor core
PSTL	postal	QR	quire	RCP	reinforced concrete pipe
PSU	power supply unit	QRY	quarry		
PSV	preserve	QT	quart	RCP	right-circular polarization
PSVT	passivate	QTR	quarter		
PSW	potential switch	QTY	quantity	RCPT	receipt
PSWBD	power switchboard	QTZ	quartz	RCPT	receptacle
PT	part	QUAD	quadrangle	RCPTN	reception
PT	pint	QUAD	quadrant (altn abbr)	RCTL	resistor-capacitor-transistor logic
PT	pipe tap	QUAL	qualitative		
PT	pneumatic tube	QUANT	quantitative	RCTN	reaction
PT	point	QUEST	question	RCVD	received
PT	point of tangency	QUOT	quotation	RCVG	receiving
PT	potential transformer			RCVR	receiver
PT	pulse time		**R**	RCVY	recovery
PTD	painted			RD	read
PTD	printed	1/4RD	quarter round	RD	register drive
PTFE	polytetrafluorethylene	R	radius	RD	road
PTL	pintle	R	ratio	RD	roof drain
PTM	pulse-time modulation	R	red	RD	root diameter
PTN	partition	R	right	RD	round (altn abbr)
PTO	power takeoff	R&D	research and development	RDC	radiac
PTR	printer			RDCN	reduction
PTY	party	R-W	read-write (head)	RDCR	reducer
PU	pickup	R/W	right of way	RDF	radio direction finding
PU	power unit	RA	rayon (insul)	RDG	ridge
PUB	publication (altn abbr)	RA	reduction of area	RDH	round head
PUBN	publication	RAACT	radioactive	RDL	radial
PUL	pulley	RACT	reverse acting	RDM	recording demand meter
PULV	pulverizer	RAD	radius		
PUR	purifier	RAD HAZ	radiation hazard	RDNG	reading
PURCH	purchase	RAD INSP	radiographic inspection	RDOUT	readout
PV	plan view	RAD OPR	radio operator	RDR	reader
PVC	polyvinyl chloride	RADL	radiological	RDTR	radiator
PVT	pivot	RADN	radiation		

RDY	ready	REWK	rework	ROT	rotate
REAC	reactance	RF	radio frequency	ROUT	routine
REAC	reactor	RF	raised face	RPDR	reproducer
REC	recess, recessed	RFC	radio-frequency choke	RPLSN	repulsion
RECIP	reciprocating	RFG	roofing	RPM	revolutions per minute
RECIRC	recirculate	RFGT	refrigerant	RPR	repair
RECM	recommend	RFI	radio-frequency interference	RPRT	report
RECP	receptacle (altn abbr)			RPS	revolutions per second
RECT	rectangular	RFLX	reflex	RPT	repeat
RECT	rectifier	RFND	refined	RPTR	repeater
REDSG	redesignate	RFP	request for proposal	RPVNTV	rust preventative
REDWM	redrawm	RFRC	refractory	RR	railroad
REF	refer	RFS	regardless of feature size	RR	relief radii
REF	reference			RR	roll roofing
REF	refinery	RGD	rigid	RS	right side
REFL	reference line	RGH	rough	RSD	raised
REFL	reflector	RGLR	regular	RSD	rolling steel door
REFR	refrigerator	RGLT	regulating	RSPTR	respirator
REG	register (altn abbr)	RGLTR	regulator	RSPV	respective
REG	regular (altn abbr)	RGN	region	RSQ	resque
REG	regulator (altn abbr)	RGNG	rigging	RST	reinforcing steel
REGEN	regenerative	RGTR	register	RSTG	roasting
REIMB	reimburse	RH	relative humidity	RSTPF	rustproof
REINF	reinforce	RH	right hand	RSVR	reservoir
REJ	reject	RH	Rockwell hardness	RT	radio telephone
REL	relative	RH DR	right-hand drive	RT	raintight
REL	release (altn abbr)	RHEO	rheostat	RT	rate
RELOC	relocated	RI	reflective insulation	RT	real time
REM	removable	RIL	red indicating light	RT	receiver-transmitter
REORG	reorganize	RIOT	real-time input-output transducer	RTC	reader tape contact
REPL	replace			RTCL	reticle
REPRO	reproduction	RIV	river	RTD	resistance temperature detector
REQ	request	RK	rack		
REQD	required	RKR	rocker	RTE	route
REQN	requisition	RL	resistance-inductance	RTG	rating
REQT	requirement	RLC	resistance-inductance-capacitance	RTL	resistor-transistor logic
RES	research			RTM	recording tachometer
RES	resistance	RLD	rolled	RTN	return
RES	resistor	RLF	relief	RTNG	retaining
RES FLD	residual field	RLG	railing	RTNR	retainer
RESC	rescind	RLR	roller	RTR	rotor
RESID	residual	RLR BRG	roller bearing	RTRSW	rotary switch
RESIL	resilient	RLSE	release	RTRY	rotary
RESN	resonant	RLV	relieve	RU	reproducing unit
RESP	respectively	RLY	relay	RUB	rubber (altn abbr)
RESP	responsible	RM	raw material	RUD	rudder
RESTR	restorer	RM	room	RV	rear view
RETP	retape	RMR	reamer	RV	relief valve
RETR	retractable	RMS	root mean square	RVLG	revolving
RETRO	retroactive	RMT	remote	RVM	reactive voltmeter
RETRO	retrograde	RND	round	RVS	reverse
RETROG	retrogressive	RNDM	random	RVSBL	reversible
REV	review	RNG	range	RVT	rivet
REV	revise	RNWBL	renewable	RVTD	riveted
REV	revision	RO	rough opening	RWG	Roebling Wire Gage
REV	revolution	RO	runout	RWND	rewind

RWY	runway	SCRDB	screwed bonnet	SH ABS	shock absorber
RY	railway	SCRN	screen	SH BL	shot blast
RYN	rayon	SCT	structural clay tile	SH TR	shunt trip
		SCTR	sector	SH & T	shower and toilet
		SCTY	security	SHCR	shipping container
S		SD	shower drain	SHF	shift
S	south	SD BL	sand blast	SHF	super-high frequency
S2S	surfaced or dressed two sides	SDG	siding	SHK	shank
S/R	send and receive	SDL	saddle	SHK	shock
SA	spectrum analyzer	SDR	sender	SHL	shell
SA	stress anneal	SE	single end	SHL	shellac
SAC	sprayed acoustical ceiling	SE	special equipment	SHLD	shield, shielding
SAE	Society of Automotive Engineers	SEC	second	SHLDR	shoulder
		SEC	secondary	SHP	shaft horsepower
SAF	safety	SECT	section	SHPBD	shipboard
SAL	salinity	SEG	sealing	SHPNG	shipping
SALV	salvage	SEG	segment	SHPRF	shakeproof
SAN	sanitary	SEJ	sliding expansion joint	SHPT	shipment
SAR	storage address register	SEL	select	SHT	short
SAT	saturate	SEL	selector	SHT DN	shut down
SATC	suspended acoustical-tile ceiling	SELS	selsyn	SHTG	shortage
		SEMICOND	semiconductor	SHTHG	sheathing
SB	service bulletin	SEN	semienclosed	SHV	sheave
SB	sideband	SENS	sensitive	SI	salinity indicator
SB	silver braze	SEP	separator	SI	standing instruction
SB	sleeve bearing	SEP	September	SI	International System of Units (Systeme International d'Unites)
SB	stove bolt	SEQ	sequence		
SB	stuffing box	SER	serial		
SBK	single-beam klystron	SER	series	SIF	single face
SBM	submersible	SERNO	serial number	SIF	selective identification feature
SBSTR	substrate	SERR	serrated		
SBU	silver brazing union	SERV	service (altn abbr)	SIL	silence
SC	scale	SERVO	servomechanism	SIL	silver
SC	single contact	SETLG	settling	SILS	silver solder
SC	smooth contour	SEW	sewage	SIM	similar
SCC	single conductor cable	SF	semifinished	SIM	simulator
SCD	screen door	SF	slip fit	SIMP	specific impulse
SCDP	steel cadmium plated	SF	spot face	SIT	situation
SCE	source	SFB	solid fiberboard	SJ	slip joint
SCH	socket head	SFC	specific fuel consumption	SK	sink
SCHED	schedule			SK	sketch
SCHEM	schematic	SFDR	single feeder	SKD	skilled
SCI	science	SFGD	safeguard	SKT	socket
SCINT	scintillator	SFO	spot face other side	SL	sea level
SCLER	scleroscope	SFT	shaft	SL	sliding
SCNG	scanning	SG	structural glass	SLBL	soluble
SCNR	scanner	SGD	signed	SLD	sealed
SCR	screw	SGL	single	SLD	sliding door
SCR	semiconductor controlled rectifier	SGW	security guard window	SLDR	solder
		SH	scleroscope hardness	SLFLKG	self-locking
SCR	silicon controlled rectifier	SH	shackle	SLFSE	self-sealing
		SH	sheet	SLFTPG	self-tapping
		SH	sheeting	SLGR	slinger
		SH	shield (electron device)	SLSP	slow speed
		SH	shower	SLT	self-loading tape
SCR GT	screen gate	SH	shunt	SLT	skylight

SLT	slate	SPKR	speaker	STA	stationary
SLTD	slotted	SPL	special (altn abbr)	STAB	stabilizer
SLV	sleeve	SPL	spiral	STAN	stanchion
SLVT	solvent	SPLC	splice	START	starter
SLYP	shortleaf yellow pine	SPLN	spline	STBD	starboard
SM	small	SPLTR	splitter	STBLN	stabilization
SM	smooth	SPLX	simplex	STBSCP	stroboscope
SMLS	seamless	SPLY	supply	STBY	standby
SMY	summary	SPM	strokes per minute	STC	sensitivity time control
SN	siren	SPNR	spanner	STD	standard
SND	sound	SPNSN	suspension	STDF	standoff
SNDG	sending	SPR	spring	STDY	steady
SNDPRF	soundproof	SPR	sprinkler	STDZN	standardization
SNL	standard nomenclature list	SPRKT	sprocket	STER	sterilizer
		SPRT	support	STFG	stuffing
SNLG	signaling	SPST	single-pole single throw	STG	stage
SNO	stock number	SPTW	desk, single-pedestal typewriter	STG	starting
SNR	signal-to-noise ratio			STGEN	steam generator
SNSR	sensor	SQ	square	STGR	stringer
SNTR	sinter	SQCG	squirrel cage	STIF	stiffener
SO	shop order	SQH	square head	STIR	stirrup
SO	stock order	SQW	square wave	STK	stack
SO	stop order	SR	selenium rectifier	STK	stock
SOL	solenoid	SR	senior	STL	steel
SOL	solid	SR	shift register	STL	studio-transmitter link
SOLN	solution	SR	slip ring	STLR	semitrailer
SOLV	solenoid valve	SR	slow release (relay)	STLT	stellite
SOV	shutoff valve	SR	stateroom	STN	stone
SP	single-pole	SRCH	search	STNG	sustaining
SP	soil pipe	SRLY	series relay	STNLS	stainless
SP	space	SRVL	survival	STOR	storage
SP	spare	SS	semisteel	STP	stamp
SP	special purpose	SS	service sink	STPD	stripped
SP	specific	SS	straight shank	STPR	stepper
SP	speed	SSB	single sideband	STPR	stripper
SP	splashproof	SSBO	single swing blocking oscillator	STR	straight
SP	spool			STR	strainer
SP	standpipe	SSCR	setscrew	STR	stream
SP GR	specific gravity	SSCRN	silkscreen	STR	strength
SP HT	specific heat	SSD	subsoil drain	STRBK	strongback
SP PH	split phase	SSF	saybolt seconds furol	STRD	stranded
SP SW	single-pole switch	SSK	soil stack	STRG	steering
SP VOL	specific volume	SSR	slate-shingle roof	STRG	strong
SPCL	special	SSS	solid-state switching	STRK	stroke
SPCR	spacer	SST	stainless steel	STRL	structural
SPDL	spindle	SSTU	seamless steel tubing	STRLN	streamline
SPDOM	speedometer	SSU	saybolt seconds universal	STRM	storeroom
SPDT	single-pole double throw			STRUCT	structure
		ST	sawtooth	STTR	stator
SPEC	specification	ST	single-throw	STU	step-up
SPEC	specimen	ST	steam	STW	storm water
SPFT	desk, single-pedestal flat-top	ST	store	STWP	steam working pressure
		ST	street	STWY	stairway
SPH	space heater	ST BRZ	statuary bronze	SUBASSY	subassembly
SPHER	spherical	ST PR	static pressure	SUBJ	subject
SPK	spark	STA	station	SUBMG	submerged

SUBMIN	subminiature
SUBQ	subsequent
SUBST	substitute
SUBSTA	substation
SUBSTR	substructure
SUBTR	subtraction
SUCT	suction
SUDT	silicon unilateral diffused transistor
SUF	sufficient
SUFF	suffix
SUPERHET	superheterodyne
SUPERSTR	superstructure
SUPHTR	superheater
SUPPL	supplement
SUPPR	suppressor
SUPSD	superseded
SUPT	supersensitive
SUPV	supervise
SURF	surface
SURG	surgical
SURV	survey
SUSP	suspend
SV	safety valve
SV	self-ventilated
SV	side view
SVCE	service
SVMTR	servomotor
SVO	servo
SW	salt water
SW	short wave
SW	spot weld
SW	switch
SWB	short wheel base
SWBD	switchboard
SWG	British Standard Wire Gage
SWG	Stubs-Wire Gage
SWG	swage
SWG	swing
SWGD	swinging door
SWGR	switchgear
SWOV	switchover
SWP	safe working pressure
SWP	sweep
SWR	standing wave ratio (voltage)
SWR	switch rails
SWS	switch stand
SWSG	security window screen and guard
SWT	sweat
SWT	switch ties
SWVL	swivel
SYM	symbol
SYMM	symmetrical
SYMP	symposium
SYN	synchronous
SYNC	synchronizer
SYNTH	synthetic
SYS	system

T

T	tee
T	teeth
T	toilet
T&G	tongue and groove
T/B	title block
TAB	tabulate
TAC	tactical
TACH	tachometer
TAF	trim after forming
TARP	tarpaulin
TAS	true air speed
TB	technical bulletin
TB	terminal board
TBD	to be determined
TBE	threaded both ends
TBG	tubing
TBL	table
TBLR	tumbler
TBO	time between overhaul
TC	tape core
TC	temperature compensating
TC	terra cotta
TC	thermocouple
TC	time constant
TC	timed closing
TC	top chord
TC	trip coil
TCC	turbine close coupled
TCD	thyratron core driver
TCG	tune-controlled gain
TCH	temporary construction hole
TCU	tape control unit
TD	temperature differential
TD	time delay
TD	transmitter distributor
TDC	time-delay closing
TDCM	transistor driver core memory
TDG	twist drill gage
TDL	tunnel-diode logic
TDM	tandem
TDO	time-delay opening
TDX	thermal demand transmitter
TE	thermal element
TE	totally enclosed

TE	trailing edge
TECH	technical
TECH	technician
TEFC	totally enclosed fan cooled
TEJ	transverse expansion joint
TEL	telephone
TELB	telephone booth
TEM	temper
TEMP	temperature
TEMP	temporary
TEMPL	template
TER	terrazzo
TER	tertiary
TERM	terminal
TERR	territory
TET	tetrode
TF	thin film
TF	thread forming
TF	tile floor
TFL	Teflon (insul)
TFT	thin-film transistor
TGC	transmit gain control
TGL	toggle
TGT	tail gate
TGT	target
TH	thermoid
THC	thermal converter
THD	thread
THD	total harmonic distortion
THEOR	theoretical
THERM	thermometer
THERMO	thermostat
THK	thick
THKNS	thickness
THMS	thermistor
THP	thrust horsepower
THPFB	treated hard-pressed fiberboard
THR	thrust
THRM	thermal
THRMSTC	thermostatic
THROT	throttle
THRT	throat
THRU	through
THTR	theater
THYR	thyristor
TIC	temperature indicating controller
TIM	time meter
TIP	turbine inlet pressure
TIR	total indicator reading
TIT	turbine inlet temperature

TJP	turbo-jet propulsion
TK	tank
TKR	tanker
TKT	ticket
TL	thrust line
TLG	telegraph
TLG	tilting
TLK	test link
TLLD	total load
TLM	telemeter
TLMY	telemetry
TLU	table lookup
TLY	tally
TM	technical manual
TM	temperature meter
TM	tone modulation
TM	training manual
TM	transverse magnetic
TMB	tumble
TMBR	timber
TMD	timed
TMG	timing
TMPD	tempered
TMR	timer
TMS	time and motion study
TMS	type model series
TMX	telemeter transmitter
TN	technical note
TN	thermonuclear
TN	tone
TN	train
TN	true north
TND	tinned
TNG	tongue
TNG	training
TNL	tunnel
TNLDIO	tunnel diode
TNR	thinner
TNSL	tensile
TNSN	tension
TNTV	tentative
TO	takeoff
TO	technical order
TO	time opening
TOB BRZ	tobin bronze
TOE	thread one end
TOL	tolerance
TOPG	topping
TOPO	topography
TOR	totalizing relay
TORNL	torsional
TOT	total
TOT	turbine outlet temperature
TP	tie plate
TP	timing point

TP	true position
TP	true profile
TP DR	tape drive
TPG	tapping
TPI	tape phase inverter
TPI	teeth per inch
TPI	threads per inch
TPL	triple
TPM	telemetry processor module
TPR	taper
TPR	teleprinter
TPS	task parameter synthesizer
TPSN	transposition
TPT	tappet
TPTG	tuned plate tuned grid
TPTOL	true position tolerance
TR	technical report
TR	trace
TR	transmitter receiver
TR	transom
TR	truss
TRAJ	trajectory
TRANS	transfer (altn abbr)
TRANS	transparent
TRANSP	transportation
TRANSV	transverse
TRB	treble
TRCR	tracer
TRD	tread
TRD	turbine reduction drive
TRF	tuned radio frequency
TRFC	traffic
TRG	trailing
TRH	truss head
TRI	triode
TRIB	tributary
TRIG	trigger
TRK	track
TRK	truck
TRK	trunk
TRKG	tracking
TRLR	trailer
TRLY	trolley
TRMR	trimmer
TRNBKL	turnbuckle
TRND	turned
TRNGL	triangle
TRNPS	transpose
TRNR	trainer
TRNSN	transition
TRNTBL	turntable
TROPR	troposphere
TRP	tripped
TRPL	terneplate

TRQ	torque
TRSBR	transcriber
TRSN	torsion
TRTD	treated
TRTMT	treatment
TRUN	trunnion
TRVLG	traveling
TRX	triplex
TS	taper shank
TS	Telegraph System
TS	tensile strength
TS	time switch
TS	tool steel
TS	tube sheet
TSL	typesetting lead
TSTG	testing
TSTR	tester
TSTRZ	transistorized
TSW	temperature switch
TT	teletype
TT	total time
TT	triple thermoplastic (insul)
TTL	transistor-transistor logic
TTNG	tightening
TTY	teletypewriter
TUN	tuning
TUNG	tungsten
TUR	turret
TURB	turbine
TVG	time variation of gain
TVM	tachometer voltmeter
TVM	transistor voltmeter
TW	temperature well
TW	traveling wave
TW	twisted
TW	typewriter
TWMBK	traveling-wave multiple-beam klystron
TWR	tower
TWSB	twin sideband
TWT	traveling-wave tube
TWX	teletypewriter exchange
TWY	taxiway
TXTL	textile
TYP	typical

U

U&L	upper and lower
U/O	used on
U/W	used with
UAR	use as required
UBL	unbleached
UC	unit cooler

UCL	upper control limit	USB	upper sideband	VEG	vegetable
UF	ultrasonic frequency	USC&GS	United States Coast	VEH	vehicle
UFN	until further notice		and Geodetic Survey	VEL	vellum
UFR	underfrequency relay	USG	United States Gage	VEL	velocity
UGND	underground	USGS	United States	VENT	ventilate
UH	unit heater		Geological Survey	VENT	ventilator
UHF	ultrahigh frequency	USP	United States	VERB	verbatim
UJT	unijunction transistor		Pharmacopoeia	VERIF	verification
UK	unit check	USS	United States Standard	VERN	vernier
ULI	Underwriters	UTIL	utility	VERT	vertical
	Laboratories, Inc.	UTN	utensil	VEST	vestibule
ULT	ultimate	UTRTD	untreated	VF	variable frequency
UMB	umbilical	UTS	universal time	VF	voice frequency
UMUS	unbleached muslin		standards	VFL PT	variable floating point
UN	unified	UV	ultraviolet	VFO	variable frequency
UN	union	UVD	undervoltage device		oscillator
UN	unit	UWT	unit weight	VH	vent hole
UNAUTHD	unauthorized	UWTR	underwater	VH	Vickers hardness
UNB	union bonnet			VHF	very high frequency
UNC	unified coarse (thread)			VI	viscosity index
UNCOND	unconditionally		V	VIB	vibrate, vibration
UNCTD	uncoated	V	valve	VID	video
UND	under	V	violet (altn abbr)	VIDAMP	video amplifier
UNDC	undercurrent	V	volt	VIDF	video frequency
UNDEF	undefined	VAC	vacant	VIL	village
UNDETM	undetermined	VAC	vacuum	VIMP	vertical impulse
UNDF	underfrequency	VAC	volt, alternating current	VINT	video integration
UNDV	undervoltage	VAL	valley	VIO	violet
UNEF	unified extra fine (thread)	VAL	value	VIP	visual identification
UNF	unified fine (thread)	VAM	voltammeter		point
UNFIN	unfinished	VAP PRF	vaporproof	VIS	visual
UNIF	uniform	VAR	variable	VISC	viscosity
UNIV	universal	VAR	variance	VISMR	viscometer
UNK	unknown	VARN	varnish	VIT	vitreous
UNL	unloading	VARR	visual aural radio range	VIZ	namely
UNLIM	unlimited	VB	valve box	VLF	very low frequency
UNS	unified special (thread)	VC	vitrified clay	VLMTRC	volumetric
UOS	unless otherwise	VC	voice coil	VLR	very long range
	specified	VCB	vertical location of	VLT	volute
UPDFT	updraft		center of buoyancy	VM	velocity modulation
UPR	upper	VCG	vertical location of	VM	voltmeter
UPS	uninterrupted power		center of gravity	VNXL	vaneaxial
	supply	VCL	vertical center line	VO	voice
UPWD	upward	VCO	voltage controlled	VOL	volume
UR	unsatisfactory report		oscillator	VOM	volt ohm milliammeter
UR	urinal	VCT	vitrified clay tile	VP	vent pipe
UR	utility room	VCT	voltage control transfer	VPR	vaporize
URG	urgent	VD	vandyke	VR	voltage regulator
URT	upright	VD	vault door	VRFY	verify
US	undersize	VD	void	VRIS	varistor
US	Uniform System (lens	VD	voltage drop	VRL	vertical reference line
	making)	VDC	volt, direct current	VRLY	voltage relay
USAS	USA Standard	VDET	voltage detector	VRYG	varying
USASI	United States of	VDI	vertical display	VS	vapor seal
	America Standards		indicator	VS	vent stack
	Institute (now ANSI)	VE	ventilating equipment	VS	versus

VS	voltmeter switch	WFS	wood furring strips	WSHLD	windshield
VSB	vestigial sideband	WG	waveguide	WSHR	washer
VSBL	visible	WG	wedge	WSL	weather seal
VST	valve seat	WG	window guard	WSP	working steam pressure
VSTM	valve stem	WG	wing	WSR	wood-shingle roof
VSWR	voltage standing wave ratio	WH	wall hydrant	WT	weight
		WH	water heater	WTG	waiting
VT	vacuum tube	WH	watt-hour	WTHPRF	weatherproof
VT	vaportight	WHL	wheel	WTRTT	watertight
VT	voice tube	WHM	watt-hour meter	WTRZ	winterize
VTM	voltage-tunable magnetron	WHSE	warehouse	WU	window unit
		WHT	white	WU	work unit
VTR	video tape recorder	WI	wrought iron	WV	wall vent
VTVM	vacuum-tube voltmeter	WIL	white indicating lamp	WV	working voltage
VTX	vertex	WJ	water jacket	WW	wire way
		WK	week	WW	wire wound
	W	WK	work		
1/W	one way	WKG	working		**X**
W	watt	WKR	wrecker		
W	west	WKS	workshop	XARM	cross arm
W	white (altn abbr)	WL	water line	XBAR	crossbar
W	wide	WL	wavelength	XCVR	transceiver
W&M GA	Washburn and Moen Gage	WL	white light	XDCR	transducer
		WL	wind load	XFMR	transformer
W/	with (comb form)	WL	wire list	XFR	transfer
W/D	withdrawn	WLD	welded	XHAIR	crosshair
W/O	without	WLDMT	weldment	XHVY	extra heavy
W/W	winding to winding	WLDR	welder	XLTR	translator
WAF	width across flats	WM	water meter	XLWB	extra-long wheel base
WAG	wagon	WM	wattmeter	XMSN	transmission
WARR	warranty	WM	wire mesh	XMT	transmit
WB	wet bulb	WMGR	worm gear	XMTD	transmitted
WB	wheel base	WN	winch	XMTG	transmitting
WB	wide band	WND	wound	XMTR	transmitter
WB	work bench	WP	waste pipe	XPL	explosive
WBF	wood block floor	WP	water pump	XSECT	cross section
WBG	webbing	WP	weatherproof (insul)	XSTR	extra strong
WBR	word buffer register	WP	wet process	XSTR	transistor
WC	water closet	WPFC	waterproof fan cooled	XTAL	crystal
WCHR	water chiller	WPG	waterproofing	XTLO	crystal oscillator
WCLD	water-cooled	WPG	wiping	XX STR	double extra strong
WCR	watercooler	WPM	words per minute		
WD	watt demand meter	WPR	working pressure		**Y**
WD	wind	WR	wall receptacle		
WD	wood	WR	washroom	Y	yellow (altn abbr)
WD	wood door	WR	weather resistant	YD	yard
WD	word	WR	wrench	YEL	yellow
WD	work day	WR	writer	YIL	yellow indicating lamp
WDF	wood door and frame	WRG	wiring	YLT	yellow light
WDF	woodruff	WRK	wrecking	YP	yield point
WDG	winding	WRN	warning	YR	year
WDO	window	WRT	wrought	YS	yield strength
WEA	weather	WS	water surface		
WEAT	weathertight	WS	weather stripping		**Z**
WF	wash fountain	WS	wrought steel	Z	zone
WFR	wafer	WSHG	washing	ZA	zero adjuster

Basic Weld Symbols and Their Location Significance

LOCATION SIGNIFICANCE	FILLET	PLUG OR SLOT	SPOT OR PROJECTION	SEAM	(FLASH OR UPSET) SQUARE	V	BEVEL	U	J
							GROOVE		
ARROW SIDE									
OTHER SIDE									
BOTH SIDES		NOT USED	NOT USED	NOT USED					
NO ARROW SIDE OR OTHER SIDE SIGNIFICANCE	NOT USED	NOT USED			NOT USED EXCEPT FOR FLASH OR UPSET WELDS	NOT USED	NOT USED	NOT USED	NOT USED

Supplementary Symbols

WELD ALL AROUND	FIELD WELD	MELT-THRU	CONTOUR		
			FLUSH	CONVEX	CONCAVE

Location of Elements of a Welding Symbol

FINISH SYMBOL
CONTOUR SYMBOL
ROOT OPENING; DEPTH OF FILLING FOR PLUG AND SLOT WELDS
SIZE; SIZE OR STRENGTH FOR CERTAIN WELDS
REFERENCE LINE

GROOVE ANGLE; INCLUDED ANGLE OF COUNTERSINK FOR PLUG WELDS
LENGTH OF WELD
PITCH (CENTER-TO-CENTER SPACING) OF WELDS
ARROW CONNECTING REFERENCE LINE TO ARROW SIDE OR ARROW-SIDE MEMBER OF JOINT

F
A
R
S
T
L-P
(N)

(SIDES) (OTHER SIDE) (BOTH) (ARROW SIDE)

SPECIFICATION, PROCESS, OR OTHER REFERENCE
TAIL (MAY BE OMITTED WHEN REFERENCE IS NOT USED)
BASIC WELD SYMBOL OR DETAIL REFERENCE

FIELD WELD SYMBOL
WELD-ALL-AROUND SYMBOL
NUMBER OF SPOT OR PROJECTION WELDS

ELEMENTS IN THIS AREA REMAIN AS SHOWN WHEN TAIL AND ARROW ARE REVERSED

Typical Welding Symbols

BACK OR BACKING WELD SYMBOL
ANY APPLICABLE SINGLE GROOVE WELD SYMBOL

SURFACING WELD SYMBOL INDICATING BUILT-UP SURFACE
SIZE (HEIGHT OF DEPOSIT). OMISSION INDICATES NO SPECIFIC HEIGHT DESIRED
1/8
ORIENTATION, LOCATION AND ALL DIMENSIONS OTHER THAN SIZE ARE SHOWN ON THE DRAWING

DOUBLE FILLET WELDING SYMBOL
SIZE (LENGTH OF LEG)
SPECIFICATION, PROCESS OR OTHER REFERENCE
1/4
12
IG
LENGTH. OMISSION INDICATES THAT WELD EXTENDS BETWEEN ABRUPT CHANGES IN DIRECTION OR AS DIMENSIONED

CHAIN INTERMITTENT FILLET WELDING SYMBOL
5/16 2-6
5/16 2-6
SIZE (LENGTH OF LEG)
LENGTH OF INCREMENTS
PITCH (DISTANCE BETWEEN CENTERS) OF INCREMENTS

STAGGERED INTERMITTENT FILLET WELDING SYMBOL
SIZE (LENGTH OF LEG)
1/2 3-8
1/2 3-8
PITCH (DISTANCE BETWEEN CENTERS) OF INCREMENTS
LENGTH OF INCREMENTS

SINGLE-V-GROOVE WELDING SYMBOL
SIZE (DEPTH OF CHAMFERING). OMISSION INDICATES DEPTH OF CHAMFERING EQUAL TO THICKNESS OF MEMBERS
1/2 1/8 60°
ROOT OPENING
GROOVE ANGLE

Supplementary Symbols Used with Welding Symbols

WELD-ALL-AROUND SYMBOL
WELD-ALL-AROUND SYMBOL INDICATES THAT WELD EXTENDS COMPLETELY AROUND THE JOINT

FIELD WELD SYMBOL
FIELD WELD SYMBOL. INDICATES THAT WELD IS TO BE MADE AT A PLACE OTHER THAN THAT OF INITIAL CONSTRUCTION

MELT-THRU SYMBOL
MELT-THRU SYMBOL IS NOT DIMENSIONED (EXCEPT HEIGHT)
ANY APPLICABLE WELD SYMBOL

Basic Joints—Identification of Arrow Side and Other Side of Joint and

ARROW OF WELDING SYMBOL
ARROW SIDE OF JOINT
JOINT
OTHER SIDE OF JOINT
BUTT JOINT

ARROW SIDE OF JOINT
OTHER SIDE OF JOINT
ARROW OF WELDING SYMBOL
CORNER JOINT

ARROW SIDE OF JOINT
JOINT
OTHER SIDE OF JOINT
ARROW OF WELDING SYMBOL

ARROW OF WELDING SYMBOL
ARROW SIDE OF JOINT
OTHER SIDE OF JOINT
TEE JOINT

DESIGNATION OF WELDING PROCESSES BY LETTERS

CAW	Carbon-Arc Welding	FW	Flash Welding
CW	Cold Welding	GMAW	Gas Metal-Arc Welding
DB	Dip Brazing	GTAW	Gas Tungsten-Arc Welding
DFW	Diffusion Welding	IB	Induction Brazing
EBW	Electron Beam Welding	IRB	Infrared Brazing
EW	Electroslag Welding	IW	Induction Welding
EXW	Explosion Welding	LBW	Laser Beam Welding
FB	Furnace Brazing	OAW	Oxyacetylene Welding
FCAW	Flux Cored Arc Welding	OHW	Oxyhydrogen Welding
FOW	Forge Welding	PAW	Plasma-Arc Welding
FRW	Friction Welding	PEW	Percussion Welding
		PGW	Pressure Gas Welding

RB	Resistance Brazing
RPW	Projection Welding
RSEW	Resistance-Seam Welding
RSW	Resistance-Spot Welding
SAW	Submerged Arc Welding
SMAW	Shielded Metal-Arc Welding
SW	Stud Welding
TB	Torch Brazing
TW	Thermit Welding
USW	Ultrasonic Welding
UW	Upset Welding

STANDARD WELDING SYMBOLS

| FLARE-V | FLARE-BEVEL | BACK OR BACKING | SURFACING | FLANGE | | ARC-SEAM OR ARC SPOT | RESISTANCE-SPOT | PROJECTION | RESISTANCE-SEAM | FLASH OR UPSET |
				EDGE	CORNER					
		GROOVE (WELD SYMBOL)	NOT USED				NOT USED		NOT USED	NOT USED
		GROOVE (WELD SYMBOL)	NOT USED				NOT USED		NOT USED	NOT USED
		NOT USED	NOT USED	NOT USED	NOT USED	NOT USED	NOT USED	NOT USED	NOT USED	NOT USED
NOT USED	NOT USED	NOT USED		NOT USED	NOT USED	NOT USED		NOT USED		

SINGLE-V-GROOVE WELDING SYMBOL INDICATING ROOT PENETRATION

DEPTH OF CHAMFERING PLUS ROOT PENETRATION
SIZE
ROOT OPENING
GROOVE ANGLE

DOUBLE-BEVEL-GROOVE WELDING SYMBOL

OMISSION OF SIZE DIMENSION INDICATES A TOTAL DEPTH OF CHAMFERING EQUAL TO THICKNESS OF MEMBERS
ARROW POINTS TOWARD MEMBER TO BE CHAMFERED
ROOT OPENING
GROOVE ANGLE

WELDING SYMBOLS FOR COMBINED WELDS

PLUG WELDING SYMBOL

SIZE (DIA. OF HOLE AT ROOT)
PITCH (DISTANCE BETWEEN CENTERS) OF WELDS
DEPTH OF FILLING IN INCHES. OMISSION INDICATES FILLING IS COMPLETE
INCLUDED ANGLE OF COUNTERSINK

SLOT WELDING SYMBOL

DEPTH OF FILLING IN INCHES. OMISSION INDICATES FILLING IS COMPLETE
ORIENTATION, LOCATION AND ALL DIMENSIONS OTHER THAN DEPTH OF FILLING ARE SHOWN ON THE DRAWING

SPOT WELDING SYMBOL

NUMBER OF WELDS (5)
SIZE (DIA. OF WELD). STRENGTH IN LB. PER WELD MAY BE USED INSTEAD
PITCH (DISTANCE BETWEEN CENTERS) OF WELDS
PROCESS REFERENCE MUST BE USED TO INDICATE PROCESS DESIRED

PROJECTION WELDING SYMBOL

PROJECTION WELDING REFERENCE MUST BE USED
SIZE (STRENGTH IN LB. PER WELD). DIA. OF WELD MAY BE USED INSTEAD FOR CIRCULAR PROJECTION WELDS
RPW 500 6
PITCH (DISTANCE BETWEEN CENTERS) OF WELDS
NUMBER OF WELDS

SEAM WELDING SYMBOL

SIZE (WIDTH OF WELD). STRENGTH IN LB. PER LINEAR INCH MAY BE USED INSTEAD
PROCESS REFERENCE MUST BE USED TO INDICATE PROCESS DESIRED
RSEW .30" 3-9
LENGTH OF WELDS OR INCREMENTS. OMISSION INDICATES THAT WELD EXTENDS BETWEEN ABRUPT CHANGES IN DIRECTION OR AS DIMENSIONED
PITCH (DISTANCE BETWEEN CENTERS) OF INCREMENTS

FLASH OR UPSET WELDING SYMBOL

FW
PROCESS REFERENCE MUST BE USED TO INDICATE PROCESS DESIRED

SQUARE-GROOVE WELDING SYMBOL

OMISSION OF SIZE INDICATES COMPLETE JOINT PENETRATION

FLARE-V- AND FLARE-BEVEL-GROOVE WELDING SYMBOL

SIZE IS CONSIDERED AS EXTENDING ONLY TO TANGENT POINTS
ROOT OPENING

EDGE- AND CORNER-FLANGE WELD SYMBOLS

RADIUS
SIZE OF WELD
HEIGHT ABOVE POINT OF TANGENCY

FLUSH-CONTOUR SYMBOL

FLUSH-CONTOUR SYMBOL. INDICATES FACE OF WELD TO BE MADE FLUSH. WHEN USED WITHOUT A FINISH SYMBOL, INDICATES WELD TO BE WELDED FLUSH WITHOUT SUBSEQUENT FINISHING
M
FINISH SYMBOL (USER'S STD.) INDICATES METHOD OF OBTAINING SPECIFIED CONTOUR BUT NOT DEGREE OF FINISH

CONVEX-CONTOUR SYMBOL

CONVEX-CONTOUR SYMBOL. INDICATES FACE OF WELD TO BE FINISHED TO CONVEX CONTOUR
G
FINISH SYMBOL (USER'S STD.) INDICATES METHOD OF OBTAINING SPECIFIED CONTOUR BUT NOT DEGREE OF FINISH

Arrow-Side and Other-Side Member of Joint

OTHER SIDE OF JOINT
ARROW SIDE OF JOINT
ARROW OF WELDING SYMBOL

ARROW-SIDE MEMBER OF JOINT
OTHER-SIDE MEMBER OF JOINT
ARROW OF WELDING SYMBOL
LAP JOINT

ARROW SIDE OF JOINT
ARROW OF WELDING SYMBOL
JOINT
OTHER SIDE OF JOINT
EDGE JOINT

DESIGNATION OF CUTTING PROCESSES BY LETTERS

AAC .... Air Carbon-Arc Cutting
AC .... Arc Cutting
AOC .... Oxygen-Arc Cutting
CAC .... Carbon-Arc Cutting
FOC .... Chemical Flux Cutting
MAC .... Metal-Arc Cutting
OC .... Oxygen Cutting
PAC .... Plasma-Arc Cutting
POC .... Metal Powder Cutting

NONPREFERRED SYMBOLS; USE PREFERRED SYMBOL WITH PROCESS REFERENCE IN THE TAIL

AWS A 2.1-68

GRAPHICAL SYMBOLS FOR PIPE FITTINGS & VALVES

	FLANGED	SCREWED	BELL & SPIGOT	WELDED	SOLDERED
JOINT					
CONNECTING PIPE					
EXPANSION					
UNION					
REDUCER					
ELBOW					
90-DEGREE					
TURNED DOWN					
TURNED UP					
TEE					
(OUTLET UP)					
(OUTLET DOWN)					
CROSS					
GLOBE VALVE					
GATE VALVE					
COCK					
CHECK VALVE					
SAFETY VALVE					

EXTRACTED FROM ANSI Z32.2.3 — 1949 (R 1953)

BOUNDARY LINES (RED)

National line
State line
County, parish, municipio
Civil township, precinct, town, barrio
Incorporated city, village, town, hamlet
Reservation, national or state
Military reservation
Small park, cemetery, airport, etc.
Land grant

U.S. PUBLIC LAND SURVEY LINES (RED)

Township, range or section line
Township, range or section line, approx. location
Section corner, found and indicated
Boundary monument: land grant and other
United States Mineral or location monument

GRID MAGNETIC DECLINATION DIAGRAM

★ True North
GN - y Grid North
- MN Magnetic North

GN 14°
1° 30'

SURVEY STATIONS (BROWN)

△ Triangulation station
BM △ 4532 Tablet, spirit level elevation (Bench Mark)
△ 4385 Other recoverable mark, spirit level elevation
VABM △ 8537 Horiz. control station: tablet, vert. angle elevation
△ 4575 Any recoverable mark, vert. angle or checked elevation
BM × 743 Vert. control station: tablet, spirit level elevation
× 738 Other recoverable mark, spirit level elevation
× 4372 Checked spot elevation
× 4370 Unchecked spot elevation
⊙ Any location station (with explanatory note)

STRUCTURES

Buildings: dwellings, place of employment, etc.
Barn (outbuilding), warehouse, etc.
Cem School, church, and cemetery
○ Gas - ○ Oil Wells other than water (labeled as to type)
●●●● ● Water ⊘ Water Tanks; oil, water, etc. (labeled as to type)
Oil
Windmill
Open pit, mine, or quarry; prospect
Shaft and tunnel entrance
×-×-×-× Barbed Wire fence
○-○-○-○ Smooth Wire fence

TRANSPORTATION AND UTILITY LINES (RED)

Hard surface, heavy duty road
Hard surface, medium duty road
Improved light duty road
Unimproved dirt road
Trail
Railroad, single track and multiple track
Tunnel, road and railroad
Telephone line, pipeline, etc. (labeled as to type)
Power transmission line
Overpass and underpass

BRIDGES AND WATERWAYS (BLUE)

Bridge, road and railroad
Drawbridge, road and railroad
Footbridge
Dam with lock
Dam with road
Canal with lock (pointing upstream)
Aqueduct, elevated and subterranean
Water well and spring
Stream and lake
Intermittent stream, intermittent lake
Large stream, River
Small rapids, small falls
Large rapids, large falls
Sounding, depth curve (fathoms)
Rock, bare or awash; dangerous to navigation
Marsh (swamp)
Submerged marsh

TERRAIN (BROWN)

600 Index contour (feet or meters)
Intermidiate contour (e.g. 580 ft.)
594 Supplimentary contour (e.g. 590 ft.)
Fill
Depression
Wash
Sand area
Gravel beach

FOLIAGE (GREEN)

Wooded marsh
Orchard
Mangrove
Scrub
Woods or brushwood
Vineyard

GRAPHICAL SYMBOLS FOR PIPING

AIR CONDITIONING

	SUPPLY OR FLOW	RETURN
BRINE	—— B ——	—— BR ——
CIRCULATING CHILLED OR HOT WATER	—— CH ——	—— CHR ——
CONDENSER WATER	—— C ——	—— CR ——
DRAIN	—— D ——	
HUMIDIFICATION LINE	—— H ——	
MAKE-UP WATER		
REFRIGERANT DISCHARGE	—— RD ——	
REFRIGERANT LIQUID	—— RL ——	
REFRIGERANT SUCTION	—— RS ——	

HEATING

	SUPPLY OR FLOW	RETURN
HIGH PRESSURE STEAM	—#—#—	—#—#—
MEDIUM PRESSURE STEAM	—/—/—	—/—/—
LOW PRESSURE STEAM		
HOT WATER HEATING		
FUEL OIL	—— FOF ——	—— FOR ——
FUEL OIL TANK VENT	—— FOV ——	
MAKE-UP WATER		
AIR RELIEF LINE		
BOILER BLOW OFF		

PLUMBING

ACID WASTE	—— ACID ——
COLD WATER	
COMPRESSED AIR	—— A ——
DRINKING-WATER FLOW	
DRINKING-WATER RETURN	
FIRE LINE	—— F —— F ——
GAS	—— G —— G ——
HOT WATER	
HOT-WATER RETURN	
SOIL, WASTE OR LEADER (ABOVE GRADE)	
SOIL, WASTE OR LEADER (BELOW GRADE)	
VACUUM CLEANING	—— V —— V ——
VENT	
SPRINKLERS	
BRANCH AND HEAD	—— O ——
DRAIN	—— S —— S ——
MAIN SUPPLIES	—— S ——

EXTRACTED FROM ANSI 232.2.3 - 1949 (R 1953)

GRAPHICAL SYMBOLS FOR HEATING, VENTILATION, & AIR CONDITIONING

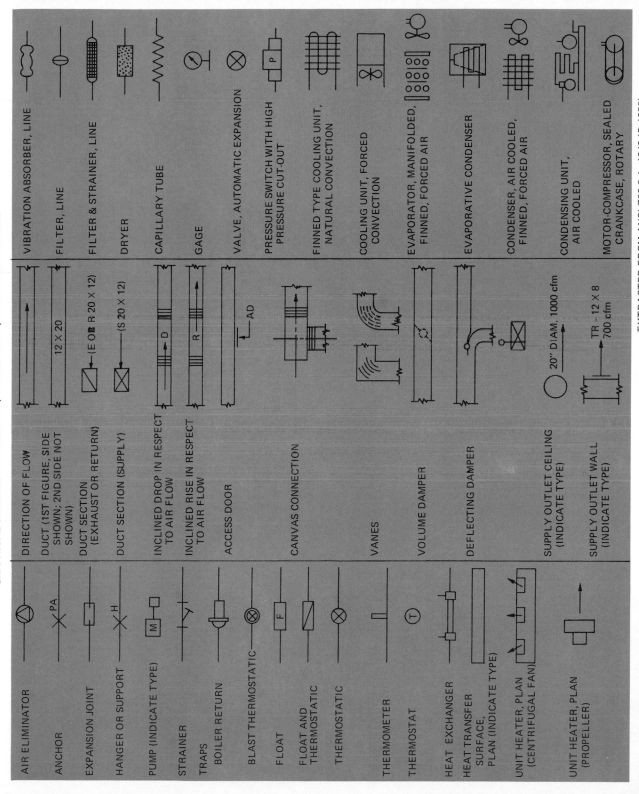

AIR ELIMINATOR	DIRECTION OF FLOW	VIBRATION ABSORBER, LINE
ANCHOR	DUCT (1ST FIGURE, SIDE SHOWN; 2ND SIDE NOT SHOWN)	FILTER, LINE
EXPANSION JOINT	DUCT SECTION (EXHAUST OR RETURN)	FILTER & STRAINER, LINE
HANGER OR SUPPORT	DUCT SECTION (SUPPLY)	DRYER
PUMP (INDICATE TYPE)	INCLINED DROP IN RESPECT TO AIR FLOW	CAPILLARY TUBE
STRAINER	INCLINED RISE IN RESPECT TO AIR FLOW	GAGE
TRAPS	ACCESS DOOR	VALVE, AUTOMATIC EXPANSION
BOILER RETURN		PRESSURE SWITCH WITH HIGH PRESSURE CUT-OUT
BLAST THERMOSTATIC	CANVAS CONNECTION	FINNED TYPE COOLING UNIT, NATURAL CONVECTION
FLOAT		COOLING UNIT, FORCED CONVECTION
FLOAT AND THERMOSTATIC	VANES	EVAPORATOR, MANIFOLDED, FINNED, FORCED AIR
THERMOSTATIC	VOLUME DAMPER	EVAPORATIVE CONDENSER
THERMOMETER	DEFLECTING DAMPER	CONDENSER, AIR COOLED, FINNED, FORCED AIR
THERMOSTAT	SUPPLY OUTLET CEILING (INDICATE TYPE)	CONDENSING UNIT, AIR COOLED
HEAT EXCHANGER	SUPPLY OUTLET WALL (INDICATE TYPE)	MOTOR-COMPRESSOR, SEALED CRANKCASE, ROTARY
HEAT TRANSFER SURFACE, PLAN (INDICATE TYPE)		
UNIT HEATER, PLAN (CENTRIFUGAL FAN)		
UNIT HEATER, PLAN (PROPELLER)		

EXTRACTED FROM ANSI Z32.2.4 - 1949 (R 1953)

GRAPHICAL SYMBOLS FOR ELECTRICAL AND ELECTRONIC DIAGRAMS

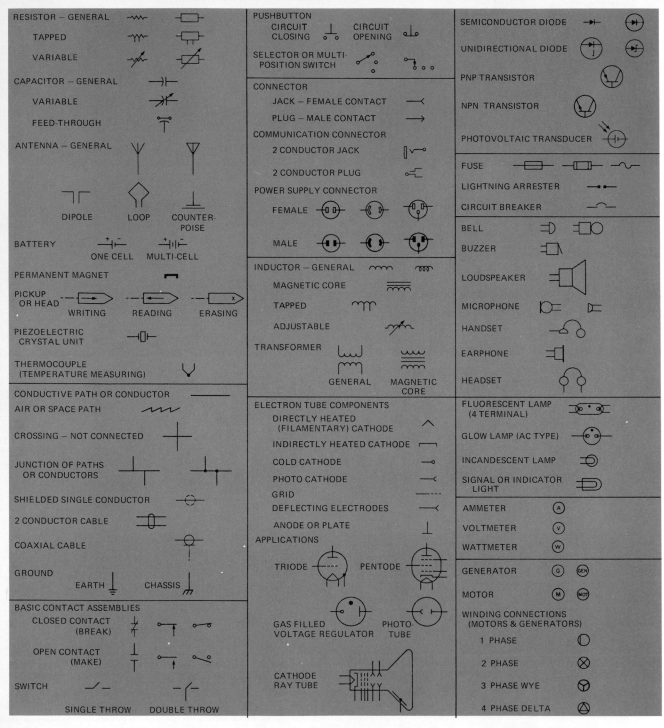

EXTRACTED FROM ANSI Y32.2 – 1970

MATERIAL SYMBOLS

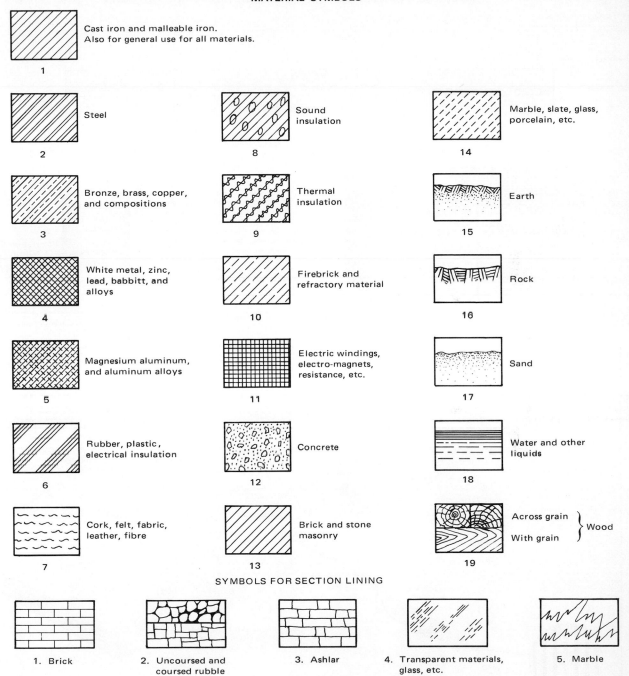

1. Cast iron and malleable iron. Also for general use for all materials.

2. Steel

3. Bronze, brass, copper, and compositions

4. White metal, zinc, lead, babbitt, and alloys

5. Magnesium aluminum, and aluminum alloys

6. Rubber, plastic, electrical insulation

7. Cork, felt, fabric, leather, fibre

8. Sound insulation

9. Thermal insulation

10. Firebrick and refractory material

11. Electric windings, electro-magnets, resistance, etc.

12. Concrete

13. Brick and stone masonry

14. Marble, slate, glass, porcelain, etc.

15. Earth

16. Rock

17. Sand

18. Water and other liquids

19. Across grain / With grain } Wood

SYMBOLS FOR SECTION LINING

1. Brick

2. Uncoursed and coursed rubble

3. Ashlar

4. Transparent materials, glass, etc.

5. Marble

SYMBOLS FOR OUTSIDE VIEWS

Extracted from ANSI Y14.2—1957.

measurements and units

THE International System of Units—officially abbreviated SI—is a modernized version of the metric system. It was established by international agreement to provide a logical and interconnected framework for all measurements in science, industry, and commerce. SI is built upon a foundation of base units and their definitions, which appear on these pages. All other SI units are derived from these base units. Multiples and submultiples are expressed in a decimal system. Use of metric weights and measures was legalized in the United States in 1866, and our customary units of weights and measures are defined in terms of the meter and the kilogram. The legal units for electricity and illumination in the United States are SI units.

THE SIX BASIC UNITS OF MEASUREMENT
LENGTH, TIME, MASS, TEMPERATURE, ELECTRIC CURRENT AND LUMINOUS INTENSITY

Length—*METER*—m The meter is defined as 1,650,763.73 wavelengths in vacuum of the orange-red line of the spectrum of Krypton-86.

INTERFEROMETER

TRANSLUCENT MIRROR SPLITS LIGHT BEAM: HALF TO 4a, HALF TO 4b

① SPECTRAL LAMP
PRODUCES ARC IN KRYPTON-86 GAS, EMITTING LIGHT WAVE RADIATION

② SPECTROSCOPE
SEPARATES LIGHT AND THE DISTINCTIVE ORANGE-RED BAND IS FOCUSED INTO THE INTERFEROMETER

④b MOVABLE MIRROR

1,650,763.73 wavelengths

ONE STANDARD METER

④a FIXED MIRROR

METER BAR

⑤ LIGHT WAVES FROM 4a INTERFERE WITH LIGHT WAVES FROM 4b, FORMING LIGHT AND DARK FRINGES

⑥ OBSERVING TELESCOPE
DISPLAYS FRINGE PROGRESSION ACROSS FIELD OF VIEW AS MIRROR 4b IS MOVED. FROM STARTING POSITION b_1, DARK FRINGES ARE COUNTED AS MIRROR 4b IS MOVED BACKWARDS SLOWLY. EACH FRINGE EQUALS EXACTLY ONE-HALF WAVELENGTH PROGRESSION. BLOCKING OR PHOTOELECTRIC DETECTION METHODS SIMPLIFY COUNTING.

Time—*SECOND*—s

The *second* is defined as the duration of 9,192,631,770 cycles of the radiation associated with a specified transition of the cesium atom. It is realized by tuning an oscillator to the resonance frequency of the cesium atoms as they pass through a system of magnets and a resonant cavity into a detector.

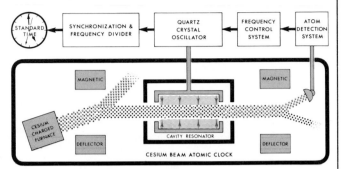

In the *atomic clock*, an electric furnace excites cesium atoms into a jet with thermal velocities, beamed into a magnetic field. Cesium, an alkali metal, has a one valance electron about a positive charge nucleus. It therefore consists of two spinning magnets, each in the field of the other, so that the atom experiences a magnetic torque when influenced by an external electromagnetic field. Entering the field, the atoms undergo a deflection according to their energy state. High-energy atoms (black dots) are selected to pass into the cavity resonator while most of the low energy atoms (color dots) are diverted away. A quartz crystal oscillates the cavity and when in resonance with the periodic frequency of the cesium atom, it causes some of the high energy atoms to emit energy and fall to the lower energy level. Flowing into another magnetic field, these low-energy atoms are deflected onto a detector and produce a positive ion current. A control system monitors this current closely and constantly tunes the crystal to the exact transition frequency. An accuracy of 1 part in 10^{11}, or 1 sec in 3000 yrs is realized.

Temperature—*KELVIN*—K

The thermodynamic or *Kelvin* scale has its origin or zero point at absolute zero and has a fixed point at the triple point of water defined as 273.16 kelvins, 0.01° Celsius, which is approximately 32.02° on the Fahrenheit scale.

The *triple point cell*, an evacuated glass cylinder filled with pure water, is used to define a known fixed temperature. When the cell is cooled until a mantle of ice forms around the reentrant well, the temperature at the interface of solid, liquid, and vapor is 0.01°C. Thermometers to be calibrated are placed in the reentrant well.

Mass—*KILOGRAM*—kg

INTERNATIONAL PROTOTYPE KILOGRAM

The standard for the unit of mass, the *kilogram*, is a cylinder of platinum-iridium alloy kept by the International Bureau of Weights and Measures at Paris. A duplicate in the custody of the National Bureau of Standards serves as the mass standard for the United States. This is the only base unit still defined by an artifact.

1 NEWTON

Closely allied to the concept of mass is that of force. The SI unit of force is the *newton* (N). A force of 1 newton, when applied for 1 second, will give to a 1 kilogram mass a speed of 1 meter per second (an acceleration of 1 meter per second).

Electric Current—*AMPERE*—A

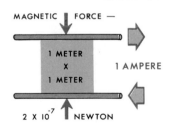

The *ampere* is defined as the magnitude of the current that, when flowing through each of two long parallel wires separated by one meter in free space, results in a force between the two wires (due to their magnetic fields) of 2×10^{-7} newton for each meter of length.

Luminous Intensity—*CANDELA*—cd

The *candela* is defined as the luminous intensity of 1/600,000 of a square meter of a radiating cavity at the temperature of freezing platinum (2042 K). A Thorium oxide tube (ThO_2) is used as a black body that absorbs all radiation falling upon it, becoming incandescent with the constant radiation during the long solidification process.

Decimal Inch
Decimal Equivalents of Common Fractions

1. Values or sizes that reflect common fractional increments shall be expressed as decimal equivalents of the fractional increments. These values should be expressed to 2, 3, or 4 decimal places as illustrated below. The number of decimal places will be determined by the tolerance required.

2. To avoid needless perpetuation of odd decimal numbers, this chart should not be used for new work. Instead, a value or size should be chosen having a final digit that is zero or an even number.

Fraction to Decimal Conversion Chart																
4ths	8ths	16ths	32nds	64ths	to 2 places	to 3 places	to 4 places	4ths	8ths	16ths	32nds	64ths	to 2 places	to 3 places	to 4 places
				1/64	0.02	0.016	0.0156					33/64	0.52	0.516	0.5156
			1/32		0.03	0.031	0.0312				17/32		0.53	0.531	0.5312
				3/64	0.05	0.047	0.0469					35/64	0.55	0.547	0.5469
		1/16			0.06	0.062	0.0625			9/16			0.56	0.562	0.5625
				5/64	0.08	0.078	0.0781					37/64	0.58	0.578	0.5781
			3/32		0.09	0.094	0.0938				19/32		0.59	0.594	0.5938
				7/64	0.11	0.109	0.1094					39/64	0.61	0.609	0.6094
	1/8				0.12	0.125	0.1250		5/8				0.62	0.625	0.6250
				9/64	0.14	0.141	0.1406					41/64	0.64	0.641	0.6406
			5/32		0.16	0.156	0.1562				21/32		0.66	0.656	0.6562
				11/64	0.17	0.172	0.1719					43/64	0.67	0.672	0.6719
		3/16			0.19	0.188	0.1875			11/16			0.69	0.688	0.6875
				13/64	0.20	0.203	0.2031					45/64	0.70	0.703	0.7031
			7/32		0.22	0.219	0.2188				23/32		0.72	0.719	0.7188
				15/64	0.23	0.234	0.2344					47/64	0.73	0.734	0.7344
1/4					0.25	0.250	0.2500	3/4					0.75	0.750	0.7500
				17/64	0.27	0.266	0.2656					49/64	0.77	0.766	0.7656
			9/32		0.28	0.281	0.2812				25/32		0.78	0.781	0.7812
				19/64	0.30	0.297	0.2969					51/64	0.80	0.797	0.7969
		5/16			0.31	0.312	0.3125			13/16			0.81	0.812	0.8125
				21/64	0.33	0.328	0.3281					53/64	0.83	0.828	0.8281
			11/32		0.34	0.344	0.3438				27/32		0.84	0.844	0.8438
				23/64	0.36	0.359	0.3594					55/64	0.86	0.859	0.8594
	3/8				0.38	0.375	0.3750		7/8				0.88	0.875	0.8750
				25/64	0.39	0.391	0.3906					57/64	0.89	0.891	0.8906
			13/32		0.41	0.406	0.4062				29/32		0.91	0.906	0.9062
				27/64	0.42	0.422	0.4219					59/64	0.92	0.922	0.9219
		7/16			0.44	0.438	0.4375			15/16			0.94	0.938	0.9375
				29/64	0.45	0.453	0.4531					61/64	0.95	0.953	0.9531
			15/32		0.47	0.469	0.4688				31/32		0.97	0.969	0.9688
				31/64	0.48	0.484	0.4844					63/64	0.98	0.984	0.9844
1/2					0.50	0.500	0.5000	1					1.00	1.000	1.0000

(a) Omit zero to left of decimal point where used on drawings.

Extracted from ANSI B87.1—1965

American National Standard
Letter Symbols for Units Used in Science and Technology

Symbols for Units

Unit	Symbol	Notes
ampere	A	SI unit of electric current
ampere per meter	A/m	SI unit of magnetic field strength
angstrom	Å	$1 \text{ Å} = 10^{-10} \text{ m}$
atmosphere, standard	atm	$1 \text{ atm} = 101{,}325 \text{ N/m}^2$
atto	a	SI prefix for 10^{-18}
barrel	bbl	$1 \text{ bbl} = 9{,}702 \text{ in}^3 = 0.15899 \text{ m}^3$
British thermal unit	Btu	
calorie	cal	$1 \text{ cal} = 4.1868 \text{ J}$
candela	cd	SI unit of luminous intensity
centi	c	SI prefix for 10^{-2}
centimeter	cm	
coulomb	C	SI unit of electric charge
cubic centimeter	cm³	
cubic foot	ft³	
cubic inch	in³	
cubic meter	m³	
curie	Ci	$1 \text{ Ci} = 3.7 \times 10^{10}$ disintegrations per second. Unit of activity in the field of radiation dosimetry.
cycle per second	Hz, c/s	See hertz. The name hertz is internationally accepted for this unit; the symbol Hz is preferred to c/s.
day	d	
decibel	dB	
degree (plane angle)	...°	
degree (temperature):		
degree Celsius	°C	Note that there is no space between the symbol ° and the letter. The use of the word *centigrade* for the Celsius temperature scale was abandoned by the Conférence Générale des Poids et Mesures in 1948.
degree Fahrenheit	°F	
degree Kelvin		See Kelvin
degree Rankine	°R	
dyne	dyn	
electronvolt	eV	
erg	erg	
farad	F	SI unit of capacitance
foot	ft	
foot per second	ft/s	
foot pound-force	ft·lb$_f$	

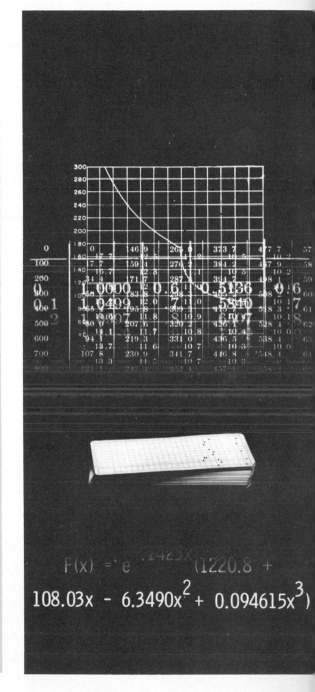

$$F(x) = e^{...1425x}(1220.8 +$$
$$108.03x - 6.3490x^2 + 0.094615x^3)$$

American National Standard
Letter Symbols for Units Used in Science and Technology

Symbols for Units (Cont'd)

Unit	Symbol	Notes
gallon	gal	The gallon, quart, and pint differ in the US and the UK, and their use in science and technology is deprecated.
gauss	G	The gauss is the electromagnetic CGS unit of magnetic flux density. Use of SI unit, the tesla, is preferred.
gram	g	
henry	H	SI unit of inductance
hertz	Hz	SI unit of frequency
horsepower	hp	The horsepower is an anachronism in science and technology. Use of the SI unit of power (the watt) is preferred.
hour	h	
joule	J	SI unit of energy
kelvin	K	In 1967 the CGPM gave the name *kelvin* to the SI unit of temperature which had formerly been called *degree Kelvin* and assigned it the symbol K (without the symbol °)
kilo	k	SI prefix for 10^3
kilogram	kg	SI unit of mass
kilogram-force	kg_f	In some countries the name *kilopond* (kp) has been adopted for this unit.
lambert	L	$1 \text{ L} = (1/\pi) \text{ cd/cm}^2$ A CGS unit of luminance. One lumen per square centimeter leaves a surface whose luminance is one lambert in all directions within a hemisphere. Use of the SI unit of luminance, the candela per square meter, is preferred.
liter	l	$1 \text{ l} = 10^{-3} \text{ m}^3$
lumen	lm	SI unit of luminous flux
mega	M	SI prefix for 10^6
megahertz	MHz	
meter	m	SI unit of length
mho	mho	CIPM has accepted the name *siemens* (S) for this unit and will submit it to the 14th CGPM for approval.

American National Standard
Letter Symbols for Units Used in Science and Technology

Symbols for Units (Cont'd)

Unit	Symbol	Notes
micro	μ	SI prefix for 10^{-6}
micron	μm	The name *micron* was abrogated by the Conférence Générale des Poids et Mesures, 1967.
mile (statute)	mi	1 mi = 5,280 ft
mile per hour	mi/h	Although use of mph as an abbreviation is common, it should not be used as a symbol.
milli	m	SI prefix for 10^{-3}
minute (time)	min	Time may also be designated by means of superscripts as in the following example: $9^h46^m30^s$.
mole	mol	SI unit of amount of substance
nano	n	SI prefix for 10^{-9}
newton	N	SI unit of force
newton per square meter	N/m^2	SI unit of pressure or stress; see pascal.
oersted	Oe	The oersted is the electromagnetic CGS unit of magnetic field strength. Use of the SI unit, the ampere per meter, is preferred.
ohm	Ω	SI unit of resistance
pascal	Pa	Pa = N/m^2 SI unit of pressure or stress. This name accepted by the CIPM in 1969 for submission to the 14th CGPM.
pico	p	SI prefix for 10^{-12}
poise	P	SI unit of absolute viscosity
pound	lb	
pound-force	lb$_f$	The symbol lb, without a subscript, may be used for pound-force where no confusion is foreseen.
pound-force per square inch	lb$_f$/in^2	Although use of the abbreviation psi is common, it should not be used as a symbol. Refer to note on pound-force regarding subscript to the symbol.
radian	rad	SI unit of plane angle
revolution per minute	r/min	Although use of rpm as an abbreviation is common, it should not be used as a symbol.

American National Standard
Letter Symbols for Units Used in Science and Technology

Symbols for Units (Cont'd)

Unit	Symbol	Notes
revolution per second	r/s	
roentgen	R	Unit of exposure in the field of radiation dosimetry
second (time)	s	SI unit of time
siemens	S	$S = \Omega^{-1}$
slug	slug	1 slug = 14.5939 kg
steradian	sr	SI unit of solid angle
stokes	St	SI unit of dynamic viscosity
tesla	T	$T = N/(A \cdot m) = Wb/m^2$ Si unit of magnetic flux density (magnetic induction)
ton	ton	1 ton = 2,000 lb
volt	V	SI unit of voltage
voltampere	VA	IEC name and symbol for the SI unit of apparent power
watt	W	SI unit of power
watt-hour	Wh	
weber	Wb	$Wb = V \cdot s$ SI unit of magnetic flux
yard	yd	

conversion tables

The number in parentheses following a value in the table indicates the power of 10 by which this value should be multiplied. Thus, 6.214(−6) means 6.214×10^{-6}.

1. Length Equivalents

cm	in	ft	m	mi*		Additional Measures		
1	3.937(−1)	3.281(−2)	1.0(−2)	6.214(−6)	*Metric:*	1 km = 10^3 m		
2.540	1	8.333(−2)	2.54(−2)	1.578(−5)		1 mm = 10^{-3} m		
3.048(+1)	1.2(+1)	1	3.048(−1)	1.894(−4)		1 μm = 10^{-6} m (micron)		
1.0(+2)	3.937(+1)	3.281	1	6.214(−4)		1 Å = 10^{-10} m (angstrom)		
1.609(+5)	6.336(+4)	5.280(+3)	1.609(+3)	1	*English:*	1 mil = 10^{-3} in.		
						1 yd = 3.0 ft		
						1 rod = 5.5 yd = 16.5 ft		
						1 furlong = 40 rod = 660 ft		

*mile.

2. Area Equivalents

m²	in²	ft²	acres	mi²		Additional Measures
1	1.55(+3)	1.076(+1)	2.471(−4)	3.861(−7)		1 hectare = 10⁴ m²
6.452(−4)	1	6.944(−3)	1.594(−7)	2.491(−10)		
9.290(−2)	1.44(+2)	1	2.296(−5)	3.587(−8)		
4.047(+3)	6.273(+6)	4.356(+4)	1	1.562(−3)		
2.590(+6)	4.018(+9)	2.788(+7)	6.40(+2)	1		

(Exponent notation: values shown as $a(\pm n)$ mean $a \times 10^{\pm n}$, e.g. 1 hectare = 10^4 m².)

3. Volume Equivalents

cm³	in³	ft³	gal (U.S.)		Additional Measures
1	6.103(−2)	3.532(−5)	2.642(−4)	*Metric:*	1 liter = 10³ cm³
1.639(+1)	1	5.787(−4)	4.329(−3)		1 m³ = 10⁶ cm³
2.832(+4)	1.728(+3)	1	7.481	*English:*	1 quart = 0.250 gal (U.S.)
3.785(+3)	2.31(+2)	1.337(−1)	1		1 bushel = 9.309 gal (U.S.)
					1 barrel = 42 gal (U.S.)
					(petroleum measure only)
					1 imperial gal = 1.20 gal (U.S.)
					approx.
					1 board-foot (wood) = 144 In³
					1 chord (wood) = 128 ft³

4. Mass Equivalents

kg	slug	lb$_m$*	g
1	6.85(−2)	2.205	1.0(+3)
1.46(+1)	1	3.22(+1)	1.46(+4)
4.54(−1)	3.11(−2)	1	4.54(+2)
1.0(−3)	6.85(−5)	2.205(−3)	1

5. Force Equivalents

N**	lb$_f$†	dyn††	kg$_f$*	g$_f$*	poundal*	Additional Measures
1	2.248(−1)	1.0(+5)	1.019(−1)	1.019(+2)	7.234	1 metric ton = 10³ kg$_f$ = 2.205 × 10³ lb$_f$
4.448	1	4.448(+5)	4.54(−1)	4.54(+2)	3.217(+1)	1 pound troy = 0.8229 lb$_f$
1.0(−5)	2.248(−6)	1	1.02(−6)	1.02(−3)	7.233(−5)	1 oz† = 6.25 × 10⁻² lb$_f$
9.807	2.205	9.807(+5)	1	1.0(+3)	7.093(+1)	1 oz troy = 6.857 × 10⁻² lb$_f$
9.807(−3)	2.205(−3)	9.807(+2)	1.0(−3)	1	7.093(−2)	
1.382(−1)	3.108(−2)	1.383(+4)	1.410(−2)	1.410(+1)	1	

*Not recommended.
**Newton.
†Avoirdupois.
††Dyne.

6. Velocity and Acceleration Equivalents

	Velocity				Acceleration			
cm/s	ft/s	mi/h (mph)	km/h		cm/s²	ft/s²	g̅*	Additional Measures
1	3.281(−2)	2.237(−2)	3.60(−2)		1	3.281(−2)	1.019(−3)	1 knot = 1.152 miles/hr
3.048(+1)	1	6.818(−1)	1.097		3.048(+1)	1	3.109(−2)	
4.470(+1)	1.467	1	1.609		9.807(+2)	3.217(+1)	1	
2.778(+1)	9.113(−1)	6.214(−1)	1					

*Standard acceleration of gravity.

7. Pressure Equivalents

					Head†			
dyn/cm²	N/m²	lb$_f$/in² (psi)	lb/ft² (psf)	atm*	in (Hg)	ft (H₂O)	Additional Measures
1	1.0(−1)	1.45(−5)	2.089(−3)	9.869(−7)	2.953(−5)	3.349(−5)	1 bar = 1 dyne/cm²
1.0(+1)	1	1.45(−4)	2.089(−2)	9.869(−6)	2.953(−4)	3.349(−4)	1 pascal = 1 N/m²
6.895(+4)	6.895(+3)	1	1.44(+2)	6.805(−2)	2.036	2.309	
4.788(+2)	4.788(+1)	6.944(−3)	1	4.725(−4)	1.414(−2)	1.603(−2)	
1.013(+6)	1.013(+5)	1.47(+1)	2.116(+3)	1	2.992(+1)	3.393(+1)	
3.386(+4)	3.386(+3)	4.912(−1)	7.073(+1)	3.342(−2)	1	1.134	
2.986(+4)	2.986(+3)	4.331(−1)	6.237(+1)	2.947(−2)	8.819(−1)	1	

*Standard atmospheric pressure.
†At std. gravity and 0°C for Hg, 15°C for H₂O.

8. Work and Energy Equivalents

J*	ft-lb$_f$	W-h	Btu**	Kcal†	kg-m	Additional Measures
1	7.376(−1)	2.778(−4)	9.478(−4)	2.388(−4)	1.020(−1)	1 Newton-meter = 1 J
1.356	1	3.766(−4)	1.285(−3)	3.238(−4)	1.383(−1)	1 erg = 1 dyne-cm = 10⁻⁷ J
3.60(+3)	2.655(+3)	1	3.412	8.599(−1)	3.671(+2)	1 cal = 10⁻³ kcal
1.055(+3)	7.782(+2)	2.931(−1)	1	2.520(−1)	1.076(+2)	1 therm = 10⁻⁵ Btu
4.187(+3)	3.088(+3)	1.163	3.968	1	4.269(+2)	
9.807	7.233	2.724(−3)	9.295(−3)	2.342(−3)	1	

*Joule.
**British thermal unit.
† = kilocalorie.

9. Power Equivalents

J/s	ft-lb$_f$/s	hp††	kW	Btu/h	Additional Measures
1	7.376(−1)	1.341(−3)	1.0(−3)	3.412	1 W = 10⁻³ kW
1.356	1	1.818(−3)	1.356(−3)	4.626	1 cal/s = 14.29 Btu/h
7.457(+2)	5.50(+2)	1	7.457(−1)	2.545(+3)	1 poncelet = 100 kg-m/sec = 0.9807 kW
1.0(+3)	7.376(+2)	1.341	1	3.412(+3)	1 ton of refrigeration = 1.2 × 10⁴ Btu/h
2.931(−1)	2.162(−1)	3.930(−4)	2.931(−4)	1	

††Horsepower.

geometric figures

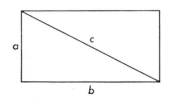

Rectangle

Area = (base)(altitude) = ab

Diagonal = $\sqrt{(\text{altitude})^2 + (\text{base})^2}$

$$C = \sqrt{a^2 + b^2}$$

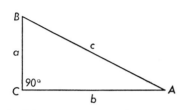

Right Triangle

Angle A + angle B = angle C = $90°$

Area = $\frac{1}{2}$(base)(altitude)

Hypotenuse = $\sqrt{(\text{altitude})^2 + (\text{base})^2}$

$$C = \sqrt{a^2 + b^2}$$

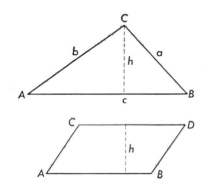

Any Triangle

Angles $A + B + C = 180°$
(Altitude h is perpendicular to base c)
Area = $\frac{1}{2}$(base)(altitude)

Parallelogram

Area = (base)(altitude)
Altitude h is perpendicular to base $A\bar{B}$
Angles $A + B + C + D = 360°$

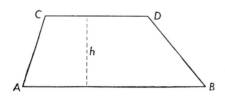

Trapezoid

Area = $\frac{1}{2}$(altitude)(sum of bases)
(Altitude h is perpendicular to sides AB and CD. Side AB is parallel to side CD.)

Regular Polygon

Area = $\frac{1}{2}\begin{bmatrix}\text{Length of} \\ \text{one side}\end{bmatrix}\begin{bmatrix}\text{Number} \\ \text{of sides}\end{bmatrix}\begin{bmatrix}\text{Distance} \\ OA \text{ to} \\ \text{center}\end{bmatrix}$

A regular polygon has equal angles and equal sides and can be inscribed in or circumscribed about a circle.

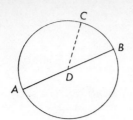

Circle

AB = diameter, CD = radius

$$\text{Area} = \pi(\text{radius})^2 = \frac{\pi(\text{diameter})^2}{4}$$

Circumference = π(diameter)

$C = 2\pi(\text{radius})$

$$\frac{\text{arc } BC}{\text{circumference}} = \frac{\text{angle } BDC}{360°}$$

$$1 \text{ radian} = \frac{180°}{\pi} = 57.2958°$$

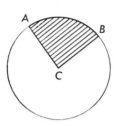

Sector of a Circle

$$\text{Area} = \frac{(\text{arc } AB)(\text{radius})}{2}$$

$$= \pi \frac{(\text{radius})^2(\text{angle } ACB)}{360°}$$

$$= \frac{(\text{radius})^2(\text{angle } ACB \text{ in radians})}{2}$$

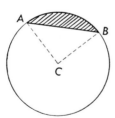

Segment of a Circle

$$\text{Area} = \frac{(\text{radius})^2}{2}\left[\frac{\pi(\angle ACB°)}{180} - \sin ACB°\right]$$

$$\text{Area} = \frac{(\text{radius})^2}{2}\left[\angle ACB \text{ in radians} - \sin ACB°\right]$$

Area = area of sector ACB − area of triangle ABC

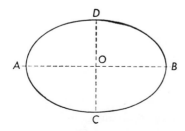

Ellipse

$$\text{Area} = \pi(\text{long radius } OA)(\text{short radius } OC)$$

$$\text{Area} = \frac{\pi}{4}(\text{long diameter } AB)(\text{short diameter } CD)$$

Volume and Center of Gravity Equations°

Volume equations are included for all cases. Where the equation for the CG (center of gravity) is not given, you can easily obtain it by looking up the volume and CG equations for portions of the shape and then combining values. For example, for the shape above, use the equations for a cylinder, Fig. 1, and a truncated cylinder, Fig. 10 (subscripts C and T, respectively, in the equations below). Hence taking moments

$$B_x = \frac{V_C B_C + V_T(B_T + L_C)}{V_C + V_T}$$

or

$$B_x = \frac{\left(\frac{\pi}{4}D^2 L_C\right)\left(\frac{L_C}{2}\right) + \frac{\pi}{8}D^2 L_T\left(\frac{5}{16}L_T + L_C\right)}{\frac{\pi}{4}D^2 L_C + \frac{\pi}{8}D^2 L_T}$$

$$B_x = \frac{L^2{}_C + L_T\left(\frac{5}{16}L_T + L_C\right)}{2L_C + L_T}$$

In the equations to follow, angle θ can be either in degrees or in radians.

Thus $\qquad \theta \text{ (rad)} = \pi\theta/180 \text{ (deg)} = 0.01745\,\theta \text{ (deg)}.$

For example, if $\theta = 30$ deg in Fig. 3, then $\sin\theta = 0.5$ and

$$B = \frac{2R(0.5)}{3(30)(0.01745)} = 0.637R$$

Symbols used are:

B = distance from CG to reference plane,
V = volume,
D and d = diameter,
R and r = radius,
H = height,
L = length.

°Courtesy of Knoll Atomic Power Laboratory, Schenectady, New York, operated by the General Electric Company for the United States Atomic Energy Commission. Reprinted from *Product Engineering*—Copyright owned by McGraw-Hill.

1. Cylinder

$$V = \frac{\pi}{4}D^2L = 0.7854D^2L \qquad B_1 = L/2$$

$$B_2 = R$$

Area of cylindrical surface = (Perimeter of base)(perpendicular height)

2. Half-cylinder

$$V = \frac{\pi}{8}D^2L = 0.3927D^2L$$

$$B_1 = L/2 \qquad B_2 = \frac{4R}{3\pi} = 0.4244R$$

3. Sector of cylinder

$$V = \theta R^2 L \qquad B = \frac{2R \sin \theta}{3\theta}$$

4. Segment of cylinder

$$V = LR^2(\theta - \tfrac{1}{2}\sin 2\theta)$$

$$V = 0.5L[RS - C(R - H)]$$

$$B = \frac{4R \sin^3 \theta}{6\theta - 3 \sin 2\theta}$$

$$S = 2R\theta$$

$$H = R(1 - \cos \theta)$$

$$C = 2R \sin \theta$$

5. Quadrant of cylinder

$$V = \frac{\pi}{4}R^2L = 0.7854R^2L$$

$$B = \frac{4R}{3\pi} = 0.4244R$$

6. Fillet or spandrel

$$V = \left(1 - \frac{\pi}{4}\right)R^2L = 0.2146R^2L$$

$$B = \frac{10 - 3\pi}{12 - 3\pi}R = 0.2234R$$

---

7. Hollow cylinder

$$V = \frac{\pi L}{4}(D^2 - d^2)$$

CG at center of part

---

8. Half-hollow cylinder

$$V = \frac{\pi L}{8}(D^2 - d^2)$$

$$B = \frac{4}{3\pi}\left[\frac{R^3 - r^3}{R^2 - r^2}\right]$$

---

9. Sector of hollow cylinder

$$V = 0.01745(R^2 - r^2)\theta L$$

$$B = \frac{38.1972(R^3 - r^3)\sin\theta}{(R^2 - r^2)\theta}$$

---

10. Truncated cylinder (with full circle base)

$$V = \frac{\pi}{8}D^2L = 0.3927D^2L$$

$$B_1 = 0.3125L$$

$$B_2 = 0.375D$$

11. Truncated cylinder (with partial circle base)

$$b = R(1 - \cos\theta)$$

$$V = \frac{R^3 L}{b}\left(\sin\theta - \frac{\sin^3\theta}{3} - \theta\cos\theta\right)$$

$$B_1 = \frac{L\left(\dfrac{\theta\cos^2\theta}{2} - \dfrac{5\sin\theta\cos\theta}{8} + \dfrac{\sin^3\theta\cos\theta}{12} + \dfrac{\theta}{8}\right)}{\left(1 - \cos\theta\right)\left(\sin\theta - \dfrac{\sin^3\theta}{3} - \theta\cos\theta\right)}$$

$$B_2 = \frac{2R\left(-\dfrac{\theta\cos\theta}{2} + \dfrac{\sin\theta}{2} - \dfrac{\theta}{8} + \dfrac{\sin\theta\cos\theta}{8} - N\right)}{\sin\theta - \dfrac{\sin^3\theta}{3} - \theta\cos\theta}$$

$$\text{where } N = \frac{\sin^3\theta}{6} - \frac{\sin^3\theta\cos\theta}{12}$$

---

12. Oblique cylinder (or circular hole at oblique angle)

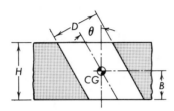

$$V = \frac{\pi}{4}D^2\frac{H}{\cos\theta} = 0.7854D^2H\sec\theta$$

$$B = \frac{H}{2} \qquad r = \frac{d}{2}$$

---

13. Bend in cylinder

$$V = \frac{\pi^2}{360}D^2R\theta = 0.0274D^2R\theta$$

$$y = R\left(1 + \frac{r^2}{4R^2}\right) \qquad \begin{aligned} B_1 &= y\tan\theta \\ B_2 &= y\cot\theta \end{aligned}$$

---

14. Curved groove in cylinder

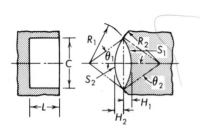

$$\sin\theta_1 = \frac{C}{2R_1} \qquad \sin\theta_2 = \frac{C}{2R_2} \qquad S = 2R\theta$$

$$H_1 = R_1(1 - \cos\theta_1) \qquad H_2 = R_2(1 - \cos\theta_2)$$

$$V = L[R_1{}^2(\theta_1 - \tfrac{1}{2}\theta_1\sin 2\theta_1) + R_2{}^2(\theta_2 - \tfrac{1}{2}\theta_2\sin 2\theta_2)]$$

Compute CG of each part separately

---

15. Slot in cylinder

$$H = R(1 - \cos \theta) \qquad \sin \theta = \frac{C}{2R}$$

$$S = 2R\theta$$

$$V = L[CN + R^2(\theta - \tfrac{1}{2} \sin 2\theta)]$$

---

16. Slot in hollow cylinder

$$S = 2R\theta \qquad \sin \theta = \frac{C}{2R}$$

$$H = R(1 - \cos \theta)$$

$$V = L[CN - R^2(\theta - \tfrac{1}{2} \sin 2\theta)]$$

$$V = L\{CN - 0.5[RS - C(R - H)]\}$$

---

17. Curved groove in hollow cylinder

$$\sin \theta_1 = \frac{C}{2R_1} \qquad \sin \theta_2 = \frac{C}{2R_2} \qquad S = 2R\theta$$

$$H_1 = R_1(1 - \cos \theta_1)$$

$$H_2 = R_2(1 - \cos \theta_2)$$

$$V = L\{[R_2{}^2(\theta_2 - \tfrac{1}{2} \sin 2\theta_2)] - [R_1{}^2(\theta_1 - \tfrac{1}{2} \sin 2\theta_1)]\}$$

$$V = \frac{L}{2}\{[R_2 S_2 - C(R_2 - H_2)] - [R_1 S_1 - C(R_1 - H_1)]\}$$

---

18. Slot through hollow cylinder

$$\sin \theta_1 = \frac{C}{R_1} \qquad \sin \theta_2 = \frac{C}{R_2}$$

$$S = 2R\theta$$

$$H_1 = R_1(1 - \cos \theta_1)$$

$$H_2 = R_2(1 - \cos \theta_2)$$

$$V = L\{CN + [R_1{}^2(\theta_1 - \tfrac{1}{2} \sin 2\theta_1)] - [R_2(\theta_2 - \tfrac{1}{2} \sin 2\theta_2)]\}$$

$$V = L\{CN + 0.5[R_1 S_1 - C(R_1 - H_1)] - 0.5[R_2 S_2 - C(R_2 - H_2)]\}$$

19. Intersecting cylinder (volume of junction box)

$$V = D^3\left(\frac{\pi}{2} - \frac{2}{3}\right) = 0.9041D^3$$

20. Intersecting hollow cylinders (volume of junction box)

$$V = \left(\frac{\pi}{2} - \frac{2}{3}\right)(D^3 - d^3) - \frac{\pi}{2}d^2(D - d)$$

$$V = 0.9041(D^3 - d^3) - 1.5708d^2(D - d)$$

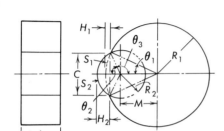

21. Intersecting parallel cylinders ($M < R_1$)

$$\theta_2 = 180° - \theta_3 \qquad \cos\theta_3 = \frac{R_2{}^2 + M^2 - R_1{}^2}{2MR_2}$$

$$\cos\theta_1 = \frac{R_1{}^2 + M^2 - R_2{}^2}{2MR_1}$$

$$H_1 = R_1(1 - \cos\theta_1)$$

$$S_1 = 2R_1\theta_1$$

$$V = L\{\pi R_1{}^2 + [R_2{}^2(\theta_2 - \tfrac{1}{2}\sin 2\theta_2)] - [R_1{}^2(\theta_1 - \tfrac{1}{2}\sin 2\theta_1)]\}$$

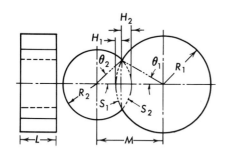

22. Intersecting parallel cylinders ($M > R_1$)

$$H_1 = R_1(1 - \cos\theta_1)$$

$$S_1 = 2R_1\theta_1$$

$$\cos\theta_1 = \frac{R_1{}^2 + M^2 - R_2{}^2}{2MR_1}$$

$$V = L\{[\pi(R_1{}^2 + R_2{}^2)] - [R_1{}^2(\theta_1 - \tfrac{1}{2}\sin 2\theta_1)] - [R_2{}^2(\theta_2 - \tfrac{1}{2}\sin 2\theta_2)]\}$$

23. Sphere

$$V = \frac{\pi D^3}{6} = 0.5236D^3$$

$$\text{Area of surface} = 4\pi(\text{radius})^2 = \pi D^2$$

24. Hemisphere

$$V = \frac{\pi D^3}{12} = 0.2618 D^3$$

$$B = 0.375 R$$

---

25. Spherical segment

$$V = \pi H^2 \left(R - \frac{H}{3} \right)$$

$$B_1 = \frac{H(4R - H)}{4(3R - H)}$$

$$B_2 = \frac{3(2R - H)^2}{4(3R - H)}$$

---

26. Spherical sector

$$V = \frac{2\pi}{3} R^2 H = 2.0944 R^2 H$$

$$B = 0.375(1 + \cos \theta)$$

$$R = 0.375(2R - H)$$

---

27. Shell of hollow hemisphere

$$V = \frac{2\pi}{3}(R^3 - r^3)$$

$$B = 0.375 \left(\frac{R^4 - r^4}{R^3 - r^3} \right)$$

---

28. Hollow sphere

$$V = \frac{4\pi}{3}(R^3 - r^3)$$

---

29. Shell of spherical sector

$$V = \frac{2\pi}{3}(R^2 H - r^2 h)$$

$$B = 0.375 \left\{ \frac{[R^2 H(2R - H)] - [r^2 h(2r - h)]}{R^2 H - r^2 h} \right\}$$

30. Shell of spherical segment

$$V = \pi\left[H^2\left(R - \frac{H}{3}\right) - h^2\left(r - \frac{h}{3}\right)\right]$$

$$B = \frac{3}{4}\left[\frac{\left(R - \frac{H}{3}\right)\dfrac{H^2(2R - H)^2}{3R - H} - \left(r - \frac{h}{3}\right)\dfrac{h^2(2r - h)^2}{3r - h}}{H^2\left(R - \frac{H}{3}\right) - h^2\left(r - \frac{h}{3}\right)}\right]$$

31. Circular hole through sphere

$$V = \pi\left[r^2 L + 2H^2\left(R - \frac{H}{3}\right)\right] \qquad H = R - \sqrt{R^2 - r^2}$$

$$L = 2(R - H)$$

32. Circular hole through hollow sphere

$$V = \pi\left[r^2 L + H_1{}^2\left(R_1 - \frac{H_1}{3}\right) - H_2{}^2\left(R_2 - \frac{H_2}{3}\right)\right]$$

$$\sin\theta_1 = \frac{r}{R_1} \qquad \sin\theta_2 = \frac{r}{R_2} \qquad H = R(1 - \cos\theta)$$

33. Spherical zone

$$V = \pi\left\{\left[H^2\left(R - \frac{H}{3}\right)\right] - \left[h_1{}^2\left(R - \frac{h_1}{3}\right)\right]\right\}$$

$$V = \frac{\pi h_2}{6}\left(\frac{3}{4}C_1{}^2 + \frac{3}{4}C_2{}^2 + h_2{}^2\right)$$

34. Conical hole through spherical shell

$$V = \frac{2\pi}{3}(R^3 - r^3)(\sin\theta_2 - \sin\theta_1)$$

$$B = \frac{0.375(R^4 - r^4)(\sin\theta_2 + \sin\theta_1)}{R^3 - r^3}$$

35. Torus

$$V = \tfrac{1}{4}\pi^2 d^2 D = 2.467 d^2 D$$

36. Hollow torus

$$V = \tfrac{1}{4}\pi^2 D(d_1^2 - d_2^2)$$

---

37. Bevel ring

$$V = \pi(R + \tfrac{1}{3}W)WH$$

$$B = H\left(\dfrac{\dfrac{R}{3} + \dfrac{W}{12}}{R + \dfrac{W}{3}}\right)$$

---

38. Bevel ring

$$B > \dfrac{H}{3}$$

$$V = \pi(R - \tfrac{1}{3}W)WH$$

$$B = H\left(\dfrac{\dfrac{R}{3} - \dfrac{W}{12}}{R - \dfrac{W}{3}}\right)$$

---

39. Quarter-torus

$$B < 0.4244R$$

$$V = \dfrac{\pi^2 R^2}{2}\left(r + \dfrac{4R}{3\pi}\right) = 4.9348R^2(r + 0.4244R)$$

$$B = \dfrac{4R}{3\pi}\left(\dfrac{r + \dfrac{3R}{8}}{r + \dfrac{4R}{3\pi}}\right) = \dfrac{0.4244Rr + 0.1592R^2}{r + 0.4244R}$$

---

40. Quarter-torus

$$V = \dfrac{\pi^2 R^2}{2}\left(r - \dfrac{4R}{3\pi}\right)$$

$$B = \dfrac{4R}{3\pi}\left(\dfrac{r - \dfrac{3R}{8}}{r - \dfrac{4R}{3\pi}}\right)$$

697

41. Curved shell ring

$$V = 2\pi\left[r - \frac{4}{3\pi}\left(\frac{R_2{}^3 - R_1{}^3}{R_2{}^2 - R_1{}^2}\right)\right]\frac{\pi}{4}(R_2{}^2 - R_1{}^2)$$

$$B = \frac{4}{3\pi}\left\{\frac{R_2{}^3\left(r - \frac{3}{8}R_2\right) - R_1{}^3\left(r - \frac{3}{8}R_1\right)}{(R_2{}^2 - R_1{}^2)\left[r - \frac{4}{3\pi}\left(\frac{R_2{}^3 - R_1{}^3}{R_2{}^2 - R_1{}^2}\right)\right]}\right\}$$

42. Curved shell ring

$$V = \frac{\pi^2}{2}\left[r(R_2{}^2 - R_1{}^2) + \frac{4}{3\pi}(R_2{}^3 - R_1{}^3)\right]$$

$$B = \frac{2}{\pi}\left[\frac{\frac{2r}{3}(R_2{}^3 - R_1{}^3) + \frac{1}{4}(R_2{}^4 - R_1{}^4)}{r(R_2{}^2 - R_1{}^2) + \frac{4}{3\pi}(R_2{}^3 - R_1{}^3)}\right]$$

43. Fillet ring

$$V = 2\pi R^2\left[\left(1 - \frac{\pi}{4}\right)r - \frac{R}{6}\right]$$

$$B = R\left[\frac{\left(\frac{5}{6} - \frac{\pi}{4}\right)r - \frac{R}{24}}{\left(1 - \frac{\pi}{4}\right)r - \frac{R}{6}}\right]$$

44. Fillet ring

$$V = 2\pi R^2\left[\left(1 - \frac{\pi}{4}\right)r - \left(\frac{5}{6} - \frac{\pi}{4}\right)R\right]$$

$$B = R\left[\frac{\left(\frac{5}{6} - \frac{\pi}{4}\right)r - \left(\frac{19}{24} - \frac{\pi}{4}\right)R}{\left(1 - \frac{\pi}{4}\right)r - \left(\frac{5}{6} - \frac{\pi}{4}\right)R}\right]$$

45. Curved-sector ring

$$V = 2\pi R_2{}^2\left[R_1 + \left(\frac{4\sin 3\theta}{6\theta - 3\sin 2\theta} - \cos\theta\right)R_2\right](\theta - 0.5\sin 2\theta)$$

46. Ellipsoidal cylinder

$$V = \frac{\pi}{4}AaL$$

---

47. Ellipsoid

$$V = \frac{4}{3}\pi ACE$$

---

48. Paraboloid

$$V = \frac{\pi}{8}HD^2 \qquad B = \frac{1}{3}H$$

---

49. Pyramid (with base of any shape)

$$A = \text{area of base} \qquad V = \tfrac{1}{3}AH \qquad B = \tfrac{1}{4}H$$

$A = $ Area of Base

---

50. Frustum of pyramid (with base of any shape)

$$V = \tfrac{1}{3}H(A_1 + \sqrt{A_1 A_2} + A_2)$$

$$B = \frac{H(A_1 + 2\sqrt{A_1 A_2} + 3A_2)}{4(A_1 + \sqrt{A_1 A_2} + A_2)}$$

$A_1 = $ Area

$A_2 = $ Area

---

51. Cone

$$V = \frac{\pi}{12}D^2 H \qquad B = \frac{1}{4}H$$

Area of conical surface (right cone) $= \tfrac{1}{2}$(circumference of base) $\times$ (slant height)

---

52. Frustum of cone

$$V = \frac{\pi}{12}H(D^2 + Dd + d^2)$$

$$B = \frac{H(D^2 + 2Dd + 3d^2)}{4(D^2 + Dd + d^2)}$$

53. Frustum of hollow cone

$$V = 0.2618H[(D_1^2 + D_1d_1 + d_1^2) - (D_2^2 + D_2d_2 + d_2^2)]$$

---

54. Hexagon

$$V = \frac{\sqrt{3}}{2}d^2L$$

$$V = 0.866d^2L$$

---

55. Closely packed helical springs

$$V = \frac{\pi^2 dL}{4}(D - d)$$

$$V = 2.4674(D - d)$$

---

56. Rectangular prism

Volume = length × width × height

Volume = area of base × altitude

---

57. Any prism

(Axis either perpendicular or inclined to base)

Volume = (area of base)(perpendicular height)

Volume = (lateral length)(area of perpendicular cross section)

materials and basic manufacturing shapes

PROPERTIES, CHARACTERISTICS, AND USES OF TYPICAL ENGINEERING MATERIALS [1]

Material & Composition [2]	Specific Weight lb/ft^3	Modulus of Elasticity 10^6 psi	Tensile [3] Strength 10^3 psi	Elong. [3] at break % at 2″	Coeff. of Thermal Expansion $10^6 \times 1/°C$	Electr. Resist. 10^{-6} Ω-cm
CARBON STEELS	487	28.5–30			12.5	10
AISI 1020 (0.2 C, 0.45 Mn, 0.25 Si)			55–61	25–15		
AISI 1045 (0.45 C, 0.75 Mn)			82–94	16–12		
AISI 1090 (0.90 C, 0.40 Mn)			122	10		
ALLOY STEELS	487	28.5–30			~12	~9
AISI 1340 (1.6–1.9 Mn)			110–230	25–11		
AISI 4140 (.9 Mn, 1 Cr, .2 Mo)			100–225	25–10		
AISI 8640 (.9 Mn, .5 Cr, .2 Mo, .55 Ni)			120–240	23–10		
STAINLESS STEELS	495	28–29			17.3	72
304 (19 Cr, 9 Ni, 2 Mn)			85–185	60–8		
316 (17 Cr, 12 Ni, 2 Mn, 2–3 Mo)			90–150	50–8		
420 (16 Cr, 2 Ni, 1 Mn)			95–230	25–8		
CAST IRON	442				12.5	
A 159 (3.4–3.7 C, 2.3–2.8 Si)		13	25	0.5		67
A 571 (2.2–2.7 C, 2 Si, 4 Mn, 2.2 Ni)		25	65	30		30
CAST STEEL	480	28.5				
A 27 (0.3 C, .75 Mn, .6 Si, .5 Ni, .25 Cr)			65	24		
A 216 (.25 C, .7 Mn, .6 Si, .5 Ni, .25 Mo)			60	24		
COPPER ALLOYS						
Beryll. Copper (1.9 Be, .25 Co)	514	19	90–200	10–2	17	
Yellow Brass (65 Cu, 35 Zn)	534	15.5	46–128	65–3	19	7
Al-Bronze (91 Cu, 7Al, 2 Fe)	481	17	76–89	45–32	17	12
TITANIUM ALLOY (8 Al, 1 Mo, 1 V)	312	16.5	150–170	18–10	8.8	80
MAGNESIUM ALLOY (1 Zr, 3 Al)	110	6.5	37–42	21–14	26	9
ALUMINUM ALLOYS	170	10–10.5			23	4
1060 (99.6 Al)			10–20	43–6		
2024 (4.5 Cu, .6 Mn, 1.5 Mg)			65–70	18–6		
6061 (.6 Si, .25 Cu, 1 Mg, .2 Cr)			18–45	25–12		
PLASTICS						10^{12} Ω-cm
Acrylic	73.5	0.3–0.5	6–12	10–2	50–60	> 100
Epoxy	72	0.3–0.6	4–13	6–2	45–90	1–100
Glass Fiber Filament Reinforced	(136)	6.0–7.5	(130–200)			
Fluorocarbon	137	0.03–0.07	2–7	200–400	21–43	10^6
Nylon 6	71	0.4	9–12	200	74	
Polycarbonate	75	0.3–0.4	8–9.5	20–100	66	2×10^4
Poly-vinyl Chloride (PVC)	87	0.2–0.6	5–9	40–2	50–180	$1 - 10^4$
REFRACTORIES						
Concrete (Unreinforced)	140	2–5	0.3–0.8	~0		
Glass (Soda-Lime)	158	10	0.5–8	~0	8.5	1
Alumina (Al_2O_3)	247	50	25–35	~0	5.4	$10^2 - 10^3$
Graphite (C)	138	1	1–2		3.6	10^{-3} Ω-cm
WOOD						
Douglas Fir	32	1.1	1.6			
White Oak	46	1.5	2.1			

[1] From various sources, primarily Parker, E. R., *Materials Data Book*, McGraw-Hill 1967, and Weast, R. C., Ed. *Handbook for Applied Engineering Sciences*, The Chemical Rubber Co., 1970.

[2] Composition in percent.

[3] Depends on thermal treatment, usually hi-strength goes with lo-elongation and vice versa.

Comments	Major Characteristics	Major Uses
Mild Steel	Moderate strength, easy to machine & weld	Bolts, nails, tubing, structural steel
	Medium strength, moderate machineability	Forgings, basic machine parts
Hot Rolled	Hard, hi-strength, takes edge, hard to weld	Springs, cutting tools, drills, dies
Typically 0.4% C		
Manganese Steel	Good machineability, hi strength	Auto & farm implements, axles, shafts
Chrome-Moly Steel	Hardenable, good hi-temp strength	Gears, aircraft & machine tool parts
Nickel-Chrome-Moly Steel	Strength, corrosion resist, hi-temp	Heavy duty gears, cams, bolts
Austenitic	Non-magnetic, weldable	General purpose, food handling, ext. trim
Austenitic	Non-magnetic, hi-temp, hi corrosion resistance	Chemical & food process equipment
Martensitic	Magnetic, will take edge	Surgical instruments
Gray C.I.	Low cost, brittle, low strength	Casting where strength is not needed
Ductile C.I.	Easy to machine	Pumps, pressure parts, engine blocks
	Easy machine & weld, moderate strength	General purpose
	Hi-temp resistance	Furnace tubes & fittings
	Tough, flexible	Springs, diaphragms, bellows
	Cold workability, strength	Radiators, lamp fixtures
	Easy to form & forge, corrosion resistant	Machine parts
	High strength, low weight, costly	Aircraft & missile parts
Type AZ 31B	Medium strength, low weight, easy to machine	Structural, where weight is critical
Type 0 – H18	Soft, hi conductivity	Electrical conductors, chemical equipment
Type T3 – T86	Hi-strength, tough, easy machining	Screw machine products, aircraft parts
Type 0 – T6	Weldable & easy machining	Structures, general use
Plexiglas, Lucite	Transparent, easy machine & glue	Aircraft windows, lighting fixtures
	Strong, Hi-temp resistance	Potting electronic parts
	Hi strength, limited shapes, costly	Missile bodies, rocket motor cases
Teflon	Lo friction, hi temp resistance	Bearings, utensil liners, chemical reactors
	Lo friction, good strength & toughness	Bearings, gears, tubing
	Hi impact strength, moderate cost	Molded parts like crash helmets
	Low cost, moderate strength	Most molded parts--decorative, household, etc.
All refractories are	Strength depends on proportions & cure	Structural
10–100 times stronger	Ordinary glass	Windows, bottles, etc.
in compression than	Very stable, melts above 2000°C, hard	Rocket nozzles, abrasives, furnace parts
in tension	Highest temp resist, melts above 2500°C	Heat shields for re-entry vehicles, furnaces
Strength in direction	Moderate strength, fast growth, little warpage	Buildings, concrete forms
of fibers	Dense, hard, uniform	Furniture, sills, floors

Specific Gravities and Specific Weights

Material	Average Specific Gravity	Average Specific Weight, lb_f/ft^3	Material	Average Specific Gravity	Average Specific Weight, lb_f/ft^3
Acid, sulfuric, 87%	1.80	112	Ice	0.91	57
Air, S.T.P.	0.001293	0.0806			
Alcohol, ethyl	0.790	49	Kerosene	0.80	50
Aluminum, cast	2.65	165			
Asbestos	2.5	153	Lead	11.34	710
Ash, white	0.67	42	Leather	0.94	59
Ashes, cinders	0.68	44	Limestone, solid	2.70	168
Asphalt	1.3	81	Limestone, crushed	1.50	95
Babbitt metal, soft	10.25	625	Mahogany	0.70	44
Basalt, granite	1.50	96	Manganese	7.42	475
Brass, cast-rolled	8.50	534	Marble	2.70	166
Brick, common	1.90	119	Mercury	13.56	845
Bronze, 7.9 to 14% Sn	8.1	509	Monel metal, rolled	8.97	555
Cedar, white, red	0.35	22	Nickel	8.90	558
Cement, Portland, bags	1.44	90			
			Oak, white	0.77	48
Chalk	2.25	140	Oil, lubricating	0.91	57
Clay, dry	1.00	63			
Clay, loose, wet	1.75	110	Paper	0.92	58
Coal, anthracite, solid	1.60	95	Paraffin	0.90	56
Coal, bituminous, solid	1.35	85	Petroleum, crude	0.88	55
Concrete, gravel, sand	2.3	142	Pine, white	0.43	27
Copper, cast, rolled	8.90	556			
Cork	0.24	15	Redwood, California	0.42	26
Cotton, flax; hemp	1.48	93	Rubber	1.25	78
Copper ore	4.2	262			
			Sand, loose, wet	1.90	120
Earth	1.75	105	Sandstone, solid	2.30	144
			Sea water	1.03	64
Fir, Douglas	0.50	32	Silver	10.5	655
Flour, loose	0.45	28	Steel, structural	7.90	490
			Sulfur	2.00	125
Gasoline	0.70	44			
Glass, crown	2.60	161	Teak, African	0.99	62
Glass, flint	3.30	205	Tin	7.30	456
Glycerine	1.25	78	Tungsten	19.22	1200
Gold, cast-hammered	19.3	1205	Turpentine	0.865	54
Granite, solid	2.70	172			
Gravel, loose, wet	1.68	105	Water, 4°C	1.00	62.4
			Water, snow, fresh fallen	0.125	8.0
Hickory	0.77	48			

Note: The value for the specific weight of water, which is usually used in problem solutions, is 62.4 lb_f/ft^3 or 8.34 lb_f/gal.

Properties of Pure Metals*

Metals	Specific Gravity	Modulus of Elasticity, millions of psi	Melting Point, °C	Coeff. of Expansion $10^{-6} \times 1/°C$**	Thermal Conductivity, kcal/hr-cm-°C†	Electrical Resistivity, $\mu\Omega$-cm
Aluminum	2.70	10	660	25	2.04	2.66
Beryllium	1.85	42	1286	12.0	1.87	4.0
Chromium	7.2	36	1860	5.9	0.77	13
Cobalt	8.9	30	1497	12.0	0.60	9
Copper	8.96	17	1082	16.5	3.42	1.673
Gold	19.32	11	1064	14.2	2.70	2.35
Iron	7.87	28.5	1538	12.0	0.69	9.7
Lead	11.35	2.0	327	29	0.30	20.6
Magnesium	1.74	6.4	649	25	1.37	4.45
Mercury	13.55	–	−39	–	0.072	98.4
Nickel	8.90	31	1452	13.1	0.77	6.85
Niobium (Columbium)	8.57	15	2470	7.0	0.45	13
Platinum	21.45	21	1772	9	0.63	10.5
Silicon	2.33	16	1410	5	0.72	1×10^5
Silver	10.50	10.5	961	20	3.67	1.59
Sodium	0.97	–	98	70	1.15	4.2
Tin	7.31	6	232	20	0.55	11.0
Titanium	4.54	16	1672	8.5	0.18	43
Tungsten	19.3	50	3400	4.5	1.53	5.65
Uranium	18.8	24	1130	13.3	0.21	30
Vanadium	6.1	19	1900	7.9	0.52	25
Zinc	7.0	12	420	34	0.99	5.92

*Compiled from various sources.
**Can also be written μin/in/°C.
†1 kcal/hr-cm-°C = 67.2 Btu/hr-ft-°F.

material specification systems

SAE Numbering System
for Wrought or Rolled Steel—SAE J402b
SAE Standard

Report of Iron and Steel Division approved January 1912 and last revised by Iron and Steel Technical Committee May 1969.

This SAE Standard is intended to supply a uniform means of designating wrought ferrous materials reported in SAE Standards and Recommended Practices.

Only compositions which conform to the SAE compositions given in the current SAE Handbook should bear the prefix "SAE."

A numeral index system is used to identify the compositions of the SAE steels, which system makes possible use of numerals on shop drawings and blueprints to describe partially the composition of the material.

The first digit indicates the type to which the steel belongs, that is, "1" indicates a carbon steel; "2" a nickel steel; and "3" a nickel–chromium steel. In the case of the simple alloy steels, the second digit generally indicates an alloy or alloy combination, and sometimes the approximate percentage of the predominant alloying element. Usually the last two or three digits indicate the approximate carbon content in "points" or hundredths of one per cent. Thus, "SAE 5135" indicates a chromium steel of approximately 1% chromium (0.80 to 1.05%) and 0.35% carbon (0.33 to 0.38%).

In some instances, in order to avoid confusion, it has been found necessary to depart from this system of identifying the approximate alloy composition of a steel by varying the second and third digits of the number. Instances of such departure are the steel numbers selected for several of the corrosion- and heat-resisting alloys and the triple alloy steels.

The basic numerals of the various types of SAE steel are given in the table.

Basic Numbering System for SAE Steels

Numerals and Digits	Type of Steel and Average Chemical Contents, %	Numerals and Digits	Type of Steel and Average Chemical Contents, %
	Carbon Steels		Nickel–Molybdenum Steels
10XX	Plain Carbon (Mn 1.00% max)	46XX	Ni 0.85 and 1.82; Mo 0.20 and 0.25
11XX	Resulfurized	48XX	Ni 3.50; Mo 0.25
12XX	Resulfurized and Rephosphorized		
15XX	Plain Carbon (max Mn range—over 1.00–1.65%)		Chromium Steels
		50XX	Cr 0.27, 0.40, 0.50, and 0.65
		51XX	Cr 0.80, 0.87, 0.92, 0.95, 1.00 and 1.05
		501XX	Cr 0.50
	Manganese Steels	511XX	Cr 1.02
13XX	Mn 1.75	521XX	Cr 1.45
	Nickel Steels		Chromium–Vanadium Steels
23XX	Ni 3.50	61XX	Cr 0.60, 0.80, and 0.95; V 0.10 and 0.15 minimum
25XX	Ni 5.00		
	Nickel–Chromium Steels		Tungsten–Chromium Steels
31XX	Ni 1.25; Cr 0.65 and 0.80	71XXX	W 13.50 and 16.50; Cr 3.50
32XX	Ni 1.75; Cr 1.07	72XX	W 1.75; Cr 0.75
33XX	Ni 3.50; Cr 1.50 and 1.57		
34XX	Ni 3.00; Cr 0.77		Silicon–Manganese Steels
		92XX	Si 1.40 and 2.00; Mn 0.65, 0.82, and 0.85; Cr 0.00 and 0.65
	Molybdenum Steels		
40XX	Mo 0.20 and 0.25		Low-Alloy High-Tensile Steels
44XX	Mo 0.40 and 0.52	9XX	Various
			Stainless Steels
	Chromium–Molybdenum Steels		(Chromium–Manganese–Nickel)
41XX	Cr 0.50, 0.80 and 0.95; Mo 0.12, 0.20, 0.25, and 0.30	302XX	Cr 17.00 and 18.00; Mn 6.50 and 8.75; Ni 4.50 and 5.00
			(Chromium–Nickel)
	Nickel–Chromium–Molybdenum Steels	303XX	Cr 8.50, 15.50, 17.00, 18.00, 19.00, 20.00, 20.50, 23.00, 25.00
43XX	Ni 1.82; Cr 0.50 and 0.80; Mo 0.25		Ni 7.00, 9.00, 10.00, 10.50, 11.00, 11.50, 12.00, 13.00, 13.50, 20.50, 21.00, 35.00
43BVXX	Ni 1.82; Cr 0.50; Mo 0.12 and 0.25; V 0.03 minimum		(Chromium)
47XX	Ni 1.05; Cr 0.45; Mo 0.20 and 0.35	514XX	Cr 11.12, 12.25, 12.50, 13.00, 16.00, 17.00, 20.50, and 25.00
81XX	Ni 0.30; Cr 0.40; Mo 0.12		
86XX	Ni 0.55; Cr 0.50; Mo 0.20	515XX	Cr 5.00
87XX	Ni 0.55; Cr 0.50; Mo 0.25		Boron–Intensified Steels
88XX	Ni 0.55; Cr 0.50; Mo 0.35	XXBXX	B denotes Boron Steel
93XX	Ni 3.25; Cr 1.20; Mo 0.12		
94XX	Ni 0.45; Cr 0.40; Mo 0.12		Leaded–Steels
97XX	Ni 0.55; Cr 0.20; Mo 0.20	XXLXX	L denotes Leaded Steel
98XX	Ni 1.00; Cr 0.80; Mo 0.25		

NOMENCLATURE FOR COMMON PRODUCT FEATURES

STOCK MATERIAL SHAPES

SLABS BLOOMS BILLETS

ARE ROLLED OR EXTRUDED

TO FORM

SHEETS & PLATES, STRUCTURAL SHAPES, BARS & RODS
AND VARIOUS IRREGULAR CROSS SECTIONS

Structural Steel Nomenclature

The shapes listed in the tabulation are those that are most commonly available. Other shapes are also available from steel producers. The nomenclature for such unlisted shapes will be related to the shape profile in the same manner as the nomenclature for each listed shape is related to its profile. For the most generally used types of shapes, this relation is as follows:

1. W shapes are doubly symmetric wide flange shapes used as beams or columns whose inside flange surfaces are substantially parallel. A shape having essentially the same nominal weight and dimensions as a W shape listed in the tabulation but whose inside flange surfaces are not parallel may also be considered a W shape having the same nomenclature as the tabulated shape, provided its average flange thickness is essentially the same shape as the flange thickness of the W shape.

2. S shapes are doubly symmetric shapes produced in accordance with dimensional standards adopted in 1896 by the Association of American Steel Manufactures for American Standard beam shapes. The essential part of these standards is that the inside flange surfaces of American Standard beam shapes have approximately a 16-2/3% slope.

3. M shapes are doubly symmetric shapes that cannot be classified as W, S, or bearing pile shapes. (Although not included in the standard nomenclature tabulation, bearing piles are doubly symmetric wide flange shapes whose inside flange surfaces are essentially parallel and whose flange and web have essentially the same thickness).

4. C shapes are channels produced in accordance with dimensional standards adopted in 1896 by the Association of American Steel Manufactures for American Standard channels. The essential part of these standards is that the inside flange surfaces of American Standard channels have approximately a 16-2/3% slope.

5. L shapes are equal-leg and unequal-leg angles.

Courtesy American Institute of Steel Construction

Shape	New Identifying Symbol
Wide Flange Shapes	W
Miscellaneous Shapes	M
American Standard Beams	S
American Standard Channels	C
Miscellaneous Channels	MC
Angles—Equal Legs	L
Angles—Unequal Legs	L
Bulb Angles	BL
Structural Tees Cut From Wide Flange Shapes	WT
Structural Tees Cut From Miscellaneous Shapes	MT
Structural Tees Cut From American Standard Beams	ST
Tees	T
Wall Tee	AT
Elevator Tees	ET
Zees	Z
Special Car Building Shapes	CZ

STRUCTURAL STEEL SHAPES

HP Shapes

M Shapes

W Shapes

HP Shapes

Designation	Depth d (in)	Flange Width b_f (in)	Flange Thickness t_f (in)	Web Thickness t_w (in)
HP 10 × 57	10	$10\frac{1}{4}$	$\frac{9}{16}$	$\frac{9}{16}$
× 42	$9\frac{3}{4}$	$10\frac{1}{8}$	$\frac{7}{16}$	$\frac{7}{16}$
HP 8 × 36	8	$8\frac{1}{8}$	$\frac{7}{16}$	$\frac{7}{16}$

M Shapes

Designation	Depth d (in)	Flange Width b_f (in)	Flange Thickness t_f (in)	Web Thickness t_w (in)
M 14 × 17.2	14	4	$\frac{1}{4}$	$\frac{3}{16}$
M 12 × 11.8	12	$3\frac{1}{8}$	$\frac{1}{4}$	$\frac{3}{16}$
M 10 × 29.1	$9\frac{7}{8}$	$5\frac{7}{8}$	$\frac{3}{8}$	$\frac{7}{16}$
× 22.9	$9\frac{7}{8}$	$5\frac{3}{4}$	$\frac{3}{8}$	$\frac{1}{4}$
M 10 × 9	10	$2\frac{3}{4}$	$\frac{3}{16}$	$\frac{3}{16}$
M 8 × 37.7	$8\frac{1}{8}$	8	$\frac{1}{2}$	$\frac{3}{8}$
× 34.3	8	8	$\frac{7}{16}$	$\frac{3}{8}$
× 32.6	8	8	$\frac{7}{16}$	$\frac{5}{16}$
M 8 × 22.5	8	$5\frac{3}{8}$	$\frac{3}{8}$	$\frac{3}{8}$
× 18.5	8	$5\frac{1}{4}$	$\frac{3}{8}$	$\frac{1}{4}$
M 8 × 6.5	8	$2\frac{1}{4}$	$\frac{3}{16}$	$\frac{1}{8}$
M 7 × 5.5	7	$2\frac{1}{8}$	$\frac{3}{16}$	$\frac{1}{8}$
M 6 × 33.75	$6\frac{1}{4}$	$6\frac{1}{8}$	$\frac{5}{8}$	$\frac{1}{2}$
× 22.5	6	6	$\frac{3}{8}$	$\frac{3}{8}$
× 20	6	6	$\frac{3}{8}$	$\frac{1}{4}$
M 6 × 4.4	6	$1\frac{7}{8}$	$\frac{3}{16}$	$\frac{1}{8}$
M 5 × 18.9	5	5	$\frac{7}{16}$	$\frac{5}{16}$
M 4 × 16.3	$4\frac{1}{4}$	4	$\frac{1}{2}$	$\frac{5}{16}$
× 13.8	4	4	$\frac{3}{8}$	$\frac{5}{16}$
× 13	4	4	$\frac{3}{8}$	$\frac{1}{4}$

W Shapes

Designation	Depth d (in)	Flange Width b_f (in)	Flange Thickness t_f (in)	Web Thickness t_w (in)
W 16 × 50	$16\frac{1}{4}$	$7\frac{1}{8}$	$\frac{5}{8}$	$\frac{3}{8}$
× 45	$16\frac{1}{8}$	7	$\frac{9}{16}$	$\frac{3}{8}$
× 40	16	7	$\frac{1}{2}$	$\frac{5}{16}$
× 36	$15\frac{7}{8}$	7	$\frac{7}{16}$	$\frac{5}{16}$
W 14 × 38	$14\frac{1}{8}$	$6\frac{3}{4}$	$\frac{1}{2}$	$\frac{5}{16}$
× 34	14	$6\frac{3}{4}$	$\frac{7}{16}$	$\frac{5}{16}$
× 30	$13\frac{7}{8}$	$6\frac{3}{4}$	$\frac{3}{8}$	$\frac{5}{16}$
W 12 × 36	$12\frac{1}{4}$	$6\frac{5}{8}$	$\frac{9}{16}$	$\frac{5}{16}$
× 31	$12\frac{1}{8}$	$6\frac{1}{2}$	$\frac{7}{16}$	$\frac{1}{4}$
× 27	12	$6\frac{1}{2}$	$\frac{3}{8}$	$\frac{1}{4}$
W 10 × 45	$10\frac{1}{8}$	8	$\frac{5}{8}$	$\frac{3}{8}$
× 39	10	8	$\frac{1}{2}$	$\frac{5}{16}$
× 33	$9\frac{3}{4}$	8	$\frac{7}{16}$	$\frac{5}{16}$
W 10 × 29	$10\frac{1}{4}$	$5\frac{3}{4}$	$\frac{1}{2}$	$\frac{5}{16}$
× 25	$10\frac{1}{8}$	$5\frac{3}{4}$	$\frac{7}{16}$	$\frac{1}{4}$
× 21	$9\frac{7}{8}$	$5\frac{3}{4}$	$\frac{5}{16}$	$\frac{1}{4}$
W 8 × 67	9	$8\frac{1}{4}$	$\frac{15}{16}$	$\frac{9}{16}$
× 58	$8\frac{3}{4}$	$8\frac{1}{4}$	$\frac{13}{16}$	$\frac{1}{2}$
× 48	$8\frac{1}{2}$	$8\frac{1}{8}$	$\frac{11}{16}$	$\frac{3}{8}$
× 40	$8\frac{1}{4}$	$8\frac{1}{8}$	$\frac{9}{16}$	$\frac{3}{8}$
× 35	$8\frac{1}{8}$	8	$\frac{1}{2}$	$\frac{5}{16}$
× 31	8	8	$\frac{7}{16}$	$\frac{5}{16}$
W 6 × 25	$6\frac{3}{8}$	$6\frac{1}{8}$	$\frac{7}{16}$	$\frac{5}{16}$
× 20	$6\frac{1}{4}$	6	$\frac{3}{8}$	$\frac{1}{4}$
× 15.5	6	6	$\frac{1}{4}$	$\frac{1}{4}$
W 5 × 18.5	$5\frac{1}{8}$	5	$\frac{7}{16}$	$\frac{1}{4}$
× 16	5	5	$\frac{3}{8}$	$\frac{1}{4}$
W 4 × 13	$4\frac{1}{8}$	4	$\frac{3}{8}$	$\frac{1}{4}$

Courtesy American Institute of Steel Construction, 1970.

STRUCTURAL STEEL SHAPES

S Shapes

Misc. Channels

Amer. Std. Channels

Designation	Depth of Section d	Flange Width b_f	Flange Thickness t_f	Web Thickness t_w
	in	in	in	in
S 15 × 50	15	$5\frac{5}{8}$	$\frac{5}{8}$	$\frac{9}{16}$
× 42.9	15	$5\frac{1}{2}$	$\frac{5}{8}$	$\frac{7}{16}$
S 12 × 50	12	$5\frac{1}{2}$	$\frac{11}{16}$	$\frac{11}{16}$
× 40.8	12	$5\frac{1}{4}$	$\frac{11}{16}$	$\frac{7}{16}$
S 12 × 25	12	$5\frac{1}{8}$	$\frac{9}{16}$	$\frac{7}{16}$
× 31.8	12	5	$\frac{9}{16}$	$\frac{3}{8}$
S 10 × 35	10	5	$\frac{1}{2}$	$\frac{5}{8}$
× 25.4	10	$4\frac{5}{8}$	$\frac{1}{2}$	$\frac{5}{16}$
S 8 × 23	8	$4\frac{1}{8}$	$\frac{7}{16}$	$\frac{7}{16}$
× 18.4	8	4	$\frac{7}{16}$	$\frac{1}{4}$
S 7 × 20	7	$3\frac{7}{8}$	$\frac{3}{8}$	$\frac{7}{16}$
× 15.3	7	$3\frac{5}{8}$	$\frac{3}{8}$	$\frac{1}{4}$
S 6 × 17.25	6	$3\frac{5}{8}$	$\frac{3}{8}$	$\frac{7}{16}$
× 12.5	6	$3\frac{3}{8}$	$\frac{3}{8}$	$\frac{1}{4}$
S 5 × 14.75	5	$3\frac{1}{4}$	$\frac{5}{16}$	$\frac{1}{2}$
× 10	5	3	$\frac{5}{16}$	$\frac{3}{16}$
S 4 × 9.5	4	$2\frac{3}{4}$	$\frac{5}{16}$	$\frac{5}{16}$
× 7.7	4	$2\frac{5}{8}$	$\frac{5}{16}$	$\frac{3}{16}$
S 3 × 7.5	3	$2\frac{1}{2}$	$\frac{1}{4}$	$\frac{3}{8}$
× 5.7	3	$2\frac{3}{8}$	$\frac{1}{4}$	$\frac{3}{16}$

Designation	Depth of Section d	Flange Width b_f	Flange Avg. Thickness t_f	Web Thickness t_w
	in	in	in	in
MC 18 × 58	18	$4\frac{1}{4}$	$\frac{5}{8}$	$\frac{11}{16}$
× 51.9	18	$4\frac{1}{8}$	$\frac{5}{8}$	$\frac{5}{8}$
× 45.8	18	4	$\frac{5}{8}$	$\frac{1}{2}$
× 42.7	18	4	$\frac{5}{8}$	$\frac{7}{16}$
MC 12 × 50	12	$4\frac{1}{8}$	$\frac{11}{16}$	$\frac{13}{16}$
× 45	12	4	$\frac{11}{16}$	$\frac{11}{16}$
× 40	12	$3\frac{7}{8}$	$\frac{11}{16}$	$\frac{9}{16}$
× 35	12	$3\frac{3}{4}$	$\frac{11}{16}$	$\frac{7}{16}$
MC 10 × 41.1	10	$4\frac{3}{8}$	$\frac{9}{16}$	$\frac{13}{16}$
× 33.6	10	$4\frac{1}{8}$	$\frac{9}{16}$	$\frac{9}{16}$
× 28.5	10	4	$\frac{9}{16}$	$\frac{7}{16}$
MC 10 × 28.3	10	$3\frac{1}{2}$	$\frac{9}{16}$	$\frac{1}{2}$
× 25.3	10	$3\frac{1}{2}$	$\frac{1}{2}$	$\frac{7}{16}$
× 24.9	10	$3\frac{3}{8}$	$\frac{9}{16}$	$\frac{3}{8}$
× 21.9	10	$3\frac{1}{2}$	$\frac{1}{2}$	$\frac{5}{16}$
MC 7 × 22.7	7	$3\frac{5}{8}$	$\frac{1}{2}$	$\frac{1}{2}$
× 19.1	7	$3\frac{1}{2}$	$\frac{1}{2}$	$\frac{3}{8}$
MC 7 × 17.6	7	3	$\frac{1}{2}$	$\frac{3}{8}$
MC 6 × 18	6	$3\frac{1}{2}$	$\frac{1}{2}$	$\frac{3}{8}$
× 15.3	6	$3\frac{1}{2}$	$\frac{3}{8}$	$\frac{5}{16}$
MC 3 × 9	3	$2\frac{1}{8}$	$\frac{3}{8}$	$\frac{1}{2}$
× 7.1	3	2	$\frac{3}{8}$	$\frac{5}{16}$

Designation	Depth of Section d	Flange Width b_f	Flange Avg. Thickness t_f	Web Thickness t_w
	in	in	in	in
C 15 × 50	15	$3\frac{3}{4}$	$\frac{5}{8}$	$\frac{11}{16}$
× 40	15	$3\frac{1}{2}$	$\frac{5}{8}$	$\frac{1}{2}$
× 33.9	15	$3\frac{3}{8}$	$\frac{5}{8}$	$\frac{3}{8}$
C 12 × 30	12	$3\frac{1}{8}$	$\frac{1}{2}$	$\frac{1}{2}$
× 25	12	3	$\frac{1}{2}$	$\frac{3}{8}$
× 20.7	12	3	$\frac{1}{2}$	$\frac{5}{16}$
C 10 × 30	10	3	$\frac{7}{16}$	$\frac{11}{16}$
× 25	10	$2\frac{7}{8}$	$\frac{7}{16}$	$\frac{1}{2}$
× 20	10	$2\frac{3}{4}$	$\frac{7}{16}$	$\frac{3}{8}$
× 15.3	10	$2\frac{5}{8}$	$\frac{7}{16}$	$\frac{1}{4}$
C 9 × 20	9	$2\frac{5}{8}$	$\frac{7}{16}$	$\frac{7}{16}$
× 15	9	$2\frac{1}{2}$	$\frac{7}{16}$	$\frac{5}{16}$
× 13.4	9	$2\frac{3}{8}$	$\frac{7}{16}$	$\frac{1}{4}$
C 8 × 18.75	8	$2\frac{1}{2}$	$\frac{3}{8}$	$\frac{1}{2}$
× 13.75	8	$2\frac{3}{8}$	$\frac{3}{8}$	$\frac{5}{16}$
× 11.5	8	$2\frac{1}{4}$	$\frac{3}{8}$	$\frac{1}{4}$
C 7 × 14.75	7	$2\frac{1}{4}$	$\frac{3}{8}$	$\frac{7}{16}$
× 12.25	7	$2\frac{1}{4}$	$\frac{3}{8}$	$\frac{5}{16}$
× 9.8	7	$2\frac{1}{8}$	$\frac{3}{8}$	$\frac{3}{16}$
C 6 × 13	6	$2\frac{1}{8}$	$\frac{5}{16}$	$\frac{7}{16}$
× 10.5	6	2	$\frac{5}{16}$	$\frac{5}{16}$
× 8.2	6	$1\frac{7}{8}$	$\frac{5}{16}$	$\frac{3}{16}$
C 5 × 9	5	$1\frac{7}{8}$	$\frac{5}{16}$	$\frac{5}{16}$
× 6.7	5	$1\frac{3}{4}$	$\frac{5}{16}$	$\frac{3}{16}$
C 4 × 7.25	4	$1\frac{3}{4}$	$\frac{5}{16}$	$\frac{5}{16}$
× 5.4	4	$1\frac{5}{8}$	$\frac{5}{16}$	$\frac{3}{16}$
C 3 × 6	3	$1\frac{5}{8}$	$\frac{1}{4}$	$\frac{3}{8}$
× 5	3	$1\frac{1}{2}$	$\frac{1}{4}$	$\frac{1}{4}$
× 4.1	3	$1\frac{3}{8}$	$\frac{1}{4}$	$\frac{3}{16}$

Courtesy American Institute of Steel Construction, 1970.

Wire and Sheet Metal Gages
In decimals of an inch

Name of Gage	*United States Standard Gage		The United States Steel Wire Gage	American or Brown & Sharpe Wire Gage	New Birmingham Standard Sheet & Hoop Gage	British Imperial or English Legal Standard Wire Gage	Birmingham or Stubs Iron Wire Gage	Name of Gage
Principal Use	Uncoated Steel Sheets and Light Plates		Steel Wire except Music Wire	Nonferrous Sheets and Wire	Iron and Steel Sheets and Hoops	Wire	Strips, Bands, Hoops, and Wire	Principal Use
Gage No.	Weight, oz/ft^2	Approx. Thickness, In			Thickness, in			Gage No.
7/0's			0.4900		0.6666	0.500		7/0's
6/0's			0.4615	0.5800	0.625	0.464		6/0's
5/0's			0.4305	0.5165	0.5883	0.432	0.500	5/0's
4/0's			0.3938	0.4600	0.5416	0.400	0.454	4/0's
3/0's			0.3625	0.4096	0.500	0.372	0.425	3/0's
2/0's			0.3310	0.3648	0.4452	0.348	0.380	2/0's
1/0			0.3065	0.3249	0.3964	0.324	0.340	1/0
1			0.2830	0.2893	0.3532	0.300	0.300	1
2			0.2625	0.2576	0.3147	0.276	0.284	2
3	160	0.2391	0.2437	0.2294	0.2804	0.252	0.259	3
4	150	0.2242	0.2253	0.2043	0.250	0.232	0.238	4
5	140	0.2092	0.2070	0.1819	0.2225	0.212	0.220	5
6	130	0.1943	0.1920	0.1620	0.1981	0.192	0.203	6
7	120	0.1793	0.1770	0.1443	0.1764	0.176	0.180	7
8	110	0.1644	0.1620	0.1285	0.1570	0.160	0.165	8
9	100	0.1495	0.1483	0.1144	0.1398	0.144	0.148	9
10	90	0.1345	0.1350	0.1019	0.1250	0.128	0.134	10
11	80	0.1196	0.1205	0.0907	0.1113	0.116	0.120	11
12	70	0.1046	0.1055	0.0808	0.0991	0.104	0.109	12
13	60	0.0897	0.0915	0.0720	0.0882	0.092	0.095	13
14	50	0.0747	0.0800	0.0641	0.0785	0.080	0.083	14
15	45	0.0673	0.0720	0.0571	0.0699	0.072	0.072	15
16	40	0.0598	0.0625	0.0508	0.0625	0.064	0.065	16
17	36	0.0538	0.0540	0.0453	0.0556	0.056	0.058	17
18	32	0.0478	0.0475	0.0403	0.0495	0.048	0.049	18
19	28	0.0418	0.0410	0.0359	0.0440	0.040	0.042	19
20	24	0.0359	0.0348	0.0320	0.0392	0.036	0.035	20
21	22	0.0329	0.0317	0.0285	0.0349	0.032	0.032	21
22	20	0.0299	0.0286	0.0253	0.0313	0.028	0.028	22
23	18	0.0269	0.0258	0.0226	0.0278	0.024	0.025	23
24	16	0.0239	0.0230	0.0201	0.0248	0.022	0.022	24
25	14	0.0209	0.0204	0.0179	0.0220	0.020	0.020	25
26	12	0.0179	0.0181	0.0159	0.0196	0.018	0.018	26
27	11	0.0164	0.0173	0.0142	0.0175	0.0164	0.016	27
28	10	0.0149	0.0162	0.0126	0.0156	0.0148	0.014	28
29	9	0.0135	0.0150	0.0113	0.0139	0.0136	0.013	29
30	8	0.0120	0.0140	0.0100	0.0123	0.0124	0.012	30
31	7	0.0105	0.0132	0.0089	0.0110	0.0116	0.010	31
32	6.5	0.0097	0.0128	0.0080	0.0098	0.0108	0.009	32
33	6	0.0090	0.0118	0.0071	0.0087	0.0100	0.008	33
34	5.5	0.0082	0.0104	0.0063	0.0077	0.0092	0.007	34
35	5	0.0075	0.0095	0.0056	0.0069	0.0084	0.005	35
36	4.5	0.0067	0.0090	0.0050	0.0061	0.0076	0.004	36
37	4.25	0.0064	0.0085	0.0045	0.0054	0.0068		37
38	4	0.0060	0.0080	0.0040	0.0048	0.0060		38
39			0.0075	0.0035	0.0043	0.0052		39
40			0.0070	0.0031	0.0039	0.0048		40

*U. S. Standard Gage is officially a weight gage, in oz/ft^2 as tabulated. The approx. thickness shown is the ''Manufacturers' Standard'' of the American Iron and Steel Institute, based on steel as weighing 501.81 lb/ft^3 (489.6 true weight plus 2.5 per cent for average overrun in area and thickness). The AISI standard nomenclature for flat-rolled carbon steel is as follows:

Classification of Rolled Stock

Thickness (Inches)	Width (Inches)					
	To 3½ incl.	Over 3½ to 6	Over 6 to 8	Over 8 to 12	Over 12 to 48	Over 48
0.2300 & thicker	Bar	Bar	Bar	Plate	Plate	Plate
0.2299 to 0.2031	Bar	Bar	Strip	Strip	Sheet	Plate
0.2030 to 0.1800	Strip	Strip	Strip	Strip	Sheet	Plate
0.1799 to 0.0449	Strip	Strip	Strip	Strip	Sheet	Sheet
0.0448 to 0.0344	Strip	Strip				
0.0343 to 0.0255	Strip		Hot-rolled sheet and strip not generally produced in these widths and thicknesses			
0.0254 & thinner						

Courtesy American Institute of Steel Construction.

713

IV standard parts specifications

fastener nomenclature[*]

A bolt is designed for assembly with a nut. A screw has features in its design that make it capable of being used in a tapped or other preformed hole in the work. Because of basic design, it is possible to use certain types of screws in combination with a nut. Any externally threaded fastener that has a majority of the design characteristics which assist its proper use in a tapped or other preformed hole is a screw, regardless of how it is used in its service application.

An externally threaded fastener that, because of head design or other feature, is prevented from being turned during assembly, and that can be tightened or released only by torquing a nut, is a bolt. (Example: round-head bolts, track bolts, plow bolts.)

An externally threaded fastener that has a thread form which prohibits assembly with a nut having a straight thread of multiple pitch length is a screw. (Example: wood screws, tapping screws.)

An externally threaded fastener that must be assembled with a nut to perform its intended service is a bolt. (Example: heavy-hex structural bolt.)

An externally threaded fastener that must be torqued by its head into a tapped or other preformed hole to perform its intended service is a screw. (Example: square-head set screw.)

Screw Thread Terminology

Right-Hand Thread

Left-Hand Thread

Single, Double, and Triple Threads

Extracted from ANSI B18.2.1–1965 and ANSI B18.12–1962.

714

Bolts

Bolt A bolt is an externally threaded fastener designed for insertion through holes in assembled parts, and is normally intended to be tightened or released by torquing a nut.

BENT BOLT A bent bolt is a cylindircal rod having one end threaded and the other end bent to some desired configuration; also, it may be a bent cylindrical rod having both ends threaded. Threads may be cut or rolled; points are usually plain sheared.

Eye Bolt, Closed Anchor Ring A closed anchor ring eye bolt is a bent bolt having a head in the form of a closed ring. An eye bolt may also be forged and have a flattened and pierced section, with or without a collar or shoulder under the head.

Hook Bolt, Right Angle Bend A right angle bend hook bolt is a bent bolt having the unthreaded end bent to form a right angle or hook.

U-Bolt, Round Bend A round bend U-bolt is a bent bolt having threads at both ends of the rod and the rod bent at the middle to a semicircle.

CARRIAGE BOLT A carriage bolt is a bolt having a thin circular head, an oval or flat top with one of various means under the head to prevent rotation of the fastener. Carriage bolts are supplied with nuts unless otherwise specified.

Countersunk Head Square Neck Bolt This bolt has a flat top, conical bearing surface, and a square shoulder under the head.

Round Head Fin Neck Bolt This bolt has two fins, 180° apart, under the head.

Round Head Ribbed Neck Bolt This bolt has a ribbed or serrated shoulder under the head.

Eye Bolt, Closed Anchor Ring

Hook Bolt, Right Angle Bend

U-Bolt, Round Bend

Counter sunk Head Square Neck Bolt

Round Head Fin Neck Bolt

Round Head Ribbed Neck Bolt

Round Head Short Square Neck Bolt This bolt has a short square shoulder under the head. It is designed for use in sheet metal where a full square shoulder would project through and present an obstruction.

Round Head Short
Square Neck Bolt

Round Head Square Neck Bolt This bolt has a square shoulder under the head. It is designed for use in wood.

Round Head
Square Neck Bolt

HANGER BOLT A hanger bolt is a threaded rod having a lag-bolt or wood screw thread and gimlet point at one end and a standard Unified thread at the other. The bolt may have a plain body or a ribbed shoulder body. It is designed for attaching hangers to woodwork. This bolt is sometimes known as a STAIR BOLT or WOOD SCREW STUD WITH THREADED END.

Plain Body Type

Ribbed Shoulder Body Type
HANGER BOLTS

HEXAGON HEAD BOLT A hexagon head bolt is a bolt having a hexagonal-shaped external wrenching head. It is available in several dimensional series, such as Finished Hexagon, Regular Hexagon, and Heavy Hexagon, and within these series in various grades with regard to materials, tolerances, and threads.

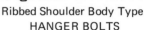

HEXAGON HEAD BOLT

HIGH-STRENGTH BOLT A high-strength bolt is a bolt developing specific high clamping loads at assembly. It may be of a type to clear the hole in the assembly or of a type that provides a bound-body fit in the assembly.

Clearance Type

Bound - Body Type
HIGH STRENGTH BOLTS

LAG BOLT*A lag bolt is a bolt having a square head, a gimlet or cone point, and a thin, sharp, coarse-pitch thread. It is designed for producing its own mating thread in wood or other resilient materials.

LAG BOLT

*More accurately called a lag screw.

716

MACHINE BOLT   A machine bolt is a bolt having a conventional head, such as a square, hexagon, button, or countersunk type, and a cylindrical body below the head. It is designed for general use in machine and other types of construction. Machine bolts are supplied with nuts unless otherwise specified.

PLOW BOLT   A plow bolt is a countersunk head bolt with head or shank designed to prevent rotation of the bolt and having coarse threads. The bolts are designed for fastening moldboards, plowshares, cultivator shoes, etc. Plow bolts are available in many types. Each type is available in a "regular head" for use on original equipment and a somewhat shallower "repair head" to fit a worn surface without grinding. Plow bolts are supplied with nuts unless otherwise specified.

Round Countersunk Head Square Neck Plow Bolt

Round Countersunk Heavy Key Head Plow Bolt

Round Countersunk Reverse Key Head Plow Bolt

Square Countersunk Head Plow Bolt

SQUARE HEAD BOLT

STOVE BOLT

Round Countersunk Head Square Neck Plow Bolt (No. 3 Head)   This bolt has a round countersunk head with an 80° head angle and a short square neck to prevent rotation.

Round Countersunk Heavy Key Head Plow Bolt (No. 6 Head)   This bolt has a round countersunk head with a 40° head angle and a triangular shaped key on one side to prevent rotation.

Round Countersunk Reverse Key Head Plow Bolt (No. 7 Head)   This bolt has a round countersunk head with a 60° head angle and a rectangular key on one side to prevent rotation.

Square Countersunk Head Plow Bolt (No. 4 Head)   This bolt has a square pyamidal shaped head with an 80° head angle in which the corners of the square prevent rotation.

SQUARE HEAD BOLT   This bolt has a square-shaped external wrenching head of standard proportions.

STOVE BOLT   A stove bolt is a former commercial standard having fractional sizes of 1/8-32, 5/32-28, 3/16-24, 7/32-22, and 1/4-18. It is now supplied as the equivalent machine screw with nut.

T-BOLT   A T-bolt is a finished bolt with a square head. It is designed for holding fixtures and other accessories in the T-slots of machine tools.

T-BOLT

TOGGLE BOLT   A toggle bolt is a bolt having a U-shaped wing rotatably attached to a nut so that it can be aligned with the shank and pushed through a hole.   It is used as a fastener in a hole that is accessible only from one side.   Toggle bolts are generally furnished with round, flat, or truss head slotted machine screws.

TOGGLE BOLT

Studs

Stud   A stud is a cylindrical rod of moderate length, threaded on either one or both ends or throughout its entire length

CONTINUOUS THREAD STUD This stud is threaded its entire length with conventional threads for the assembly of nuts on both ends. It is a variation of the Double End Stud (clamping type). It is known in some industries as BOLT STUD.

CONTINUOUS THREAD STUD

DOUBLE END STUD   A double end stud is a stud threaded on both ends with a plain or unthreaded portion between the threaded ends.   The double end stud is of two general types: the interference thread type and the clamping type.

Double End Stud (clamping type)   This stud has conventional threads on both ends of the stud. It serves the function of clamping two bodies together with a nut on either end. It is known in some industries as STUD BOLT and BOLT STUD.

Nut End   Nut End
Double End Stud (clamping type)

Double End Stud (interference thread type)   This stud has conventional threads on the "nut" end and threads on the "stud" end that will give an interference fit in the hole in which it is installed. Its application dictates that the tightness of the stud end thread in a tapped hole should not be disturbed by the removal of the nut from the nut end.   The studs may have coarse, fine, or spaced series threads. The pitch diameter on the stud end is enlarged an amount depending on the individual application. It is also known as a TAP END STUD.

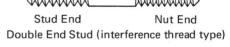

Stud End   Nut End
Double End Stud (interference thread type)

SCREWS

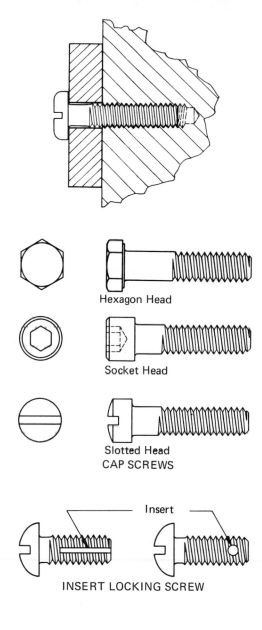

Screw. A screw is an externally threaded fastener capable of being inserted into holes in assembled parts, of mating with a preformed internal thread or forming its own thread, and of being tightened or released by torquing the head.

CAP SCREW   A cap screw is a screw having all surfaces machined or of an equivalent finish, closely controlled body diameter, and a flat chamfered point, with a wrench, slotted, recessed, or socket head of proportions and tolerances designed to assume full and proper loading when wrenched or driven into a tapped hole. Cap screws usually have hexagon, spline socket, hexagon socket, button, flat, fillister, or round head styles.

Hexagon Head

Socket Head

Slotted Head
CAP SCREWS

INSERT LOCKING SCREW   An insert locking screw is a screw having a metallic or nonmetallic insert in the threaded portion.

Insert

INSERT LOCKING SCREW

INSERT SCREW   An insert screw is a screw designed for permanent assembly of the head or shank within a cast or molded material, such as hard rubber, organic plastics, or die castings. The head or shank or both are provided with serrations, knurling, or other projections or indentations to prevent its rotation in the molded material.

INSERT SCREW

MACHINE SCREW A machine screw is a screw having a slotted, recessed, or wrenching head and threaded for assembly with a preformed internal thread. Machine screws are generally available in the following standard head styles: binding, fillister, 80° and 100° flat, flat trim, hexagon, hexagon washer, oval, oval trim, pan, round, and truss.

They are also made in numerous special head styles to suit particular requirements. They are generally furnished with plain points, but for special purposes may have chamfered, header, pilot, or other type points.

MACHINE SCREW WITH NUT has practically replaced the term STOVE BOLT.

METALLIC DRIVE SCREW (Type U) A metallic drive screw is a hardened screw having a blunt or sharp pilot point, single or multiples threads of steep lead angle, and generally furnished with a round or flat head.

It is used with a clearance hole in one of the parts to be fastened and designed for assembly by impact in sheet metal, castings, fiber, plastics, etc.

ONE-WAY HEAD SCREW A one-way head screw is a round head screw that is slotted but has side clearances at diagonally opposite sides of the slot so that the screw can be driven only in the direction of assembly; designed to prevent tampering or theft.

SET-SCREW A set screw is a hardened screw with or without a head, threaded the entire length and having a formed point designed to bear on a mating part. Set screws are regularly furnished in square head, headless slotted, hexagon socket and spline socket styles in combination with the POINT STYLES illustrated and described below.

MACHINE SCREW

METALLIC DRIVE SCREW

Feather Edge

ONE-WAY HEAD SCREW

SET SCREW

SQUARE HEAD	SQUARE HEAD	SLOTTED HEAD	HEX SOCKET	SPLINE SOCKET	SPLINE SOCKET

FLAT POINT	CONE POINT	OVAL POINT	CUP POINT	FULL DOG POINT	HALF DOG POINT

SHOULDER SCREW A shoulder screw is a slotted, flat fillister head screw having a cylindrical shoulder under the head to serve as a bearing or spacer.

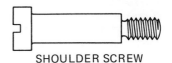

SHOULDER SCREW

SOCKET HEAD SHOULDER SCREW A socket head shoulder screw is a socket head screw having a cylindrical shoulder under the head to serve as a bearing or spacer, and a necked portion between the thread and the shoulder. (Formerly called STRIPPER BOLT.)

SOCKET HEAD SHOULDER SCREW

TAPPING SCREW A tapping screw is a screw having a slotted, recessed, or wrenching head designed to form or cut a mating thread in one or more of the parts to be assembled. Tapping screws are generally available in various combinations of the following head and screw styles: Fillister, flat, flat trim, hexagon, hexagon washer, oval, oval trim, pan, round, and truss head styles with thread-forming screws, Types AB, A, B, BP, and C, or thread-cutting screws, Types D, F, G, T, BF, and BT as illustrated and described below.

TAPPING SCREW

Type Designation of Tapping Screws and Metallic Drive Screws

Type	ANSI Standard	Manufacturer
	AB [1]	AB [1]
NOT RECOMMENDED – USE TYPE AB	A	A
	B	B
	BP	BP
	C	C
	D	1

Type	ANSI Standard	Manufacturer
	F	F
	G	G
	T	23
	BF	BF
	BT	25
DRIVE SCREW	U	U

[1] Formerly designated "Type BA"

THREAD LOCKING SCREW A thread locking screw is a screw having a thread designed to produce interference with its mating thread.

THREAD LOCKING SCREW

THUMB OR WING SCREW A thumb or wing screw is a screw having a flattened or wing shaped head, designed for manual turning without a driver or wrench.

THUMB OR WING SCREW

721

WELDING SCREW A welding screw is a headed screw provided with lugs or weld projections on the top or underside of the head to facilitate attachment to a metal part by resistance welding.

WELDING SCREW

WOOD DRIVE SCREW A wood drive screw is a thread-forming screw having a cone or pinch point, multiple threads of steep lead angle, a reduced diameter body, and generally available with flat, oval, or round head styles, designed for rapid assembly in wood.

WOOD DRIVE SCREW

WOOD SCREW A wood screw is a thread-forming screw having a slotted or recessed head, gimlet point, and a sharp crested, coarse pitch thread, and generally available with flat, oval and round head styles. It is designed to produce a mating thread when assembled into wood or other resilient materials.

WOOD SCREW

SCREW AND WASHER ASSEMBLY This is a preassembled screw and washer unit in which the washer is retained free to rotate under the screw head by the rolled thread. These units expedite assembly operations and assure the presence of a washer in each assembly. They are generally available in various combinations of head styles and washer types as indicated.

Truss Head Screw and External Tooth Lock Washer | Fillister Head Screw and Internal Tooth Lock Washer | Round Head Screw and Internal-External Tooth Lock Washer

Hexagon Head Screw and Spring Lock Washer | Pan Head Screw and Conical Spring Washer | Pan Head Screw and Plain Flat Washer

SCREW AND WASHER ASSEMBLIES (SEMS)

NUTS

Nut. A nut is a block or sleeve having an internal thread designed to assemble with external thread on a bolt, screw, or other threaded part. It may serve as the fastening means, an adjusting means, a means for transmitting motion, or a means for transmitting power with a large mechanical advantage and nonreversible motion.

CAPTIVE NUT A captive nut consists of a threaded member, usually a square nut, held loosely in a shaped sheet metal box. The variations in mating assembly parts are usually over-come by this type nut since it can float laterally.

CAPTIVE NUTS

CASTLE NUT A castle nut is a slotted hexagon nut having a cylindrical portion at the slotted end equal in length to the slot depth and slightly smaller in diameter than the hexagon width.

This nut is designed for the insertion of a cotter pin to secure the nut in place when it is used with a drilled shank fastener. This nut was formerly known as a CASTELLATED NUT.

CLINCH NUT A clinch nut is a solid nut having a pilot or other feature to be inserted in a preformed hole. The pilot may be clinched, staked, or expanded to retain the nut and prevent rotation. It is available in a large variety of types, some of which are capable of piercing the holes for assembly. It is sometimes designated ANCHOR NUT.

CONDUIT NUT A conduit nut is a thin nut, usually stamped. It may be square with scalloped corners or hexagonal or octagonal in shape.

CROWN NUT A crown nut is a hexagon nut having an acorn-shaped top and a blind threaded hole.

Crown nuts are generally furnished in two types, high crown and low crown. It is sometimes designated as ACORN NUT or CAP NUT.

FLANGE NUT A flange nut is an integral nut and washer designed for increased bearing area.

HEXAGON NUT A hexagon nut has a hexagonal base with or without a washer face. The six essentially rectangular sides serve as wrenching flats.

Hexagon nuts are available in various dimensional series, such as Finished Hexagon, Heavy Hexagon, Regular Hexagon, and in various thicknesses, such as standard, jam or thin, and thick, as shown in the illustrations. See MACHINE SCREW NUT.

CASTLE NUTS

CLINCH NUTS

CONDUIT NUTS

High   Low
CROWN NUTS

FLANGE NUT

Standard

Thick   Jam Nut
HEXAGON NUTS

LOCK NUT There are two basically different types of lock nuts: (1) a prevailing torque type that resists relative bolt–nut movement with or without an axially applied load to the bolt–nut combination, and (2) a free-running type that exhibits a locking ability when there is an axial load applied to the base of the nut. The "locking" or stopping action of the nut is accomplished by thread deformation, or clamping, or by the addition of nonmetallic inserts. The free-running type usually has a design feature that adds to the elastic elongation of the bolt–nut combination.

MACHINE SCREW NUT A machine screw nut is a hexagon or square nut of proportions suitable for use with a machine screw.

Hexagon

Square

MACHINE SCREW NUT

PLATE NUT A plate nut is a nut consisting of an internally threaded unit and a plate, which is designed to hold the threaded unit in place relative to the work. The threaded unit may be integral with the plate or held by a retainer and may have conventional or locking threads. Two-piece plate nuts are generally of the floating type in which the threaded unit has a limited movement with respect to the plate and normal to the thread axis to facilitate alignment with the mating fastener. Plates may be of the following types: (1) the hole type, for riveting, nailing, or otherwise fastening the plate to work, (2) the boss type, having weld embossments for resistance welding, the plate to work (the embossments may be on the top of the plate—internal boss, or on the bottom of the plate—external boss), or (3) the prong type, having projections to grip soft materials such as wool.

Two Rivet Type

Two Rivet, Locking, Floating Type

Nonmetallic Insert

Three-weld Boss, Internal Type

Two Rivet, Locking, Corner Type

PLATE NUTS

Standard

Thick

SLOTTED NUTS

SLOTTED NUT A slotted nut is a hexagon nut having opposed slots through the centers of the flats. The slots are on the end opposite the bearing surface and are perpendicular to the axis of the nut. Slotted nuts are designed for the insertion of a cotter pin to secure the nut in place when it is used with a drilled shank fastener.

Flat-Rectangular   Flat-Round   "J" Shape

SPRING NUTS

SPRING NUT A spring nut is a nut fabricated from thin spring steel having an impression designed to accommodate the mating thread. It is used in place of a solid nut. Spring nuts are available in many shapes and styles.

SQUARE NUT

SQUARE NUT A square nut is a solid nut with a square base, generally without a washer face. The four essentially rectangular sides serve as wrenching flats. These nuts are available in the regular and heavy series with varying proportions.

STAMPED NUTS

STAMPED NUT A stamped nut is a hexagon nut, sometimes with an integral washer, stamped from thin spring steel, having prongs formed to engage the mating thread. It is used in place of a solid nut in low-stress applications or as a retaining nut against a solid nut.

WELD NUTS

WELD NUT A weld nut is a solid nut provided with lugs, annular rings, or embossments to facilitate its attachment to a metal part by resistance welding.

WING NUT

WING NUT A wing nut is a nut having "wings" designed for manual turning. It may be forged, machined, stamped, or cast. It is sometimes called THUMB NUT.

Washers

Washer A washer is a part usually thin, having a centrally located hole or partial slot. The washer performs various functions when assembled between the bearing surface of a fastener and the part being attached. Insulation, lubrication, spanning of large clearance holes, and improved stress distribution are a few design uses.

BEVEL WASHER

BEVEL WASHER A bevel washer is a flat, square, or circular washer with a definite taper between opposite bearing faces.

CONICAL SPRING WASHER A conical spring washer is a hardened circular steel washer formed with a slight dish and having edges sheared parallel to the center line. This type of washer is designed to store a large amount of energy and also provides a "scaling" effect as the sharp edges are tightened into the bearing surfaces. This washer is also known as BELLEVILLE WASHER and CONE LOCK WASHER.

CONICAL SPRING WASHER

FINISH WASHER A finish washer is a formed circular washer designed to accommodate the head of a flat or oval head screw and provide additional bearing area on the material being fastened. Finish Washers are available in the Raised Type and Flush Type.

Raised Type   Flush Type
FINISH WASHERS

FLAT WASHER See PLAIN WASHER for definition.

Ears Bent

LOCKPLATE A lockplate is a flat plate fastened to an assembled element with screws, or held by lanced ears. The lockplate provides projections that are bent into place against a flat of the screw head, effectively preventing rotation of the head.

Assembled

LOCKPLATE

726

OPEN OR HORSESHOE WASHER   An open or horseshoe washer is a flat circular washer having a slot of width equal to the hole diameter and extending from the hole to the periphery. It is designed for installation on or removal from the shank of the fastener without removing the fastener from the assembly. This washer is also known as a C-WASHER.

OPEN OR HORSESHOE WASHER

PLAIN WASHER   A plain washer is a flat, circular, or square washer with a central hole designed to fit around a bolt or screw and under the head or nut.

PLAIN WASHER

RIVETING BURR   A riveting burr is a small plain washer assembled with a small rivet before peening the end to provide a large area of contact on the part.

RIVETING BURR

SPRING LOCK WASHER   A spring lock washer is a coiled, hardened, split circular washer having a slightly trapezoidal wire section. It is designed to serve as a spring take-up device to compensate for developed looseness and loss of tension between the parts of an assembly and to function as a hardened thrust bearing. The ends of the washer are designed to bite into the bearing surfaces.

SPRING LOCK WASHER

External Tooth

Internal Tooth

TOOTH LOCK WASHER   A tooth lock washer is a hardened circular washer, having twisted or bent prongs or projections that are deformed when assembled. The prongs, on which the pressure is localized, resist loosening of the fastener. It is generally furnished in External Tooth, Internal Tooth, and Internal-External Tooth Types,

Internal - External Tooth
TOOTH LOCK WASHER

Rivets

Rivet A rivet is a headed metal fastener of malleable material used to join parts of structures and machines by inserting the shank through the aligned holes in each piece and forming a head on the headless end by upsetting.

LARGE RIVET A large rivet is a solid rivet having a body diameter of $\frac{1}{2}$ inch or more and a head of one of the following forms: button, high button, cone, countersunk, or pan. Large rivets are usually driven at forging heat.

BUTTON HEAD   HIGH BUTTON HEAD (ACORN)   CONE HEAD   FLAT TOP COUNTERSUNK HEAD   ROUND TOP COUNTERSUNK HEAD   PAN HEAD

SMALL RIVET A small rivet is a rivet, usually solid, having a body diameter of less than $\frac{1}{2}$ inch and a head of one of the following forms: button, countersunk, flat, oval, pan, or truss. Small rivets are usually driven cold.

BUTTON HEAD   COUNTERSUNK HEAD   FLAT HEAD   OVAL HEAD   PAN HEAD   TRUSS HEAD (WAGON BOX)

BELT RIVET A belt rivet is a small solid rivet having a flat top, countersunk head, and chamfer point. It is used with a riveting burr for joining leather.

Riveting Burr

Belt Rivet

BLIND RIVET A blind rivet is a rivet designed for use where only one side of the work is accessible. The rivet will have a suitable means for expanding or forming the rivet end on the blind side, which is actuated after the rivet is inserted from the open side. Blind rivets are generally further categorized by the expanding or forming features such as: collar, drive pin, explosive, and pull stem. A few examples of the various types of blind rivets are shown in the accompanying illustrations.

Before Riveting   After Riveting   Before Driving   After Driving   Before Exploding   After Exploding

Collar Type   Drive Pin Type   Explosive Type

Before Riveting   After Riveting   Before Riveting   After Riveting

Pull Through   Self Plugging

Pull Stem Type

BLIND RIVET TYPES

BOILER RIVET A boiler rivet is a large rivet with a cone head.

BOILER RIVET

COMPRESSION RIVET A compression rivet is a rivet consisting of two parts: a solid rivet and a deep-drilled tubular rivet. The diameters of the solid shank and the drilled hole are selected so as to produce a compression or pressed fit when the two parts are assembled. Most rivets of this type have flat heads. This rivet is sometimes referred to as CULTERY RIVET.

COMPRESSION RIVET

COOPERS' RIVET A coopers' rivet is a small solid rivet having a flat top, countersunk head, and chamfer point. It is used for joining the ends of barrel hoops.

COOPERS' RIVET

SPLIT RIVET A split rivet is a small rivet having a split end for securing by spreading the ends. It is commonly furnished with an oval or countersunk head.

SPLIT RIVET

TINNERS' RIVET A tinners' rivet is a small solid rivet having a head of the same form as a flat head rivet but larger in diameter. It is designed for use in sheet-metal work.

TINNERS' RIVET

TUBULAR RIVET A tubular rivet is a small rivet having a co-axial cylindrical or tapered hole in the headless end. It is commonly furnished with a countersunk, flat, oval, or truss head. The top of the flat-top countersunk head may be slightly chamfered, as shown. Tubular rivets are designed to be secured by splaying or curling the end. They are further classified as semitubular, those having hole depths which do not exceed 112 per cent of the mean shank diameter, measured on the wall; and full tubular, those having hold depths which do exceed 112 per cent of the mean shank diameter.

Semi-Tubular   Full Tubular

Flat Top Countersunk Head
With Chamfered Top
(Brake Lining Rivet)
TUBULAR RIVETS

PINS

Pin A pin is a straight cylindrical or tapered fastener, with or without a head, designed to perform a semipermanent attaching or locating function.

CLEVIS PIN A clevis pin is a solid pin having a cylindrical head on one end with a chamfer point and drilled hole for a cotter pin at the other; designed for use with clevises and rod ends.

CLEVIS PIN

COTTER PIN A cotter pin is a double bodied pin formed from semicircular wire, a loop at one end of which provides a head. Available in various point styles as illustrated.

DOWEL PIN A dowel pin is a solid headless straight pin. Its diameter is closely controlled. Hardened and ground dowel pins have one end chamfered and the other end radiused to form a crown. Unhardened ground pins have both ends chamfered.

ESCUTCHEON PIN An escutcheon pin is a pin having a semispherical head with a flat bearing surface formed on one end and a long cone or pinch point on the other.

GROOVED PIN A grooved pin is a solid headless pin having controlled diameter and length, with multiple longitudinal grooves either rolled or pressed into the body, displacing the pin stock within predetermined limits. The grooves may extend over the full length or only portions of the pin and the ends are generally crowned. During installation, the pin material is pressed back within its elastic limits and the compressive forces actuated through the constraining action of the hole wall produce a force fit having very high resistance to loosening under shock and vibration.

SPRING PIN A spring pin is a hollow, headless pin having controlled length with rounded or chamfered ends, formed to a diameter somewhat greater than that of the hole into which it is to be assembled. Spring pins are available in two styles, slotted and coiled, as illustrated.

TAPER PIN   A taper pin is a headless, solid pin having controlled diameter, length, and taper, with crowned ends.

TAPER PIN

Miscellaneous Fasteners

BINDING POST   A binding post is a special type of subassembly used for clamping or holding electrical conductors in a rigid position. It commonly consists of a screw having a collar head or body with one or more clamping screws.

BINDING POST

CEILING HOOK   A ceiling hook is a fastener similar to an open eye bolt except that it has lag threads.

CEILING HOOK

EXPANSION FASTENER   One type of expansion fastener consists of a machine bolt, an expansion shield, and an expander nut. The shield body expands in a wedgelike manner when the expander nut is tightened. This fastener is commonly used in fastening to masonry.

Another type of expansion fastener consists of a lag bolt and an internally threaded split sleeve. It is designed for fastening to stone or concrete by inserting the sleeve into a hole in the stone or concrete and expanding to a tight fit in the hole by turning the lag bolt.

EXPANSION FASTENERS

EYELET   An eyelet is a flanged tubular fastener designed for securing by curling or splaying the tubular end.

EYELET

GROMMET   A grommet is a large eyelet–type fastener designed for securing by curling the tubular end over a formed washer to provide strength in holes through resilient materials.

GROMMET

THREAD INSERT   A thread insert is an internally threaded bushing designed to be molded in or inserted into soft or brittle materials to provide greater strength and minimize wear of threaded assembly.

THREAD INSERT

Helical Thread Insert   A helical thread insert is a wire of diamond shaped cross section coiled in the form of a helix designed to form a thread insert when assembled into a tapped hole. The insert is designed to lock itself in the tapped hole.

Helical Thread Insert

Tapping Thread Insert   A tapping thread insert is a thread insert having an external thread and cutting slots for cutting and forming a mating thread when assembled into an untapped drilled or cored hole.

Tapping Thread Insert

TURNBUCKLE   A turnbuckle is a loop or sleeve usually internally threaded with a left-hand thread at one end and a right-hand thread at the other end, intended for assembly with a threaded stud, eye, hook, or jaw at each end, used for applying tension to rods, wire rope, etc. Turnbuckles are sometimes made with a swivel feature at one end.

TURNBUCKLE

Unified Screw Threads

SIZES Primary	SIZES Secondary	Basic Major Diam.	Coarse UNC Thds. per in.	Coarse UNC Tap Drill	Fine UNF Thds. per in.	Fine UNF Tap Drill	Extra-Fine UNEF Thds. per in.	Extra-Fine UNEF Tap Drill
0		0.0600			80	$\frac{3}{64}$		
	1	0.0730	64	53	72	53		
2		0.0860	56	50	64	50		
	3	0.0990	48	47	56	45		
4		0.1120	40	43	48	42		
5		0.1250	40	38	44	37		
6		0.1380	32	36	40	33		
8		0.1640	32	29	36	29		
10		0.1900	24	25	32	21		
	12	0.2160	24	16	28	14	32	13
$\frac{1}{4}$		0.2500	20	7	28	3	32	$\frac{7}{32}$
$\frac{5}{16}$		0.3125	18	F	24	I	32	$\frac{9}{32}$
$\frac{3}{8}$		0.3750	16	$\frac{5}{16}$	24	Q	32	$\frac{11}{32}$
$\frac{7}{16}$		0.4375	14	U	20	$\frac{25}{64}$	28	$\frac{13}{32}$
$\frac{1}{2}$		0.5000	13	$\frac{27}{64}$	20	$\frac{29}{64}$	28	$\frac{15}{32}$
$\frac{9}{16}$		0.5625	12	$\frac{31}{64}$	18	$\frac{33}{64}$	24	$\frac{33}{64}$
$\frac{5}{8}$		0.6250	11	$\frac{17}{32}$	18	$\frac{37}{64}$	24	$\frac{37}{64}$
	$\frac{11}{16}$	0.6875					24	$\frac{41}{64}$
$\frac{3}{4}$		0.7500	10	$\frac{21}{32}$	16	$\frac{11}{16}$	20	$\frac{45}{64}$
	$\frac{13}{16}$	0.8125					20	$\frac{49}{64}$
$\frac{7}{8}$		0.8750	9	$\frac{49}{64}$	14	$\frac{13}{16}$	20	$\frac{53}{64}$
	$\frac{15}{16}$	0.9375					20	$\frac{57}{64}$
1		1.0000	8	$\frac{7}{8}$	12	$\frac{59}{64}$	20	$\frac{61}{64}$
	$1\frac{1}{16}$	1.0625					18	1
$1\frac{1}{8}$		1.1250	7	$\frac{63}{64}$	12	$1\frac{3}{64}$	18	$1\frac{5}{64}$
	$1\frac{3}{16}$	1.1875					18	$1\frac{9}{64}$
$1\frac{1}{4}$		1.2500	7	$1\frac{7}{64}$	12	$1\frac{11}{64}$	18	$1\frac{3}{16}$
	$1\frac{5}{16}$	1.3125					18	$1\frac{17}{64}$
$1\frac{3}{8}$		1.3750	6	$1\frac{7}{32}$	12	$1\frac{19}{64}$	18	$1\frac{5}{16}$
	$1\frac{7}{16}$	1.4375					18	$1\frac{3}{8}$
$1\frac{1}{2}$		1.5000	6	$1\frac{11}{32}$	12	$1\frac{27}{64}$	18	$1\frac{7}{16}$
	$1\frac{9}{16}$	1.5625					18	$1\frac{1}{2}$
$1\frac{5}{8}$		1.6250					18	$1\frac{9}{16}$
	$1\frac{11}{16}$	1.6875					18	$1\frac{5}{8}$
$1\frac{3}{4}$		1.7500	5	$1\frac{9}{16}$				
2		2.0000	$4\frac{1}{2}$	$1\frac{25}{32}$				
$2\frac{1}{4}$		2.2500	$4\frac{1}{2}$	$2\frac{1}{32}$				
$2\frac{1}{2}$		2.5000	4	$2\frac{1}{4}$				
$2\frac{3}{4}$		2.7500	4	$2\frac{1}{2}$				
3		3.0000	4	$2\frac{3}{4}$				
$3\frac{1}{4}$		3.2500	4	3				
$3\frac{1}{2}$		3.5000	4	$3\frac{1}{4}$				
$3\frac{3}{4}$		3.7500	4	$3\frac{1}{2}$				
4		4.0000	4	$3\frac{3}{4}$				

All dimensions given in inches.
Tap drill sizes not American Standard.
Extracted from ANSI 81.1–1960.

Straight Shank Twist Drills

Dia. of Drill	Decimal Equivalent	Dia. of Drill	Decimal Equivalent	Dia. of Drill	Decimal Equivalent	Dia. of Drill	Decimal Equivalent	Dia. of Drill	Decimal Equivalent
97	0.0059	3/64	0.0469	19	0.166	21/64	0.3281	27/32	0.8438
96	0.0063	55	0.052	18	0.1695	Q	0.332	55/64	0.8594
95	0.0067	54	0.055	11/64	0.1719	R	0.339	7/8	0.875
94	0.0071	53	0.0595	17	0.173	11/32	0.3438	57/64	0.8906
93	0.0075	1/16	0.0625	16	0.177	S	0.348	29/32	0.9062
92	0.0079	52	0.0635	15	0.180	T	0.358	59/64	0.9219
91	0.0083	51	0.067	14	0.182	23/64	0.3594	15/16	0.9375
90	0.0087	50	0.070	13	0.185	U	0.368	61/64	0.9531
89	0.0091	49	0.073	3/16	0.1875	3/8	0.375	31/32	0.9688
88	0.0095	48	0.076	12	0.189	V	0.377	63/64	0.9844
87	0.010	5/64	0.0781	11	0.191	W	0.386	1	1.000
86	0.0105	47	0.0785	10	0.1935	25/64	0.3906	1 1/64	1.0156
85	0.011	46	0.081	9	0.196	X	0.397	1 1/32	1.0312
84	0.0115	45	0.082	8	0.199	Y	0.404	1 3/64	1.0469
83	0.012	44	0.086	7	0.201	13/32	0.4062	1 1/16	1.0625
82	0.0125	43	0.089	13/64	0.2031	Z	0.413	1 5/64	1.0781
81	0.013	42	0.0935	6	0.204	27/64	0.4219	1 3/32	1.0938
80	0.0135	3/32	0.0938	5	0.2055	7/16	0.4375	1 7/64	1.1094
79	0.0145	41	0.096	4	0.209	29/64	0.4531	1 1/8	1.125
1/64	0.0156	40	0.098	3	0.213	15/32	0.4688	1 9/64	1.1406
78	0.016	39	0.0995	7/32	0.2188	31/64	0.4844	1 5/32	1.1562
77	0.018	38	0.1015	2	0.221	1/2	0.500	1 11/64	1.1719
76	0.020	37	0.104	1	0.228	33/64	0.5156	1 3/16	1.1875
75	0.021	36	0.1065	A	0.234	17/32	0.5312	1 13/64	1.2031
74	0.0225	7/64	0.1094	15/64	0.2344	35/64	0.5469	1 7/32	1.2188
73	0.024	35	0.110	B	0.238	9/16	0.5625	1 15/64	1.2344
72	0.025	34	0.111	C	0.242	37/64	0.5781	1 1/4	1.250
71	0.026	33	0.113	D	0.246	19/32	0.5938	1 9/32	1.2812
70	0.028	32	0.116	E & 1/4	0.250	39/64	0.6094	1 5/16	1.3125
69	0.0292	31	0.120	F	0.257	5/8	0.625	1 11/32	1.3438
68	0.031	1/8	0.125	G	0.261	41/64	0.6406	1 3/8	1.375
1/32	0.0312	30	0.1285	17/64	0.2656	21/32	0.6562	1 13/32	1.4062
67	0.032	29	0.136	H	0.266	43/64	0.6719	1 7/16	1.4375
66	0.033	28	0.1405	I	0.272	11/16	0.6875	1 15/32	1.4688
65	0.035	9/64	0.1406	J	0.277	45/64	0.7031	1 1/2	1.500
64	0.036	27	0.144	K	0.281	23/32	0.7188	1 9/16	1.5625
63	0.037	26	0.147	9/32	0.2812	47/64	0.7344	1 5/8	1.625
62	0.038	25	0.1495	L	0.290	3/4	0.750	1 11/16	1.6875
61	0.039	24	0.152	M	0.295	49/64	0.7656	1 3/4	1.750
60	0.040	23	0.154	19/64	0.2969	25/32	0.7812	1 13/16	1.8125
59	0.041	5/32	0.1562	N	0.302	51/64	0.7969	1 7/8	1.875
58	0.042	22	0.157	5/16	0.3125	13/16	0.8125	1 15/16	1.9375
57	0.043	21	0.159	O	0.316	53/64	0.8281	2	2.000
56	0.0465	20	0.161	P	0.323				

Extracted from ANSI B94.11–1967.

BOLTS AND HEX CAP SCREWS

	Square Bolts			Hex Bolts				Hex Cap Screws (Finished Hex Bolts)		
	F	G	H	F	G	H		F	G	H
	Width Across Flats	Width Across Corners	Head Height	Width Across Flats	Width Across Corners	Head Height		Width Across Flats	Width Across Corners	Head Height
Nominal Size or Basic Product Dia.	Basic	Max.	Basic	Basic	Max.	Basic	Nominal Size or Basic Product Dia.	Basic	Basic	Basic
1/4 0.250	3/8	0.630	11/64	7/16	0.505	11/64	1/4 0.250	7/16	0.505	5/32
5/16 0.3125	1/2	0.707	13/64	1/2	0.577	7/32	5/16 0.3125	1/2	0.577	13/64
3/8 0.375	9/16	0.795	1/4	9/16	0.650	1/4	3/8 0.375	9/16	0.650	15/64
7/16 0.4375	5/8	0.884	19/64	5/8	0.722	19/64	7/16 0.4375	5/8	0.722	9/32
1/2 0.500	3/4	1.061	21/64	3/4	0.866	11/32	1/2 0.500	3/4	0.866	5/16
5/8 0.625	15/16	1.326	27/64	15/16	1.083	27/64	9/16 0.5625	13/16	0.938	23/64
3/4 0.750	1 1/8	1.591	1/2	1 1/8	1.299	1/2	5/8 0.625	15/16	1.083	25/64
7/8 0.875	1 5/16	1.856	19/32	1 5/16	1.516	37/64	3/4 0.750	1 1/8	1.299	15/32
							7/8 0.875	1 5/16	1.516	35/64
1 1.000	1 1/2	2.121	21/32	1 1/2	1.732	43/64				
1 1/8 1.125	1 11/16	2.386	3/4	1 11/16	1.949	3/4	1 1.000	1 1/2	1.732	39/64
1 1/4 1.250	1 7/8	2.652	27/32	1 7/8	2.165	27/32	1 1/8 1.125	1 11/16	1.949	11/16
1 3/8 1.375	2 1/16	2.917	29/32	2 1/16	2.382	29/32	1 1/4 1.250	1 7/8	2.165	25/32
	2 1/4	3.182	1				1 3/8 1.375	2 1/16	2.382	27/32
1 1/2 1.500				2 1/4	2.598	1				
1 3/4 1.750				2 5/8	3.031	1 5/32	1 1/2 1.500	2 1/4	2.598	15/16
							1 3/4 1.750	2 5/8	3.031	1 3/32
2 2.000				3	3.464	1 11/32				
							2 2.000	3	3.464	1 7/32

All dimensions given in inches.
Bolt need not be finished on any surface except threads.
Top of head shall be flat and chamfered.
Minimum thread length shall be twice the basic bolt diameter plus 0.25 in for lengths up to and including 6 in, and twice the basic diameter plus 0.50 in for lengths over 6 in.
Bolts too short for the formula thread length shall be threaded as close to the head as practical.
Threads shall be in the Unified coarse thread series (UNC series), Class 2A.
Extracted from ANSI B18.2.1 – 1965.

All dimensions given in inches.
Top of head shall be flat and chamfered.
Minimum thread length shall be twice the basic product diameter plus 0.25 in for lengths up to and including 6 in, and twice the basic diameter plus 0.50 in for lengths over 6 in. On products too short for minimum thread lengths, the distance from the bearing surface of the head to the head to the first complete thread shall not exceed the length of 2½ threads for sizes up to and including 1 in, and 3½ threads for sizes larger than 1 in.
Threads shall be in the Unified coarse, fine, or 8 thread series (UNC, UNF, or 8UN series), Class 2A.
Unification of fine thread products is limited to sizes 1 in and under.
Extracted from ANSI B18.2.1 – 1965.

NUTS

Square Nuts				Hex. Nuts and Hex. Jam Nuts				
	F	G	H		F	G	H	H
Nominal Size or Basic Major Dia. of Thread	Width Across Flats	Width Across Corners	Thickness	Nominal Size or Basic Major Dia. of Thread	Width Across Flats	Width Across Corners	Thickness Hex. Nut	Thickness Hex. Jam Nut
	Basic	Max.	Basic		Basic	Max.	Basic	Basic
1/4 0.250	7/16	0.619	7/32	1/4 0.250	7/16	0.505	7/32	5/32
5/16 0.3125	9/16	0.795	17/64	5/16 0.3125	1/2	0.577	17/64	3/16
3/8 0.375	5/8	0.884	21/64	3/8 0.375	9/16	0.650	21/64	7/32
7/16 0.4375	3/4	1.061	3/8	7/16 0.4375	11/16	0.794	3/8	1/4
1/2 0.500	13/16	1.149	7/16	1/2 0.500	3/4	0.866	7/16	5/16
5/8 0.625	1	1.414	35/64	9/16 0.5625	7/8	1.010	31/64	5/16
3/4 0.750	1 1/8	1.591	21/32	5/8 0.625	15/16	1.083	35/64	3/8
7/8 0.875	1 5/16	1.856	49/64	3/4 0.750	1 1/8	1.299	41/64	27/64
				7/8 0.875	1 5/16	1.516	3/4	31/64
1 1.000	1 1/2	2.121	7/8					
1 1/8 1.125	1 11/16	2.386	1	1 1.000	1 1/2	1.732	55/64	35/64
1 1/4 1.250	1 7/8	2.652	1 3/32	1 1/8 1.125	1 11/16	1.949	31/32	39/64
1 3/8 1.375	2 1/16	2.917	1 13/64	1 1/4 1.250	1 7/8	2.165	1 1/16	23/32
1 1/2 1.500	2 1/4	3.182	1 5/16	1 3/8 1.375	2 1/16	2.382	1 11/64	25/32
				1 1/2 1.500	2 1/4	2.598	1 9/32	27/32

All dimension given in inches
Tops of nuts shall be flat and chamfered or washer crowned.
Threads shall be in the Unified coarse thread series (UNC series), Class 2B.
Extracted from ANSI B18.2.2 — 1965.

All dimensions given in inches.
Nuts in sizes up to and including $\frac{5}{8}$ in. shall be double chamfered or have washer faced bearing surface and chamfered top.
Threads shall be in the Unified coarse, fine, or 8 thread series (UNC, UNF or 8UN series), Class 2B.
Unification of fine-thread products is limited to sizes 1 in. and under.
Extracted from ANSI B18.2.2 — 1965.

CAP SCREWS

Round Head Cap Screws	Flat Head Cap Screws	Fillister Head Cap Screws	Hex. Socket Head Cap Screws

	D	A	H	J	T	A	H	J	T	A	H	O	J	T	A	H	J	T
Nom-inal Size	Body Dia.	Head Dia.	Head Height	Slot Width	Slot Depth	Head Dia.	Head Height	Slot Width	Slot Depth	Head Dia.	Head Height	Total Head Height	Slot Width	Slot Depth	Head Dia.	Head Height	Hex. Socket Size	Key Engage-ment
	Max.	Max.	Max.	Min.	Min.	Max	Aver-age	Min.	Min.	Max.	Max.	Max.	Min.	Min.	Max.	Max.	Nom.	Min.
1/4	0.250	0.437	0.191	0.064	0.097	0.500	0.140	0.064	0.045	0.375	0.172	0.216	0.064	0.077	0.375	0.250	3/16	0.120
5/16	0.3125	0.562	0.245	0.072	0.126	0.625	0.177	0.072	0.057	0.437	0.203	0.253	0.072	0.090	0.469	0.312	1/4	0.151
3/8	0.375	0.625	0.273	0.081	0.138	0.750	0.210	0.081	0.068	0.562	0.250	0.314	0.081	0.112	0.562	0.375	5/16	0.182
7/16	0.4375	0.750	0.328	0.081	0.167	0.8125	0.210	0.081	0.068	0.625	0.297	0.368	0.081	0.133	0.656	0.438	3/8	0.213
1/2	0.500	0.812	0.354	0.091	0.178	0.875	0.210	0.091	0.068	0.750	0.328	0.413	0.091	0.153	0.750	0.500	3/8	0.245
9/16	0.5625	0.937	0.409	0.102	0.207	1.000	0.244	0.102	0.080	0.812	0.375	0.467	0.102	0.168	0.938	0.625	1/2	0.307
5/8	0.625	1.000	0.437	0.116	0.220	1.125	0.281	0.116	0.091	0.875	0.422	0.521	0.116	0.189	1.125	0.750	5/8	0.370
3/4	0.750	1.250	0.546	0.131	0.278	1.375	0.352	0.131	0.115	1.000	0.500	0.612	0.131	0.223	1.312	0.875	3/4	0.432
7/8	0.875					1.625	0.423	0.147	0.138	1.125	0.594	0.720	0.147	0.264	1.500	1.000	3/4	0.495
1	1.000					1.875	0.494	0.166	0.162	1.312	0.656	0.803	0.166	0.291				
1 1/8	1.125					2.062	0.529	0.178	0.173						1.688	1.125	7/8	0.557
1 1/4	1.250					2.312	0.600	0.193	0.197						1.875	1.250	7/8	0.620
1 3/8	1.375					2.562	0.665	0.208	0.220						2.062	1.375	1	0.682
1 1/2	1.500					2.812	0.742	0.240	0.244						2.250	1.500	1	0.745

All dimensions given in inches.

Points shall be flat and chamfered.

For slotted-head cap screws the minimum length of thread shall be equal to 2D plus ¼ in. When too short, for the specified minimum thread length, the complete threads shall extend to within 2½ threads of the head.

The threads on slotted-head cap screws shall be coarse, fine, or 8-thread series, Class 2A.

The threads on hexagon socket head cap screws shall be Unified external threads with radius root: Class 3A UNRC and UNRF.

Series for screw sizes ¼ in through 1 in; Class 2A UNRC and UNRF Series for sizes over 1 in to 1½ in inclusive.

Hexagon socket head cap screws shall be designated by the following data in the sequence shown: Nominal size; threads per inch; length; product name; material; and protective coating, if required.

Extracted from ANSI B18.6.2 – 1956 (Slotted-Head Cap Screws); ANSI B18.3 – 1969 (Socket-Head Cap Screws).

MACHINE SCREWS

	Round Head Machine Screws					Truss Head Machine Screws					Flat Head Machine Screws				Fillister Head Machine Screws				
	D	A	H	J	T	A	H	J	T	R	A	H	J	T	A	H	O	J	T
Nom-inal Size	Diameter of Screw	Head Dia.	Head Height	Slot Width	Slot Depth	Head Dia.	Head Height	Slot Width	Slot Depth	Radius	Head Dia	Head Height Ref.	Slot Width	Slot Depth	Head Dia.	Head Side Height	Total Head Height	Slot Width	Slot Depth
	Basic	Max.	Max.	Min.	Min.	Max.	Max.	Min.	Min.	Max.	Max. Sharp		Min.	Min.	Max.	Max.	Max.	Min.	Min.
0	0.060	0.113	0.053	0.016	0.029	0.131	0.037	0.016	0.014	0.087	0.119	0.035	0.016	0.010	0.096	0.045	0.059	0.016	0.015
1	0.073	0.138	0.061	0.019	0.033	0.164	0.045	0.019	0.018	0.107	0.146	0.043	0.019	0.012	0.118	0.053	0.071	0.019	0.020
2	0.086	0.162	0.069	0.023	0.037	0.194	0.053	0.023	0.022	0.129	0.172	0.051	0.023	0.015	0.140	0.062	0.083	0.023	0.025
3	0.099	0.187	0.078	0.027	0.040	0.226	0.061	0.027	0.026	0.151	0.199	0.059	0.027	0.017	0.161	0.070	0.095	0.027	0.030
4	0.112	0.211	0.086	0.031	0.044	0.257	0.069	0.031	0.030	0.169	0.225	0.067	0.031	0.020	0.183	0.079	0.107	0.031	0.035
5	0.125	0.236	0.095	0.035	0.047	0.289	0.078	0.035	0.034	0.191	0.252	0.075	0.035	0.022	0.205	0.088	0.120	0.035	0.040
6	0.138	0.260	0.103	0.039	0.051	0.321	0.086	0.039	0.037	0.211	0.279	0.083	0.039	0.024	0.226	0.096	0.132	0.039	0.045
8	0.164	0.309	0.120	0.045	0.058	0.384	0.102	0.045	0.045	0.254	0.332	0.100	0.045	0.029	0.270	0.113	0.156	0.045	0.054
10	0.190	0.359	0.137	0.050	0.065	0.448	0.118	0.050	0.053	0.283	0.385	0.116	0.050	0.034	0.313	0.130	0.180	0.050	0.064
12	0.216	0.408	0.153	0.056	0.073	0.511	0.134	0.056	0.061	0.336	0.438	0.132	0.056	0.039	0.357	0.148	0.205	0.056	0.074
1/4	0.250	0.472	0.175	0.064	0.082	0.573	0.150	0.064	0.070	0.375	0.507	0.153	0.064	0.046	0.414	0.170	0.237	0.064	0.087
5/16	0.3125	0.590	0.216	0.072	0.099	0.698	0.183	0.072	0.085	0.457	0.635	0.191	0.072	0.058	0.518	0.211	0.295	0.072	0.110
3/8	0.375	0.708	0.256	0.081	0.117	0.823	0.215	0.081	0.100	0.538	0.762	0.230	0.081	0.070	0.622	0.253	0.355	0.081	0.133
7/16	0.4375	0.750	0.328	0.081	0.148	0.948	0.248	0.081	0.116	0.619	0.812	0.223	0.081	0.066	0.625	0.265	0.368	0.081	0.135
1/2	0.500	0.813	0.355	0.091	0.159	1.073	0.280	0.091	0.131	0.701	0.875	0.223	0.091	0.065	0.750	0.297	0.412	0.091	0.151
9/16	0.5625	0.938	0.410	0.102	0.183	1.198	0.312	0.102	0.146	0.783	1.000	0.260	0.102	0.077	0.812	0.336	0.466	0.102	0.172
5/8	0.625	1.000	0.438	0.116	0.195	1.323	0.345	0.116	0.162	0.863	1.125	0.298	0.116	0.088	0.875	0.375	0.521	0.116	0.193
3/4	0.750	1.250	0.547	0.131	0.242	1.573	0.410	0.131	0.182	1.024	1.375	0.372	0.131	0.111	1.000	0.441	0.612	0.131	0.226

All dimensions given in inches.
Unless otherwise specified, machine screws shall have plain sheared ends.
Threads on machine screws shall be UNC or UNF, Class 2A.
Screws up to and including 2 in in length shall have full form threads extending to within two threads of the bearing surface of the head or closer if practicable. Screws over 2 in in length shall have a minimum thread length of 1¾ in.
Extracted from ANSI B18.6.3 – 1962.

MACHINE SCREWS AND NUTS

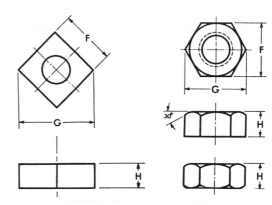

Hex. Head Machine Screws

Square and Hexagon Machine Screw Nuts

Nominal Size	D Diameter of Screw Basic	F Width Across Flats Max.	G Width Across Corners Min.	H Head Height Max.
2	0.086	0.125	0.134	0.050
3	0.099	0.187	0.202	0.055
4	0.112	0.187	0.202	0.060
5	0.125	0.187	0.202	0.070
6	0.138	0.250	0.272	0.093
8	0.164	0.250	0.272	0.110
10	0.190	0.312	0.340	0.120
12	0.216	0.312	0.340	0.155
1/4	0.250	0.375	0.409	0.190
5/16	0.3125	0.500	0.545	0.230
3/8	0.375	0.562	0.614	0.295

Nominal Size	Major Diameter of Thread Basic	F Width Across Flats Basic	G Width Across Corners Square Max.	G Width Across Corners Hex. Max.	H Thickness Nom.
0	0.060	5/32	0.221	0.180	3/64
1	0.073	5/32	0.221	0.180	3/64
2	0.086	3/16	0.265	0.217	1/16
3	0.099	3/16	0.265	0.217	1/16
4	0.112	1/4	0.354	0.289	3/32
5	0.125	5/16	0.442	0.361	7/64
6	0.138	5/16	0.442	0.361	7/64
8	0.164	11/32	0.486	0.397	1/8
10	0.190	3/8	0.530	0.433	1/8
12	0.216	7/16	0.619	0.505	5/32
1/4	0.250	7/16	0.619	0.505	3/16
5/16	0.3125	9/16	0.795	0.650	7/32
3/8	0.375	5/8	0.884	0.722	1/4

All dimensions given in inches.
Unless otherwise specified, machine screws shall have plain sheared ends.
Threads on machine screws shall be UNC or UNF, Class 2A.
Screws up to and including 2 in length shall have full form threads extending to within two threads of the bearing surface of the head or closer if practicable.
Screws over 2 in in length shall have a minimum thread length of 1 ¾ in.
Extracted from ANSI B18.6.3 — 1962.

All dimensions given in inches.
Hexagon machine screw nuts shall have tops flat and chamfered.
Bottoms are flat but for special purposes may be chamfered if so specified.
Square machine screw nuts shall have tops and bottoms flat without chamfer.
Threads in hexagon machine screw nuts shall be UNC or UNF, Class 2B; and in square machine screw nuts shall be UNC, Class 2B.
Extracted from ANSI B18.6.3 — 1962.

SET SCREWS

Hexagon and Spline Socket Set Screws

Nominal Size or Basic Screw Diameter		Hexagon Socket Size (J) Nom.		Spline Socket Size (M) Nom.	Min. Key Engagement to Develop Functional Capability of Key		Cup and Flat Pt. Dia. (C) Max.	Oval Point Radius (R) Basic	Cone Point Angle 90° ±2° For these Nominal Lengths or Longer; 118° ±2° For Shorter Nominal Lengths (Y)	Half Dog Point Dia. (P) Max.	Half Dog Point Length (Q) Max.
					Hex. Socket T_H Min.	Spline Socket T_S Min.					
0	0.060		0.028	0.033	0.050	0.026	0.033	0.045	5/64	0.040	0.017
1	0.073		0.035	0.033	0.060	0.035	0.040	0.055	3/32	0.049	0.021
2	0.086		0.035	0.048	0.060	0.040	0.047	0.064	7/64	0.057	0.024
3	0.099		0.050	0.048	0.070	0.040	0.054	0.074	1/8	0.066	0.027
4	0.112		0.050	0.060	0.070	0.045	0.061	0.084	5/32	0.075	0.030
5	0.125	1/16	0.062	0.072	0.080	0.055	0.067	0.094	3/16	0.083	0.033
6	0.138	1/16	0.062	0.072	0.080	0.055	0.074	0.104	3/16	0.092	0.038
8	0.164	5/64	0.078	0.096	0.090	0.080	0.087	0.123	1/4	0.109	0.043
10	0.190	3/32	0.094	0.111	0.100	0.080	0.102	0.142	1/4	0.127	0.049
1/4	0.250	1/8	0.125	0.145	0.125	0.125	0.132	0.188	5/16	0.156	0.067
5/16	0.3125	5/32	0.156	0.183	0.156	0.156	0.172	0.234	3/8	0.203	0.082
3/8	0.375	3/16	0.188	0.216	0.188	0.188	0.212	0.281	7/16	0.250	0.099
7/16	0.4375	7/32	0.219	0.251	0.219	0.219	0.252	0.328	1/2	0.297	0.114
1/2	0.500	1/4	0.250	0.291	0.250	0.250	0.291	0.375	9/16	0.344	0.130
5/8	0.625	5/16	0.312	0.372	0.312	0.312	0.371	0.469	3/4	0.469	0.164
3/4	0.750	3/8	0.375	0.454	0.375	0.375	0.450	0.562	7/8	0.562	0.196
7/8	0.875	1/2	0.500	0.595	0.500	0.500	0.530	0.656	1	0.656	0.227
1	1.000	9/16	0.562	—	0.562	—	0.609	0.750	1 1/8	0.750	0.260
1 1/8	1.125	9/16	0.562	—	0.562	—	0.689	0.844	1 1/4	0.844	0.291
1 1/4	1.250	5/8	0.625	—	0.625	—	0.767	0.938	1 1/2	0.938	0.323
1 3/8	1.375	5/8	0.625	—	0.625	—	0.848	1.031	1 5/8	1.031	0.354
1 1/2	1.500	3/4	0.750	—	0.750	—	0.926	1.125	1 3/4	1.125	0.385
1 3/4	1.750	1	1.000	—	1.000	—	1.086	1.312	2	1.312	0.448
2	2.000	1	1.000	—	1.000	—	1.244	1.500	2 1/4	1.500	0.510

All dimensions given in inches.
Threads shall be Unified standard, Class 3A, UNC and UNF Series.
Hexagon and spline socket set screws shall be designated by the following data in the sequence shown: nominal size; threads per inch; length; product name; point style; material; and protective coating, if required.
W is normally 45° (30° minimum for very short screws).
Extracted from ANSI B18.3 — 1969.

WASHERS

Preferred Sizes of Type A Plain Washers

Nominal Washer Size			Inside Dia. A	Outside Dia. B	Thickness C
–	–		0.078	0.188	0.020
–	–		0.094	0.250	0.020
–	–		0.125	0.312	0.032
No. 6	0.138		0.156	0.375	0.049
No. 8	0.164		0.188	0.438	0.049
No. 10	0.190		0.219	0.500	0.049
3/16	0.188		0.250	0.562	0.049
No. 12	0.216		0.250	0.562	0.065
1/4	0.250	N	0.281	0.625	0.065
1/4	0.250	W	0.312	0.734	0.065
5/16	0.312	N	0.344	0.688	0.065
5/16	0.312	W	0.375	0.875	0.083
3/8	0.375	N	0.406	0.812	0.065
3/8	0.375	W	0.438	1.000	0.083
7/16	0.438	N	0.469	0.922	0.065
7/16	0.438	W	0.500	1.250	0.083
1/2	0.500	N	0.531	1.062	0.095
1/2	0.500	W	0.562	1.375	0.109
9/16	0.562	N	0.594	1.156	0.095
9/16	0.562	W	0.625	1.469	0.109
5/8	0.625	N	0.656	1.312	0.095
5/8	0.625	W	0.688	1.750	0.134
3/4	0.750	N	0.812	1.469	0.134
3/4	0.750	W	0.812	2.000	0.148
7/8	0.875	N	0.938	1.750	0.134
7/8	0.875	W	0.938	2.250	0.165
1	1.000	N	1.062	2.000	0.134
1	1.000	W	1.062	2.500	0.165
1 1/8	1.125	N	1.250	2.250	0.134
1 1/8	1.125	W	1.250	2.750	0.165
1 1/4	1.250	N	1.375	2.500	0.165
1 1/4	1.250	W	1.375	3.000	0.165
1 3/8	1.375	N	1.500	2.750	0.165
1 3/8	1.375	W	1.500	3.250	0.180
1 1/2	1.500	N	1.625	3.000	0.165
1 1/2	1.500	W	1.625	3.500	0.180
1 5/8	1.625		1.750	3.750	0.180
1 3/4	1.750		1.875	4.000	0.180
1 7/8	1.875		2.000	4.250	0.180
2	2.000		2.125	4.500	0.180
2 1/4	2.250		2.375	4.750	0.220
2 1/2	2.500		2.625	5.000	0.238
2 3/4	2.750		2.875	5.250	0.259
3	3.000		3.125	5.500	0.284

All dimensions given in inches.
Preferred sizes are for the most part from series previously designated "Standard Plate" and "SAE." Where common sizes existed in the two series, the SAE size is designated "N" (narrow) and the Standard Plate "W" (wide). These sizes as well as all other sizes of Type A Plain Washers are to be ordered by ID, OD, and thickness dimensions.
Nominal Washer sizes are intended for use with comparable nominal screw or bolt sizes.
Extracted from ANSI B27.2 – 1965.

Regular Helical Spring Lock Washers

Nominal Washer Size		Inside Diameter A	Outside Diameter B	Thickness $\frac{T+t}{2}$
		Min.	Max.	Min.
No. 22	0.086	0.088	0.172	0.020
No. 3	0.099	0.101	1.195	0.025
No. 44	0.112	0.115	0.209	0.025
No. 5	0.125	0.128	0.236	0.031
No. 6	0.138	0.141	0.250	0.031
No. 8	0.164	0.168	0.293	0.040
No. 10	0.190	0.194	0.334	0.047
No. 12	0.216	0.221	0.377	0.056
1/4	0.250	0.255	0.489	0.062
5/16	0.312	0.318	0.586	0.078
3/8	0.375	0.382	0.683	0.094
7/16	0.438	0.446	0.779	0.109
1/2	0.500	0.509	0.873	0.125
9/16	0.562	0.572	0.971	0.141
5/8	0.625	0.636	1.079	0.156
11/16	0.688	0.700	1.176	0.172
3/4	0.750	0.763	1.271	0.188
13/16	0.812	0.826	1.367	0.203
7/8	0.875	0.890	1.464	0.219
15/16	0.938	0.954	1.560	0.234
1	1.000	1.017	1.661	0.250
1 1/16	1.062	1.080	1.756	0.266
1 1/8	1.125	1.144	1.853	0.281
1 3/16	1.188	1.208	1.950	0.297
1 1/4	1.250	1.271	2.045	0.312
1 5/16	1.312	1.334	2.141	0.328
1 3/8	1.375	1.398	2.239	0.344
1 7/16	1.438	1.462	2.334	0.359
1 1/2	1.500	1.525	2.430	0.375

All dimensions given in inches.
Formerly designated Medium Helical Spring Lock Washers.
Extracted from ANSI B27.1 – 1965.

WOOD SCREWS

		D	Slotted Round Head				Slotted Flat Head			
			A	H	J	T	A	H	J	T
Nom-inal Size	Threads per Inch	Diameter of Screw	Head Dia.	Head Height	Slot Width	Slot Depth	Head Dia.	Head Height	Slot Width	Slot Depth
		Basic	Max.	Max.	Min.	Min.	Max. Sharp	Max.	Min.	Min.
0	32	0.060	0.113	0.053	0.016	0.029	0.119	0.035	0.016	0.010
1	28	0.073	0.138	0.061	0.019	0.033	0.146	0.043	0.019	0.012
2	26	0.086	0.162	0.069	0.023	0.037	0.172	0.051	0.023	0.015
3	24	0.099	0.187	0.078	0.027	0.040	0.199	0.059	0.027	0.017
4	22	0.112	0.211	0.086	0.031	0.044	0.225	0.067	0.031	0.020
5	20	0.125	0.236	0.095	0.035	0.047	0.252	0.075	0.035	0.022
6	18	0.138	0.260	0.103	0.039	0.051	0.279	0.083	0.039	0.024
7	16	0.151	0.285	0.111	0.039	0.055	0.305	0.091	0.039	0.027
8	15	0.164	0.309	0.120	0.045	0.058	0.332	0.100	0.045	0.029
9	14	0.177	0.334	0.128	0.045	0.062	0.358	0.108	0.045	0.032
10	13	0.190	0.359	0.137	0.500	0.065	0.385	0.116	0.050	0.034
12	11	0.216	0.408	0.153	0.056	0.073	0.438	0.132	0.056	0.039
14	10	0.242	0.457	0.170	0.064	0.080	0.491	0.148	0.064	0.044
16	9	0.268	0.506	0.187	0.064	0.087	0.544	0.164	0.064	0.049
18	8	0.294	0.555	0.204	0.072	0.094	0.597	0.180	0.072	0.054
20	8	0.320	0.604	0.220	0.072	0.101	0.650	0.196	0.072	0.059
24	7	0.372	0.702	0.254	0.081	0.116	0.756	0.228	0.081	0.069

All dimensions given in inches.
The length of thread on wood screws shall be equal to approximately $\frac{2}{3}$ of the screw length.
Extracted from ANSI B18.6.1 — 1961.

WOODRUFF KEYS AND KEYSEATS

KEY   KEYSEAT-SHAFT   KEYSEAT-HUB

Key No.	Nominal Key Size W X D	Height of Key H (Max.)	Distance Below Center E	Keyseat in Shaft Depth A	Keyseat in Hub Depth B
204	1/16 X 1/2	0.203	3/64	0.1668	0.0372
304	3/32 X 1/2	0.203	3/64	0.1511	0.0529
404	1/8 X 1/2	0.203	3/64	0.1355	0.0685
305	3/32 X 5/8	0.250	1/16	0.1981	0.0529
405	1/8 X 5/8	0.250	1/16	0.1825	0.0685
505	5/32 X 5/8	0.250	1/16	0.1669	0.0841
406	1/8 X 3/4	0.313	1/16	0.2455	0.0685
506	5/32 X 3/4	0.313	1/16	0.2299	0.0841
606	3/16 X 3/4	0.313	1/16	0.2143	0.0997
507	5/32 X 7/8	0.375	1/16	0.2919	0.0841
607	3/16 X 7/8	0.375	1/16	0.2763	0.0997
807	1/4 X 7/8	0.375	1/16	0.2450	0.1310
608	3/16 X 1	0.438	1/16	0.3393	0.0997
808	1/4 X 1	0.438	1/16	0.3080	0.1310
1008	5/16 X 1	0.438	1/16	0.2768	0.1622
609	3/16 X 1 1/8	0.484	5/64	0.3853	0.0997
809	1/4 X 1 1/8	0.484	5/64	0.3540	0.1310
1009	5/16 X 1 1/8	0.484	5/64	0.3228	0.1622
810	1/4 X 1 1/4	0.547	5/64	0.4170	0.1310
1010	5/16 X 1 1/4	0.547	5/64	0.3858	0.1622
1210	3/8 X 1 1/4	0.547	5/64	0.3545	0.1935
811	1/4 X 1 3/8	0.594	3/32	0.4640	0.1310
1011	5/16 X 1 3/8	0.594	3/32	0.4328	0.1622
1211	3/8 X 1 3/8	0.594	3/32	0.4015	0.1935
812	1/4 X 1 1/2	0.641	7/64	0.5110	0.1310
1012	5/16 X 1 1/2	0.641	7/64	0.4798	0.1622
1212	3/8 X 1 1/2	0.641	7/64	0.4485	0.1935

All dimensions are in inches.
The key numbers indicate nominal key dimensions. The last two digits give the nominal diameter D in eighths of an inch and the digits preceding the last two give the nominal width W in thirty-seconds of an inch.
Extracted from ANSI B17.2 — 1967.

PARALLEL KEYS

Key Size Versus Shaft Diameter

NOMINAL SHAFT DIAMETER		NOMINAL KEY SIZE			NOMINAL KEYSEAT DEPTH	
Over	To (Incl)	Width, W	Height, H		H/2	
			Square	Rectangular	Square	Rectangular
5/16	7/16	3/32	3/32		3/64	
7/16	9/16	1/8	1/8	3/32	1/16	3/64
9/16	7/8	3/16	3/16	1/8	3/32	1/16
7/8	1-1/4	1/4	1/4	3/16	1/8	3/32
1-1/4	1-3/8	5/16	5/16	1/4	5/32	1/8
1-3/8	1-3/4	3/8	3/8	1/4	3/16	1/8
1-3/4	2-1/4	1/2	1/2	3/8	1/4	3/16
2-1/4	2-3/4	5/8	5/8	7/16	5/16	7/32
2-3/4	3-1/4	3/4	3/4	1/2	3/8	1/4
3-1/4	3-3/4	7/8	7/8	5/8	7/16	5/16
3-3/4	4-1/2	1	1	3/4	1/2	3/8
4-1/2	5-1/2	1-1/4	1-1/4	7/8	5/8	7/16
5-1/2	6-1/2	1-1/2	1-1/2	1	3/4	1/2
6-1/2	7-1/2	1-3/4	1-3/4	1-1/2*	7/8	3/4
7-1/2	9	2	2	1-1/2	1	3/4
9	11	2-1/2	2-1/2	1-3/4	1-1/4	7/8
11	13	3	3	2	1-1/2	1
13	15	3-1/2	3-1/2	2-1/2	1-3/4	1-1/4
15	18	4		3		1-1/2
18	22	5		3-1/2		1-3/4
22	26	6		4		2
26	30	7		5		2-1/2

*Some key standards show 1-1/4 in. Preferred size is 1-1/2 in.

All dimensions given in inches.
For a stepped shaft, the size of a key is determined by the diameter of the shaft at the point of location of the key, regardless of the number of different diameters on the shaft.
Square keys are preferred through 6½ inch diameter shaft and rectangular keys for larger shafts. Sizes and dimensions in shaded area are preferred.
Extracted from ANSI B17.1 — 1967.

Welded and Seamless Steel Pipe and Pipe Threads

Size Nominal (in.)	Size O.D. (in.)	Wall Thickness (in.)	I.D. (in.)	Plain End Weight (lb/ft)	API Standard	Standard (STD) X-strong(XS) XX-strong(XXS)	Schedule No.	Threads Per Inch	Tap Drill	Handtight Engagement
$\frac{1}{8}$	0.405	0.068	0.269	0.24	5L	STD	40	27	R	0.1615
		0.095	0.215	0.31	5L	XS	80			
$\frac{1}{4}$	0.540	0.088	0.364	0.42	5L	STD	40	18	$\frac{7}{16}$	0.2278
		0.119	0.302	0.54	5L	XS	80			
$\frac{3}{8}$	0.675	0.091	0.493	0.57	5L	STD	40	18	$\frac{37}{64}$	0.240
		0.126	0.423	0.74	5L	XS	80			
$\frac{1}{2}$	0.840	0.109	0.622	0.85	5L	STD	40			
		0.147	0.546	1.09	5L	XS	80	14	$\frac{23}{32}$	0.320
		0.188	0.464	1.31			160			
		0.294	0.252	1.71	5L	XXS				
$\frac{3}{4}$	1.050	0.113	0.824	1.13	5L	STD	40			
		0.154	0.742	1.47	5L	XS	80	14	$\frac{59}{64}$	0.339
		0.219	0.612	1.94			160			
		0.308	0.434	2.44	5L	XXS				
1	1.315	0.133	1.049	1.68	5L	STD	40			
		0.179	0.957	2.17	5L	XS	80	11.5	$1\frac{5}{32}$	0.400
		0.250	0.815	2.84			160			
		0.358	0.599	3.66	5L	XXS				
$1\frac{1}{4}$	1.660	0.140	1.380	2.27	5L	STD	40			
		0.191	1.278	3.00	5L	XS	80	11.5	$1\frac{1}{2}$	0.420
		0.250	1.160	3.76			160			
		0.382	0.896	5.21	5L	XXS				
$1\frac{1}{2}$	1.900	0.145	1.610	2.72	5L	STD	40			
		0.200	1.500	3.63	5L	XS	80	11.5	$1\frac{47}{64}$	0.420
		0.281	1.338	4.86			160			
		0.400	1.100	6.41	5L	XXS				
		0.083	2.209	2.03	5L 5LX					
		0.109	2.157	2.64	5L 5LX					
		0.125	2.125	3.00	5L 5LX					
		0.141	2.093	3.36	5L 5LX					
		0.154	2.067	3.65	5L 5LX	STD	40			
		0.172	2.031	4.05	5LX					
2	2.375	0.188	1.999	4.39	5LX			11.5	$2\frac{7}{32}$	0.436
		0.218	1.939	5.02	5L 5LX	XS	80			
		0.250	1.875	5.67	5LX					
		0.281	1.813	6.28	5LX					
		0.344	1.687	7.46			160			
		0.436	1.503	9.03	5L 5LX	XXS				

Extracted from ANSI B36.10—1970 and ANSI B2.1—1968
Tap drill sizes not American Standard.

MALLEABLE IRON SCREWED PIPE FITTINGS—150 Lb.

ELBOW   TEE   CROSS   45° ELBOW   45° Y-BRANCH

STREET ELBOW   45° STREET ELBOW   STREET TEE   COUPLING

Nominal Pipe Size	Center to End, Elbows, Tees, and Crosses	Center to End, 45-deg Elbows	Length of Thread Min	Width of Band, Min	Inside Dia Min	Metal Thickness	Outside Diameter of Band Min	Center to Male End Elbows Tees	Center to Male End 45-deg Elbows	Center to End Outlet	End to End	Length of Straight Couplings
	A	C	B	E	F	G	H	J	K	U	V	W
1/8	0.69	....	0.25	0.200	0.405	0.090	0.693	*1.00	...			0.96
1/4	0.81	0.73	0.32	0.215	0.540	0.095	0.844	1.19	0.94			1.06
3/8	0.95	0.80	0.36	0.230	0.675	0.100	1.015	1.44	1.03	1.43	1.93	1.16
1/2	1.12	0.88	0.43	0.249	0.840	0.105	1.197	1.63	1.15	1.71	2.32	1.34
3/4	1.31	0.98	0.50	0.273	1.050	0.120	1.458	1.89	1.29	2.05	2.77	1.52
1	1.50	1.12	0.58	0.302	1.315	0.134	1.771	2.14	1.47	2.43	3.28	1.67
1 1/4	1.75	1.29	0.67	0.341	1.660	0.145	2.153	2.45	1.71	2.92	3.94	1.93
1 1/2	1.94	1.43	0.70	0.368	1.900	0.155	2.427	2.69	1.88	3.28	4.38	2.15
2	2.25	1.68	0.75	0.422	2.375	0.173	2.963	3.26	2.22	3.93	5.17	2.53
2 1/2	2.70	1.95	0.92	0.478	2.875	0.210	3.589	*3.86	2.57	4.73	6.25	2.88
3	3.08	2.17	0.98	0.548	3.500	0.231	4.285	*4.51	3.00	5.55	7.26	3.18
3 1/2	3.42	2.39	1.03	0.604	4.000	0.248	4.843					
4	3.79	2.61	1.08	0.661	4.500	0.265	5.401	5.69	3.70	6.97	8.98	3.69
5	4.50	3.05	1.18	0.780	5.563	0.300	6.583	*6.86	....			
6	5.13	3.46	1.28	0.900	6.625	0.336	7.767	*8.03	....			

All dimensions are given in inches.

*This dimension applies to street elbows only. Street tees are not made in these sizes.

Extracted from ANSI B16.3 — 1963.

WROUGHT STEEL BUTTWELDING PIPE FITTINGS

LONG RADIUS ELBOWS

TEES

CROSSES

LONG RADIUS RETURNS

Nominal Pipe Size	Outside Diameter at Bevel	Long Radius Elbows Center to End		Tees and Crosses Center to End		Long Radius Returns	
		90° Elbows A	45° Elbows B	Run C	Outlets* M	Center to Center O	Back to Face K
1/2	0.840	1 1/2	5/8	1	1	3	1 7/8
3/4	1.050	1 1/8	7/16	1 1/8	1 1/8	2 1/2	1 11/16
1	1.315	1 1/2	7/8	1 1/2	1 1/2	3	2 3/16
1 1/4	1.660	1 7/8	1	1 7/8	1 7/8	3 3/4	2 3/4
1 1/2	1.900	2 1/4	1 1/8	2 1/4	2 1/4	4 1/2	3 1/4
2	2.375	3	1 3/8	2 1/2	2 1/2	6	4 3/16
2 1/2	2.875	3 3/4	1 3/4	3	3	7 1/2	5 3/16
3	3.500	4 1/2	2	3 3/8	3 3/8	9	6 1/4
3 1/2	4.000	5 1/4	2 1/4	3 3/4	3 3/4	10 1/2	7 1/4
4	4.500	6	2 1/2	4 1/8	4 1/8	12	8 1/4
5	5.563	7 1/2	3 1/8	4 7/8	4 7/8	15	10 5/16
6	6.625	9	3 3/4	5 5/8	5 5/8	18	12 5/16
8	8.625	12	5	7	7	24	16 5/16
10	10.750	15	6 1/4	8 1/2	8 1/2	30	20 3/8
12	12.750	18	7 1/2	10	10	36	24 3/8
14	14.000	21	8 3/4	11	11	42	28
16	16.000	24	10	12	12	48	32
18	18.000	27	11 1/4	13 1/2	13 1/2	54	36
20	20.000	30	12 1/2	15	15	60	40
22	22.000	33	13 1/2	16 1/2	16 1/2	66	44
24	24.000	36	15	17	17	72	48

All dimensions given in inches.
*Outlet dimension "M" for run sizes 14 in. and larger is recommended but not mandatory.
Extracted from ANSI B16.9 – 1964.

V anthropometric tables

ANTHROPOMETER

Table V-1 (All dimensions in inches)*

Measurement	Range	Mean	Standard Deviation	Percentiles				
				1st	5th	50th	95th	99th
Weight								
1. Weight (pounds)	104. – 265.	163.66	20.86	123.1	132.5	161.9	200.8	215.9
Body Lengths								
2. Stature	59.45 – 77.56	69.11	2.44	63.5	65.2	69.1	73.1	74.9
3. Nasal root height	56.30 – 73.23	64.95	2.39	59.4	61.0	65.0	68.9	70.7
4. Eye height	56.30 – 73.23	64.69	2.38	59.2	60.8	64.7	68.6	70.3
5. Tragion height	54.72 – 74.41	63.92	2.39	58.4	60.0	64.0	67.8	69.6
6. Cervicale height	50.39 – 66.93	59.08	2.31	53.7	55.3	59.2	62.9	64.6
7. Shoulder height	47.24 – 64.17	56.50	2.28	51.2	52.8	56.6	60.2	61.9
8. Suprasternale height	48.03 – 63.78	56.28	2.19	51.3	52.7	56.3	59.9	61.5
9. Nipple height	42.13 – 57.09	50.41	2.08	45.6	47.0	50.4	53.9	55.3
10. Substernale height	41.34 – 55.51	48.71	2.02	44.0	45.6	48.7	52.1	53.5
11. Elbow height	36.61 – 49.21	43.50	1.77	39.5	40.6	43.5	46.4	47.7
12. Waist height	34.65 – 48.82	42.02	1.81	37.7	39.1	42.1	45.0	46.4
13. Penale height	27.95 – 41.34	34.52	1.75	30.6	31.6	34.5	37.4	38.7
14. Wrist height	27.56 – 39.76	33.52	1.54	30.1	31.0	33.6	36.1	37.1
15. Crotch height (inseam)	26.77 – 38.19	32.83	1.73	29.3	30.4	32.8	35.7	37.0
16. Gluteal furrow height	25.20 – 37.01	31.57	1.62	27.9	29.0	31.6	34.3	35.5
17. Knuckle height	24.80 – 35.04	30.04	1.45	26.7	27.7	30.0	32.4	33.5
18. Kneecap height	15.75 – 23.23	20.22	1.03	17.9	18.4	20.2	21.9	22.7

*Adapted from H. T. E. Hertzberg, G. S. Daniels, and E. Churchill, *Anthropometry of Flying Personnel*—1950, WADC Technical Report 52–321, USAF, Wright Air Development Center, Wright-Patterson AFB, Ohio, September, 1964. It should be noted that these data represent measurements made on approximately 4,000 male USAF personnel and thus do not specifically represent the U.S. population at large.

Table V-2 (All dimensions in inches)

Measurement	Range	Mean	Standard Deviation	Percentiles				
				1st	5th	50th	95th	99th
19. Sitting height	29.92 – 40.16	35.94	1.29	32.9	33.8	36.0	38.0	38.9
20. Eye	26.38 – 36.61	31.47	1.27	28.5	29.4	31.5	33.5	34.4
21. Shoulder	18.90 – 27.17	23.26	1.14	20.6	21.3	23.3	25.1	25.8
22. Waist height, sitting	6.30 – 12.99	9.24	0.76	7.4	7.9	9.3	10.4	10.9
23. Elbow rest height, sitting	4.33 – 12.99	9.12	1.04	6.6	7.4	9.1	10.8	11.5
24. Thigh clearance height	3.94 – 7.09	5.61	0.52	4.5	4.8	5.6	6.5	6.8
25. Knee height, sitting	17.32 – 24.80	21.67	0.99	19.5	20.1	21.7	23.3	24.0
26. Popliteal height, sitting	14.17 – 19.29	16.97	0.77	15.3	15.7	17.0	18.2	18.8
27. Buttock-knee length	18.50 – 27.56	23.62	1.06	21.2	21.9	23.6	25.4	26.2
28. Buttock-leg length	35.43 – 50.00	42.70	2.04	38.2	39.4	42.7	46.1	47.7
29. Shoulder-elbow length	11.42 – 18.11	14.32	0.69	12.8	13.2	14.3	15.4	15.9
30. Forearm-hand length	15.35 – 22.05	18.86	0.81	17.0	17.6	18.9	20.2	20.7
31. Span	58.27 – 82.28	70.80	2.94	63.9	65.9	70.8	75.6	77.6
32. Arm reach from wall	27.56 – 39.76	34.59	1.65	30.9	31.9	34.6	37.3	38.6
33. Maximum reach from wall	31.10 – 46.06	38.59	1.90	34.1	35.4	38.6	41.7	43.2
34. Functional reach	26.77 – 40.55	32.33	1.63	28.8	29.7	32.3	35.0	36.4

Table V-3 (All dimensions in inches)

Measurement	Range	Mean	Standard Deviation	Percentiles				
				1st	5th	50th	95th	99th
Body Breadths and Thicknesses								
35. Elbow-to-elbow breadth	11.42 – 23.62	17.28	1.42	14.5	15.2	17.2	19.8	20.9
36. Hip breadth, sitting	11.42 – 18.11	13.97	0.87	12.2	12.7	13.9	15.4	16.2
37. Knee-to-knee breadth	6.30 – 10.24	7.93	0.52	7.0	7.2	7.9	8.8	9.4
38. Biacromial diameter	12.60 – 18.50	15.75	0.74	14.0	14.6	15.8	16.9	17.4
39. Shoulder breadth	14.57 – 22.83	17.88	0.91	15.9	16.5	17.9	19.4	20.1
40. Chest breadth	9.45 – 15.35	12.03	0.80	10.4	10.8	12.0	13.4	14.1
41. Waist breadth	7.87 – 15.35	10.66	0.94	8.9	9.4	10.6	12.3	13.3
42. Hip breadth	8.27 – 15.75	13.17	0.73	11.3	12.1	13.2	14.4	15.2
43. Chest depth	6.69 – 12.99	9.06	0.75	7.6	8.0	9.0	10.4	11.1
44. Waist depth	5.51 – 11.81	7.94	0.88	6.3	6.7	7.9	9.5	10.3
45. Buttock depth	6.30 – 11.81	8.81	0.82	7.2	7.6	8.8	10.2	10.9
Circumferences and Body Surface Measurements								
46. Neck circumference	10.24 – 19.29	14.96	0.74	13.3	13.8	14.9	16.2	16.8
47. Shoulder circumference	35.43 – 56.69	45.25	2.43	40.2	41.6	45.1	49.4	51.5
48. Chest circumference	31.10 – 49.61	38.80	2.45	33.7	35.1	38.7	43.2	44.8
49. Waist circumference	24.41 – 47.24	32.04	3.02	26.5	27.8	31.7	37.5	40.1
50. Buttock circumference	29.92 – 46.85	37.78	2.29	33.0	34.3	37.7	41.8	43.5
51. Thigh circumference	14.57 – 28.74	22.39	1.74	18.3	19.6	22.4	26.3	26.4
52. Lower thigh circumference	11.81 – 23.23	17.33	1.41	14.2	15.1	17.3	19.6	20.9
53. Calf circumference	9.84 – 18.50	14.40	0.96	12.2	12.9	14.4	16.0	16.7
54. Ankle circumference	7.09 – 12.99	8.93	0.57	7.8	8.1	8.9	9.8	10.5

Table V-4 (All dimensions in inches)

Measurement	Range	Mean	Standard Deviation	Percentiles				
				1st	5th	50th	95th	99th
55. Scye circumference	11.02 – 22.83	18.09	1.38	15.1	16.1	18.0	20.5	21.8
56. Axillary arm circumference	7.87 – 16.54	12.54	1.10	10.2	10.9	12.4	14.4	15.2
57. Biceps circumference	8.27 – 16.93	12.79	1.07	10.5	11.2	12.8	14.6	15.4
58. Elbow circumference	8.27 – 15.35	12.26	0.80	10.7	11.1	12.2	13.6	14.3
59. Lower arm circumference	8.66 – 15.35	11.50	0.73	9.9	10.4	11.5	12.7	13.3
60. Wrist circumference	3.94 – 8.27	6.85	0.40	6.0	6.3	6.8	7.5	7.8
61. Sleeve inseam	15.35 – 24.80	19.83	1.14	17.1	18.0	19.8	21.7	22.6
62. Sleeve length	27.56 – 38.98	33.64	1.50	30.2	31.3	33.7	36.0	37.3
63. Anterior neck length	1.38 – 5.31	3.40	0.64	1.8	2.3	3.4	4.4	4.9
64. Posterior neck length	1.57 – 6.10	3.64	0.61	2.3	2.7	3.6	4.7	5.2
65. Shoulder length	4.33 – 8.66	6.77	0.56	5.5	5.9	6.8	7.7	8.1
66. Waist back	11.81 – 22.83	17.72	1.07	14.8	16.1	17.7	19.4	20.2
67. Waist front	10.63 – 21.26	15.24	1.12	12.3	13.5	15.2	17.0	18.1
68. Gluteal arc	7.87 – 17.32	11.71	0.92	9.7	10.4	11.7	13.1	14.8
69. Crotch length	20.08 – 38.19	28.20	2.00	23.7	25.1	28.2	31.6	33.5
70. Vertical trunk circumference	54.72 – 74.41	64.81	2.88	58.3	60.2	64.8	69.7	71.7
71. Interscye	12.20 – 24.41	19.62	1.40	16.3	17.3	19.6	22.0	22.9
72. Interscye maximum	17.72 – 27.17	22.85	1.33	19.8	20.7	22.9	25.1	26.0
73. Buttock circumference	33.46 – 52.36	41.74	2.82	36.1	37.4	41.5	46.7	49.3
74. Knee circumference	11.42 – 20.47	15.39	0.92	13.5	14.0	15.4	16.9	17.7

Table V-5 (All dimensions in inches)

Measurement	Range	Mean	Standard Deviation	Percentiles				
				1st	5th	50th	95th	99th
The Foot								
75. Foot length	8.86 – 12.24	10.50	0.45	9.5	9.8	10.5	11.3	11.6
76. Instep length	6.42 – 8.86	7.64	0.34	6.9	7.1	7.6	8.2	8.4
77. Foot breadth	3.19 – 4.65	3.80	0.19	3.40	3.50	3.78	4.10	4.36
78. Heel breadth	2.13 – 3.27	2.64	0.15	2.30	2.40	2.63	2.87	3.01
79. Bimalleolar breadth	2.44 – 3.58	2.95	0.15	2.61	2.70	2.95	3.19	3.32
80. Medial malleolus height	2.60 – 4.29	3.45	0.21	3.0	3.1	3.5	3.8	4.0
81. Lateral malleolus height	2.01 – 3.70	2.73	0.22	2.2	2.4	2.7	3.1	3.3
82. Ball of foot circumference	7.87 – 12.60	9.65	0.48	8.6	8.9	9.6	10.4	10.8
The Hand								
83. Hand length	5.87 – 8.74	7.49	0.34	6.7	6.9	7.5	8.0	8.3
84. Palm length	3.39 – 5.04	4.24	0.21	3.77	3.89	4.24	4.60	4.74
85. Hand breadth at thumb	3.23 – 4.76	4.07	0.21	3.59	3.73	4.08	4.42	4.57
86. Hand breadth at metacarpale	2.99 – 4.09	3.48	0.16	3.12	3.22	3.49	3.74	3.86
87. Thickness at metacarpale III	0.75 – 1.54	1.17	0.07	1.00	1.05	1.17	1.28	1.35
88. First phalanx III length	2.21 – 3.07	2.67	0.12	2.40	2.49	2.67	2.85	2.95
89. Finger diameter III	0.75 – 1.00	0.86	0.05	0.77	0.79	0.85	0.93	0.96
90. Grip diameter (inside)	1.37 – 2.63	1.90	0.14	1.52	1.62	1.83	2.05	2.16
91. Grip diameter (outside)	3.15 – 4.72	4.09	0.21	3.58	3.72	4.09	4.44	4.57
92. Fist circumference	7.09 – 13.39	11.56	0.57	10.2	10.7	11.6	12.4	12.8

Table V-6
(All dimensions in inches)

Measurement	Range	Mean	Standard Deviation	Percentiles				
				1st	5th	50th	95th	99th
The Head and Face								
93. Head length	6.89 – 8.78	7.76	0.25	7.2	7.3	7.7	8.2	8.3
94. Head breadth	5.35 – 6.89	6.07	0.20	5.61	5.74	6.05	6.40	6.56
95. Minimum frontal diameter	3.54 – 5.00	4.35	0.19	3.88	4.04	4.35	4.68	4.80
96. Maximum frontal diameter	4.02 – 5.47	4.71	0.20	4.26	4.39	4.72	5.05	5.20
97. Bizygomatic diameter	4.72 – 6.22	5.55	0.20	5.07	5.21	5.54	5.88	6.02
98. Bigonial diameter	3.50 – 5.08	4.27	0.22	3.8	3.9	4.3	4.6	4.8
99. Bitragion diameter	4.76 – 6.30	5.60	0.21	5.1	5.3	5.6	5.9	6.1
100. Interocular diameter	0.87 – 1.65	1.25	0.10	1.03	1.09	1.25	1.42	1.50
101. Biocular diameter	3.19 – 4.45	3.78	0.17	3.38	3.48	3.78	4.06	4.19
102. Interpupillary distance	2.01 – 2.99	2.49	0.14	2.19	2.27	2.49	2.74	2.84
103. Nose length	1.46 – 2.56	2.01	0.14	1.69	1.79	2.00	2.23	2.33
104. Nose breadth	0.91 – 1.85	1.31	0.11	1.09	1.16	1.31	1.49	1.58
105. Nasal root breath	0.28 – 0.91	0.61	0.08	0.42	0.48	0.61	0.74	0.81
106. Nose protrusion	0.43 – 1.42	0.89	0.11	0.63	0.72	0.90	1.08	1.17
107. Philtrum length	0.35 – 1.46	0.77	0.14	0.48	0.54	0.76	0.98	1.09
108. Menton–Subnasale length	1.81 – 3.54	2.63	0.27	2.05	2.19	2.62	3.07	3.28
109. Menton–Crinion length	6.18 – 8.58	7.36	0.36	6.6	6.8	7.4	8.0	8.2
110. Lip-to-Lip distance	0.16 – 1.26	0.64	0.12	0.35	0.44	0.63	0.83	0.94
111. Lip length (Bichelion Dia.)	1.34 – 2.64	2.03	0.14	1.72	1.81	2.02	2.27	2.38
112. Ear length	1.69 – 3.15	2.47	0.16	2.08	2.21	2.47	2.73	2.85
113. Ear breadth	1.10 – 1.93	1.44	0.11	1.20	1.27	1.44	1.61	1.70
114. Ear length above tragion	0.79 – 1.61	1.17	0.11	0.92	0.99	1.17	1.35	1.42
115. Ear protrusion	0.31 – 1.54	0.84	0.14	0.55	0.63	0.83	1.10	1.23

code of ethics for engineers*

Preamble

The Engineer, to uphold and advance the honor and dignity of the engineering profession and in keeping with high standards of ethical conduct:

- *Will be honest and impartial, and will serve with devotion his employer, his clients, and the public;*
- *Will strive to increase the competence and prestige of the engineering profession;*
- *Will use his knowledge and skill for the advancement of human welfare.*

Section 1—The Engineer will be guided in all his professional relations by the highest standards of integrity, and will act in professional matters for each client or employer as a faithful agent or trustee.

a. *He will be realistic and honest in all estimates, reports, statements, and testimony.*
b. *He will admit and accept his own errors when proven obviously wrong and refrain from distorting or altering the facts in an attempt to justify his decision.*
c. *He will advise his client or employer when he believes a project will not be successful.*
d. *He will not accept outside employment to the detriment of his regular work or interest, or without the consent of his employer.*
e. *He will not attempt to attract an engineer from another employer by unfair methods.*
f. *He will not actively participate in strikes, picket lines, or other collective coercive action.*
g. *He will not use his professional affiliations or public office to secure personal advantage and will avoid any act tending to promote his own interest at the expense of the dignity and integrity of the profession.*

Section 2—The Engineer will have proper regard for the safety, health, and welfare of the public in the performance of his professional duties. If his engineering judgment is overruled by nontechnical authority, he will clearly point out the consequences. He will notify the proper authority of any observed conditions which endanger public safety and health.

*Adopted by the National Society of Professional Engineers.

a. *He will regard his duty to the public welfare as paramount.*

b. *He shall seek opportunities to be of constructive service in civic affairs and work for the advancement of the safety, health and well-being of his community.*

c. *He will not complete, sign, or seal plans and/or specifications that are not of a design safe to the public health and welfare and in conformity with accepted engineering standards. If the client or employer insists on such unprofessional conduct, he shall notify the proper authorities and withdraw from further service on the project.*

Section 3—The Engineer will avoid all conduct or practice likely to discredit or unfavorably reflect upon the dignity or honor of the profession.

a. *The Engineer shall not advertise his professional services but may utilize the following means of identification:*

    1. *Professional cards and listings in recognized and dignified publications, provided they are consistent in size and are in a section of the publication regularly devoted to such professional cards and listings. The information displayed must be restricted to firm name, address, telephone number, appropriate symbol, name of principal participants, and the fields of practice in which the firm is qualified.*

    2. *Signs on equipment, offices and at the site of projects for which he renders services, limited to firm name, address, telephone number and type of services, as appropriate.*

    3. *Brochures, business cards, letterheads and other factual representations of experience, facilities, personnel and capacity to render service, providing the same are not misleading relative to the extent of participation in the projects cited, and provided the same are not indiscriminately distributed.*

    4. *Listings in the classified section of telephone directories, limited to name, address, telephone number, and specialties in which the firm is qualified.*

b. *The Engineer may advertise for recruitment of personnel in appropriate publications or by special distribution. The information presented must be displayed in a dignified manner, restricted to firm name, address, telephone number, appropriate symbol, name of principal participants, the fields of practice in which the firm is qualified, and factual descriptions of positions available, qualifications required, and benefits available.*

c. *The Engineer may prepare articles for the lay or technical press which are factual, dignified, and free from ostentations or laudatory implications. Such articles shall not imply other than his direct participation in the work described unless credit is given to others for their share of the work.*

d. The Engineer may extend permission for his name to be used in commercial advertisements, such as may be published by manufacturers, contractors, material suppliers, etc., only by means of a modest dignified notation acknowledging his participation and the scope thereof in the project or product described. Such permission shall not include public endorsement of proprietary products.

e. The Engineer will not allow himself to be listed for employment using exaggerated statements of his qualifications.

Section 4—The Engineer will endeavor to extend public knowledge and appreciation of engineering and its achievements and to protect the engineering profession from misrepresentation and misunderstanding.

a. He shall not issue statements, criticisms, or arguments on matters connected with public policy which are inspired or paid for by private interests, unless he indicates on whose behalf he is making the statement.

Section 5—The Engineer will express an opinion of an engineering subject only when founded on adequate knowledge and honest conviction.

a. The Engineer will insist on the use of facts in reference to an engineering project in a group discussion, public forum, or publication of articles.

Section 6—The Engineer will undertake engineering assignments for which he will be responsible only when qualified by training or experience; and he will engage, or advise engaging, experts and specialists whenever the client's or employer's interests are best served by such service.

Section 7—The Engineer will not disclose confidential information concerning the business affairs or technical processes of any present or former client or employer without his consent.

a. While in the employ of others, he will not enter promotional efforts or negotiations for work or make arrangements for other employment as a principal or to practice in connection with a specific project for which he has gained particular and specialized knowledge without the consent of all interested parties.

Section 8—The Engineer will endeavor to avoid a conflict of interest with his employer or client, but when unavoidable, the Engineer shall fully disclose the circumstances to his employer or client.

a. The Engineer will inform his client or employer of any business connections, interests, or circumstances which may be deemed as influencing his judgment or the quality of his services to his client or employer.

b. When in public service as a member, advisor, or employee of a governmental body or department, an engineer shall not participate in considerations or actions with respect to services provided by him or his organization in private engineering practice.

c. An engineer shall not solicit or accept an engineering contract from a governmental body on which a principal or officer of his organization serves as a member.

Section 9—The Engineer will uphold the principal of appropriate and adequate compensation for those engaged in engineering work.

a. He will not undertake or agree to perform any engineering service on a free basis, except for civic, charitable, religious, or eleemosynary nonprofit organizations when the professional services are advisory in nature.

b. He will not undertake work at a fee or salary below the accepted standards of the profession in the area.

c. He will not accept remuneration from either an employee or employment agency for giving employment.

d. When hiring other engineers, he shall offer a salary according to the engineer's qualifications and the recognized standards in the particular geographical area.

e. If, in sales employ, he will not offer, or give engineering consultation, or designs, or advice other than specifically applying to the equipment being sold.

Section 10—The Engineer will not accept compensation, financial or otherwise, from more than one interested party for the same service, or for services pertaining to the same work, unless there is full disclosure to and consent of all interested parties.

a. He will not accept financial or other considerations, including free engineering designs, from material or equipment suppliers for specifying their product.

b. He will not accept commissions or allowances, directly or indirectly, from contractors or other parties dealing with his clients or employer in connection with work for which he is responsible.

Section 11—The Engineer will not compete unfairly with another engineer by attempting to obtain employment or advancement or professional engagements by competitive bidding, by taking advantage of a salaried position, by criticizing other engineers, or by other improper or questionable methods.

a. *The Engineer will not attempt to supplant another engineer in a particular employment after becoming aware that definite steps have been taken toward the other's employment.*

b. *He will not offer to pay, either directly or indirectly, any commission, political contribution, or a gift, or other consideration in order to secure work, exclusive of securing salaried positions through employment agencies.*

c. *He shall not solicit or submit engineering proposals on the basis of competitive bidding. Competitive bidding for professional engineering services is defined as the formal or informal submission, or receipt, of verbal or written estimates of cost or proposals in terms of dollars, man days of work required, percentage of construction cost, or any other measure of compensation whereby the prospective client may compare engineering services on a price basis prior to the time that one engineer, or one engineering organization, has been selected for negotiations. The disclosure of recommended fee schedules prepared by various engineering societies is not considered to constitute competitive bidding. An engineer requested to submit a fee proposal or bid prior to the selection of an engineer or firm subject to the negotiation of a satisfactory contract shall attempt to have the procedure changed to conform to ethical practices, but if not successful he shall withdraw from consideration for the proposed work. These principles shall be applied by the Engineer in obtaining the services of other professionals.*

d. *An Engineer shall not request, propose, or accept a professional commission on a contingent basis under circumstances in which his professional judgment may be compromised, or when a contingency provision is used as a device for promoting or securing a professional commission.*

e. *While in a salaried position, he will accept part-time engineering work only at a salary or fee not less than that recognized as standard in the area.*

f. *An engineer will not use equipment, supplies, laboratory, or office facilities of his employer to carry on outside private practice without consent.*

Section 12—The Engineer will not attempt to injure, maliciously or falsely, directly or indirectly, the professional reputation, prospects, practice, or employment of another engineer, nor will he indiscriminately criticize another engineer's work in public. If he believes that another engineer is guilty of unethical or illegal practice, he shall present such information to the proper authority for action.

a. *An Engineer in private practice will not review the work of another engineer for the same client, except with the knowledge of such engineer, or unless the connection of such engineer with the work has been terminated.*

b. *An Engineer in governmental, industrial, or educational employ is entitled to review and evaluate the work of other engineers when so required by his employment duties.*

c. *An Engineer in sales or industrial employ is entitled to make engineering comparisons of his products with products by other suppliers.*

Section 13—The Engineer will not associate with or allow the use of his name by an enterprise of questionable character, nor will he become professionally associated with engineers who do not conform to ethical practices, or with persons not legally qualified to render the professional services for which the association is intended.

a. *He will conform with registration laws in his practice of engineering.*

b. *He will not use association with a nonengineer, a corporation, or partnership, as a "cloak" for unethical acts, but must accept personal responsibility for his professional acts.*

Section 14—The Engineer will give credit for engineering work to those to whom credit is due, and will recognize the proprietary interests of others.

a. *Whenever possible, he will name the person or persons who may be individually responsible for designs, inventions, writings, or other accomplishments.*

b. *When an engineer uses designs supplied to him by a client, the designs remain the property of the client and should not be duplicated by the Engineer for others without express permission.*

c. *Before undertaking work for others in connection with which he may make improvements, plans, designs, inventions, or other records which may justify copyrights or patents, the Engineer should enter into a positive agreement regarding the ownership.*

d. *Designs, data, records, and notes made by an engineer and referring exclusively to his employer's work are his employer's property.*

Section 15—The Engineer will cooperate in extending the effectiveness of the profession by interchanging information and experience with other engineers and students, and will endeavor to provide opportunity for the professional development and advancement of engineers under his supervision.

a. *He will encourage his engineering employees' efforts to improve their education.*

b. *He will encourage engineering employees to attend and present papers at professional and technical society meetings.*

c. *He will urge his engineering employees to become registered at the earliest possible date.*

d. *He will assign a professional engineer duties of a nature to utilize his full training and experience, insofar as possible, and delegate lesser functions to subprofessionals or to technicians.*

e. *He will provide a prospective engineering employee with complete information on working conditions and his proposed status of employment, and after employment will keep him informed of any changes in them.*

murphy's law and its corollaries*

In general Murphy's Law states that

If anything can possibly go wrong with a design, test, or experiment—it will.

From this basic statement concerning the nature and behavior of inanimate objects a number of corollaries have been drawn, as follows:

General Corollaries

1. When a design has been completely defined and all avenues of inquiry exhausted, an uninformed, independent, amateur experimenter will discover a fact that either abolishes the need for the design or expands the scope of the need to such extent that the design is worthless.

2. The necessity for making a major change in a design increases in direct proportion to the decrease in time remaining to complete the design.

3. The more innocuous an alteration in a design appears to be, the more extensive will be its influence.

4. Units will always be expressed in the least usable terms. For example, acceleration is most apt to be expressed in furlongs/fortnight^2 and specific weight in stones/angstrom^3.

5. It is impossible for overall dimensions to be totaled correctly after 4:30 P.M. on Friday.

---

*Versions of Murphy's Law have appeared in numerous technical journals for many years. The authors have surveyed the literature extensively to search out those laws and corollaries that seem to be most pertinent for the young engineer. Reference credit is not given here, because it is not common practice to credit the quotation or statement of fundamental relationships, such as the *law of gravity,* the *law of the conservation of mass, energy, and momentum, Ohm's law,* or the *second law of thermodynamics.* Note: The serious student should carefully place tongue in cheek before reading these reflections on "real life."

6. The probability that a particular dimension has been omitted from a drawing will be directly proportional to its importance.

Purchasing Corollaries
1. All warranty and guarantee clauses in an equipment purchase agreement become null and void upon payment of the invoice.
2. Any mechanical or electrical device used in a design will most likely fail to operate the day after the manufacturer's guarantee expires.
3. All engineering instrumentation with any malfunction short of complete failure will function perfectly in the presence of an experienced serviceman.
4. Important equipment operating manuals will always be lost, discarded, or misplaced prior to need. Don't be dismayed, however. Your assistant will interpret this as a call for originality.

Analysis Corollaries

1. In any collection of data, the figures that are obviously correct will contain errors.
2. It is customary for a decimal to be misplaced.
3. An error that can creep into a calculation, will. Also, it will always be in the direction that will cause the most damage to the calculation.

Testing and Production Corollaries

1. If a circuit cannot fail, it will.
2. Interchangeable parts aren't.
3. Identical equipment, tested under identical conditions, will not perform identically when needed.
4. In a test setup the most delicate component is most certain to be dropped. If a part is heavy and inexpensive, it will always land on the most delicate component.
5. Instrumentation will be damaged in direct proportion to its overall value.
6. A fast-acting fuse designed to protect a transistor will, in fact, be protected by the transistor blowing first.
7. Any wire cut to length will always be too short.
8. After an instrument has been fully assembled and tested, unused components will be found on the workbench.
9. After the last 24 mounting screws have been removed from an access cover, it will be discovered that the wrong access cover has been removed.
10. After an access cover has been secured by 24 hold-down screws, it will be discovered that the Teflon gasket has been omitted.
11. A motor will always have the tendency to rotate in the wrong direction.
12. A component selected at random from a group having 99 per cent reliability will be a member of the 1 per cent group.
13. In any test, experience is directly proportional to the number of failures recorded.
14. Good experiments should be reproducible. They should always fail in the same way.
15. If it jams—force it. If it breaks, you probably needed a new one anyway.

the planning of engineering projects

In every walk of life, we notice and appreciate evidence of well-planned activities. You may have noticed that good planning involves more than "the assignment of tasks to be performed," although this frequently is the only aspect of planning that is given any attention. Planning in the broad sense must include the enumeration of all the activities and events associated with a project and a recognition and evaluation of their interrelationships and interdependencies. The assignment of tasks to be performed and other aspects of scheduling should follow.

Since "time is money," planning is a very important part of the implementation of any engineering design. Good planning is often the difference between success and failure, and the young engineering student would do well, therefore, to learn some of the fundamental aspects of planning as applied to the implementation of engineering projects.

In 1957 the US Navy was attempting to complete the Polaris Missile System in record time. The estimated time for completion seemed unreasonably long. Through the efforts of an operations research team, a new method of planning and coordinating the many complex parts of the project was finally developed. The overall saving in time for the project amounted to more than 18 months. Since that time a large percentage of engineering projects, particularly those which are complex and time consuming, have used this same planning technique to excellent advantage. It is called PERT (Program Evaluation and Review Technique).

PERT enables the engineer in charge to view the total project as well as to recognize the interrelationships of the component parts of the design. Its utility is not limited to the beginning of the project, but rather it continues to provide an accurate measure of progress throughout the work period. Pertinent features of PERT are combined in the following discussion.

How Does PERT Work?

Basically PERT consists of events (or jobs) and activities arranged into a *time-oriented network* to show the interrelationships and interdependencies that exist. One of the primary objectives of such a network is to identify where bottlenecks may occur that would slow down the process. Once such bottlenecks have been identified, extra resources such as time and effort can be applied at the appropriate places to make certain that the entire process will not be slowed.

The network is also used to portray the events as they occur in

A-VII-1

A-VII-2   A-VII-3

the process of accomplishing missions or objectives, together with the activities that necessarily occur to interconnect the events. These relationships will be discussed more fully below.

The Network. A PERT network is one type of pictorial representation of a project. This network establishes the *precedent relationships* that exist within a project. That is, it identifies those activities which must be completed before other activities are started. It also specifies the time that it takes to complete these activities. This is accomplished by using *events* (points in time) to separate the project *activities*. In other words, project events are connected by activities to form a project network. Progress from one event to another is made by completing the activity that connects them. Let us examine each component of the network in more detail.

Events. An event is the *start* or *completion* of a mental or physical task. It does not involve the actual performance of the task. Thus, events are *points in time* which require that action be taken or that decisions be made. Various symbols are used in industry to designate events, such as circles, squares, ellipses, or rectangles. In this book circles, called *nodes,* will be used [A-VII-1].

Events are joined together to form a project network. It is important that the events be arranged within the network in logical or time sequence from left to right. If this is done, the completion of each event will occupy a discrete and identifiable point in time. An event cannot consume time and it cannot be considered to be completed until all activities leading to it have been completed. After all events have been identified and arranged within the network, they are assigned identification numbers. Since events and activities may be altered during the course of the project, the logical order of the events will not necessarily follow in exact numerical sequence, 1, 2, 3, 4, 5, etc. The event numbers, therefore, serve only for identification purposes. The final or terminal node in the network is usually called the *sink;* the beginning or initial node is called the *source.* Networks may have varying numbers of sources and sinks.

Activities. An activity is the actual performance of a task and, as such, it consumes an increment of time. Activities separate events. An activity cannot begin until all preceding activities have been completed. An arrow is used to represent the time span of an activity, with time flowing from the tail to the point of the arrow [A-VII-2]. In a PERT network an activity may indicate the use of time, manpower, materials, facilities, space, or other resources. A *phantom* activity may also represent waiting time or *interdependencies.* A phantom activity, represented by a dashed arrow [A-VII-3], may be inserted into the network for clarity of the logic, although it represents no real physical activity. Waiting time would also be noted in this manner. Remember that

> *Events* "happen or occur."
> *Activities* are "started or completed."

The case of Mr. Jones getting ready for work each morning can be examined as an example.

<table>
<tr><td>Events</td><td>Activities</td></tr>
</table>

Events	Activities
1. The alarm rings.	
	A. Jones stirs restlessly.
2. Jones awakens.	
	B. Jones nudges his wife.
	C. Jones lies in bed wishing that he didn't have to go to work.
3. Wife awakens.	
	D. Wife lies in bed wishing that it were Saturday.
4. Jones's wife gets up and begins breakfast.	
	E. Wife cooks breakfast.
	Meanwhile
5. Jones begins morning toilet.	
	F. Jones shaves, bathes, and dresses.
6. The Joneses begin to eat breakfast.	
	G. The Joneses eat part of their breakfast.

7. Jones realizes his bus is about to pass the bus stop.

H. Jones jumps up, grabs his briefcase, and runs for the bus.
I. Wife goes back to bed.

8. Jones boards bus.
9. Wife falls asleep.

His PERT network can now be drawn as shown in [A-VII-4].

A-VII-4

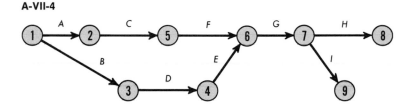

This is a very elementary example, but it does point up the constituent parts of a PERT network. Note that Jones and his wife must wait until he is dressed (F) and the breakfast is cooked (E) before they can eat.

In a PERT network each activity should be assigned a specified time for expected accomplishment. The time units chosen should be consistent throughout the network, but the size of the time unit (years, work-weeks, days, hours, etc.) should be selected by the engineer in charge of the project. The time value chosen for each activity should represent the mean of the various times that the activity would take if it were repeated many times.

By using the network of events and activities and by taking into account the times consumed by the various activities, a *critical path* can be established for the project. It is this path that controls the successful completion of the project, and it is important that the engineer be able to isolate it for study. Let us consider the PERT network in [A-VII-5], where the activity times are represented by Arabic numbers and are indicated in days. Activities represent the expenditure of time and effort. For example, activity A (from event

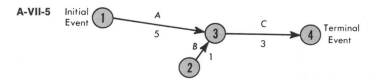

1 to event 3) requires 5 days and is likely devoted to planning the project; activity B requires 1 day and may represent the procurement of basic supplies. Event 1 is the beginning of the project and event 4 is the end of the project. The first step in locating the *critical path* is to determine the "earliest" event times (T_E), the "latest" event times (T_L), and the "slack" time ($T_L - T_E$).

Earliest Event Times (T_E)

The earliest expected time of an event refers to the time, T_E, when an event can be expected to be completed. T_E for an event is calculated by summing all the activity duration times from the beginning event to the event in question *if the most time-consuming route is chosen*. To avoid confusion, the T_E times of events are usually placed near the network as Arabic numbers within rectangular blocks. For reference purposes, the beginning of the project is usually considered to be *time zero*. In [A-VII-6], T_E for event 3 would be $\boxed{0} + 5 = \boxed{5}$ and T_E for event 4 would be $\boxed{0} + 5 + 3 = \boxed{8}$. However, there are two possible routes to event 4 (A + C, or B + C). The *maximum* duration of these event times should be selected as the T_E for event 4. Summing the times, we find

By path A + C: $\boxed{0} + 5 + 3 = \boxed{8}$ ← Select as T_E for event 4

By path B + C: $\boxed{0} + 1 + 3 = \boxed{4}$

Latest Event Times (T_L)

The latest expected time, T_L, of an event refers to the longest time that can be allowed for an event, assuming that the entire project is kept on schedule. T_L for an event is determined by beginning at the terminal event and working backward through the various event circuits, subtracting the value T_E at each event *assuming the least time-consuming route is chosen*. The resulting values of T_L are recorded as Arabic numbers in small ellipses located near the T_E times. Thus, in [A-VII-6] T_L for event 3 would be $\textcircled{8} - 3 = \textcircled{5}$; for event 2, $\textcircled{8} - 3 - 1 = \textcircled{4}$; and for event 1, $\textcircled{8} - 3 - 5 = \textcircled{0}$.

Remember that T_L is determined to be the *minimum* of the differences between the succeeding event T_L and the intervening activity times. Also, in calculating T_L values one must always proceed backward through the network—from the point of the arrows to the tail of the arrows.

Slack Times

The *slack* time for each event is the difference between the latest event time and the earliest possible time ($T_L - T_E$). Intuitively, one may verify that it is the "extra time that an event can slip" and not affect the scheduled completion time of the project. For example,

A-VII-6

A-VII-7

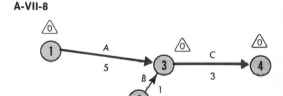

in [A-VII-7] the slack time for event 2 is ④ − ⓪ = 4. For this reason activity B may be started as much as 4 days late and still not cause any overall delay in the minimum project time of 8 days

A-VII-8

The Critical Path

The *critical path* through a PERT network is a path that is drawn from the initial event of the network to the terminal event by connecting the events of zero slack. The critical path is usually emphasized with a very heavy thick line. Color is sometimes used. In the example problem above, the critical path would be shown connecting events 1-3-4 [A-VII-8]. Slack times for each event are indicated as small Arabic numbers located in triangles adjacent to the events.

Remember that the critical path is the path that controls the successful completion of the project. It is also the path that requires the most time to get from the initial event to the terminal event. Any event on the critical path that is delayed will cause the final event to be delayed by the same amount. Conversely, putting an extra effort on noncritical activities will not speed up the project.

Although calculations in this appendix have been done manually, it is conventional practice to program complex networks for solution by digital computer. In this way thousands of activities and events may be considered, and one or more critical paths can be located for additional study. Finally, the PERT network should be updated periodically as the work on the project progresses.

The following example will show how a typical PERT diagram is analyzed. It should be noted here, however, that in real-life situations the most difficult task is to identify the precedent relationships

A-VII-9

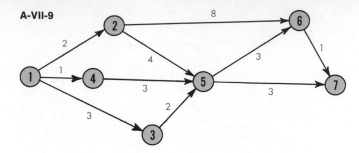

that exist and to draw a realistic network of the events and activities. After this is accomplished, following through with a solution technique becomes a relatively routine task.

EXAMPLE: In the PERT network diagram of [A-VII-9] assume that all activity times are given in months and that they exist as indicated on the proper activity branch. Find the earliest times, T_E, the latest times, T_L, and the slack times for each event. Identify the critical path through the network.

SOLUTION:

A-VII-10

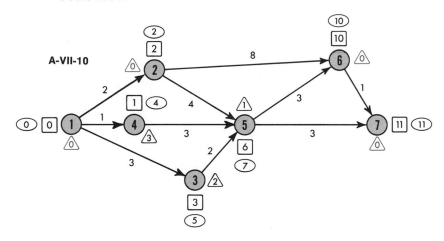

It is usually advisable to construct a summary table of the calculations.

Event ○	Path	T_E □	Path	T_L ○	Slack, $T_L - T_E$ △	On Critical Path
1	—	0	7-6-2-1	0	0	*
2	1-2	2	7-6-2	2	0	*
3	1-3	3	7-6-5-3	5	2	
4	1-4	1	7-6-5-4	4	3	
5	1-2-5	6	7-6-5	7	1	
6	1-2-6	10	7-6	10	0	*
7	1-2-6-7	11	—	11	0	*

The critical path then is 1-2-6-7 [A-VII-11]. This means that as the project is now organized, it will take 11 months to complete.

A-VII-11

VIII case studies

What is a typical engineering problem? How does it come to the engineer and how does he handle it? The best we can say is that there is no "typical" or unique way. Problems come in different ways, from different sources. They are rarely defined better than "There is a problem at the XYZ plant (or with the ABC machine). Will you please see what you can do about it?" It is up to the engineer to gather the information he needs, to formulate the problem so that a technical solution becomes possible, and then to try one or more solutions. We showed in Chapters 5 and 6 how this process works, how information is gathered, how assumptions are made to arrive at a model, how the model is analyzed, and how the results and assumptions are tested.

Here we present a few realistic examples of engineering projects to illustrate this process of problem solving. The cases are neither more nor less "typical" than any one person is typical of the human race. When you dig into the details, they are all different. But the study of cases—like the study of people—makes you better able to handle problems when they come to you.

an example of the development of an engineering design

There are many well-known engineering designs on the American scene that have, over a period of many years, almost become a "way of life." Although the authors of this text are reluctant to pick any one of these as being superior to another, they are eager that the students who study this text gain an appreciation for the concepts that "good ideas plus good engineering design practice equals success," and "all good engineering designs can be improved." For this reason the story of the developing design of the safety razor is given here.*

The idea for the safety razor that the American public knows today was the brainchild of a traveling salesman, King C. Gillette, who on a summer morning in 1895 became irritated and exasperated with his inability to shave with a dull straight razor. In an instant the idea of a replaceable flat blade secured in a holder for maximum safety was born. In Gillette's own words,

I saw it all in a moment, and in that same moment many unvoiced questions were asked and answered more with the rapidity of a dream than by the slow process of reasoning. A razor is only a sharp edge and all back of

*Much of the material presented here was made available by and is used with the permission of the Gillette Safety Razor Company, Boston, Massachusetts.

that edge is but a support for that edge. Why do they spend so much material and time in fashioning a backing which has nothing to do with the shaving? Why do they forge a great piece of steel and spend so much labor in hollow grinding it when they could get the same result by putting an edge on a piece of steel that was only thick enough to hold an edge? At that time and in that moment it seemed as though I could see the way the blade could be held in a holder. Then came the idea of sharpening the two opposite edges on the thin piece of steel that was uniform in thickness throughout, thus doubling its service; and following in sequence came the clamping plates for the blade with a handle equally disposed between the two edges of the blade. All this came more in pictures than in thought as though the razor were already a finished thing and held before my eyes. I stood there before that mirror in a trance of joy at what I saw.

A-VIII-1
The morning shave in 1568 was not without its difficulties, as shown in the above English woodcut.

Previous to this time, men of wealth and influence of all nationalities frequented barbershops in which the customer was lathered from the community mug and shaved with an unsterilized razor [A-VIII-1]. Such a barbershop shave was a luxury that poor people could not afford, but many men of modest means did purchase their own straight razors. Ladies of respect would not think of using a razor to remove unsightly hair, although it is reported that such practice was not uncommon for burlesque queens.

Several years previous to the inspirational moment of 1895, King

Gillette was talking with a successful inventor friend who advised him:

King, you are always thinking and inventing something; why don't you try to think of something like the Crown Cork; when used once, it is thrown away, and the customer keeps coming back for more—and with every additional customer you get, you are building a permanent foundation of profit.

Although Gillette often thought of this advice, he never was able to capitalize on it until that moment—holding in his hand a dull razor which was beyond the point of successful stropping and in need of honing—when the idea in his subconscious emerged to reinforce his need for a new and novel solution.

Gillette knew very little about razors and practically nothing about steel, and he could not foresee the trials and frustrations that were to come his way before the "safety razor" was a success. On the same day that he received the inspiration to devise a razor which could use interchangeable and disposable blades, and which were safe to use, Gillette went to a local hardware store and purchased

A-VIII-2
King Gillette's moment of triumph came when he discovered that his idea could be made to work.

several pieces of brass, some steel ribbon used for clock springs, and some hand tools. Using some rough pencil sketches and the recently purchased hand tools, he fashioned a crude model of his new design, [A-VIII-2]. Gillette's invention did not consist primarily in a particular form of blade or design of a blade holder, but in the conception of a blade so cheap as to be discarded when dull. To obtain such a blade he abandoned the forged type and fashioned one of thin steel, so that it might be cut from a strip, avoiding the expense of forging or hollow grinding. Prior to this invention, razor makers produced an expensive blade that was expected to give service as long as possible, even a lifetime, and to be honed and stropped indefinitely. The new idea was a complete reversal of this practice and was a really unique invention.

In his new razor Gillette carried his theory to great completeness. The blade was to be made of relatively thin steel and thereby achieve economy through the saving of both material and labor. It was to have two edges, one on each side, thus giving double shaving service. The adjustment of the blade edge in relation to the guard was to be obtained by flexing the blade so as to bring the edge nearer to or farther from the guard teeth, in order to obtain a finer or coarser cut [A-VIII-3].

However, all was not bright for this new idea. No one but Gillette had any faith in a razor the blades of which were to be used once and then wasted. Such a proposal did not seem to be within the bounds of reason, and even Gillette's friends looked upon it as a joke. Actually, he had thought originally that the blades might be made very cheaply from a thin ribbon of steel, but he was, of course, aware that new machines and processes would need to be invented and developed before such "ribbon blades" could be manufactured cheaply. This did not seem to be a likely prospect. For more than five years Gillette clung tenaciously to his razor theories. He made a number of models with minor variations and sought through others to get blades made with shaving qualities. He got very little encouragement either from his helpers and advisers or from the results of his experiments. People who knew most about cutlery and razors in particular were most discouraging. Years later Gillette said, "They told me I was throwing my money away; that a razor was only possible when made from cast steel forged and fashioned under the hammer to give it density so it would take an edge. But I didn't know enough to quit. If I had been technically trained, I would have quit or probably would never have begun." In spite of this discouragement, Gillette did not falter in his faith and persistence.

Faced with an inability to cope with the technical difficulties surrounding his idea, Gillette began to search for others to help him. He associated himself with several men, one of whom—W. E. Nickerson—was a mechanical engineering graduate of the Massachusetts Institute of Technology. The design capability of Nickerson soon became apparent. A notation from the Gillette Safety Razor Co. Silver Jubilee history relates the following:

. . . after a very urgent plea, he [Nickerson] agreed to turn the problem over in his mind and give a decision within a month. On giving the problem serious thought, he began to see the proper procedure and felt that he could develop the razor into a commercial proposition. Things began to take definite shape in his mind, he could visualize the hardening process and sharpening machines, and definite ideas were developed as to the type of handle necessary to properly hold the blade.

Hardening apparatus and sharpening machines could not be properly designed until the form and size of the blade were known, so the first step was to decide just what the blade and the handle were to be like. Mr. Gillette's models were amply developed to disclose the fundamental ideas, but there was left a wide range of choice in the matter of carrying out these ideas; and furthermore, the commercial success of the razor was sure to depend very much upon the judgment used in selecting just the right form and thickness of blade and the best construction in the handle.

Mr. Nickerson's fundamental thought in relation to the remodeled razor was that the handle must have sufficient stability to make possible very great accuracy of adjustment between the edge of the blade and the protecting guard. Here is a point upon which he laid great stress, and which we are constantly endeavoring to drive home today: "No matter how perfect the blade is, you cannot get the best result unless the handle is perfect also." The Gillette handle is made to micrometric dimensions and is an extremely accurate instrument. If damaged or thrown out of alignment, poor shaves are likely to result. This idea of great stability led Mr. Nickerson to design a handle to be "machined" out of solid metal, in contra-distinction to one stamped from relatively thin sheet metal. To this fact much of the Gillette commercial success is due. In fact, it is doubtful if great success could have been achieved without it.

The shape and thickness of the blade were determined as follows: Sheet steel thinner than six one-thousandths of an inch appeared to lack sufficient firmness to make a good blade, and a thickness greater than that seemed too difficult to flex readily; so six thousandths was chosen. In the matter of width, one inch was thought to be unnecessarily wide and three-quarters of an inch was found to be too narrow, especially when flexing was considered. Thus seven-eighths of an inch was adopted. As to contour, a circle one and three-quarters inches in diameter if symmetrically crossed by two parallel lines seven-eighths of an inch apart give chords corresponding to the cutting edges, one and one-half inches long, which was thought to be the right length for the edges. The rounded ends to the blade form thus produced strengthened the blade among the center where holes were to be and gave the blade its well-known and pleasing shape. After twenty-five years of use nothing has transpired to cause regret that some other shape was not selected. These early decisions were of the utmost importance and almost seemed inspired.

On September 9, 1901, Mr. Nickerson sent a report of his findings and recommendations to Mr. Heilborn of which the following is an exact copy:

A-VIII-3

Boston, Mass., Sept. 9, 1901.

Jacob Heilborn, Esq.,
Boston, Mass.

Dear Sir:

I have had your proposition, in regard to the manufacture of the Gillette Safety Razor, under consideration for rather more than a month and desire to report as follows:

It is my confident opinion that not only can a successful razor be made on the principles of the Gillette patent, but that if the blades are made by proper methods a result in advance of anything known can be reached. On the other hand, to put out these razors with blades of other than the finest quality of temper and edge would be disastrous to their reputation and to their successful introduction.

With an almost unlimited market, and with such inducements as are offered by this razor, in the way of cheapness of manufacture and of convenience and effectiveness in use, I can see no reason why it cannot easily compete for popular favor with anything in its line ever put before the public.

I wish to reiterate that in my opinion the success of the razor depends very largely, if not almost wholly, on the production at a low price of a substantially perfect blade. This blade must possess an edge that shall, at least, be equal of any rival on the market, and should combine extreme keenness with a hardness and toughness sufficient to stand using a number of times without much deterioration.

For the past month I have been giving much thought to the subject of manufacturing these blades, and I now feel justified in offering to undertake the construction of machines and apparatus to that end. I am confident that I have grasped the situation and can guarantee, as far as such a thing can be guaranteed, a successful outcome. Your knowledge of my long experience with inventions and machine building will, perhaps, cause you to attach considerable weight to my opinion in this matter. You are of course aware that special machines will have to be designed and built for putting on the blades that delicate edge which is necessary for easy shaving. The problem is entirely different from that involved in the tempering and grinding of ordinary razors and other keen tools, not only on account of the thinness of the blades, but also on account of the cheapness with which it must be done. I believe that with the machines which I have in mind, an edge can be put upon these blades which will be unapproachable by ordinary hand sharpened razors. The machinery and methods for making the blades will naturally be of a novel character and admit of sound patents, which would become the property of the Company and would be of great advantage in disposing of foreign rights. It is not unlikely that the machines for honing these blades may be adapted for any of the present form of razors and do away with hand honing. I will also add that I have in mind a convenient and simple method of adjusting the position of the blade for different beards.

In reply to your questions as to the probable expense of fitting up to manufacture the razor on a scale suitable for a beginning on a commercial basis, I will make the following approximation:

Drawings for machines for tempering, grinding, honing and
stropping . . . . $ 100
Patterns for ditto   250
Materials for machines (one each)   300
Cost of building (one each)   700
Special dies and tools   150

Tools for making holders
- Small turret lathe
- Power punch
- Small plain milling machine   1500
- Sensitive drill
- Bench lathe
- Bench tools, etc.

Foreign patents:
England, Germany, Belgium, France,
Canada, Spain, Italy, Austria—about   800
Labor services, etc.   1200
                                                                    $5000

I have made what seems to me to be fairly liberal but by no means extravagant figures. It may cost considerably less or possibly a little more, but I think the sum given will not come out very far from the truth.

I should recommend that the machines for making the blades be built in some shop already established, and when they are completed, a suitable room be engaged and they and the holder tools set up in it. It is not easy to say just how long it would take to be ready for manufacturing, but if there are no serious delays it is possible that four months might cover it.

In conclusion let me add that so thoroughly am I satisfied that I can perfect machinery described on original lines which will be patentable, that I am ready to accept for my compensation stock in a Company which I understand you propose forming.

Very truly yours,
(Signed) Wm. E. Nickerson

Nickerson did design a machine for sharpening the blades and an apparatus for hardening the blades in packs. Thus through the application of fundamental engineering principles a successful new industry was born.

Success was not immediate because two years later, in 1903, when Gillette put his first razor on the market only 51 razors and 168 blades were sold. Barbers, who believed that their business would be ruined if this new fad caught on, were particularly scathing in their reproof. However, the new razor caught on, sales soared, and by 1905 manufacturing operations had to be moved to larger quarters. By 1917 razor sales had risen to over 1 million a year, and blade sales averaged 150 million a year. As a result of World War I, self-shaving became widespread and returning servicemen carried the habit home with them. While World War I taught thousands of men the self-shaving habit, World War II introduced millions of men to daily shaving practice.

BLADE EDGE AT MAXIMUM EXPOSURE

BLADE EDGE AT MINIMUM EXPOSURE

9 • 7

A-VIII-4

Adjustable Gillette Razor

12" STAINLESS STEEL RAZOR BAND

SHAVING HEAD WIDTH 1¾"

DIRECTION OF EDGE TRAVEL

CONTINUOUS STAINLESS STEEL RAZOR BAND CONTAINS SIX SHAVING EDGE EXPOSURES

"PHANTOM VIEW" OF RAZOR BAND CARTRIDGE

THICKNESS OF SHAVING EDGE .0015"

CONTINUOUS STAINLESS EDGE ⅓ THICKNESS OF STAINLESS STEEL BLADES THINNEST, SHARPEST BLADE STEEL EVER MADE

STORAGE ARBOR FOR USED EDGES

CARTRIDGE DIAL INDICATES NUMBER OF EDGE EXPOSURES REMAINING IN RAZOR BAND

PRECISION-ENGINEERED CARTRIDGE SNAPS IN PLACE GIVES WEEKS OF SHAVES

RAZOR HEAD IS ANGLED 15° FOR OPTIMUM SHAVING EASE

1½"

CARTRIDGE SNAP LOCK

EDGE ADVANCE LEVER ROTATES CLOCKWISE 360° TO EXPOSE NEW LENGTH OF SHAVING EDGE

ACTUAL LENGTH 4½"

1¾"

SIDE VIEW

FRONT VIEW

BACK VIEW

A-VIII-5
The Techmatic Razor with razor band.

Year	New Design	Improvements
1932	Gillette Blue Blade	Better shaving edge
1934	One-Piece Razor	Convenience, more exact edge exposure
1938	Thin Gillette Blade	Reduced cost by one half
1947	Blade Dispenser	Blade edges protected, simplified blade changing
1957	Adjustable Safety Razor	Variable cut, ease of adjustment
1960	Super Blue Blade	Longer life, first coated edge, less pull
1963	Stainless Steel Blade	Comfort, coated edge, durability
1963	Lady Gillette Razor	Designed expressly for women
1965	Super Stainless Steel Blade	Better steel, longer life, new coating
1965	Techmatic Razor with Razor Band	Cartridge load, convenience, no blades
1968	Injector-Type Single-Edge Blade	Provides alternative shaving method
1969	Platinum-Plus Double-Edge Blade	Stronger, harder, corrosion-resistant edges
1972	Trac II	Twin shaving blades for improved comfort and safety

In the 62 years since Gillette razors first went on sale, the company has produced over $\frac{1}{2}$ billion razors and over 100 billion blades. Throughout this period of time, however, many modifications and redesigns have been made [A-VIII-4].

The latest of these designs, the Techmatic Razor with razor band [A-VIII-5], is a complete departure from the blade-changing routine which has been so successfully sold to the American public. Interestingly enough, the idea of shaving with a "ribbon of steel' is a simple adaption of the original material purchased by King Gillette on that summer day in 1895. It has, however, taken 70 years for engineering design to make possible mass-produced "ribbon blades." Other improvements will undoubtedly follow in the years ahead.

Many other American industries have equally exciting engineering histories. In many respects the engineering students of today live in the most challenging period of history ever, and a *good idea*, together with the application of sound engineering design principles, will still produce *success*.

howard arneson's pool-sweep*

In 1958 Mr. Howard Arneson, rather fortuitously, came across an idea for a device to clean swimming pools automatically. To pursue

*Written by Mr. Prem C. Garg under the direction of Professor H. O. Fuchs with support from the National Science Foundation. By permission of the Engineering Case Program, Stanford University.

this idea further he started a tiny company with $8,000 in 1960. By 1965 the device was in production and in 1969 his company had sales exceeding 6 million dollars. Mr. Arneson now heads the company he sold to Castle and Cooke Inc. for 9 million dollars in 1969.

Howard Arneson's Pool-Sweep

"Practically all the 40,000 Pool-Sweeps (trade name of the device) sold so far have been sold in California. We have yet to make a serious effort for markets outside California," says Mr. Arneson with a glow in his eyes, emphasizing that he is not daydreaming. Not that daydreaming is something unfamiliar to Arnie; for that matter in fact, Pool-Sweep has been the only "genuine break" he has had during a career extending over the past thirty years.

Too ambitious and independent-minded to work for anyone, he has been living off his "own wits" for most of the time since his high school graduation in 1939. "Going to college was out of the question; my parents just couldn't afford it and I wasn't all that bright either to get some scholarship," recollects Arnie. "I used to get A's in the subjects I liked, but then there weren't too many of them," he adds with his characteristic smile. Mechanical things had a special fascination for Arnie and he often tinkered with appliances at home. Drawing was his favorite subject in school, and thanks to his high school training, he could read blueprints "half way." His interest in mechanical things was further reinforced during the Second World War in which he served as an Aviation Gunnery Instructor.

After the war he started a Skeet Trap Field in Vallejo, a small town in California.* However, he made little headway in this venture and after a couple of years sold the trap field to work as a sporting goods salesman. During the early fifties he sold TV sets for Sears and he was extremely successful in this. "From my earnings," he says, "they used to withhold as income tax more than what most other guys took home." This success, however, did not dampen his interest in mechanical things and, working with a colleague, he invented a light for emergency vehicles. Highway officials showed quite a bit of interest in that and he became very enthusiastic about its prospects. When in 1951 someone offered to invest in his venture he decided, contrary to the advice of all his colleagues, to quit Sears. "Most of them thought I was insane to leave a job like that," he remembers. During his three years involvement in this venture he did manage to sell these lights to a number of public services (among them the police forces of Washington, D.C., Kansas City, and New Orleans), but he isn't sure if, on the whole, he managed to break even or not. "Aside from the financial aspect," he says, "the venture

*Himself a versatile sportsman, his love for sports is perhaps second only to that for "mechanical things." In addition to being a past California Trap Shooting Champion, he is an expert fisherman as well. Competing in races on water as well as on land are some of his other hobbies.

was an extremely educational experience. Before then I never realized the importance of having the right distributors with 'proper contacts' in selling a product like this." (Incidentally, he still isn't sorry for his decision to quit Sears. "If I had to make that decision all over again, I would quit again.")

Finding himself in an unprofitable concern, he gradually phased out of the emergency-light business and spent the next four years producing and marketing fishing tackle.

"None of these ventures was a major disaster, but then neither were they a 'success.' I always had the feeling that I was going to do something better than what I was doing at that time." The opportunity to do that "something" came in a rather inconspicuous and accidental manner.

Sometime in early 1958 he was contacted by a San Rafael engineer named Andrew Pansini (Arnie doesn't remember the exact date). "Our contact was purely accidental. Mr. Pansini had happened to mention to a friend in Los Angeles that he was looking for someone who could help him in the development of a product based upon his ideas for a swimming pool cleaning device. This friend of his knew me pretty well and he suggested that my experience and aptitude for this kind of work could be very helpful to Mr. Pansini."

"Mr. Pansini felt that his idea, if successful, would completely revolutionize the irksome task of pool cleaning.* His idea was rather simple. Many people refill their swimming pools by letting garden hoses run into the pool. When you take those hoses out, you always find the area where they discharged water to be nice and clean. Now if you were to take a hose and try to clean the pool by just walking around it, you would never get it cleaned because you would just be chasing dirt from one corner to another—or perhaps if someone had the patience and the time he could clean it, but that certainly is not the best way to do it. Mr. Pansini was thinking of carrying this idea further: he wanted to simulate this action automatically by directing high-pressure water jets on the walls and the floor of the pool in some organized fashion.

"Mr. Pansini's approach was to have some kind of platform floating in the pool and connected to a high pressure water source. A small part of the incoming water was to be used for propelling the platform, while the rest was to clean the bottom and sides of the pool. Obviously there were two major design problems involved: first to feed the high pressure water to the mobile platform and second to

*As any pool owner would testify, the most irritating aspect of owning a swimming pool is the job of keeping it clean. The conventional methods include manual brushing of sides and bottom as well as vacuum cleaning to remove the foreign matter. For those who neither like the nuisance of cleaning their pools themselves nor the sight of disgruntled teenage sons, there are pool service companies. For a monthly charge of about 30 dollars they provide 2 cleanings a week, each of about 15 minutes duration.

A-VIII-6
Schematic of Mr. Pansini's pool-sweep.

AUTOMATIC SWIMMING POOL CLEANER

Filed May 12, 1958   3 Sheets-Sheet 1

NOZZLE FOR CLEANING JET

SWIVEL JOINT

FLOATS

SWIVEL JOINT
&
THRUST NOZZLE

MAIN DRAIN

HIGH
PRESSURE
WATER

INVENTOR.
ANDREW L. PANSINI
BY *Naylor & Neal*
ATTORNEYS

EXHIBIT 1.

propel the platform in some desirable fashion. Of course nobody knew what such a desirable pattern might be. We exchanged our ideas on these problems and working on those ideas we had a crude model fabricated within a few days time. Mr. Pansini was impressed with my work and asked me to continue helping him in the development."

In the same year Mr. Pansini filed a patent application for a jet-propelled cleaning device. (The patent was subsequently granted in 1962.) Exhibit 1, an excerpt from his patent, shows schematically the main features of his system. The device was extremely simple in construction. It consisted of a stationary steel pipe AB supported on the surface of the pool and connected to a high-pressure water source (at about 40 psi). Another steel pipe CD was connected to AB through a swivel joint. The swivel joint permitted the pipe CD to rotate about vertical axis BC, without any leakage. A flexible cleaning hose EF was connected at the other end of CD, through a second swivel joint. At the free end F of hose EF was attached a nozzle through which the cleaning jets were discharged. There was also a secondary nozzle at joint DE. Reaction from the secondary jet rotated pipe CD, along with hose EF, about BC. The reaction from the main nozzle at F made the hose EF execute a wavy pattern, spraying high-pressure water jets over the bottom and sides of the pool. The agitated dirt gradually gravitated toward the main drain where it was aspirated by the pool filter system. A specially designed plate P placed over the main drain induced currents in the water around the main drain to assist in collecting the dirt.

"I kept fooling around with various ideas to improve the crude device for about a year. My interest in the product at that time was rather peripheral, however. At that time I was sold on the idea of some hose coupling devices and was trying to get patents on those. In fact during that period I didn't really take the device very seriously; it seemed more of a novelty than a practical product. Mr. Pansini was extremely pleased with my work, however, and in 1959 he asked me to work for him full time on the development of this device. In addition to the regular salary, he offered me a 10% interest in the patents he might get on this product."

"It didn't take us long to realize that the original device needed many modifications and improvements. With the kind of model Mr. Pansini had in his patent, it was extremely difficult to cover the whole pool; especially if the pool happened to be of an odd shape, say 'L' shaped or a narrow rectangle where the pipe CD could cover only a small part by its rotation. To get better coverage we made substantial changes. Instead of keeping pipe AB stationary, it was made to oscillate. Also a tripping mechanism was introduced to diversify the pattern of movement of the cleaner hose. By late 1959 we had a fairly good workable prototype; in fact, we sold some of these prototypes to some overly enthusiastic customers."

"In 1960 Mr. Pansini decided to sell the rights to commercialize this product to Anthony Pools, a large pool building company in Los Angeles. In the contract he offered to make arrangements so that I could get a license from Anthony Pools for exclusive rights to Northern California."

"I had to make a big decision. While the product did seem to hold a lot of promise, there was no guarantee of anything.* In fact, by that time the initial enthusiasm of some of our earliest customers had started to wane; they still felt that the device was great but added that it was rather cumbersome to have in the pool. It appeared to me that any large scale commercialization of this product would require nothing short of a complete redesign. Transforming the excellent idea of a jet-propelled cleaning device into a functional product undoubtedly held a lot of challenge and excitement and possibly a fortune too. I felt that even though I could keep working on the development as a 'diversion,' I would have to give my full attention to this product to do a good job. By accepting Mr. Pansini's offer I could continue working on the development while at the same time supporting myself by selling the old models. Consequently, in spite of the long range financial uncertainties involved, I decided to accept the offer."

Having made his plans, Arnie discussed them with his wife Eva. "Notwithstanding my previous adventures she was very encouraging in her response and showed full faith in my plans. She was working for the Board of Education at that time. She quit that job and decided to join me in this venture."

"Over the years we had been able to save some money. Eva was also able to get some money out of her retirement fund, and we were able to raise about $8,000 to start with."

It was a modest beginning for Arneson. He decided to concentrate on marketing the device based upon the existing model, at that stage. He rented a small basement shop. Most of the parts for the device were available on the market and needed only assembling. However there were some which he could not get. "Having a workshop of my own was just not feasible at that time; so I arranged to have the parts made by a man who ran a small workshop and did odd jobs for a variety of customers."

"Apart from Eva's assistance I was taking care of everything myself. One day I would be out soliciting new customers; the next day I would be busy with installation or maintenance or something else. This total involvement proved very useful later on. On the one hand I became aware of the product's strong points and weak points as regards manufacturing, maintenance, assembly and installation,

---

*In the United States there were about 1 million pools in 1969 and over 80,000 new ones being built every year.

A-VIII-7
Mr. Arneson's floating-hose sweep-system.

How it works

1. Automatic timer turns pump on.

2. Filtered water from pool filter system is drawn into pump.

3. Pump boosts water at 60 lbs (shut off pressure) to deck stand.

4. Water passes through deck stand on pool edge (pressure gauge and regulator valve enable pool owner to set cleaning pattern and speed of pool sweep).

5. Ribbed floating hose with pressure chamber inside air chamber carries water to floating cleaning head.

6. Some water flows through skimmer jet and driving jet—the latter transports cleaning hose about pool in systematic patterns.

7. Main portion of water flows through cleaning hoses and out jets at hose ends.

8. Jets blast dirt out of pool's pores and drives hoses about pool bottom and sides.

9. Loose dirt and debris are washed into main drain and into pool filtering system.

10. Leaf trap catches and holds larger dirt particles and leaves (may be lifted out by means of pool pole for emptying).

EXHIBIT 2.

etc.; on the other hand from the way my customers reacted to it I could look at it from their point of view. This insight avoided numerous pitfalls which so often occur when someone tries to design something without knowing what he really needs to have.

"In spite of all my attempts to economize, I soon realized that $8,000 wouldn't go too far. It wasn't long before all the money was tied up and we were living on petty cash. Things weren't going badly, however, on paper at least; during the first nine months we sold about 200 of these cleaners and showed a net profit of $36,000. This was good enough to help us get loans from commercial banks."

His main opportunity, however, came in 1961 when Anthony Pools failed to keep up their contract with Mr. Pansini and their license was withdrawn. "Not only did they fail on promised sales figures, but they also didn't do anything to further develop the product. They did make some changes, but they were moving backwards; they were trying things we had already discarded." Mr. Arneson bought the license himself from Mr. Pansini and now had the exclusive rights on the jet-propelled cleaning devices. (To complete the full cycle, Mr. Arneson now sublicensed Anthony Pools to make these cleaners for their own use.)

Over a year's association with the device had confirmed Arnie's belief that while the basic idea was brilliant, the product as it was at that time left much to be desired. "It was just a mechanical monster. The unshapely steel pipes lying in the pool were not only an eyesore but were also a potential hazard to swimmers. They needed a carton over 15′ long for shipping and every pool required different sizes and configurations of these pipes. The installation was so involved that I had to do all the selling myself; you just couldn't teach anyone the way to install it. It wasn't something you could sell wholesale or sell by mail. The last and most important drawback was the fact that while in some pools it worked beautifully, in others it would simply chase the dirt from one corner to the other. Evidently we needed something which would be foolproof in operation, easy to install and ship, and would not obstruct the use of the swimming pool.

"I felt that there was really no reason for those steel pipes to be there at all. Their only function was to supply the cleaning hose with water and to move it around the pool. I felt that it should be possible to accomplish this without using the steel pipes."

In an attempt to eliminate the steel pipes Arnie replaced them with a flexible hose to which the cleaning hoses were connected as previously (see Exhibit 2; note there are two cleaning hoses instead of one). The propulsion was again achieved by the reaction from the jet at the end of the flexible (feeder) hose. While the introduction of the flexible hose removed many of the shortcomings of the first model, it did create some new problems. There were leakage problems due to puncturing of the floating hose and also the fact that the device drifted aimlessly on windy days. Even without the winds, there was much less control over the pattern of movement of the cleaning hoses. Consequently, in some pools it worked and in some others it just didn't. So it turned out that this solution, though better than the previous one, was still far from satisfactory.

In late 1963 Arnie first conceived of the product in its present form. "Really it is an offshoot of the floating hose concept. Since the main trouble with the floating hose model was the lack of control over the propulsive thrust from the drive jet, I felt that what we needed was some mechanism through which we could control the magnitude and direction of the drive jet thrust, at will. Further thought on these lines indicated that this should not be very difficult to do, e.g., a system of valves operated in some periodic fashion could control the flow through the drive jet nozzle thus controlling the thrust. The valves could be operated by using part of the high pressure water energy, say by running a small turbine wheel in the mobile platform and using its rotation to run the valves. The more I thought about it, the more convinced I became that this approach was workable. In my mind I began to see the whole thing very clearly. I could see the water wheel turning; I could see the gears meshing with each other; I could see the valves opening and closing. I had the functional design pretty well figured out. But that's not quite the same thing as the actual design; I still had to make numerous decisions, e.g. the pattern for the movement of the hoses, the thrust combinations to be used or even the duration of the valve cycle to get best results. Admittedly, I didn't have the training to calculate all those things but I don't think mathematics would have helped anyway. There were just so many variables involved that an engineer could have spent months working on a big computer just to prove that such a thing won't even work. I think my ignorance was an advantage in this case. Since I didn't know what was there in the books, I was able to work with freedom and an open mind.

"I decided not to bother about the details; I thought I could let someone else worry about them later on. Instead, I concentrated on verifying if my approach was workable. I tried to keep my design simple using standard parts as far as I could. Often I used parts scavenged from junk; I remember some of the gears I used in the early models were reclaimed from discarded lawn sprinklers."

Exhibit 3 shows a photograph of one of the earliest models Arnie made to check his ideas regarding the propulsion mechanism. Though this model was far off from the final product envisioned by Arnie, it worked well enough to assure him of the soundness of his approach.

"Developing these ideas further was important but at the same time I could not afford to have a decline in the sale of the floating hose cleaners—profits from them were the only source of income I had at that time. So during the daytime I would be out selling or installing those cleaners. Whenever some new idea came to my

A-VIII-8
Photograph of an early pool-sweep head fabricated by Mr. Arneson.

EXHIBIT 3.

POOL·SWEEP AUTOMATIC SWIMMING POOL CLEANER
INSTALLATION & OPERATING INSTRUCTIONS

1971

NOMENCLATURE AND ELEMENTS OF POOL-SWEEP SYSTEM

1. Automatic Timer (Optional, additional charge)
Separate time clock, installed when desired, to provide automatic turning on and off.

2. Booster Pump
Special pump installed to increase water pressure to approximately 50 lbs. working pressure for proper operation of Pool-Sweep system.

3. Supply Hose (For existing pool)
Heavy flexible hose (in some installations, may be buried pipe) which carries water from booster pump to deck stand. (Not included due to variety of individual requirements.)

4. Deck Stand (For existing pool)
Designed to transfer water from supply hose to feeder hose, and portable for placement at desired position at pool coping.
Note: In new pools, a buried pipe and suitable wall fitting are provided to attach feeder hose.

5. Feeder Hose
Water supply hose which extends from deck stand or wall fitting to floating Pool-Sweep.

6. Float Arm
Special floating device designed to keep Pool-Sweep in vertical position and aid in floatation of hoses.

7. Pool-Sweep Head
Basic unit designed to float on water and transport cleaning hoses into every portion of pool to be cleaned.

8. Floor Hose
Longer of the two sweep hoses, whose principal function is the cleaning of the pool's floor.

9. Wall Hose
Shorter of the two cleaning hoses, whose principal function is the cleaning of the pool walls.

10. Housing Bumper
Special bumper, which keeps Pool-Sweep on desired tracking path around pool and steps.

11. Leaf Trap
Special screen unit designed to catch leaves and other large objects as dirt is swept down drain.

A-VIII-9
Schematic of Mr. Arneson's pool-sweep system.

EXHIBIT 4.

Skimming Jet

Water In

Propulsion Jet

To Cleaning Hoses

Wall Traction Tire

INCHES

Back-up Jet

Valve

Drive Jet Shaft

Propulsion Jet

Main Shaft

To Skimming Jet

Turbine Wheel

EXHIBIT 5.

A-VIII-10
Details of pool-sweep head.

A-VIII-11
Movement pattern of pool-sweep head.

MAIN DRAIN

DECK STAND

a

f

d

e

b

c

EXHIBIT 6.

mind I would scribble it down on some scratch paper. Late in the evening I would meet the machinist and we would make parts based upon my 'blueprints' and then I would be out trying those ideas at some neighbor's swimming pool.*

"Progress was slow. While it didn't take long to get the basic ideas about the functional design, to come up with something which actually worked the way I wanted it to work was quite another story. The actual design took thousands of hours of just standing around the pools and watching the device move around and figuring out ways to make it do better. There were hundreds of changes in the design. A design would work beautifully in one pool, you take it to another pool and it would start doing all sorts of crazy things. During those days it was nothing for me to come home at four in the morning after trying my ideas the whole night. Often the machinist would complete some part at midnight and then I wouldn't have the patience to wait 'til the next morning. Mostly it was trial and error. At times it was very depressing; however I never got depressed enough to think of leaving it. It never once occurred to me that I wouldn't succeed."

Gradually Arnie's never-say-die approach began to pay off. Within a period of six months he had a prototype which satisfied most of the stringent requirements he had set for the device. Exhibit 4 shows schematically the working of such a system. Exhibit 5 gives the details of the Pool-Sweep head (Item 7, Exhibit 4), the unit responsible for transporting the cleaning hoses into the various parts of the pool. As shown in Exhibit 4, high-pressure water is fed into the head through the feeder hose. There it drives a turbine wheel which in turn rotates the main shaft as well as the drive jet shaft, through worm gear reductions (see Exhibit 5). There is a 25:1 reduction from the turbine wheel to the main shaft and a further 100:1 reduction from the main shaft to the drive jet shaft. During operation the drive jet shaft completes one revolution about every 4 minutes. The water, after driving the turbine wheel, leaves the head in the form of five different jets as indicated below:

1. Two jets through the cleaning hoses for cleaning the sides and bottom of the pool.
2. Two propulsion jets through the drive jet shaft for the backward and forward propulsion of the unit in the pool.
3. A small jet through the top of the main shaft to clean the above water tiles as well as to skim the pool water surface so as to settle down any floating dirt particles.

---

*Since Mr. Arneson did not have a swimming pool of his own during those days, he had to work around the pools of his friends and neighbors. "To a certain extent this was a handicap; I often had to work at odd hours so as not to interfere with normal usage. In the long run, however, it proved a blessing. If I had had my own pool, I would have been wedded to one pool. Working in pools of all kinds of different shapes and sizes resulted in a product which worked perfectly in every pool."

Flow is continuous through the cleaning jets, but a valve mounted on the drive jet shaft controls the flow through the propulsion jets. Both the forward and backward propulsion jets rotate with the drive jet shaft. However while the backward jet nozzle is concentric with the shaft axis, the forward jet nozzle is tilted by about 15° from the drive jet shaft axis. The backward jet is operated for a small part of the cycle only (about $\frac{1}{12}$). The forward jet operates all the time except when the backward jet is working. As a reaction to the propulsion jets, the head, along with the hoses connected to it, moves around in the pool. While the path followed by the unit during any cycle of the drive jet shaft is predictable with reasonable accuracy, over a period of a couple of hours there is enough variation in the motion so as to cover practically every spot in the pool.

It is impossible to list all the design problems Arnie faced during the development period. The one mentioned below, known in the company as "Tangling Hose Problem," may give some idea of their nature and magnitude.

This problem was among the earliest to be encountered and last to be solved. As the name implies the problem concerned the tangling of the feeder and cleaning hoses with each other. It is obvious that every time the head circled around the pool once, the feeder hose would get twisted and unless the unit could get rid of the twist it would quickly jam up. This meant that there had to be a joint in the feeder hose which would turn freely but at the same time would be leakproof against 40–50 psi pressure. A conventional joint with an O-ring didn't work; it had too much friction. In looking for a solution to this problem Arnie came up with a very simple and inexpensive swivel joint. (The joint proved to be patentable in itself.)

To his dismay, however, Arnie found that in many pools the hoses got tangled even with the swivel joint. Evidently there were many other factors involved, e.g.,

1. Length of the feeder hose vis-à-vis the pool size and shape.
2. Pressure in the Pool-Sweep head (affects the drive jet thrust).
3. Material of the hoses.
4. Temperature of the pool water.
5. Position of floats on the feeder hose.

The importance of these and some other factors was realized by Mr. Arneson rather early in the development by his hit-and-miss approach. Working around these parameters he managed to design his system so that it worked most of the time in most pools. During the early years of marketing it worked out satisfactorily; there were complaints but not too many. Later when the number of units in operation increased, the number of complaints rose accordingly. By 1969 they were getting as many as 30 complaints a day (there were

A-VIII-12
Improved feeder hose setup.

FEEDER HOSE

CORRECT LENGTH OF FEEDER HOSE

The *feeder* hose carries water under pressure from the deck stand, or wall fitting, as the case may be, to the cleaner head. The deck stand (D28) or wall fitting (W10) should be positioned at the middle of a long pool side. If a wall fitting is used, it should be located below the tiles.

The feeder hose comes in three sections: a 6-ft length of hose with two feeder hose weights (w) attached that connects to the deck stand or wall fitting; a 10-ft length which is usually shortened, depending on the size of the pool; a 16-ft length with three floats, A, B, and C attached. The weights on the 6-ft section and the floats on the 16-ft section are properly installed at the factory.

To determine the proper length, temporarily connect the entire hose and fill it with water by connecting it to the deck stand or wall fitting and turning on the pump for a few seconds. Walk the free end of the hose to the farthest corner of the pool from the deck stand. With the hose in a natural working position, there should be 3 feet of hose beyond the water's edge. The feeder hose will usually need to be shortened. Cut the excess from the 10-ft middle section. For example, if you have 5 feet of feeder hose beyond the water's edge, then 2 feet must be cut from the 10-ft middle section.

MEASURE TO FARTHEST CORNER FROM DECK STAND*

FLOAT ARM

"FOR CORRECT LENGTH" LET HOSE FILL WITH WATER AND ASSUME A NATURAL WORKING POSITION AS SHOWN BELOW

PLACE DECK STAND IN THE MIDDLE OF POOL SIDE

*If pool has odd shape make sure that you measure to corner of pool furthest away from deck stand location.

FEEDER HOSE ARRANGEMENT

FLOAT ARM — FLOAT "A" — FARTHEST CORNER — FLOAT "B" — FLOAT "C" — SWIVEL "A" — SWIVEL "B" — FLOAT "D" — IF REQUIRED — DECK STAND — WEIGHT "W"

Extra float

The float on the hose extension (the 10-ft middle section), should be positioned as follows:

(1) If the extension is 6 ft or less, *no* float is added, but if more than 6 ft then position one float, "D," 2 ft from swivel "A" as seen above.

(2) Rarely will more than 10 ft of extension hose be required but the factory will provide up to 16-ft lengths if needed. If more than 10 ft is used, a second float (not shown above) will be needed and should be positioned on the extension hose 5 ft from float "D."

In order to connect to the swivel connector (D5) proceed as follows: Take the $\frac{5''}{8}$ mender nut (D2) that comes with the box of hoses, slip it on the swivel connector with the beveled edge of the nut facing toward the middle of the connector.

Push the free hose end over the swivel connector and thread the mender nut over the hose end tightly. (See illustration Detail C.)

DETAIL C—TYPICAL SWIVEL CONNECTION

Feeder Hose D3 — Mender Nut D2 — Swivel D5 — Mender Nut D2 — Feeder Hose D3

Wetting the quick-disconnect coupling for easier installation attach the feeder hose to the deck stand (D28), or wall fitting (W5), depending on the type of installation. Again, wetting the quick-disconnect coupling, connect the other end of the feeder hose assembly to the float arm assembly (F3).

EXHIBIT 7.

POOL-SWEEP

PARTS LIST

EXHIBIT 8.

PARTS LIST

PART NO.	DESCRIPTION	QTY.
A1	Pump-Motor Assembly	1
B2	Gate Valve, 3/4", Brass	1
B3	Hose Adapter, 3/4" x 3/4" male	3
B5	Suction Hose, 3/4"	1
B10	Male Elbow, 3/4" x 90 degrees	1
D2	Mender Nut, 5/8"	6
D3A	Feeder Hose, 6-ft length	1
D3B	Feeder Hose, 10-ft length	1
D3C	Feeder Hose, 16-ft length	1
D5	Swivel Connector	2
D9	Screen	1
D10	Washer for 3/4" hose	3
D14	Float, small	4
D20	Feeder hose, complete	1
D27	Weight for Feeder Hose	1
D28	Deck Stand, complete (for existing pool)	1
F1	Float, large	1
F7	"O"-ring, #014, 5/8" x 1/16"	4
F8	Float arm assembly	1
G4	Flat washer, 7/16" nickel-plated	1
G6	3/8" Housing Nut, nickel	1
G9	Housing Tire	2
G15	Thumb screw for sweep hose adjustment	2
G39	Tile Rinser Assembly	1
G44	Jam Nut, 3/8"—16 plated	1
H1	Hose weight	2
H2	Hose mender, 7/16"	2
H3	Mender Nut, 7/16"	4
H5W	Wall Sweep hose, 10-ft length	1
H5F	Floor Sweep hose, 10-ft length	1
H6	Floor hose extension, 8-ft length	1
H7	Hose Sleeve without insert, Floor Hose	18
H7	Floor Hose Ext....8, Wall Hose	19
H8	Hose Jet	2
H9	Hose Jet Sleeve	3
H10	Stop ring for hose weight	2
H12	Floor Hose, 13, Ext...1, Wall Hose	9
*J2	Ladder Guard (including screw, J8)	1
J8	Self-tapping screw for ladder guard	2
J27	Quick-disconnect coupling for 7/16" hose	2
J28	Quick-disconnect coupling for 5/8" hose	2
K9	Supply Hose, 3/4"	1
L1	Leaf Trap Assembly	1
L2	Harness for leaf trap	1
*S1	Saddle Tee (give size when ordering)	1
W5	Wall Fitting only, 1-1/2" (for new pool)	1
W9	Screen retainer	1
W10	Wall Fitting, 1-1/2", complete (including W5, D9, W9, F7)	1

*The Ladder Guard (J2 & J8) and the Saddle Clamp (S1) are not included with the Pool-Sweep.

around 25,000 units in operation). So in 1969 renewed efforts were made to solve the problem. At that time the setup shown in Exhibit 7 was found, rather accidentally, which all but eliminated the problem. The only essential difference between this setup and the previous setups is the weight "W" ($\approx$4 lb) mounted on the feeder hose.

By late 1964 Arnie was more or less through with the technical problems and the prototype was refined enough to start thinking in terms of production. "'Til then I had given very little thought to the production aspect. For the prototypes, we had been machining most of the components from thick plastic sheets and gluing them together; you can't do that in mass production. Also there was the need for selecting appropriate materials for various components. Practical considerations limited the choice to plastics for most components; however there still was the need for picking up the proper ones from an endless variety of available plastics. It was here that assistance from Jupiter Engineering Inc., a plastic injection molding company in Menlo Park, California, came in handy to us. Mr. Reinbacher, Jupiter's President, had just started his own company after working for a long time with DuPont and was looking for clients. The Pool-Sweep provided Jupiter with an ideal opportunity. On the one hand it had enough complexities to let them establish a reputation for the company; on the other it had a big market potential. The arrangement with Jupiter proved good for us as well; we were able to get their exclusive attention as they did not have very many clients at that time." The whole unit was redesigned by Jupiter after taking into consideration the manufacturing, materials and aesthetic aspects. Exhibit 8 shows the arrangement of the major components in the redesigned system. In Exhibit 9 is shown an exploded view of the Pool-Sweep head, the "brain" of the system.

"In about six months time Jupiter Engineering provided us with the molded specimens for testing and evaluation. Most of the components did very well during the tests; the gear housing (see Exhibit 9), however, proved to be troublesome. It just couldn't withstand the pressure. Either it would burst under pressure or there would be such large deformations that the gears would get out of alignment and the whole unit would get stalled. Naturally enough 'increase the thickness' was my immediate reaction; Mr. Reinbacher felt, however, that this wouldn't be of much help—the housing was already close to 'critical thickness'; and any further increase would have resulted in excessive molded-in stresses. To make the housing stronger, Jupiter changed the mold to add ribs to the housing; even this, however, did not solve the problem. Then Mr. Reinbacher suggested trying some other plastic. Luckily they were able to find a material which could be used with the old mold. The switching in materials proved to be effective and the crisis was averted. There were some other troubles too, but all of them were solved and we were ready to sell these units during the summer of 1965.

"From that time on, things have just mushroomed. We had sales of about half a million dollars during the first year and since then they have been doubling every year. The same thing happened with the number of our employees; 20 was a big number at one time and then all of a sudden I found myself with over 200 people to manage. This has certainly put some strains on the organization. Often there is lack of coordination between various departments. Sometimes we feel that we have too much paper flow and at other times we feel that we have too little. Also, so far it has been too much of a one-man show. There has been lack of strong leadership in various departments, which primarily is my fault since I didn't delegate authority to other people."

Arnie isn't overly worried with these problems. "We are just suffering growing pains. Normally, if your sales increase 10% every year, your organization will grow accordingly. But when the sales get doubled every year you just have to live with these problems."

Reflecting back on the past Arnie feels that his success was due to a rather unique combination. "I was personally involved with the design while at the same time I was in touch with the customers. I have always been successful as a salesman. I could talk to people and sell." Talking about his sales policy, Arnie feels that the most important thing in selling is that you must have something to sell, and further if you can convince your customer that you are not trying to take advantage of him, you are a good salesman. "Not a small part of my success was due to the fact that never for once did I give my customers a chance to complain. I would rather let my customers take advantage of me than let anybody in the organization take advantage of them by not doing his job properly."

Interestingly, Arnie feels that a big factor in his success during the development stages was the fact that he never had any problems with his machinist. "He made what I wanted. He was happy if it worked but it wasn't 'I told you so' if it did not. He never had any opinions of his own. Only one of us did the thinking and we thus eliminated many fruitless arguments." (Later Mr. Arneson bought all his equipment and engaged him as his shop supervisor.)

The exceptional success of the product hasn't closed Arnie's mind to the possibilities of further improvement. Neither has his interest in mechanical things been diminished by the organizational responsibilities. Often he still attends to the service calls himself. The disbelieving look on the startled faces of his customers has to be seen to be believed when a balding, medium-statured man dressed in a sport shirt rings the door bell and introduces himself, "I am Mr. Arneson. I am here to attend to. . . ."

A-VIII-14
Details
of the
redesigned
pool-sweep
head.

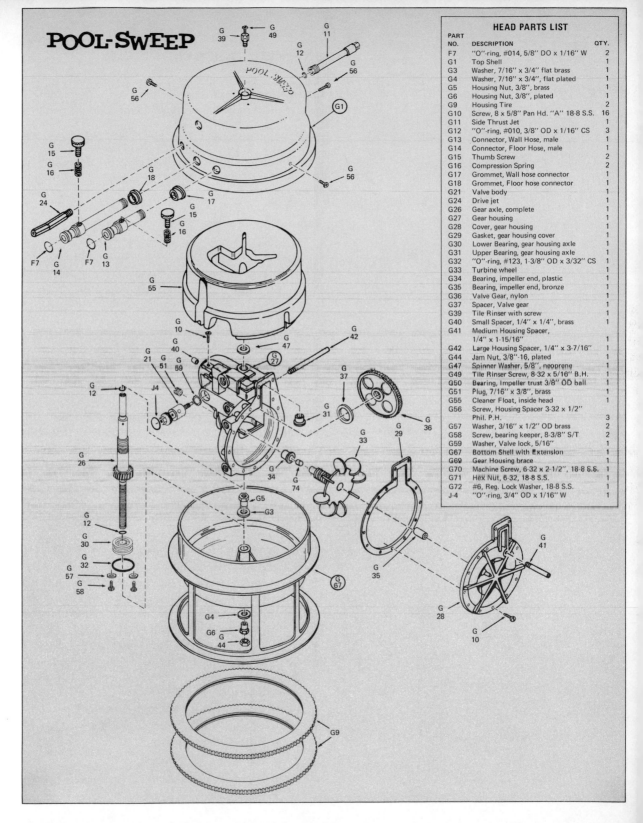

POOL·SWEEP

HEAD PARTS LIST

PART NO.	DESCRIPTION	QTY.
F7	"O"-ring, #014, 5/8" DO x 1/16" W	2
G1	Top Shell	1
G3	Washer, 7/16" x 3/4" flat brass	1
G4	Washer, 7/16" x 3/4", flat plated	1
G5	Housing Nut, 3/8", brass	1
G6	Housing Nut, 3/8", plated	1
G9	Housing Tire	2
G10	Screw, 8 x 5/8" Pan Hd. "A" 18-8 S.S.	16
G11	Side Thrust Jet	1
G12	"O"-ring, #010, 3/8" OD x 1/16" CS	3
G13	Connector, Wall Hose, male	1
G14	Connector, Floor Hose, male	1
G15	Thumb Screw	2
G16	Compression Spring	2
G17	Grommet, Wall hose connector	1
G18	Grommet, Floor hose connector	1
G21	Valve body	1
G24	Drive jet	1
G26	Gear axle, complete	1
G27	Gear housing	1
G28	Cover, gear housing	1
G29	Gasket, gear housing cover	1
G30	Lower Bearing, gear housing axle	1
G31	Upper Bearing, gear housing axle	1
G32	"O"-ring, #123, 1-3/8" OD x 3/32" CS	1
G33	Turbine wheel	1
G34	Bearing, impeller end, plastic	1
G35	Bearing, impeller end, bronze	1
G36	Valve Gear, nylon	1
G37	Spacer, Valve gear	1
G39	Tile Rinser with screw	1
G40	Small Spacer, 1/4" x 1/4", brass	1
G41	Medium Housing Spacer, 1/4" x 1-15/16"	1
G42	Large Housing Spacer, 1/4" x 3-7/16"	1
G44	Jam Nut, 3/8"-16, plated	1
G47	Spinner Washer, 5/8", neoprene	1
G49	Tile Rinser Screw, 8-32 x 5/16" B.H.	1
G50	Bearing, Impeller trust 3/8" OD ball	1
G51	Plug, 7/16" x 3/8", brass	1
G55	Cleaner Float, inside head	1
G56	Screw, Housing Spacer 3-32 x 1/2" Phil. P.H.	3
G57	Washer, 3/16" x 1/2" OD brass	2
G58	Screw, bearing keeper, 8-3/8" S/T	2
G59	Washer, Valve lock, 5/16"	1
G67	Bottom Shell with Extension	1
G69	Gear Housing brace	1
G70	Machine Screw, 6-32 x 2-1/2", 18-8 S.S.	1
G71	Hex Nut, 6-32, 18-8 S.S.	1
G72	#6, Reg. Lock Washer, 18-8 S.S.	1
J-4	"O"-ring, 3/4" OD x 1/16" W	1

EXHIBIT 9.

an electric accelerometer[*]

Let us suppose that the engineer who was studying the liquid-level accelerometer in Chapter 6 is seeking a direct-reading accelerometer for permanent mounting in an automobile. He decides that the liquid type is unsuitable for this purpose because of its sensitivity to the level of the vehicle, and that, anyway, he would prefer a device indicating acceleration on an electric instrument, such as a voltmeter or ammeter.

It occurs to him that a dc generator, geared directly to the drive shaft of the car, would give a voltage accurately proportional to car speed provided the magnetic flux remained constant, as it would with a permanent-magnet field. Now if he could connect the generator terminals to something that would draw a current proportional to the rate of change of voltage, that is, proportional to the rate of change of speed, acceleration, he would have a solution. He considers the common circuit elements: resistance, inductance, and capacitance, and their effects on the flow of current. He chooses a condenser for his purpose because its charge will be proportional to its terminal voltage, $q = Cv$; hence the rate of change of charge, or current $i = dq/dt$, will be proportional to rate of change of voltage.

Thus the engineer decides to try a condenser in series with an ammeter, and to fix ideas he sketches and labels the diagram [A-VIII-15] and writes

The dc generator is geared directly to the drive shaft of the automobile and is connected in series with a condenser and ammeter. How will the current vary with car speed?

It is significant that, although this statement of the problem is much like those which fill common engineering textbooks, it was not given to the engineer in this clearly defined form. Rather, he made up the problem statement himself in an effort to answer the broader question, also put by himself, "How can I make an instrument that will measure acceleration electrically?" He hopes that solution of the definite problem which he has stated will supply the answer to his question, but he fully realizes that it may not, in which case he must try again; and he realizes also that there may be many answers.

Having formulated for himself a definite problem, the engineer next seeks a plan for its solution. Observing that he has a simple

A-VIII-15
Circuit for accelerometer.

*From D. W. Ver Planck and B. R. Teare, Jr., *Engineering Analysis*, New York: Wiley, 1954, by permission. Some knowledge of elementary electric circuit elements is required for an understanding of this problem.

series circuit, he sees that Kirchhoff's voltage law will yield a relationship involving the current. So, to fix ideas, he writes his plan:

Apply Kirchhoff's voltage law to the circuit and solve for the current. Assume that the voltage generated will be exactly proportional to car speed and independent of current (that is, neglect armature reaction) and assume that inductance is negligibly small.

In execution of this plan, he writes

Voltage generated equals the sum of the voltage drops through the condenser and the circuit resistance.

Translating this statement into mathematical form, he writes

$$Ku = \frac{q}{C} + Ri \qquad \text{Equation A}$$

where K = constant of proportionality between generated voltage and car speed (volts second per foot). This involves generator constants, gear ratios, and wheel diameter.

u = car speed (feet per second).
q = charge on the condenser at any instant (coulombs).
C = capacitance of the condenser (farads).
R = total resistance of the circuit (ohms).

$i = \dfrac{dq}{dt}$ = current in the circuit (amperes).

This gives a relationship between car speed, condenser charge, ammeter current, and the system constants. Does it show that current is in proportion to rate of change of car speed? To try to answer this question, the engineer proceeds and writes

Differentiate with respect to time

$$K\frac{du}{dt} = \frac{1}{C}\frac{dq}{dt} + R\frac{di}{dt} \qquad \text{Equation B}$$

But $$i = \frac{dq}{dt}$$

so $$K\frac{du}{dt} = \frac{i}{C} + R\frac{di}{dt} \qquad \text{Equation C}$$

Inspection of this equation indicates that i will be proportional to du/dt as is desired if the last term is negligibly small compared to the other two, or, as may be seen from Equation A, if the Ri drop can be neglected. The engineer continues:

Assume Ri negligible in comparison with q/C at all times. Then

$$K\frac{du}{dt} = \frac{1}{C}\frac{dq}{dt} \qquad\qquad \text{Equation D}$$

or

$$i = \frac{dq}{dt} = CK\frac{du}{dt} \qquad\qquad \text{Equation E}$$

that is, the current is proportional to du/dt, which is the acceleration of the car.

Before putting any faith in this very promising result, the engineer checks it in various ways.

Dimensional check:

$$i(\text{amperes}) = C(\text{farads})\, K\left(\frac{\text{volt second}}{\text{feet}}\right)\frac{du}{dt}\left(\frac{\text{feet}}{\text{second}^2}\right)$$

$$= (\text{farads})\left(\frac{\text{volts}}{\text{second}}\right)$$

$$= (\text{amperes}) \qquad \text{check} \qquad\qquad \text{Equation F}$$

The basis for the last step is that capacitance in farads times voltage is charge in coulombs $(q = Cv)$, and rate of change of charge in coulombs per second is current in amperes.

The result appears reasonable because, if the acceleration is zero, so is the current, and, if the acceleration increases, so does the current. Having K and C in the numerator appears reasonable, because the larger C, the greater the current; also the larger K, the greater the voltage and hence the greater the current.

Satisfied with these checks, the engineer turns to a consideration of what he has learned about the answer to his original question, which was how to make an electric accelerometer. He writes the following conclusion:

A permanent-magnet dc generator geared directly to the wheels and connected to a condenser will give a current proportional to acceleration if resistance drop, armature inductance, and armature reaction can be neglected. If, in addition, the mechanical transient in the ammeter may be ignored, the reading will be proportional to acceleration.

Apparently, the engineer had a glimmering of this idea or he would not have thought of trying the circuit he did. On the other hand, had he been perfectly familiar with differentiating circuits, he might have used this knowledge as a fundamental basis for a solution instead of proceeding as he did.

The seemingly favorable result obtained above immediately raises a number of questions that also must be answered before the engineer would be justified in considering his original question answered. For example: Are the sizes of the components necessary in the generator–condenser scheme practically realizable? Is it possible for the resistance drop to be negligibly small? Is it safe to ignore the effect of inductance of the circuit? Is it reasonable to neglect armature reaction in a small permanent-magnet generator? Can the mechanical transient in the ammeter be neglected? Are there wholly different electrical schemes that might be better?

Let us see how the engineer might answer the question, "Will the scheme work with readily available components?" To answer a question such as this requires some experience with apparatus, or perhaps some searching through sources of data, such as handbooks and manufacturers' catalogs. It is remarkable, though, how far one can go on a very modest fund of experience. For example, let us see how the engineer might proceed in answering this question. Thinking over the components, the generator, the ammeter, and the condenser, the engineer plans to solve the new problem he has set himself in this way:

Choose a generator and ammeter arbitrarily and see how big a condenser will give a suitable meter deflection.

The engineer recalls his engineering laboratory experience and decides on a generator that he remembers using as a component of an electric tachometer. He writes

Use a tachometer generator that develops 200 volts at a maximum speed, and gear it so that this voltage is reached at 100 miles per hour (2 volts per mile per hour).

The voltage output of commercially available tachometer generators varies widely among manufacturers. A common rating is 6 volts per 1,000 revolutions per minute, but models are available in which this figure is as high as 75 volts per 1,000 revolutions per minute. It is probably one of these latter that our friend has in mind. Then, thinking of a small portable meter he once used, which was quite sensitive and still fairly rugged, he decides to

Use an ammeter with center zero and a full scale reading of 1 milli-ampere (0.001 ampere).

Then he writes further

It would be desirable to be able to read a moderate rate of acceleration, say from 10 to 60 miles per hour in 20 seconds, at half scale on the meter. Thus the change of voltage will be 100 volts in 20 seconds or

$$K\frac{du}{dt} = 5 \text{ volts/second} \qquad \text{Equation G}$$

The current corresponding to this should be 0.5 milliampere or

$$i = 0.0005 \text{ ampere} \qquad \text{Equation H}$$

Then from the formula developed

$$C = \frac{i}{K(du/dt)} = \frac{0.0005}{5} = 10^{-4} \text{ farad}$$

$$= 100 \text{ microfarads} \qquad \text{Equation I}$$

If this value turns out to be uneconomically high, it could be reduced by using a more sensitive ammeter or a generator which gives a still higher voltage.

So far the scheme looks feasible. In considering a generator of higher voltage and a more sensitive meter, the engineer would realize at once that these probably would involve increased resistance. Thus, as the next step, he might set himself the problem of determining how much resistance can be tolerated. In attacking this problem, he writes

What is the effect of circuit resistance? Return to Equation A, in which resistance was included, and attempt to solve it without neglecting Ri.

$$Ku = \frac{q}{C} + Ri$$

Differentiate and rearrange the terms:

$$\frac{di}{dt} + \frac{i}{RC} = \frac{K}{R}\frac{du}{dt} \qquad \text{Equation J}$$

For simplicity, assume a constant rate of acceleration suddenly applied; that is, let

$$\frac{du}{dt} = A \qquad \text{Equation K}$$

Then separate variables in Equation J and integrate between limits:

$$\int_0^i \frac{di}{(KA/R) - (i/RC)} = \int_0^t dt \qquad \text{Equation L}$$

In choosing the lower limits as he did, the engineer reasoned as follows: Assuming the acceleration applied with the vehicle initially at rest, the voltage generated at the first instant will be zero. Also, the charge on the condenser, and hence its voltage, will be zero. Therefore, at the first instant there is no voltage available to cause current to flow through the resistance of the circuit; consequently, $i = 0$ at $t = 0$. Integrating Equation L, he proceeds:

$$-RC \, ln \frac{(KA/R) - (i/RC)}{(KA/R)} = t \qquad \text{Equation M}$$

$$1 - \frac{i}{KCA} = \varepsilon^{-t/RC} \qquad \text{Equation N}$$

and finally

$$i = KCA(1 - \varepsilon^{-t/RC}) \qquad \text{Equation P}$$

Dimensional check of the coefficient:

$$i(\text{amperes}) = K\left(\frac{\text{volt second}}{\text{feet}}\right) C(\text{farads}) \, A\left(\frac{\text{feet}}{\text{second}^2}\right)$$

$$= \frac{\text{volts}}{\text{second}} \times \text{farads} = \text{amperes} \qquad \text{check}$$

The exponent should be dimensionless:

$$\frac{t(\text{second})}{R(\text{ohms}) \, C(\text{farads})} = \frac{\text{second}}{(\text{volts/amperes}) \times \text{farads}}$$

$$= \frac{\text{amperes}}{(\text{volts/seconds}) \times \text{farads}}$$

$$= \frac{\text{amperes}}{\text{amperes}} \qquad \text{check}$$

With $R = 0$, the result, Equation P, becomes $i = KCA$. This agrees with Equation E derived directly for the case of zero resistance if the acceleration du/dt has the constant value A. With $R = \infty$, Equation P gives $i = 0$, which evidently is correct.

Thus the engineer has derived a formula showing the effect of resistance in the circuit for the case of a suddenly applied constant acceleration. To interpret his formula (Equation P) to himself, he sketches roughly a graph [A-VIII-16], showing as functions of time

A-VIII-16
Sketch to interpret equation P.

the acceleration and the currents that would result with different values of resistance. As further interpretation of the result, he writes

The current approaches the value corresponding to the steady acceleration exponentially with a time constant equal to RC. At a time equal to RC, the current will reach about 63 per cent of its final value. In three time constants, the current will be within 5 per cent of its final value.

In addition to this time lag, there also will be a mechanical transient dependent on the characteristics of the meter. The part of the transient associated with the circuit would be imperceptible to the eye if the time constant RC is made $\frac{1}{20}$ second.

$$RC = 0.05$$

$$R = \frac{0.05}{C} = \frac{0.05}{10^{-4}}$$

$$= 500 \text{ ohms}$$

using the value of $C = 100$ microfarads found in the earlier calculation. This is the maximum tolerable resistance, and is probably higher than the resistances likely for the assumed generator and meter.

Thus far it appears that this scheme for an electric accelerometer is practically feasible. Before embarking on an experimental installation, however, the engineer certainly would analyze carefully the effects of the mechanical behavior of the meter element, for these effects might well determine the success of the scheme. Moreover, he might consider the influence of other factors and possibly also entirely different schemes.

index

coolness of, 157
warmness of, 157
Colt, Samuel, v
Column, 605
Combustion engine, 249
Combustion gas, 248
Comfort zone, 351
Command societies, 371
Communicate, 357
Communication, 228, 262
visual, 418
Communism, 370
Communities, 117
Community Chest, 52
Compass, 425
beam, 425
bow, 425
Compass needle, 191
Compatibility, 173
Component, 186, 216, 239
Compost piles, 86
Compounds, 18
inorganic, 302
organic, 302
Compression, 299
Computer, 224
electronic, 211
Computer-aided graphics, 629
Computer simulation, 175
Conant, James B., 60
Concentration, 247
Conclusion, 258–59
Concrete, 299, 300
Concrete structure, 308
Conduction, 111
Cone, development of, 593
Conover, D.W., 347
Conservatism, 288, 405
Construction, 434
graphic, 642
modular, 149
Construction line, 433
Consumer acceptance, 376
Consumer market, 274
Contract, 372
Contraction, 111
Contrast, 153, 431
brightness, 344
Control, death, 10
Conversion tables, 684
Converter, basic oxygen-process, 295
Cook, R.C., 6
Cook, Theodore Andrea, 78, 97, 118, 154
Cooking, 15
Cooling liquid, 311
Cooper, James Fenimore, 6
Coordinate, Cartesian, 488
Coordinate system, 571
Copernicus, 67
Coral, 100
Corn, 256
Cornea, 81
Corrode, 245
Corrosion fatigue, 245
Cost, 238, 389
Cost estimate, 261
Cottonwood, 91
Cows, 7, 61
Cox, Coleman, 60
Cracker, 351

Crank, bell, 324
Cream, 212
Creative ability, 55
Creative behavior, barriers to, 61
Creative effort, 55
Creative thinking, 49
Creative thought, 55
Creativity, 50
Crime, 35
United States, 36
Critical path, 769
Criticism, 212
Cross hairs, 97
Cross-hatching, 433
Cruciform, 185
Crustacean, 100
Cultural barriers, 65
Cultural restraints, 67
Culture, Indian, 67
vision based, 342
Cumberland, Bishop Richard, 67, 71
Current, 228
alternating, 228
direct, 228
electrical, 679
Curve, growth, 40, 382
Customer appeal, 189
Customer reaction, 274
Cutters, milling, 315
Cutting plane, 574
Cutting plane line, 433
Cutting plane method, 581
Cutting tools, 310
Cuttlefish, 80
Cuyahoga River, 18, 21
Cycle, life, 381
Cycloid, 222
Cylinder, development of, 590
Czurles, Stanley, 52

Dacron, 99
Damages, 175
Damsel, 217
Dandelion, 91
Daniels, G.S., 337
Darrow, Clarence, 52
Darwin, 114
Data, anthropometric, 185
DDT, 4, 250
Dead men, 194
Death control, 10
DeBall, Garrett, 29
Deceleration, 354
Decibel, 26, 346
Decimal equivalents of common fractions, 680
Decision, 398–99
Decision matrix, 399
Decision processes, 174, 398
Decision theory, 398
Decisions under certainty, 401
Decisions under risk, 402
Decisions under uncertainty, 403
Defoe, Daniel, 357
Degreaser, 321
Delhi, 10
Demand, 370
De Montaigne, Michel Eyquem, 57, 401
Descriptive geometry, 512
De Setanti, Joaquin, 402
Design, detail, 171

engineering, 194
phases of, 169
phases of engineering, 171
preliminary, 171
process of, 170
systems, 194
Design criteria, 177
Design parameters, 207
Design phase, detail, 181
preliminary, 175
Design philosophy, 187
Design process, 193, 197
Designers, characteristics of, 170
Designs, living, 75
Detail design, 171
Detail design phase, 181
Detailers, 186
Detergent, 21
Deterioration, 245
Development, 373, 586
of cone, 593
of cylinder, 590
of engineering design, 773
of prism, 588
of pyramid, 592
Dewey, John, 202
Diagnosis, 221
Diagram, 219, 275, 278
block, 278
circuit, 279
energy, 279
flow, 279
free-body, 230, 278
Dialing stop, 503
Dialyzing fluid, 98
Diameter, pitch, 324
Diamonds, 310
Diatom, 114
Diatomaceous earth, 114
Die, 308
wire-drawing, 309
Die casting, 307
Dihedral angle, 536
Dimension, 180, 559
location, 566
size, 564
Dimension line, 433, 560
Dimensional homogeneity, 233
Dimensional lettering, 562
Dimensional notes, 562
Dimensional number system, 562
Dimensioning, 558
Dip, 539
Direct current, 228
Direct labor, 390
Direct material, 389
Discovery, 212
Discrimination, 343
Discussion, 259
Dishwasher, 323
Disraeli, Benjamin, v, 370
Distance, shortest, 527
true, 540
Distortion, visual, 467
Distribution, 370
Divider, 429
Divine proportion, 149
Doe, John, 54
Dollar, 189
Dolphin, 103